SCIENTIFIC THEORY AND RELIGION

LONDON
Cambridge University Press
FETTER LANE

NEW YORK · TORONTO
BOMBAY · CALCUTTA · MADRAS
Macmillan

TOKYO
Maruzen Company Ltd

SCIENTIFIC THEORY AND RELIGION

The World described by Science and its Spiritual interpretation

by

ERNEST WILLIAM BARNES *Bp. of*

Sc.D. Camb., Hon. D.D. Aber. and Edin., Hon. LL.D. Glas.,
F.R.S., Bishop of Birmingham

Birmingham
1874 –

THE GIFFORD LECTURES AT ABERDEEN
1927–1929

215

33- 17816

CAMBRIDGE
AT THE UNIVERSITY PRESS
1933

CONTENTS

FOREWORD   *page* xxiii

LECTURE I. INTRODUCTION

§ 1. Jewish cosmology   1
  2. The different picture created by modern science   2
  3. Repercussions of scientific progress: free-will: invariable
     sequence   2
  4. The constant progress of science constitutes a series of
     ever closer approximations to the truth   4
  5. Theology cannot be based solely on human spiritual ex-
     perience: it must take account of the God of Nature
     revealed by science   5
  6. The philosophical assumption of these lectures is a
     moderate realism: the physical world exists inde-
     pendently of any human mind   6
  7. The external world a somewhat unexpected synthesis
     gradually being constructed by the observation and
     thought of humanity   7
  8. Rational and irrational faith   9
  9. The limitations of scientific knowledge   10
 10. The opportunity of superstition   11
 11. The laws of Nature   12
 12. The range of the lectures   13

LECTURE II. MATTER

 13. The physicist's definition of matter: inertia   14
 14. The Galilean principle of inertia an experimental fact 14
 15. Matter in ancient speculation   15
 16. The nature of combustion   16
 17. The law of 'conservation of matter'   16
 18. Force   17
 19. The implications of Newton's second and third laws of
     motion   17
 20. The law of conservation of energy   18
 21. Mass and weight: inertia and gravity   18

15545

§ 22. Einstein's revolution: energy has inertia   *page* 20
   23. Dalton's atomic law   21
   24. Atoms: their existence and size   22
   25. Mendeléev's Periodic Table   25
   26. Atomic number and the true order of the elements   26

LECTURE III. SPACE

   27. Our intuitions of space and time   28
   28. Measurements of time and of space   28
   29. The arbitrary separation of space from time   30
   30. The straight line and ideal measuring rod   30
   31. Coordinates: three-dimensional space and its numerical
        representation   30
   32. The fundamental assumptions of our geometries   32
   33. Consideration of Lobatchewskyan or hyperbolic plane
        geometry   34
   34. Hibbert's axiom   34
   35. Saccheri's quadrilateral   35
   36. The limiting curves of sets of parallel lines and the funda-
        mental congruence theorem associated with them   36
   37. The line-element in hyperbolic geometry   38
   38. The value of the angle of parallelism in hyperbolic space 38
   39. The self-consistency of hyperbolic geometry   39
   40. The analogue with sets of circles orthogonal to a given
        circle   40
   41. The analogue to displacements of a rigid body   41
   42. The utility of the circular analogue. Various examples 42
   43. Riemannian or spherical geometry, and its assumptions   44
   44. The pole of a line: spherical and 'elliptic' geometry   44
   45. Riemannian plane geometry is, in effect, that of a sphere 45
   46. The theory of groups of displacements of a rigid body as
        the basis of geometry   46
   47. The idea of space as homogeneous, isotropic and un-
        bounded   47
   48. The two sub-groups of rotation which exist for all types
        of space   47
   49. Euclidean space and the parallel displacement sub-group 48
   50. "If there were no solid bodies we should not have geo-
        metry"   49

LECTURE IV

RIEMANN'S GENERAL THEORY OF SPACE

§ 51. Introduction   *page* 51
52. Intrinsic geometry of a surface   52
53. Gaussian coordinates   53
54. The line-element in Riemann's generalised space   53
55. Geodesics of a manifold   55
56. Outline of Riemann's investigation   55
57. The measurement of angles   58
58. Parallelism with respect to a surface   59
59. Infinitesimal parallel displacement   59
60. Such displacements satisfy the parallelogram rule   62
61. The extension to n-dimensional manifolds   63
62. Parallel displacement round an infinitesimal parallelo-
       gram   64
63. The Riemann-Christoffel tensor   66
64. Sections of a manifold and the change in a vector after
       describing an infinitesimal circuit lying in a given
       section. Pérès' formula   74
65. The total or Gaussian curvature of a two-dimensional
       surface   76
66. Use of geodesic surfaces to determine the curvatures of
       an n-dimensional manifold at an assigned point   79
67. The condition that generalised space should be flat   80
68. Application to our three-dimensional space and to
       similar n-dimensional manifolds   81
69. The canonical form for the line-element in generalised
       space of constant curvature   83
70. Some transformations of the canonical form for three-
       dimensional space   87
71. A geometrical interpretation of three-dimensional space
       of constant positive curvature   88
72. Canonical forms for homogeneous and isotropic three-
       dimensional space   88
73. The true range and value of Riemann's achievement   89
74. The nature of the space of common experience in the
       light of Riemann's analysis   90
     Résumé of properties of (1) Euclidean, (2) hyperbolic and
       (3) spherical space   90

§ 75. The analytical investigation of plane hyperbolic geo-
        metry   *page* 92
76. Lobatchewskyan geometry of the plane is that of the
        pseudo-sphere in Euclidean space   93
77. The volume of Lobatchewskyan space   93
78. Riemannian geometry of the plane is that of the sphere
        in Euclidean space   94
79. The volume of spherical or Riemannian space of three
        dimensions   94
80. Properties of Riemannian space   96
81. To which of the three possible types does our space belong? 96

LECTURE V

SPACE-TIME: THE SPECIAL THEORY OF RELATIVITY

82. The measurement and interconnection of space and time   98
83. Absolute space   99
84. Does absolute rotation exist? The views of Newton and
        Mach   100
85. The belief in absolute chronometric time   101
86. The belief in absolute simultaneity   103
87. Two fundamental enquiries   103
88. The Michelson-Morley experiment   104
89. The fundamental result of the special theory of relativity 105
90. The restricted principle of relativity   107
91. The Fitzgerald-Lorentz contraction   108
92. The equations of the Lorentz transformation   109
93. Einstein's deduction of the Lorentz transformation   110
94. The Lorentz transformation for infinitesimals   112
95. Time-measurements in the special theory of relativity   112
96. The space-time continuum and the interval   114
97. Minkowski's world and its stratification   116
98. Geometrical illustration of the way in which different
        observers break up the space-time continuum   117
99. The order of events in the world   119
100. Weyl's picture of 'the scene of reality'   122
101. Composition of velocities according to the special theory
        of relativity   122
102. Fizeau's experiment   123
103. The fundamental definitions of the mechanics of the
        special theory of relativity   123

§ 104. The fundamental law of kinetics, and its transformation
in the special theory of relativity   *page* 126
105. Minkowski's world. Time and proper-time. The 'four-velocity' and 'four-acceleration' vectors   126
106. The fundamental dynamical equations of the special
theory of relativity   128
107. The equivalence of mass and energy   131

LECTURE VI.   GENERAL RELATIVITY

108. The fundamental limitation of the special theory of
relativity   134
109. The 'reality' of centrifugal forces   134
110. Does absolute rotation exist?   134
111. The equality of inertial and gravitational mass   135
112. The likeness between gravitational and uniformly accelerated regions   136
113. The passage from the special to the general theory of
relativity   136
114. The type of mathematical analysis needed in the
general theory of relativity   137
115. Riemann's symbols and other tensors deducible there-
from   138
116. Divergence. Covariant differentiation   142
117. The fundamental identities of the general theory of
relativity   147
118. The stress-tensor at a point in a continuous material
medium   148
119. The Newtonian equations of motion in such a medium   150
120. A symmetrical form for such equations   151
121. A modified form of these equations in which time has
not a privileged position   152
122. The energy-momentum-stress tensor   154
123. The connection between mechanics and geometry   159
124. Einstein's gravitational equations of the general theory
of relativity   160
125. The curvature of a region of space-time containing
neither matter nor energy   161
126. The justification of Einstein's gravitational equations   166

§ 127. The problem of two bodies is insoluble in Einsteinian
          dynamics   *page* 169
128. The gravitational field of an isolated particle   170
129. Einstein's equations for the orbit of a planet moving
          round the sun   172
130. The motion of the perihelion of Mercury   173
131. The bending of rays of light near the sun   174
132. The spectrum-shift due to a strong gravitational field   176
133. Gravitation is due to the warping of space-time   177
134. The law of gravitation is a disguised identity   178
135. Our measures of matter and momentum are determined
          by the warping of space-time   178
136. The position of the law of conservation of energy in
          Einsteinian mechanics   180
137. Is space finite?   183
138. The objection to a Newtonian-Euclidean cosmos   184
139. Einstein's time-cylindrical cosmos   184
140. de Sitter's cosmos   187
141. General relativity and the Maxwell field-equations   189
142. Conclusions and speculations   190

LECTURE VII

THE ELECTRICAL THEORY OF MATTER

143. Electricity and magnetism: the original discoveries   193
144. Maxwell's achievement   193
145. Electricity and matter   193
146. Coulomb's law. What is electricity? Electrons. Ions   194
147. The nature of an electron   197
148. Radiation   200
149. The inertia of an electron   202
150. The ether   202
151. The inertia of light   204
152. The energy of matter   204
153. Can we create electrons?   205
154. X-rays: origin: properties and spectra   206
155. The radio-active process: and the law of radio-active
          decomposition   207
156. The age of the earth   209
157. The puzzle of uranium   210

§ 158. The products of radio-active disintegration: and the nature of the process   *page* 211

159. The electrical constitution of matter   212

160. The ordering of the elements   213

161. The sizes of atoms, electrons and protons   215

162. Bohr's model of the atom   217

163. Chemical combination   219

164. Isotopes   219

165. The spectrum of an element and its origin   221

166. A comparison with the solar system   222

167. The spectrum of hydrogen   222

168. Perplexities due to the Bohr model   223

169. Is free-will possible in inanimate nature?   224

170. Some further enquiries   225

LECTURE VIII.   HEAT AND LIGHT

171. Heat and change of state of bodies   227

172. Pressure and temperature   227

173. Boyle's law: Charles' law   228

174. The graduation of an air thermometer   229

175. Absolute zero   229

176. Work done by an expanding gas   230

177. The first law of thermodynamics   231

178. The character and origin of the second law of thermo-dynamics   231

179. Carnot's reversible engine   231

180. Carnot's principle and efficiency function   232

181. The absolute (Kelvin) scale of temperature   233

182. An expression for the efficiency of a reversible engine   234

183. The indicator-diagram for Carnot's cycle. Isothermals and adiabatics   235

184. Entropy: must increase with spontaneous change in a physical system   236

185. The two fundamental principles of thermodynamics   237

186. The nature of entropy   238

187. Entropy and the direction of time: the end of the Universe   238

188. Light: an electro-magnetic phenomenon   240

§ 189. The polarisation of light   *page* 242
190. The intensity of radiation: radiation pressure: comets
        and their tails   242
191. The Doppler effect   244
192. Isotropic radiation   246
193. Equilibrium of radiation: the balancing of absorption
        and emission   247
194. Black-body radiation   249
195. Radiation from the sun and stars: from planets: within
        a star   249
196. Absorption lines   251
197. Stefan's law   253
198. Planck's law   254
199. Visual magnitudes and Fechner's law   255
200. Measures of magnitude: absolute magnitude: the
        Purkinje effect   256
201. Radiation and human sight   258

LECTURE IX

THE QUANTUM THEORY AND RÖNTGEN RAYS

202. The first form of the quantum theory   261
203. The photo-electric effect   262
204. The connection between energy emitted by an atom
        and the frequency of the radiation produced   263
205. The generalised form of the quantum theory: action is
        atomic   264
206. Bohr's theory of the hydrogen spectrum   267
207. Elliptic orbits for the hydrogen atom   269
208. The periodic system of the elements   273
209. Wave mechanics and the Born-Dirac calculus   275
210. The Heisenberg uncertainty-relations   279
211. The present state of the quantum theory. Lindemann's
        speculations. The concepts of space and time   281
212. Röntgen radiation: the two types   284
213. The origin of characteristic X-rays   286
214. The connection between such rays and the atomic
        number of an element   287
215. The K-, L- and M-series of spectral lines   288
216. The interference of light   290

§ 217. The diffraction of light: diffraction gratings   *page* 291
218. The direct passage of plane waves through a slit   293
219. Theory of a plane transmission grating   295
220. Diffraction by a crossed grating or lattice   297
221. Diffraction by a space-lattice: equivalent to a series of
reflections   298
222. Crystals   300
223. The diamond   301
224. Arrangement and Creative Activity   302
225. Crystal measurements of, and by, X-rays   303
226. The achievement of X-ray analysis   304
227. General conclusions   306

LECTURE X.   THE SOLAR SYSTEM

228. Ancient speculation   311
229. The rise and triumph of the heliocentric theory. Kepler's laws   312
230. Newton's fundamental assumption   313
231. The members of the solar system   314
232. The earth: its shape, size, density and mass   314
233. The distance and size of the sun   314
234. The sun's mass and density   315
235. The planets in general   317
236. Laplace's theory of the origin of the solar system   318
237. The modern theory   318
238. The origin of the earth-moon system   319
239. The moon   320
240. Velocity of escape   321
241. Conditions of escape of a gas from a planet's atmosphere. Atmospheres of moon, sun and earth   322
242. Other worlds than ours   323
243. Are Venus and Mars inhabited?   324
244. The tides: the equilibrium theory   327
245. The tides in theory and observation   329
246. Tidal friction: the lengthening of the day: ancient observations: effect of tidal friction on the moon's motion   329
247. The past of the earth-moon system: its future   333
248. The end of the earth-moon system   334

LECTURE XI

THE GALACTIC UNIVERSE AND THE GREAT NEBULAE

THE GALACTIC UNIVERSE

§ 249. The 'fixed' stars   *page* 336
250. Instruments   336
251. The interferometer   337
252. Astronomical measures of distance   339
253. The shape and size of the galactic universe   340
254. The unity of the galactic universe   341
255. The distances of the stars   343
256. The open and globular clusters   343
257. The cepheid variables   345
258. Giant and dwarf stars   346
259. White dwarfs   348
260. Spectroscopic parallaxes   349
261. The total number of the stars   350
262. Stellar radiation   351
263. The radiant energy emitted by the sun   353
264. Radiation emitted by the stars   354
265. Where does the sun's energy come from?   355
266. Consequences of the annihilation hypothesis   356
267. The motions of the stars   357
268. Binary stars   358
269. Visual and spectroscopic binaries   358
270. The mass-luminosity relation   361
271. Eclipsing binaries   362
272. The contrast between visual and spectroscopic binaries 362
273. The ages of the stars   363
274. Moving clusters   364
275. Star-streaming and differential galactic rotation   365
276. Novae or temporary stars   368
277. The future of stars, sun and earth   371
278. The observing of the nebulae   372
279. Galactic nebulae   372

THE GREAT NEBULAE

280. The great nebulae: their number   374
281. The shapes of the great nebulae: their spectra   375
282. The distances of the great nebulae   377

§ 283. The sizes of the great nebulae   *page* 378
284. The velocities of the great nebulae   379
285. Lemaître's expanding (or contracting) cosmos   381
286. The instability of the Einstein cosmos   384
287. Geodesics in the Lemaître cosmos   384
288. Pressure, density and mass in this cosmos   385
289. The Doppler effect in this cosmos   387
290. The present size of our cosmos: its mass   389
291. Some general reflections. Man and the cosmos   392
292. The probable origin of the cosmos: and of stars   395
293. A final enigma   397
294. Are there other planetary systems?   398
295. The frequency of stellar encounters   398
296. The number of planetary systems in regions of local
        star-density   401
297. Life elsewhere in the galactic universe   401
298. Is the whole cosmos the home of intelligent beings?   403
299. The final state of the cosmos   404
300. Cosmic rays and the annihilation of matter   404
301. Extrapolation and its risks   406
302. Need we postulate Divine intervention?   408

LECTURE XII

THE ORIGIN OF LIFE AND THE GEOLOGICAL RECORD

THE ORIGIN OF LIFE

303. The coming of life to the earth   411
304. Geology and the origin of life   411
305. The living probably emerged from the non-living   412
306. Arguments in favour of 'spontaneous generation'   413
307. 'In the beginning'   413
308. The three fundamental elements of organic chemistry   414
309. The preparation for life   415
310. The ascent to life   415
311. The first life   416
312. Primitive organisms: of one type or many?   416
313. Was the earth's initial covering of gases essential or
        merely convenient?   417
314. Does life's supposed origin give any clue to its nature?   419

THE GEOLOGICAL RECORD

§ 315. The rise of geological investigation   *page* 420
316. Gaps in the geological record   421
317. The ages of the different strata of the earth   421
318. Measurements by radio-active decomposition   422
319. The main geological formations   423
320. The Archaeozoic era   424
321. The Palaeozoic era   425
322. The Mesozoic era   427
323. The origin of the birds   427
324. The early mammals   428
325. The Tertiary era: its divisions   428
326. Tertiary geography   430
327. The destruction of species   431
328. The history of the horse   431
329. A mammalian slaughter   432
330. Man's end?   432

LECTURE XIII

THE EVOLUTION OF PLANTS AND SEX

THE EVOLUTION OF PLANTS

331. The similarity of animals and plants   434
332. The most primitive plants   435
333. Liverworts and mosses: club-mosses   436
334. Spores and seeds   437
335. Ferns and seed-ferns   437
336. The great botanical eras   438
337. The age of cycads: descent or independent evolution   438
338. The last botanical transformation   440
339. Mammals and angiosperms   441
340. Dicotyledons and monocotyledons   441
341. Change in the Tertiary era   442
342. Conclusion   442

SEX

343. The basal facts: secondary differences   443
344. The reproductive cells   444
345. Sexual fusion   445

§ 346. The distribution of the sex-chromosomes: the two sexes
        must be roughly equal in numbers   *page* 446
347. An alternative sex-mechanism   447
348. Inter-sexes and super-sexes   448
349. Parthenogenesis: haploid males and diploid females.
        Artificial parthenogenesis   451
350. Ants, bees and wasps   452
351. The termites   453
352. The advance of social organisation among the bees   454
353. Instinct and intelligence: the salt of life   456
354. The Virgin Birth   457

LECTURE XIV

THE EVOLUTION OF ANIMALS AND MENDELISM

THE EVOLUTION OF ANIMALS

355. Evolution and religious prejudice   459
356. The nature of species   460
357–360. The main arguments for evolution:
            (1) The geological record   462
            (2) The evidence from embryology   462
            (3) The existence of useless organs   465
            (4) The geographical distribution of animals 467
361. Missing links   469
362. The origin of the vertebrates   470
363. The transition to the amphibians and thence to the
        mammals   471
364. The moral significance of the development of the herd-
        instinct   473
365. Mind versus material protection   474

MENDELISM

366. Mendel's work and its significance   475
367. Mendel's fundamental experiment   475
368. Mendel's first law   477
369. The law of independent assortment   478
370. Linkage-groups   479
371. Morgan's restatement of Mendel's laws of inheritance 480
372. Mutant characters   482

§ 373. The contrast between Mendelian and blending inheritance   *page* 484

374. Mutations in humanity   485

375. The persistence of mutations in humanity   488

376. Sex-linked defects   489

377. Mental mutations in humanity   491

378. Feeble-mindedness   491

379. Insanity   495

380. Lethal mutations   497

381. Inbreeding   498

382. Can dysgenic mutations be reversed?   498

383. Mutations and short-wave radiation   499

384. The sexual cycle in animals and plants   501

385. Has the sex-mechanism arisen independently in animals and plants?   501

386. The future of the evolutionary process   502

LECTURE XV. THE MACHINERY OF EVOLUTION

387. Charles Darwin's achievement   504

388. The fact of variation   505

389. Fluctuation   506

390. Natural selection   506

391. How does variability arise?   508

392. Weismann's position   509

393. Criticisms of Lamarckism   510

394. Dürken's experiments   511

395. Johannsen's experiments: fluctuations are not inherited   512

396. Further arguments against the inheritance of acquired characters   514

397. The raw material of evolution   515

398. Genetic variation the vehicle of emergence   518

399. Evolution the result of external creative activity   519

400. Is God's creative activity non-moral?   520

401. Man and the cosmic process   522

402. The sternness of God   523

403. The genetic process and predestination   523

LECTURE XVI.   MAN'S ORIGIN AND PAST

§ 404. Man's place among the Primates   *page* 525
  405. The earliest Primates   525
  406. The development of the Primates   526
  407. Man's emergence   527
  408. Where and when did man emerge?   528
  409. The Java ape-man   530
  410. The Piltdown remains   530
  411. Pekin man   531
  412. Heidelberg man   532
  413. Neanderthal man   532
  414. The coming of *homo sapiens*   534
  415. The men and culture of the Reindeer Age   535
  416. The differences between Palaeolithic and Neolithic
         culture   537
  417. Iberians and Nordics   537
  418. The cradle of humanity   538
  419. The antiquity of man   539
  420. The evolution of human intelligence   542
  421. The development of brain and speech   543
  422. The faint dawn of civilisation   543
  423. The Reindeer Age civilisation   544
  424. Characteristics of primitive religion   545
  425. Animism   546
  426. The practical nature of primitive magic and religion 546
  427. The relation between magic and primitive religion   547
  428. Primitive religion and totemism   549
  429. The development of primitive religion   550

LECTURE XVII

SCIENTIFIC THEORY AND THE 'REAL' WORLD

  430. Introduction   552
  431. Naïve realism: physical realism   553
  432. Individual experience   554
  433. Collective experience: public knowledge   555
  434. The synthetic activity of the intellect   556
  435. The Newtonian philosophy   557

§ 436. Space and time   *page* 559
437. Realism and Idealism: moderate realism: theism   562
438. A possible cosmos of monads   566
439. Cause   567
440. Substance   570
441. Phenomenalism   573
442. Materialism and agnostic naturalism   575
443. Mechanistic determinism   577
444. The problem of consciousness: psycho-physical parallelism   580
445. Freedom and natural law   582

LECTURE XVIII

GOD AND OUR BELIEF IN HIS EXISTENCE

446. Scientific experience: general conclusions   586
447. Experience and 'Spiritualism'   587
448. The dualism of natural and supernatural rejected   588
449. Emergence   590
450. Purposiveness in emergence   592
451. The existence of God   593
452. The ontological argument and its rejection   594
453. The cosmological argument   595
454. The teleological argument   597
455. Faith in God   599
456. The natural sciences and qualitative judgments   600
457. Individuality, value and quality   601
458. The rise of moral consciousness   601
459. Ethical judgments   603
460. The realms of Nature and of moral order   604
461. The moral argument for God's existence   605
462. The absolute values   606

LECTURE XIX. RELIGIOUS EXPERIENCE

463. Normal religious experience   609
464. Prayer   611
465. Does God answer prayer?   612
466. Conversion   613
467. The psychology of conversion   614
468. The value of conversion   615

§ 469. Conversion and 'fundamentalism'   *page* 616
470. Mystical experience   617
471. Illustrations of mystical experience   619
472. The 'dark night of the soul'   621
473. The worth of mystical experience   623
474. Induced experience   624
475. The problem of public worship   626
476. Sacraments   626
477. The necessity for guided religious experience   628
478. The revival of pagan sacramentalism   629
479. Religious degeneration   631
480. Religious ecstasy must be subject to morality and reason   632
481. Religious experience and dogmatic assertion   633
482. The duty of religious teachers   635

LECTURE XX. IMMORTALITY

483. Soul and body   636
484. The resurrection of the body   637
485. Man's decisive separation from the lower animals   638
486. The background of belief in immortality: pantheism and impersonal immortality   638
487. Spinoza and immortality   640
488. God as the Absolute   641
489. The rejection of Absolutist theories   642
490. The self as *Ego*   643
491. Christian theism and immortality   644
492. Immortality and the conservation of values   646
493. Pantheism and theism   647
494. Immortality and time   650
495. Personality and the psycho-physical organism   652

CONCLUSION

496. The present and the immediate future of religious faith   653
497. The character of the lectures   654
498. The advance of knowledge   655
499. Here and hereafter   656

Appendix   658
Index   661

FOREWORD

In publishing these lectures I would first of all thank the Senatus Academicus of the University of Aberdeen for the honour which they conferred upon me in the year 1925 by inviting me to be Gifford Lecturer. To Sir George Adam Smith, the Principal of the University, I am indebted for many kindnesses both in connection with the lectures and on other occasions: of the hospitality which was received from Lady Adam Smith and himself, when the lectures were being delivered, most happy memories remain. There were many in Aberdeen who combined to make visits there enjoyable; and not least would I thank those who attended the lectures and made the lecturer feel that his labour in preparing them had not been in vain.

Of the lectures themselves I would merely say that, wide as is their range, they have an inner coherence. I trust that they express the attitude of the modern man of science who, as he hopefully makes theories, is aware of the limitations of his knowledge and also, in part because of his loyalty to truth, bears in mind the reality and the claims of the spiritual world.

Since the lectures were given they have been extensively revised and some recent developments of knowledge have been included.

Acknowledgments are, I trust, adequately made in the lectures. Of those now living in this country to whom I am specially indebted I would mention my old teacher, Professor E. W. Hobson, whose own Gifford Lectures I have constantly consulted, Professor S. Alexander and Professor J. S. Haldane. If Hastings Rashdall, lately Dean of Carlisle, had not died before his time, I would rejoice to say how much talks with him had helped me in my thinking. He and Fenton John Anthony Hort were, among those no longer living, the greatest men of the Modernist movement in English theology.

Finally, my wife has helped me with constant encouragement and criticism: and my secretary, Miss N. M. V. Owen, daughter of the late Bishop of St David's, has been unwearied in preparing clean type-script from rough and illegible manuscript. I am ashamed to recall how often certain passages have been recast without, from her, a murmur of complaint.

E. W. B.

BISHOP'S CROFT
BIRMINGHAM
November, 1932

Lecture i

INTRODUCTION

§1. *Jewish cosmology.*

The Christian Church at an early period of its existence took over from the Jews beliefs as to the creation and early history of the world and as to the origin of man. Such beliefs, as every educated person knows full well, can no longer be accepted. The beliefs, however, formed a background to Catholic theology and were consequently associated with the Christian idea of God. That idea rests primarily on the teaching of Jesus of Nazareth; and it is not erroneous to say that He regarded it as an intuition which man's richest and deepest spiritual experience would confirm. But human thought naturally and rightly refuses to rest content with such an intuition. The God to whom man's spiritual experience leads him must be also the God revealed in Nature. Hence the picture of earth's beginnings framed by Jewish speculation was used to supplement and confirm the belief as to God's character to which Jesus Christ gave the weight of His authoritative understanding. Until quite modern times the synthesis thus made was deemed satisfactory. In fact many traditional types of argument were so framed as to leave the impression that the Christian conception of God was derived from Jewish cosmology; and that it would not be true unless the Biblical accounts of the Creation and the Fall were, in substance, historical facts. It was an axiom of Catholic orthodoxy that the Creation took place in time: and, though opinions varied as to its exact date B.C., the belief was general that the Universe came into existence less than 10,000 years ago. Further, the earth was assumed to be the centre of this Universe. Sun, moon, planets and stars were all subordinate to it. On the earth and on the earth alone existed man, specially created 'in the image of God'. Furthermore, all the manifold defects of human nature which lead to individual corruption and social disorder were deemed to be the result of a Fall, an act of disobedience on the part of the 'first man' Adam, by reason of which all his descendants inherited a moral taint. Christ had insisted alike on the inherent value of the individual human soul and on the goodness of God. For traditional theology man's inherent value was preserved by the fact that he was created with unique attributes to rule the earth, which itself was of supreme significance in the cosmos: God's goodness was preserved by attributing all the evil, alike of nature and of human society, to the fact of Adam's Fall.

§ 2. *The different picture created by modern science.*

Within the last four centuries the old Jewish cosmology has vanished. Science has created an entirely different picture of the nature and duration of the Universe. The single act—or week—of 'Creation' is replaced by a process of unimaginable extent whose beginnings elude us, though soberly argumentative speculation carries them back for at least tens of thousands of millions of years. The earth, far from being the centre of the Universe, is a minor planet of a solar system whose central luminary is one of, at least, some 50,000 millions of suns. Even this vast aggregate of suns does not exhaust the visible Universe: it is, in fact, but one of many 'island universes' of comparable magnitude. For the age of the earth astronomers and physicists compute periods which exceed a thousand million years. During the latter part of that time life has been developing upon it. Biological evolution upon this planet has continued for many hundreds of millions of years; and finally by such evolution man has emerged from an ape-like stock. Sub-human types were probably in existence upon the earth a million years ago: and traces of rudimentary human civilisation have been found which can hardly be less than 150,000 years old. Pre-history may be said to have begun in Europe, Egypt and the Euphrates valley 20,000 years ago: and written history goes back for something like 6000 or 8000 years.

§ 3. *Repercussions of scientific progress: free-will: invariable sequence.*

While the coordinated discoveries of modern times have thus emphasised the idea of development, and while they have led to an amazing extension of knowledge, I must warn my readers that they have not enabled us to solve the great problems of philosophy. There has now been built up a coherent plan of the evolution of the Universe, a plan which concludes with that development of terrestrial life which has led to man. The scheme, though vague in many details, is magnificent, and we need not fear that its main outlines are wrongly drawn. But little has been discovered which helps us to an understanding of such fundamental enquiries of philosophy as relate, say, to the nature of time, or to the existence of evil, or to human free-will. In fact, new difficulties confront us.

If Einstein's speculations have made it probable that space is finite and have thereby freed human thinking from one scandal, they have also forced us to conclude that space and time together form a single continuum into which all events must be placed. It is obvious that such a conclusion is highly satisfactory to those who hold that we are mere automata. They can now contend that time, like space, lies before us to be explored, and that consciousness meets but does not cause events. Yet it belongs to our constant and invariable experience that we have some measure of free-will, that our mental states cause and are not mere concomitants of events in the material world. In short, the darkness which clouds all enquiries into human freedom is no less dense than of old. The Heisenberg uncertainty-relations, immensely important though they must be, have brought controversy rather than light.

Again, it cannot be said that the so-called 'laws of Nature' have become easier to understand. For the theist all such laws are the expressions of God's will; and they are regular because God is self-consistent and His action not capricious. But the man of science, who, as such, makes no metaphysical assumptions, rightly thinks of such laws as mere sequences: as to their cause he does not speculate. Our laws of nature are descriptions of behaviour. But the progress of science has not given us a clearer insight into their range or character. It is not outside the bounds of possibility that some laws are disguised truisms, results of our own modes of measurement, and that others express statistical averages resulting from the free behaviour of individual monads, or units, possessing some freedom of choice. Moreover, we do not know whether it will ultimately be possible to bring the whole of Nature under the reign of law. It appears, for instance, that biological mutations are the raw material of evolution: yet in the present state of our knowledge such mutations are merely inexplicable facts.

There are, of course, some among us who cannot satisfy themselves that God exists, as they contemplate that progressive development of life which has led to man, because they do not see in it purpose and plan. Such desire rather to be shewn signs of the free creative activity of God. Yet it will not help them to be told that such activity is most typically expressed in the production of mutations, inasmuch as in such biological changes there is, so far as we can see, no ethical quality whatever. In fact, our present knowledge of changes in the germ-plasm seems to shew that evil and good alike are present at the very basis of the evolutionary process. I personally hold that God must be good in that He has made man to seek goodness; but recent additions to our knowledge of evolution do not make it any easier to solve the problem of evil.

I have thought it well thus to allude to enquiries, which in later lectures we shall consider in detail, in order that on the one hand I may
indicate the repercussions of scientific progress in the domains of philosophy and religion and in order that, on the other hand, I may not at the
beginning of my course excite false hopes. We must set our religious intuitions and aspirations against the background created by the new
knowledge. We must, whenever possible, test religious dogmas by the
methods of scientific enquiry and refashion them in the light of scientific
progress. But also we must, in the end, allow that our minds are finite
and that, even after the unparalleled intellectual advance which culminated in the first quarter of the twentieth century, we cannot solve
all the puzzles of the Universe.

§ 4. *The constant progress of science constitutes a series of ever closer
approximations to the truth.*

We must be content with partial knowledge, ready to admit that, in
regard to many matters of the highest importance, we must balance
opposing theories and reach probability rather than certainty. An
element of agnosticism, a willingness to say 'I don't know', is necessary
in the attitude of every honest thinker. But we have no right to use
scepticism as a support of superstition. To decry the value of human
reason in order that one may continue to hold beliefs that will not stand
the test of rational enquiry is discreditable. Similarly we have no right
to take refuge in the obscurantism which, because our knowledge of
Nature is progressive, alleges that 'the scientific theories of one generation are repudiated by the next'. The man of science builds upon the
labours of his predecessors. He seldom, if ever, entirely rejects their
conclusions when these are the result of scientific method; that is to say,
when they result from careful observation and experiment. He usually
finds that such conclusions are, as it were, first approximations to the
truth. They become, in the development of his research, rough outlines
of theories to which he gives more accurate form. Sometimes he can
make a higher synthesis, as when the laws of conservation of mass and
conservation of energy are combined into a single law in consequence of
the discovery that energy has inertia and therefore weight. But to
fancy that the main development of any great branch of modern scientific theory may ultimately be proved to be valueless is absurd. Whatever, for example, may be the machinery of evolution, the facts that
man has evolved from lower forms of terrestrial life and they in turn
from primitive organisms will not be overthrown. Einstein's success in

bringing gravitation within the scope of the general relativity-principle
has shewn that Newton's empirical law of gravitation is not absolutely
exact; but no competent student imagines that the Newtonian scheme
of planetary motions is not an exceedingly accurate approximation to
the truth.

§ 5.   *Theology cannot be based solely on human spiritual experience: it*
      must take account of the God of Nature revealed by science.

By reason of the knowledge laboriously built up from the application
of scientific method to various branches of enquiry, we have now a picture of the nature and past history of the Universe on which, so far as it
is clear and not blurred, we can place considerable reliance. We have
already said that it differs fundamentally from that associated with
traditional Christian theology. Now any scheme of theology must, to
be adequate, take account of the way in which God has fashioned and
controls the Universe and must therefore be permeated by the new
knowledge. Moreover, no adequate theology can be limited to human
spiritual experience. Man is the outcome of Nature's processes. He is
a product of the general scheme of the Universe. No one of his faculties
is entirely independent of his ancestry and environment. Without exaggeration we can assert that man's spiritual experience is as unreal as
a dream unless the God to Whom it leads him is also the God Whose
nature is shewn in the Universe as a whole.

The right starting-point for theology, as Inge* has well said, "is to
examine the conception of the world as known to science". I propose
in these lectures to make such an examination as my ignorance will
permit. To this end I shall try to set out in some detail the general
results which have been reached in those branches of science to which
we owe the modern picture. Often enough it is not possible to relate
them directly to theology. But my object is not a narrow apologetic.
I would rather say: "Such is our world. Such is its past development.
Such is man's place within it. Is it reasonable or necessary to believe
that the Christian God Whose character is goodness and truth is alike
its Creator and Ruler?" I believe, as will become apparent, that the
scientific conception of the world leads us to postulate the guidance of
a single controlling Intelligence. The philosophic view termed Naturalism suffices when we merely *describe* phenomena. To *explain* them we
need to assume the existence of a unifying and directing Mind. I maintain further that, though an examination of such facts as are available

* W. R. Inge, *Outspoken Essays, Second Series.* Longmans, 1922, p. 27.

to us does not lead of necessity to a conviction that the God thus postulated is good, yet this conclusion is more reasonable than any other.
We can, I believe, claim that the new conception of the world which
science now lays before us does not increase the doubts to which the
problem of evil has always given rise.

§ 6. *The philosophical assumption of these lectures is a moderate realism:
the physical world exists independently of any human mind.*

These lectures are intended for educated men and women who have
no technical knowledge of science or philosophy. They will therefore, so
far as possible, be free from the technical terms to be found in scientific
and philosophical discussions. The concrete is more easily apprehended
by us all than is the abstract. From the concrete results obtained by
scientific method we can, I believe, draw conclusions valuable for
theology even though we avoid processes which the profane call 'logic-
chopping'. To make fine-drawn distinctions, which had no counterpart
in the world of sense observation, was a vice of medieval scholasticism.
To such distinctions the mind which works upon itself is naturally led.
The modern philosopher, however, can use the theories reached by the
man of science as material for critical examination. His work is of the
greatest value as he lays bare the assumptions which underlie 'obvious'
arguments and as he estimates the extent to which the human mind
creates that knowledge of the external world which we believe ourselves
to possess. Of the rival systems of philosophy which have been built up
as a result of such enquiries we must choose one. But in making our
choice we must needs join faith to reason. Rival systems would not
exist if it were possible to prove that one was true and all the others
false. My own philosophical position, which I shall assume throughout
these lectures, is that known as moderate realism. I believe that a
physical world exists independently of any human mind. I hold, in fact,
that we may trust the evidence of our senses when they tell us that there
is an external world from which we derive our sensations. If I were the
only human being in the Universe, I might reasonably assume that the
data thus presented for investigation were themselves engendered in
my mind. But I assume that other human beings, other centres of consciousness, exist. I compare notes with these people and find that the
data presented by their senses have a general likeness to those which I
get myself. As a consequence I believe that the ultimate source of these
data is an external world which would still exist should my own
consciousness of it cease.

But the external world thus postulated is not necessarily the world as conceived by humanity. Though it is not constructed by my mind, my supposed knowledge of it is the construction of the general human mind. We can only believe that we have some, not entirely inaccurate, knowledge of the external world as it really is, as it is known to God, if we make the further assumption that our minds are akin to the Divine Mind; or, in other words, that there is some ground of unity between man and God. Belief in the existence of such a fundamental unity is regarded by some of our theologians as the necessary foundation of the Christian doctrine of the Incarnation. Rashdall* (1858–1924) has well said: "If 'Divine' and 'human' are thought of as mutually exclusive terms, if God is thought of as simply the Maker of man, if man is thought of as merely a machine or an animal having no community of nature with the Universal Spirit who is the cause or source or 'ground' of the existence alike of Nature and of other spirits", then the Christian doctrine of the Incarnation cannot be maintained. With Rashdall I postulate that there is a certain community of nature between God and man, that all human minds are reproductions 'in limited modes' of the Divine Mind, that in all true human thinking there is a reproduction of the Divine thought; and, above all, that in the highest ideals which the human conscience recognises there is a revelation of the ideal eternally present in the Divine Mind. Bethune-Baker† maintains the same standpoint even more firmly than Rashdall. In connection with the Incarnation he says that "we know enough of the order of Nature now to discredit the ancient idea that the new can only come about by a break in the continuity of the order of Nature". "The being of God and the being of Man are indissolubly interrelated.... The Creator is not separated from His creatures.... God is always being actualised, fulfilled, expressed in Man."

§ 7. *The external world a somewhat unexpected synthesis gradually being constructed by the observation and thought of humanity.*

We need continually to emphasise that the external world whose existence we postulate is not the world of any one individual: it results from a synthesis of the appearances which it presents to different observers. The actual synthesis which our physicists make is, in fact, much

* Hastings Rashdall, *Jesus Human and Divine*. Melrose, 1922, p. 17.
† J. F. Bethune-Baker, *The Way of Modernism and other Essays*. Cambridge University Press, 1927, pp. 94 and 99, 100. The full passage from which I have compressed the second quotation is well worth careful study.

more recondite than would result from the acceptance of a mere aggregate of appearances to unreflective observers. From that which is actually observed our men of science use the faculty of imagination (which must be sharply distinguished from fancy) to construct what would be observed under conditions which humanity cannot reach or in circumstances in which no human being could place himself. In the theory of relativity we have to imagine a man moving relatively to ourselves with velocities so large that they are comparable with the velocity of light: and we then construct the framework of space and time in which he would put events which we perceive. It is only thus that we reach the amazing conclusion that man's instinct that his measures of space and time are independent is mistaken. Similarly in atomic physics we have to imagine what would be the appearance of matter were it to be observed by a human being whose dimensions were smaller than those of a 'filter-passer', which is a micro-organism so small that it can pass through a porcelain filter and much smaller than can be seen under our most powerful microscopes. For such a being the most solid matter of our experience would appear to be, so we believe, electric charges either rotating with tremendous rapidity round oppositely charged nuclei, or existing in regions of space-time indeterminacy as satellites to such nuclei, charges and nuclei alike being so small as to occupy less than a billionth* of the volume which to us the matter appears continuously to fill. These instances shew conclusively that our direct knowledge of the external world is by no means as satisfactory as men who have given no thought to the subject naïvely fancy.

A further illustration will emphasise the same truth. Physiologists give good reasons for thinking that, of all man's faculties, vision is the most important. Now we see things because the retina of the eye is sensitive to light-rays. These rays have different wave-lengths which correspond to the different colours which we perceive. But the total range of wave-lengths to which our eyes are sensitive is but a very small fragment indeed of the range of all such rays as exist. We are unconscious of 'wireless rays' which may be passing around us; yet these belong to the same system as rays of light. Suppose that, instead of our eyes, we had different organs sensitive to another group of rays. The appearance of the external world for us would be entirely changed. Yet it would be, so we postulate, the same world differently perceived. We need always to bear in mind the fact that our minds, and the faculties that minister to them, have been by the process of evolution developed

* We use the English billion of one million millions.

in special directions. Certain kinds of perception have been practically useful: they have had survival-value, so that animal ancestors of our own who have developed them have survived in the struggle for existence. Scientific progress is a somewhat artificial development of human intelligence by which we transcend the limitations due to our ancestral history. We may, however, fairly claim that, because such progress enlarges our understanding, it should therefore enable us the better to know the nature of the Supreme Activity which, as it seems to me, directs, or is the ground of, the Universe.

Although the external world is very different from what it appears to be before we analyse the sensations which reveal its existence, the realism which I personally accept denies that it is in any true sense created by being known. As Plato taught, knowledge is the discovery of that which was there to be discovered before the discovery was made. This holds good, as it seems to me, alike in the domain of morality and in that of physical science. No doubt there is some kinship between the mind and the ideas which it rightly constructs from experience. But I believe that this kinship results from the fact that the human mind is akin to the guiding Intelligence of the Universe. The extent to which we frame true ideas is a measure of our capacity to 'think the thoughts of God'.

§8. *Rational and irrational faith.*

This philosophical position, as I have said, must be accepted as an act of reasonable faith. In stating my acceptance of it I would protest against any philosophical assumptions that ultimately lead to discord with the results of rational enquiry. Whatever may be said for the Idealism which asserts that whatever is known is thereby given some nature or quality of reality which it did not otherwise possess, I would protest against the misuse of such a standpoint. By religious apologists of a certain type it is sometimes said that all reality is a creation of the mind and that therefore—a strange *non sequitur*—any belief which can find a place in our scheme of reality can be accounted true if it have emotional value. The result of this type of argument is that we may believe what we like provided the belief gives us emotional satisfaction.

Such a misuse of Idealism is disguised scepticism and the whole scheme is the familiar, and odious, combination of scepticism and superstition. Against it we assert that all beliefs must be subjected to rational enquiry, whether they be scientific or religious. Among fit subjects for experimental investigation are, for instance, the disguised forms of 'animism' which still survive, and allied beliefs that spiritual presences can be attached to, or made to inhere in, non-living matter. These beliefs will disappear when the possibility of experimental en-quiry into the psychology of the religious consciousness becomes under-stood. Science has freed itself from the sway of irrational fancy: we may hope to free religion from similar contamination by linking it up with science.

§ 9. *The limitations of scientific knowledge.*

I can easily imagine that complaint will be made, with regard to some of the earlier of these lectures, that certain fundamental questions, especially of geometry, are treated at inordinate length. Such treatment is, however, essential to my scheme for two reasons. In the first place, I desire to shew that in science we are never free from possible errors of perception. The axioms of geometry, though often regarded as among the fundamental certainties of scientific knowledge, are dubious deduc-tions from empirical observation. In mathematical analysis we start with certain postulates or conventions and work out their consequences without necessarily troubling ourselves as to whether the initial pos-tulates or conventions belong to the objective world of our experience. In geometry, however, we seek to describe relations in this objective world; and the assumptions which we perforce make are only true so far as our observations are free from error. The existence of alternative systems of geometry, which may equally serve to describe relations in the world of our experience, is a significant illustration of the difficulty of reaching ultimate truth. In the second place, I have been anxious to make it clear that even in such a science as geometry we do not, to use an expressive phrase of the French, 'touch reality with the finger'. We seek, of course, to discover properties of space: we actually investigate consequences of our belief that ideally rigid bodies can be moved from one position to another without change of size or shape. Once this fact is grasped it will probably be admitted that an investigation of such consequences, however far continued, is unlikely to give us a complete insight into the nature of space. Moreover, the special theory of rela-tivity will make us hesitate even to accept the fundamental belief of which I have just spoken, for in that theory we learn that no physical disturbance can be propagated more quickly than with the velocity of light. If then we move a rigid body by disturbing two points of it, the disturbances will expand in spheres surrounding the two points; and, so long as these spheres expanding with the velocity of light do not overlap, the parts of the body surrounding the two points will move independently of one another. In other words, a body which can be moved cannot be ideally rigid! In geometry, as a matter of fact, we disentangle space from time by making a cross-cut of the space-time continuum in such a way that for this cross-cut the time is, according to our arbitrary method of measurement, everywhere the same: thus motion, because it involves change of time, ought to be excluded from the fundamental postulate of geometry. Only when such facts are thrust upon our attention do we begin to see that, as a picture of what is a completely satisfactory description of the actual space of the external world, geometry is by no means as adequate as the intelligent citizen believes.

So too with regard to matter. We shall try to bring out clearly that we study almost exclusively, not matter in its essential nature, whatever that may be, but matter so far as we can get at its properties by measuring its inertia. Matter which is the vehicle of life certainly has other properties, or is associated with other qualities, than can be grasped by the measurement of inertia. It is therefore difficult to believe that we can ultimately explain, by means of its physical properties, why the brain of a living man is a thinking machine. In short, physics, which is our most fully developed science, at present merely allows us to investigate certain measurable properties of things; but we must never forget, in contemplating the very extensive conquests made by this science, that there are possibly vast regions of the phenomenal world to which its methods, so far as they have been developed, do not apply.

§ 10. *The opportunity of superstition.*

It is my duty to emphasise such facts because they are true and we seek truth. But I am only too well aware that, if we admit the existence of realms which science has not conquered, we give to religious quacks and obscurantists domains where only too probably they will house superstition. As against their consequent claims we can only protest that for any belief there must be some evidence, some fact of observation which substantiates the belief: and further that, as between rival theories to account for facts that are not within the present domain of science, we must choose the one which best accords with that view of the inner nature and meaning of the Universe which a general survey leads us to create. We can thus, as I believe, repel most of the common superstitions of our age.

§ 11. *The laws of Nature.*

At one period of the nineteenth century science seemed to be well on the way to exclude religion from a world where everything could be known and freedom did not exist. To-day, however, the state of science is such that, wherever we probe, we are conscious that reality is evading our touch. In artificially isolated realms we can, from certain percepts derived from our physical experience, construct schemes embracing sequences of events. These schemes have, as it were, a predictive power in such limited realms: they tell us what will happen under certain conditions and, as has been stated in § 3, we call them *laws of Nature*. Such laws of Nature are to some extent a construction of the mind; for the mind creates by isolation the realm in which any particular law holds good. But, in seeking to make intelligible the sequences which he observes, the man of science is always in danger of introducing conceptual schemes derived from facts of experience which are so frequent in life that we think that we understand them. For instance, we are as children made so familiar by sad experience with the properties of hard bodies that we feel that there is nothing unintelligible in collisions between balls on a billiard-table. If therefore we can reduce any phenomenon to such collisions we feel that we have understood it. Hence in the nineteenth century certain physicists sometimes wrote as though the whole of reality was becoming comprehensible on the theory that atoms were tiny billiard-balls and that the properties of all material bodies were in process of being explained by mutual collisions of the atoms of which they were composed. Poincaré (1854–1912) satirised this attitude of mind when he asked whether we are to believe that God, in contemplating His work, experienced the same sensations as a man at a billiard match*.

We must, as I have already indicated, guard against the idea that a law of Nature is nothing but a construction of the mind: it is our way of expressing sequences which humanity continues to observe in the physical Universe. On the other hand, because it is *our* way, there is in it a human element liable to change as our understanding is enlarged. Our percepts, so far as they are accurate, convey to us knowledge of the external world. But a law of nature is a conceptual scheme determined by the action of the human mind in arranging such percepts: and only by continued reflection and experiment can we determine how far the conceptual scheme is adequate: how far, that is to say, it can be made

---

* H. Poincaré, *La Science et l'Hypothèse*. Paris, Flammarion, n.d., p. 193. The suggestiveness of Poincaré's satire is emphasised at the end of Lecture IX.

to embrace all percepts relevant to the particular class of phenomena
to which it relates.

§12. *The range of the lectures.*

This course of lectures falls naturally into four divisions: Space and
Time: Matter and Stars: Life and Evolution: Man and Mind. Unfortunately, the discussions of space and matter cannot be kept separate: hence, in the investigation of the first two divisions, the order that
we have indicated cannot be maintained. Throughout we shall be
concerned with the search for ultimate Reality. We try to see how far
modern knowledge will take us that we may thereby get some inkling
of what lies beyond the confines of the known. In such a way we may be
led to a knowledge of God less inadequate than if we trusted to speculation that was largely *à priori*. The difficulty with the scheme is that in
its initial stages we cannot entirely dispense with mathematics. But,
then, 'knowledge is measurement'; and mathematics is the science of
number. Alternatively, in words attributed to Robert Boyle, "mathematics is the alphabet in which God wrote the world". In the thirteenth
century Roger Bacon* said with truth, "he who knows not mathematics cannot know any other sciences; what is more, he cannot discover his own ignorance or find its proper remedies".

* *Roger Bacon*, Essays collected and edited by A. G. Little. Clarendon Press,
1914, p. 167.

Lecture ii

MATTER

§ 13. *The physicist's definition of matter: inertia.*

The physical Universe of our experience is built up of matter. We can give no definition of matter which could convey its nature to a being who lived in a Universe where it had no place. It is the stuff of our physical experience. Of it earth, air and sea, the distant stars and every living organism, including ourselves, are made. From it we derive our sensations of touch, taste, sound and sight.

The mathematical physicist, making a great abstraction, says that matter is that which has inertia. And following Galileo (1564–1642) and Newton (1642–1727) he gives the law or principle of inertia: "A body (i.e. a piece of matter) removed away from all other bodies would continue in a state of rest or of uniform (i.e. steady) motion in a straight line". This law at once forces us to ask what we mean by a straight line and by uniform motion. The law does not help us to know what matter is; but it shews that there is an intimate relation between a fundamental property of matter and the geometry of space. To seize upon this property of matter is rather like defining a man by his laziness: it is, however, the best basis that has so far been discovered.

The law states that the characteristic property of matter is inertia. Moreover, corresponding to every piece of matter there is a definite constant, its inertial mass. This constant is often mistakenly believed to measure 'the quantity of matter' in a body. Its connection with the weight of the body we shall discuss shortly: still later we shall discover that the physical measure of the constant depends upon the velocity of the body and we shall have to discriminate between the inertial mass of Newtonian physics and what is called the invariant inertial mass of the more accurate relativity-mechanics. When we affirm that matter has inertia we affirm that which is its most characteristic property. But it is not true to say that everything which has inertia is matter. Light, as we shall see, has inertia: it possesses mass and yet it is certainly not matter in the sense in which the term is commonly used.

§ 14. *The Galilean principle of inertia an experimental fact.*

The principle of inertia is by no means obvious. The ancients believed that the motion of a body ceased when the cause of the motion ceased to operate: this belief of Aristotle persisted until Galileo* denied it. We might reasonably have expected that Aristotle's assumption would be true or that some 'perfect' form of motion, like motion in a circle, would go on for ever.

The Galilean law of inertia must be regarded as an experimental fact: but it is a fact most difficult to establish rigorously by experiment, for we can never observe a body so far removed from all other bodies that they do not influence it. However, such experiments as we can make lead us to believe that the law is true. We may state it in the form that a body which is not subject to any force can only have a uniform rectilinear motion. On this basis Newtonian dynamics has been built up. When that system of dynamics and, still more, when the relativity-dynamics of Einstein are applied to the motion of the bodies which constitute the solar system, the agreement between theory and observation is so exact that we may feel justified in accepting the principle of inertia.

§15. *Matter in ancient speculation.*

In the Golden Age of Greece the nature of matter was an object of speculative enquiry by Greek philosophers. Aristotle put forward a scheme which was accepted for nearly two thousand years and played an important part in medieval Christian thought. He assumed that matter was continuous; and he further held that it was in some way made up of four 'elements': earth, air, fire and water. With these elements were associated, two by two, the qualities which make things hot and cold, dry and wet. The unsatisfactory nature of this scheme became evident when the foundations of the modern science of chemistry were gradually laid down. Effective experimental enquiry may be said to have been begun in the seventeenth century by Robert Boyle (1627–1691), "father of chemistry and uncle of the Earl of Cork". With him we get the modern view of the 'elements' of which matter consists. They are those kinds of matter which cannot be decomposed by chemical experiments. To discover the elements it was necessary to experiment, to try to decompose every chemical substance which Nature provides. The first steps of the enquiry were, of course, the most difficult. As soon as a few of the more common elements were

* Though Galileo used the law of inertia and applied it in particular instances, he did not formulate it as a general principle. See A. V. Vasilief, *Space—Time—Motion.* Translated by Lucas and Sanger. Chatto and Windus, 1924, p. 48.

isolated and their properties known, the character of the compounds which they formed by chemical combination, one with another, indicated the course of further enquiry.

§ 16. *The nature of combustion.*

During the eighteenth century there was a protracted conflict which led finally to the discovery of the true nature of combustion. The question was at bottom: 'Is fire an element?' We know now that, when carbon burns freely, it produces heat in uniting with the oxygen of the air to produce a compound called carbon-dioxide. But an influential school of chemists, following Stahl (1660–1734), for long maintained that in combustion there was an escape of the 'element' phlogiston. Ultimately decisive experiments were made. Substances were weighed both before and after combustion. The weight of the oxygen taken from the air was found to be approximately (that is to say, within the limits of experimental error) equal to the weight of that added to the carbon in making carbon-dioxide. 'Phlogiston' is, in fact, energy: heat is a form of energy. Fire is simply a manifestation of the energy which escapes during certain chemical combinations. It is not produced by the combinations but is liberated when they take place, just as water is not produced by turning a tap but is then liberated from the pipe which supplies the tap.

§ 17. *The law of 'conservation of matter'.*

Lavoisier (1743–1794) was thus led to formulate the law of conservation of matter. Matter, according to this law, is never destroyed: in all chemical transformations it merely enters into new combinations. Strictly speaking we have no right to affirm the conservation of *matter*. The experimental fact on which the principle is based is that the total weight of any group of substances is unaltered by any chemical combination which may take place between them. Now weight is a way of measuring inertial mass. Hence Lavoisier's principle should be formulated as the law of conservation of *mass*. It is based on experiment; and recent research goes to shew that its experimental basis is not rigorously true. In a chemical experiment in which heat is evolved, the heat escapes as energy. Now within the present century Einstein has shewn that energy itself has mass; but so small is the mass of the heat produced in ordinary chemical experiments that the most delicate balances would fail to reveal its loss. We may not say that, in a chemical experiment in which energy is given out, the total mass of the substances remains unaltered. The difference between the initial and final masses of the substances involved is a minute quantity which measures the mass of the energy lost.

§18. *Force.*

What now is the nature of energy? Before we can answer this question we must explain what is meant by the terms *force* and *acceleration*. We have said that heat is a form of energy and we all know that the heat obtained by burning coal can be used to drive a railway train. The engine pulls the train with a *force* exerted through the couplings. We exert force whenever we push bodies. Force, says the mathematical physicist, is that which when applied to matter produces change of velocity in the direction of the force. The rate of change of velocity is termed acceleration. The acceleration of a train is the rate at which it increases its speed. Retardation is negative acceleration, the rate at which a train's speed is diminished. Newton laid down the law that the force acting on a body is to be measured by the product of the inertial mass of the body and the acceleration produced in it by the force. Newton's second law of motion thus states that the acceleration of a body is equal to the force which acts upon it divided by its mass.

§19. *The implications of Newton's second and third laws of motion.*

In this law there are three terms, acceleration, mass and force. If we assume that we can measure acceleration or change of velocity—and this assumption is by no means as obvious as we might think—we are left with two unknown terms, *mass* and *force*. Mass, you may say, we can measure. Yes, but by weighing bodies, i.e. by comparing the forces with which the earth pulls them. We all know vaguely what force is. We experience certain sensations in our muscles when we try to move a body. We can then state that force is the cause of movement: but this is a metaphysical statement useless for the measurement of force. What Newton's second law does is to state how we can measure force when we assign to bodies certain numbers which we term their mass-measurements. As these mass-measurements are determined by the law, it is really a definition or, according to Poincaré, a convention and not an experimental fact.

The third law of motion states that to every action there is an equal and opposite reaction. In other words, if there is a force between the bodies A and B, the action of A on B is equal to the reaction of B on A. If we measure the forces by the convention assigned by the second law of motion, we can theoretically verify the third law by experiment. When A and B act upon one another we can approximately (that is to say, within the limits of experimental error) demonstrate that the mass of A multiplied by its acceleration is equal and opposite to the mass of B multiplied by its acceleration. But the convention of the second law of motion determines the numbers by which we measure the masses of A and B.

§ 20. *The law of conservation of energy.*

A force does *work*, that is to say it produces energy, when it moves the body to which it is applied. Thus the force in the coupling which attaches a train to its engine does work in moving the attached carriages relatively to the rails on which the train is moving. The energy produced is measured by the product of the force and the distance through which its point of application is moved in the direction of the force. A moving train thus acquires *kinetic energy* which ultimately comes from the coal which is burnt in the engine. Let us now suppose that the coupling, which attaches the train to the engine, snaps. The guard immediately applies his brakes to bring the train to rest. He thus applies frictional force to the wheels. The force of friction does work in stopping the train. Where has the energy of the train gone to? It has been dissipated in heat. Wherever the brake has been applied heat has been generated. Now comes a most important question: has any energy been destroyed in the whole process which began with the burning of the coal and ended with the stopping of the train? Joule (1818–1889), a great English physicist of the middle of the nineteenth century, by careful experiments was led to give a negative answer. He discovered the *mechanical equivalent of heat,* the connection between heat and kinetic energy. Energy is indestructible. We can transform it and, in so doing, deprive it of utility; but we cannot destroy it. The two laws of 'conservation of mass' and 'conservation of energy' were the great generalisations of nineteenth-century physics. They both rest upon experiment and therefore we can only affirm that they are true within the limits of experimental error. That the first of these two laws is erroneous we have already stated: the fusion of the two laws we shall shortly describe.

§ 21. *Mass and weight: inertia and gravity.*

We have seen that, if the first and third laws of motion be accepted on experimental facts, the inertial mass of a body is a number assigned to it by the definition contained in the second law. Now, in practical life, we always associate mass with the idea of quantity of matter; and, when we wish to determine the quantity of matter in a body, we weigh it. We are sure that there is twice as much butter in a lump which weighs two pounds as in a lump which weighs one pound: and we believe that there is as much matter in a pound of feathers as in a pound of lead. We cannot, however, measure quantity of matter: we measure either inertial mass or weight. Now the weight of a body is the force with which the earth attracts the body. Why then should measurement of this force lead us to assign to different bodies the same set of mass-numbers as we get by measuring inertia? The reason is a consequence of a remarkable fact which can be verified by experiment. In a vacuum a bullet and a feather fall with equal acceleration. We may say, more generally, that the acceleration of a body under the influence of gravity is independent alike of its material and of its physical state. Thus there is associated with every body a number, which we may term its *gravitational mass*, such that its weight is equal to its gravitational mass multiplied by the intensity of gravity.

Now by Newton's second law, the force acting on a body is equal to its inertial mass multiplied by its acceleration. When gravity is the cause of the acceleration, the force is the gravitational mass of the body multiplied by the intensity of gravity. Thus the acceleration of a body falling under gravity

$$= \frac{\text{gravitational mass}}{\text{inertial mass}} \times \text{intensity of gravity.}$$

Hence because of the truth of the experimental fact to which we have just referred the ratio of the gravitational mass of a body to its inertial mass must be a constant which is the same for every body we may care to investigate. By a suitable choice of units we can make this constant equal to unity. In this manner we reach the law that the gravitational mass of a body is equal to its inertial mass. This result Einstein has made fundamental in the general theory of relativity.

We thus see how, by weighing bodies, we can measure their relative masses. The weight of a body, however, depends on the intensity of gravity. This intensity varies slightly at different parts of the earth's surface, as is proved by the fact that bodies *in vacuo* fall with slightly different accelerations at different places. Thus, though weight gives us a convenient because roughly accurate measure of the inertial mass of a body, the weight of a body in London (i.e. the force with which the earth attracts it in London) will differ slightly from, say, its weight in

Calcutta. The ordinary man, confronted by terms like inertial mass and gravitational mass, is apt to say indignantly: 'But I wish to know the quantity of matter in a body'. Before he can get an answer he must tell us how to measure 'quantity of matter'. We can only measure mass or weight.

§ 22. *Einstein's revolution: energy has inertia.*

We have said that matter is not the only thing which possesses mass. A moving electron (atom of negative electricity) possesses inertia and, therefore, has inertial mass. When some radio-active elements break up such electrons are one result of their decomposition. Now the whole mass of an electron appears to be due to its electrical properties, its inertia being derived from the electro-magnetic field associated with it. That is why an electron has been described as content without a container. A Cheshire cat has been defined as a smile apart from a cat: similarly an electron, as a measurable entity, is believed to be inertia apart from matter. Hence, if we could attach any meaning to the principle of the conservation of matter, it could hardly be equivalent to the law of conservation of mass. Moreover, as we have already indicated, the latter law has lost its old independence of the law of conservation of energy. Einstein, as a deduction from the special principle of relativity, has shewn* that, if a body takes up an amount of energy E, its inertial mass increases by E/c^2, where c is the velocity of light. Thus the inertial mass of a body is not a constant but varies with the change in the energy of the body. Further, the aggregate inertial mass of a system of bodies can be regarded as the measure of the energy of the system. Hence the law of the conservation of mass becomes identical with the law of the conservation of energy and is only true of a system which neither takes up nor gives out energy.

The velocity of light is very great, some 186,000 miles a second. Hence it is impossible to shew directly by experiment that the inertial mass of a moving body increases with its velocity. But the fact has been established for the electrons (the so-called β-rays) which are ejected from radio-active bodies with speeds approximating to the speed of light. The inertial mass of those electrons which travel at 99 per cent. of the speed of light has been shewn to be about seven times as great as the inertial mass of an electron travelling with the ordinary velocities of our normal experience. Other indirect consequences of the relativity

* The theoretical investigation will be given in the concluding paragraphs of Lecture V.

theory have successfully satisfied experimental tests; and the great generalisation which Einstein calls the principle of the inertia of energy, that mass may be considered as a form in which energy appears, can hardly be doubted.

Matter *may* be nothing but congealed energy. On the other hand, inertia may be quite inadequate if it is regarded as a property which completely reveals the true nature of matter. The wise man will probably conclude that, in any such analysis of matter as we have summarised, reality has eluded us.

§ 23. *Dalton's atomic law.*

We were led to Einstein's great generalisation that mass is a manifestation of energy by the fact that the progress of chemistry was long impeded by modifications of the old belief that fire was one of the 'elements'. As soon as the phlogiston doctrine had been decisively abandoned, the analysis of material substances into their elements proceeded rapidly. One by one the common elements were separated and the more simple laws of their combination discovered. A theoretical advance of the greatest importance was made by Dalton* (1766–1844) with his Atomic Theory. It was found that the elements combined in fixed proportions as measured by weight. Thus, when carbon and oxygen combine to make carbon-monoxide (the familiar and poisonous 'water-gas' now commonly mixed with the coal-gas supplied to our houses), 12 parts by weight of carbon unite with 16 parts by weight of oxygen to given carbon-monoxide of weight 28. Similarly when carbon burns in oxygen to make carbon-dioxide, 12 parts by weight of carbon unite with 32 parts by weight of oxygen to give carbon-dioxide of weight 44. A similar law of combination by weight was discovered to be general. What did it imply? Dalton assumed that matter was not indefinitely divisible: it was not continuous, as Aristotle had taught, but, as Democritus had surmised, was built up of atoms (and molecules). An *atom* we may define to be the smallest particle of matter which can enter into chemical combination. According to the atomic theory each element is such that a quantity of it ultimately consists of atoms, indistinguishable from one another, each atom having a definite fixed weight. If the weight of an atom of hydrogen, the lightest element, be taken as unity†, that of an atom of carbon will be 12, and of an atom of

* Dalton's main conclusions, which almost inevitably contained errors, appeared in the first decade of the nineteenth century.

† More accurately, as will be seen later, 1·0078.

oxygen 16. In the language usually used, the *atomic weight* of hydrogen is 1 and that of carbon 12. When two or more elements combine to form a compound substance, one or more of the atoms of each unite to form a *molecule* of the compound: and the weight of the molecule will be the sum of the weights of the constituent atoms. The atoms of a single element may similarly unite to form molecules of the element. I would have you notice how the whole basis of the atomic theory is weight: we are still building on that fundamental property of matter which we term inertia.

§ 24. *Atoms: their existence and size.*

The atomic theory remained for some time no more than a speculation derived from the experimental law of combination by weight. Within the limits of experimental error (as to which we shall have something to say later) the law was true. But was the speculative deduction a fact? Did atoms really exist, or were they convenient figments of the mind? It was impossible to see an atom. Matter appeared to be infinitely divisible. If the atom existed, it was certain that it must be so small that even the most powerful microscopes could not reveal the atomic structure of matter.

Answers to enquiries as to the size and weight of an atom were given in the first place by ingenious deductions from the theory of gases. We are all familiar with the fact that water exists in three states. Normally it is a liquid. It becomes solid ice when sufficiently cooled; and it takes the state of a gas, steam, when sufficiently heated. As ice, its molecules are, roughly speaking, fixed relatively to one another: more accurately, the atoms oscillate about fixed mean positions, and their quivering produces such heat as the ice has. As water, they are in close contact but can move freely. As steam, they are dissociated one from another. The properties of a gas, some of which we shall consider in Lecture VIII, shew the behaviour of the free molecules of which it is composed. By investigating these properties, both the size and weight of the atoms of the various elements were theoretically determined long before there was any direct experimental evidence for the existence of an atom.

In these investigations certain assumptions were made. One of the most important was what is now called Avogadro's hypothesis, because it was first adumbrated by him in the year 1811, that equal volumes of different gases at the same pressure and temperature contain equal numbers of molecules. It follows from this hypothesis that, even in gases which are not compounds, the atoms are often united to form molecules. Most elements have diatomic molecules; but a number of metallic elements, such as mercury-vapour, are monatomic. A second assumption of the kinetic theory of gases is that the molecules of a gas are perfectly elastic, so that no energy is lost when they collide with each other or with the vessel in which they are contained. A third assumption is that the molecules of every gas are in a state of rapid motion. Each molecule travels with a high velocity for a very short distance when it meets another molecule (or exceptionally the vessel in which the gas is contained). Moreover it is a part of the third assumption that the heat of a gas is supposed to be due solely to the kinetic energy of the molecules. Under these assumptions the pressure on a vessel containing a gas will be due to the impacts of the molecules of the gas. Hence the pressure of a gas will be doubled when its volume is halved, provided the temperature be unchanged: this fact can be verified experimentally and is known as Boyle's law.

Avogadro's hypothesis can be deduced from our third assumption. For if two gases are at the same temperature, heat will not be transferred when they are in contact. Hence the average kinetic energy of the molecules of the two gases must be the same. Further, it will be shewn in Lecture VIII in connection with isotropic radiation that, if the pressures of two gases be the same, their energy density, i.e. the energy per unit volume, must be the same. Hence, if two gases are at the same pressure and temperature, their molecular density must be the same: in other words, equal volumes of each will contain equal numbers of molecules.

The average short distance that each molecule of a gas, at a given pressure and temperature, travels between successive impacts is called its *mean free path* for such pressure and temperature. Suppose now that two portions of the same gas at different temperatures are brought together. It is an experimental fact that they will gradually reach a common temperature: in other words, the average kinetic energies of their molecules will become uniform. Now the molecular velocities will become uniform as a result of collisions. Hence the rate at which a gas conducts heat at a given pressure and temperature will depend on the magnitude of its average molecular velocity and on the length of the corresponding mean free path. In this way a relation between the conductivity (which can be found experimentally), the average molecular velocity and the mean free path of a gas can be obtained.

But, as Joule first shewed, the average molecular velocity of a gas can be calculated when its pressure and mass-density are known. Hence the length of the mean free path of a gas can always be obtained.

As illustrating the size of the quantities under consideration, we may state that the average molecular velocity of hydrogen at 0° C. and atmospheric pressure is 1·8 km. per sec. and its mean free path is ·000017 cm.

Assume now that all molecules of a gas, even those which are not monatomic, are spherical. Then when the gas is condensed to a liquid all the spherical molecules are closely packed. Hence in any gas, compressible to a liquid, we can obtain a relation between the size of the molecules and their density at a given pressure and temperature. But obviously the length of the mean free path of a gas depends upon its average molecular velocity combined with the size and density of its molecules. If then we know the mean free path and also the average velocity of the molecules of a gas we have a second relation connecting their size and density. We can then theoretically find an approximate value for the size of the molecules of a gas.

Though based on assumptions that were not entirely satisfactory, the kinetic theory of gases thus led to the very probable conclusion that in size the molecules are all of the same order of magnitude, about 10^{-8} cm. in radius, so far as a radius can be said to exist. The number of molecules in one cu. cm. of a gas at 0° C. and atmospheric pressure is roughly 27×10^{18}. Further, an atom of hydrogen weighs $1·6 \times 10^{-24}$ grammes. The weight of an atom of any other element is obtained by multiplying this number by its atomic weight.

What does an atom look like? It is natural to think of the atoms of any solid substance as tiny billiard-balls. We shall see later that the true picture is rather a nucleus, small compared even with the dimensions of the atom, round which a number of electrons form a satellite system. The difficult question as to whether the satellites can be rightly pictured as moving in definite orbits will be considered in Lecture IX. The 'size' of the atom is the size of the small sphere within which the whole system can be contained.

It is an important philosophical principle that distinctions which make no difference to observable phenomena should not be introduced into physics. This principle was used by Mach (1838–1916) as the basis of speculations which paved the way for the theory of relativity. It led him also to regard the atomic theory as merely transitory. Until the present century his scepticism was shared by many; and a group of physicists and chemists regarded atoms and molecules as merely imaginative and sought to remove the atomic theory from physical chemistry. They urged in defence of this desire that atoms and molecules were, and always would be, inaccessible to observation. Since then, however, ingenious experiment has put an end to such pleas. Incredible though it sounds, "we are now in a position to examine many of the activities of a single atom, and even to count atoms, one by one, and to photograph the path of an individual atom. All these discoveries depend upon the behaviour of electrically charged atoms moving under the influence of electrical forces". We cannot indicate the character of these experiments until we come to that great triumph of physical theory, associated especially with the names of Sir J. J. Thomson and Lord Rutherford, the electrical constitution of matter.

§ 25. *Mendeléev's Periodic Table.*

The discovery of the atomic weights of the elements led men to consider whether any principle of connection between them could be discovered. When the elements were arranged in increasing order of atomic weight it was found that elements with similar properties tended to recur at periodic intervals. Mendeléev (1834–1907), about the year 1870, formed a Periodic Table in which such similarities were graphically exhibited. Only some 60 of the elements were known at that time: there are now places in the Periodic Table for 92 elements and all but two are believed to have been discovered. But the Table, even sixty years ago, shewed a striking periodicity of the elements: and its value was enhanced as newly discovered elements were gradually fitted into the gaps or vacant places which existed.

In the Table as we have it to-day the similar elements fluorine, chlorine, bromine and iodine occupy the 9th, 17th, 35th and 53rd places. The alkalis lithium, sodium and potassium occupy the 3rd, 11th and 19th places. The 'alkaline earths' beryllium, magnesium, calcium, strontium and barium occupy the 4th, 12th, 20th, 38th and 56th places. Obviously there was some reason for this periodicity: and it became still more challenging when the inert gases were discovered. These gases, helium, neon, argon, krypton, xenon and niton, are all monatomic; they will not combine chemically with other elements (or with one another) and they occupy the 2nd, 10th, 18th, 36th, 54th and 86th places of the Table.

But the Table was not wholly satisfactory, for in certain cases an element of larger atomic weight had to precede an element of smaller atomic weight in order to get the sequences of like elements satisfactorily spaced. Thus argon of atomic weight 39·94 precedes potassium of atomic weight 39·10. Similarly tellurium precedes iodine and cobalt precedes nickel.

§ 26. *Atomic number and the true order of the elements.*

An explanation of Mendeléev's Table was not forthcoming until the electrical theory of matter was developed. Then it was seen that, for the right order of the elements, *atomic weight* must be replaced by a new measure, *atomic number*; and the chemical properties of atoms were discovered to depend mainly on the outer rings of the planetary electrons which form groups of satellites to the central nuclei in the different atoms of matter. The total number of electrons which, in the electrically neutral atom of any element, are satellites of the central nucleus is equal and opposite to the positive charge on that nucleus and is defined to be the atomic number of that element. H. G. J. Moseley (1887–1915), a brilliant young English physicist who was killed in the Great War, demonstrated decisively, by investigating X-ray spectra, that the elements in Mendeléev's Table are properly arranged according to their atomic numbers and not according to their atomic weights. The great importance which chemists formerly assigned to atomic weight has been finally destroyed by Aston's discovery of the existence of *isotopes*, elements with identical chemical properties but of different atomic weights. But an adequate discussion of such matters belongs to the exposition of the electrical theory of matter which we shall discuss in a later lecture.

What I would, in conclusion, now insist upon is that in the Periodic Table we pass from deductions from measures of inertia to more general likenesses and dissimilarities between elements. Further, we reach the fact that all the elements are built to plan and are, so to speak, manufactured articles. Moseley's re-ordering of Mendeléev's Table is, in fact, a sort of manufacturer's catalogue. We are thus led to think of a cosmic factory and its products, and to reflect that from these products the whole material Universe is built. Is there not intelligence behind the whole elaborate scheme? I confess that I can form no satisfactory understanding of the process which has led to the creation of matter, as we now know it, save on the assumption that some Cosmic Artificer has been at work with the result that we can observe, even in the building of raw matter, creation according to plan.

Two generations ago Clerk Maxwell (1831–1879) ended his treatise on the *Theory of Heat* by a prophecy that molecules would be ultimately discovered to be uniform in size. He allowed himself for a moment to lift the veil by which, in his scientific work, he hid his religious convictions. In the light of subsequent discovery his words are worth recalling. "If we suppose the molecules to be made at all, or if we suppose them to consist of something previously made, why should we expect any irregularity to exist among them? If they are, as we believe, the only material things which still remain in the precise condition in which they first began to exist, why should we not rather look for some indication of that spirit of order, our scientific confidence in which is never shaken by the difficulty which we experience in tracing it in the complex arrangements of visible things, and of which our moral estimation is shewn in all our attempts to think and speak the truth, and to ascertain the exact principles of distributive justice?"*

The physicist of the present day would not allow that the molecules "remain in the precise condition in which they first began to exist". But, on the other hand, he certainly finds in the structure of matter a spirit of order. Yet there is a profound difference between orderly arrangement in the physical realm and the moral order associated with truth and justice. 'I am the Lord, I change not', could be said by a consistently unjust God. We must admit that in mechanical perfection, as such, there is no moral quality; just as there is no spiritual principle, save a bare consistency, in the uniformity of the law of inertia.

* J. Clerk Maxwell, *Theory of Heat*. Longmans, 1891, p. 342.

Lecture iii

SPACE

§ 27. *Our intuitions of space and time.*

From our experience of the external world we get our intuitions of space and time. We derive our idea of space from distances between objects. Time we think of as a something which flows uniformly or steadily. Newton defined absolute time as that which flows uniformly; but the definition is really only a description: we could not give any meaning to steady flow unless we already had a conception of time. This conception is an abstraction from experience. In actual life time is filled with values: it is qualitative. Lines of Scott and Tennyson expressing this fact have become hackneyed.

> One crowded hour of glorious life
> Is worth an age without a name.

> Better fifty years of Europe than a cycle of Cathay.

Time, we say, goes quickly when we are pleased or excited, slowly when we are bored. We can thus draw a distinction between 'psychological time', which is measured by our sensations, and 'clock-time', which is the public time of the community to which we belong. Now clock-time we can measure by numbers: it is quantitative. Hence it can be used in physical science. But necessarily in such science we ignore all the qualitative aspects of time. When we abstract from psychological time in this way we may even ignore the primary quality of time for our experience, the fact that it is irreversible. We cannot go backwards in time; but the numbers by which we measure it form a sequence which is not thus limited. These numbers, in fact, form what is called a one-dimensional continuum. By this we mean that they constitute a single sequence and that near any one we can find two others on either side of it and as close to it as we desire.

§ 28. *Measurements of time and of space.*

Our clock-time is public time: it is independent of estimates of the passage of time peculiar to particular individuals. The most obvious phenomena from which to get standard measurements, common to all, are furnished by the day and the year. Unfortunately, Nature has provided no satisfactory astronomical clock: it is a rather complicated process to get accurate averages of such varying quantities as the length of the day or month. A different physical phenomenon gives us a more simple way of measuring time. The beats of an ideally perfect pendulum are of equal duration. This is a fact which can be verified experimentally, by comparing the motions of pendulums of different lengths placed near together: it can also be deduced from physical theory. Clock-time as measured by such beats replaces the use of the earth as a time-keeper. Of course no clock which we can construct is perfect. Our measures of time may therefore be vitiated by the small errors which enter into all practical measurements. When, however, time is measured by aid of the refinements which the astronomer employs, such errors are very small indeed.

We thus see that ideally perfect clock-time, which we represent by the numbers of a one-dimensional continuum, is an abstraction from our ordinary physical experience. The conception of space which we use in natural science is similarly an abstraction. We get it partly from sight, partly from movement and touch. Our senses tell us that space has three dimensions, up or down, right or left, in front or behind. But things are seen, as we say, in perspective. A geometry based on sight alone would be what is called projective geometry. No two different individuals see the world around them in exactly the same way.

In order to get public space, an abstraction which shall correspond to the experience of all individuals, we start with the distance between two material points. Of 'space', apart from material bodies* which (as we say) are in space, our experience tells us nothing. We can, however, by means of a rigid rod measure the distance between two material points. (The question as to whether the rod, in view of the quivering of the atoms at its ends, has a definite length must be considered later: it leads to the idea that space is a statistical concept.) By moving the rod we can determine whether the distance between two other points of a material body is the same. But, in so doing, we use the assumption that the rod does not alter in length by being thus moved. Is this assumption true? We believe it to be a fact of experience. So far as we can test it empirically, it holds good. Euclid assumed its truth in his method of superposition. If we state the assumption accurately it takes the form: The distance or line-interval between two points of a rigid body is un-altered by any change of position of the body. Of course, no body is absolutely rigid. All may vary under strain or change of temperature. Our assumption applies to the ideally rigid body.

* We ignore, for the present, the determination of space by the existence within it of electrons or radiation.

§ 29. *The arbitrary separation of space from time.*

At this point it is necessary to say explicitly that in our measurements we cannot actually detach space from time. We observe 'point-instants': there is a time-succession in the operation of measurement and this time-measure we ignore in constructing a geometry of space independent of time. How far such a proceeding is legitimate is an enquiry which must be made later in connection with the doctrine of relativity.

§ 30. *The straight line and ideal measuring rod.*

How, now, are we to determine the distance between two points? The natural answer is: Measure the length of the straight line joining the two points. But what is the straight line? Euclid defines it as that which lies evenly between the two points. In different words, a point C lies on the straight line between the points A and B if it is in the line of sight from A to B. But this assumes that the path of a ray of light is a straight line. To avoid this assumption we define the straight line as the shortest distance from A to B, a definition which agrees with our intuition of straightness.

A distinguished ecclesiastical lawyer* of a generation ago wrote a book, *How to draw a straight line.* It was an interesting lecture on link-ages. An equally interesting book might be written on the subject, *How to define a straight line.* Obviously we cannot use the idea of shortest distance unless we have some method of measuring lengths; and, in practice, this method depends upon our having as a unit of measure-ment some standard of length or, in other words, a short piece of a straight line. Empirically we can determine the shortest distance be-tween the two points which we call the ends of this 'bit' of straight line; but there is little basis for a rigorous theory in the processes of measure-ment used in practical life. In the next lecture I shall describe the assumptions on which Riemann built the general geometry of space: and then it will become apparent that the lines of shortest distance between assigned points (or *geodesics* as they are called) form the naturally fundamental lines of space.

§ 31. *Coordinates: three-dimensional space and its numerical representa-tion.*

With our ideal measuring rod we can measure distances. The use of the measuring rod thus enables us to construct a scheme whereby the

* Sir A. B. Kempe (1849–1922).

position of any point in space can be determined by three numbers. To do this, we take three plane surfaces perpendicular to each other and attached to one another so as to form a rigid body. The planes themselves are called *planes of reference* and the intersections of these planes are called *axes of reference*. We may conveniently think of the three planes as two adjacent sides and the floor of a room. Then the position of any assigned point will be uniquely settled if we know the lengths of its perpendicular distances from the three planes. We must, of course, have a convention of positive and negative. If the distance of a point from the floor of a room is positive when the point is above the floor it must be negative when the point is in the cellar. The three (positive or negative) numbers which represent the distance of the point from the planes of reference are called its coordinates. There will be an indefinite number of points near an assigned point whose coordinates differ from those of the point itself by numbers less than the smallest number which we care to choose: as the numbers vary we cover (if we include irrational numbers) the whole of the possible space to which the point may pass. Thus we arrive at an abstraction from our experience, a space which is a three-dimensional continuum. Each point of the space is determined by three coordinates, x_1, x_2, x_3. As the numbers which measure these coordinates change, we get all points of the continuum. The advantage of this abstraction is that geometry is replaced by schemes of relations between sets of points, each of which is a triplet of numbers. We thus reduce geometry to algebraical analysis, of which number is the basis. To shew how this abstraction can be used would be to write a treatise on analytical geometry.

It is important to notice that our arbitrarily chosen framework of reference is essential in the scheme. To the notion of the position of a point in vague 'space' we can attach no meaning. "Every description of events in space involves the use of a rigid body to which such events have to be referred."

The three mutually perpendicular planes which we have used as the framework of reference, though the simplest, do not constitute the only framework which can be employed. Analytical expression of the relation of other possible frameworks of reference to that chosen is obtained by using a set of numbers u, v, w, where u, v and w are each functions of x_1, x_2, x_3. (A quantity q is said to be a function of quantities x_1, x_2, x_3, when the value of q is determined from the values of x_1, x_2, x_3, by a definite scheme of mathematical operations.) These functions are to a great extent arbitrary: that is to say, the scheme of operations can to a large extent be arbitrarily assigned. The relations which connect u, v, w with x_1, x_2, x_3 are called the equations of transformation from the one framework of reference to the other. Such transformations may involve the element of time when one framework is moving with respect to the other.

The most remarkable use of the general continuous transformation which corresponds to the choice of different fixed frameworks of reference was made by Riemann. His work we shall describe in the next lecture.

§ 32. *The fundamental assumptions of our geometries.*

The fundamental assumption made in all systems of geometry which we can construct to correspond with what we imagine to be our experience is, as we have said, that *rigid bodies can be moved in space without change of size or shape*. Euclid made a further assumption, equivalent to what is now known as Playfair's axiom, that from a point outside a straight line one, and only one, coplanar straight line can be drawn which does not cut the first line. This is the famous 'parallel postulate'. From it we derive the theorem that the sum of the angles of a triangle is equal to two right angles. From it also comes Pythagoras' theorem that the sum of the squares of the two sides of a right-angled triangle is equal to the square on the hypotenuse. For long attempts were made to prove Euclid's parallel postulate. All failed. Finally in the years 1826–1829 Lobatchewsky (1793–1856), followed independently in the years 1823–1832 by Bolyai (1802–1860), constructed a system of geometry in which a whole sheaf of coplanar lines can be drawn through a point outside a straight line so as not to cut the line. This so-called *hyperbolic* geometry of space is entirely self-consistent. It differs remarkably from the system of Euclid. For instance, the sum of the angles of a triangle is less than two right angles, the difference depending on the size of the triangle. In it, as in Euclidean geometry, space is infinite.

It was left for Riemann (1826–1866) to shew that hyperbolic geometry was not the only self-consistent scheme alternative to that of Euclid in which the fundamental hypothesis of the mobility of rigid bodies holds good. He constructed a scheme of what is often called *spherical* geometry, in which it is not possible to draw a single coplanar line through a point outside a straight line which does not intersect it. In other words, all coplanar straight lines intersect. In spherical geometry there are no parallels such as Euclid postulated. The three angles of a triangle are together greater than two right angles; and, further, every straight line returns into itself and is of finite length. Spherical three-dimensional space is of finite volume but has no bounds.

At this stage I will assume that the elements of Euclidean geometry are known to my readers and will proceed* to indicate the way in which the two types of non-Euclidean geometry can be built up by elementary considerations.

Before we begin our discussion two facts must be emphasised.

We shall, in the first place, speak of *straight lines* in non-Euclidean geometries. But it must be remembered that such lines are defined as lines of shortest (or longest) distance between assigned points. If a two-dimensional non-Euclidean surface were immersed in our own sup-posedly three-dimensional Euclidean space, such straight lines would appear to us to be curved and would not be lines of shortest distance between assigned points. When, however, we have three-dimensional non-Euclidean space there can be in it no lines joining assigned points which are shorter than the geodesics. The latter we can rightly call straight lines because they are paths of rays of light; and any point C on the 'straight line' joining A and B will be in the line of sight from A to B.

Secondly, we shall throughout speak of the two-dimensional spaces in which Lobatchewskyan and Riemannian geometries hold good as *planes*. It must not, however, be supposed that such two-dimensional areas are planes in three-dimensional Euclidean space. In such space they would be represented by curved surfaces for which what is called 'the Gaussian measure of curvature' is everywhere a constant, positive for Riemannian space and negative for Lobatchewskyan. Such curved surfaces cannot, by any process of bending without stretching, be made to coincide with Euclidean planes. Though we may visualise non-Euclidean 'planes' as curved surfaces in three-dimensional Euclidean space, such a proceeding is dangerous in so far as it may lead to the idea that non-Euclidean three-dimensional geometries are fanciful con-structions in three-dimensional Euclidean space. They are, of course, nothing of the kind. If the actual space of our experience is non-Euclidean, it cannot be also Euclidean. We shall see later (§71) that three-dimensional space of constant positive (Riemannian) curvature could exist in four-dimensional Euclidean space, if such space itself existed; but such Riemannian space cannot be changed into three-

* In the succeeding paragraphs I have made use of the exposition of H. S. Carslaw, *Elements of Non-Euclidean Plane Geometry*. Longmans, 1916.

dimensional Euclidean space. The two types are, in fact, radically different forms of space.

§33. *Consideration of Lobatchewskyan or hyperbolic plane geometry.*

In this geometry we accept Euclid's tacit assumption that the unlimited straight line is infinite in length. We do not, however, assume the truth of his postulate with regard to parallel lines. This postulate is by him stated in the form: "If a straight line falling on two other straight lines makes the interior angles on the same side less than two right angles, the two straight lines, if produced indefinitely, will meet on that side on which the angles are together less than two right angles".

This postulate is not used by Euclid to establish the earlier propositions of the first book of his *Elements*. In fact, these propositions hold good for hyperbolic geometry.

Euclid defines parallel lines as "straight lines which being in the same plane and being produced indefinitely in both directions do not meet one another in either direction". Then he finds it necessary to use his parallel postulate to prove (1. 29) that "if a straight line falls on two parallel straight lines, it makes the alternate angles equal to one another and the interior angles on the same side together equal to two right angles".

From this proposition it follows that the sum of the three angles of a triangle is equal to two right angles and the whole scheme of Euclidean geometry can be deduced in the familiar manner.

Euclid assumed, in effect, that if we have a straight line AB and a point P, we can through P draw a single parallel to AB.

Lobatchewsky rejected this postulate and, on the contrary, assumed that through P we can draw a whole sheaf of lines which, by Euclid's definition, are parallel to AB. Formal shape was given to the assumption by Hilbert.

§34. *Hilbert's axiom.*

This axiom states that through any point P, not on a straight line AB, we can draw in the plane PAB two lines b_1Pa_1 and a_2Pb_2, as in the figure, such that *any line through P within or on the boundary of the angle a_1Pb_2 will not meet AB*, while every other line, which passes through P, within the region a_1Pa_2, will meet AB.

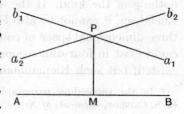

In hyperbolic geometry the lines Pa_1 and Pa_2 are called the *right-handed* and *left-handed parallels* through P to AB. The other lines through P which do not meet AB are not termed parallels in hyperbolic geometry, though they are parallels by Euclid's definition.

The angle between either Pa_1 or Pa_2 and the perpendicular PM from P on AB (both angles are readily proved to be equal) is called the angle of parallelism and is usually denoted by $\Pi(p)$ when $p = PM$.

When $\Pi(p) = \dfrac{\pi}{2}$, the lines Pa_1 and Pa_2 will be in the same straight line; and we have Euclidean geometry.

A peculiar feature of hyperbolic geometry of the plane at once strikes us. With every length p there is *associated by the very nature of space* an angle $\Pi(p)$. Thus, when we have settled the measure of an angle, the measure of length is thereby determined. In Euclid's geometry, after the measure of an angle is settled, the measure of length is still arbitrary.

Simple considerations shew that in hyperbolic geometry a straight line Pa_1 preserves at all its points its property of being parallel to a given line AB.

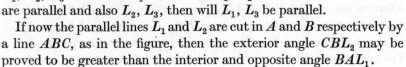

Moreover if Pa_1 is parallel to AB, then AB is parallel to Pa_1.

Further, if we have three straight lines L_1, L_2, L_3 in the same plane and if L_1, L_2 are parallel and also L_2, L_3, then will L_1, L_3 be parallel.

If now the parallel lines L_1 and L_2 are cut in A and B respectively by a line ABC, as in the figure, then the exterior angle CBL_2 may be proved to be greater than the interior and opposite angle BAL_1.

§35. *Saccheri's quadrilateral.*

Saccheri (1667–1733) was an Italian Jesuit, professor of mathematics at Pavia, and a younger contemporary of Newton. He was firmly convinced that Euclid's scheme was the uniquely possible geometry of the space of our experience and was led to frame alternatives to Euclid's postulate so that by the process of *reductio ad absurdum* he might leave Euclid's scheme alone in possession of the field. Had he been a little more adventurous* he would by a century have anticipated the work of Lobatchewsky and Bolyai. As it was, he made important advances, and the quadrilateral called by his name is associated with propositions

---

* Perhaps one cannot fairly expect that a Jesuit should be adventurous in upsetting established belief.

often made fundamental in modern elementary expositions of non-Euclidean geometry.

Saccheri's quadrilateral is an isosceles quadrilateral $ABCD$ of which the base angles A and B are both right angles and of which the sides AD and BC are equal.

If we use congruence theorems, which depend on the principle that rigid bodies can be freely moved without change of size or shape, it can be shewn that the angles at C and D are equal. Furthermore, in hyperbolic geometry the angles

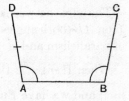

at C and D can fairly easily be proved to be both acute. Thence it follows by quite elementary considerations that the sum of the angles of every triangle is less than two right angles.

In Euclidean geometry the angles at C and D of Saccheri's quadrilateral are both right angles: we shall see later that in Riemannian or spherical geometry they are both obtuse.

§36. *The limiting curves of sets of parallel lines and the fundamental congruence theorem associated with them.*

We have seen that between the parallels b_1Pa_1 and a_2Pb_2 to a given line AB there is a whole sheaf of lines which according to Euclid's definition would be parallel to AB. As these lines are not called parallels in hyperbolic geometry we may describe them as lines which neither intersect nor are parallel to AB. In connection with such lines there is a somewhat important proposition that "if two straight lines neither intersect nor are parallel, they must have a common perpendicular". The converse of this proposition is also true: "if two straight lines have a common perpendicular, they will neither intersect nor be parallel".

If then we have a set of parallel lines they cannot have a common perpendicular. The curved line which corresponds to the common perpendicular of Euclidean geometry is in hyperbolic geometry often called the *limiting curve*.

On two parallel lines L_1 and L_2 take points P_1 and P_2 such that the angle $L_1P_1P_2 = L_2P_2P_1$, these angles being on the same side of the line P_1P_2: then P_1 and P_2 are called *corresponding* points and the *locus of points corresponding to a given point on a sheaf of parallel lines is the limiting curve.*

If P_1P_2 and Q_1Q_2 are two limiting curves, cutting the parallels L_1 and L_2 in P_1, Q_1 and P_2, Q_2 respectively, then $P_1Q_1 = P_2Q_2$.

It can further be established that any two limiting curves of the same sheaf of parallel lines are congruent: in other words, if we take up Q_1Q_2 and its parallels and put Q_1 on P_1 and Q_1L_1 along P_1L_1, then Q_1Q_2 will lie along P_1P_2 and the line Q_2L_2 will fall along a parallel to L_1 through the point P_2' of the curve P_1P_2 which corresponds to Q_2. This important proposition serves to measure arcs of limiting curves. From it we deduce that, if a third parallel L_3 cuts the limiting curves in P_3, Q_3, then

$$\frac{\text{arc } P_1P_3}{\text{arc } P_1P_2} = \frac{\text{arc } Q_1Q_3}{\text{arc } Q_1Q_2}.$$

We can now shew that, if the parallel straight lines OV and UP be cut by two limiting curves in OU and VP re- 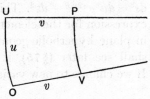 spectively, and if $u = OU$, the length being measured along the limiting curve, and if $v = OV = UP$, then arc $PV = ue^{-v/R}$, where R is a constant.

The proof is rapid. Let $PV = \phi(v)$. From the congruence theorem we have, for all general real values of v and t,

$$\frac{\phi(v+t)}{\phi(v)} = \frac{\phi(v)}{\phi(v-t)}.$$

Let t be small: expand by Taylor's theorem and equate coefficients of t^2. We get

$$\phi\frac{d^2\phi}{dv^2} - \left(\frac{d\phi}{dv}\right)^2 = 0,$$

whence $\phi(v) = Ce^{-v/R}$, where C and R are constants. When $v = 0$, $\phi(v) = u$. Hence $C = u$.

If O be taken as origin of coordinates and if we take axes $u = 0$ and $v = 0$ (namely the line through O and the corresponding limiting curve), any point P in the plane may be defined by coordinates u and v. Obviously, therefore, our theorem opens the way to an analytical investigation of hyperbolic geometry.

The constant R which has been introduced in integration is *the natural constant of hyperbolic space*. We shall see later that it can be used to measure the curvature of that space. For different types of hyperbolic space R varies: in other words some are more curved than others. Evidently for Euclidean space R is infinite, so that Euclidean space is not curved. Inasmuch as the space of our experience is, at most, only slightly different from Euclidean space we may be certain that, if our space is Lobatchewskyan, R is a very large number.

§37. *The line-element in hyperbolic geometry.*

Let P be the point (u, v), and let Q be the point $(u + du, v + dv)$. Further let ds be the line-element
PQ. Then, in the figure,

$$PR = dv \text{ and } QR = TU e^{-v/R}$$
$$= du\, e^{-v/R}.$$

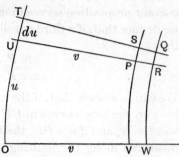

Now, since Pythagoras' theorem holds good for infinitesimal triangles, we have $PQ^2 = PR^2 + QR^2$; and hence $ds^2 = du^2 e^{-2v/R} + dv^2$. This gives the expression for the element of length in plane hyperbolic geometry. As we shall see later (§75), it can be made fundamental in the theory. If we change to new variables x and y by means of the equations

$$e^{x/R} = \frac{u}{R} \coth \frac{y}{R},$$

$$\sinh \frac{y}{R} = \frac{u}{R} e^{-v/R},$$

we have

$$ds^2 = dx^2 \cosh^2 \frac{y}{R} + dy^2.$$

Let A be the area $OVPU$, and let dA be the change in A corresponding to an increase of v to $v + dv$. Then we have $dA = PVWR = PV \times PR$; or $dA = dv\, u e^{-v/R}$. Hence

$$A = uR\{1 - e^{-v/R}\}.$$

If we make $v \to \infty$, we shall have $A \to uR$. Thus we see that the total area between any two parallel lines and a limiting curve is finite and equal to uR, where u is the length of the limiting curve intercepted between the lines and R is the constant of hyperbolic space.

§38. *The value of the angle of parallelism in hyperbolic space.*

Suppose that Pa be a parallel through a point P to a line OL, and let p be the length of the perpendicular PM on OL. Then θ, the angle MPa, is the angle of parallelism $\Pi\,(p)$ corresponding to the distance p.

We have already stated that, by the very nature of hyperbolic space, an angle $\Pi(p)$ is always associated with a length p. But we have also seen that in such geometry there is a natural constant R which measures the curvature of space. We now proceed to connect $\Pi(p)$, p and R.

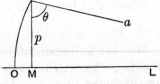

Let OP be the limiting curve of the parallels OL and Pa.

Let $OP = u$, $OM = x$, $PM = y$. Then, by the elementary geometry of congruent figures, we may shew* that

$$e^{x/R} = \cosh y/R,$$
$$u = R \sinh y/R.$$

From these results it follows that, since $\sin \theta = \dfrac{dy}{du}$, we have

$$\cos \theta = \tanh y/R.$$

We therefore have

$$\tan \frac{\theta}{2} = e^{-y/R}.$$

Thus the angle of parallelism $\Pi(p)$ is such that

$$\tan \tfrac{1}{2} \Pi(p) = e^{-p/R},$$

which is the relation required.

When $R \to \infty$ we have Euclidean geometry and $\Pi(p) \to \pi/2$.

§ 39. *The self-consistency of hyperbolic geometry.*

We need not further work out the geometry of the hyperbolic plane. So far as we have gone such geometry is fantastic but self-consistent: and these properties it retains however far we may carry it. For long it was thought that some self-contradiction would emerge from the scheme if only it were carried sufficiently far. That belief, however, within the second half of the nineteenth century was finally dissipated.

The most simple proof of the inherent consistency of Lobatchew-skyan geometry is derived from the general theory of transformations; but it can be expressed in terms of elementary geometry. It consists in establishing a unique correspondence between lines in the hyperbolic plane and Euclidean arcs of circles within and, when produced, ortho-gonal to a given circle.

Poincaré calls this the 'dictionary' method of proof. We take pro-positions in hyperbolic geometry and translate them into propositions affecting circles orthogonal to a given circle in the Euclidean plane.

* The investigation is not reproduced as the analytical methods adumbrated in the next lecture are more powerful and much less tedious. (*Vide* §§ 75, 76.)

Because every proposition of the hyperbolic plane can be so translated and because also there are no inconsistencies in Euclidean geometry, it follows that hyperbolic geometry is self-consistent.

§40. *The analogue with sets of circles orthogonal to a given circle.*

We take a fundamental circle K and call points inside it h-points.

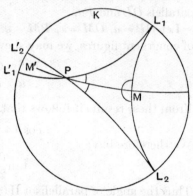

Points on the circumference of K are excluded from the domain of h-points. The h-line through two h-points is the arc of a circle through the two points orthogonal to K. The angle between two h-lines is the angle at which they meet.

The parallels through an h-point P to an h-line L_1L_2 are the h-lines PL_1 and PL_2, where L_1 and L_2 are the points in which the h-line meets the fundamental circle. Surprise at this definition diminishes if we remember that from our circular figure we exclude all points on or outside K. To see that the definition is reasonable we construct PM, the h-line perpendicular to L_1L_2, i.e. the arc of the circle which cuts both K and L_1L_2 at right angles.

Then, as we readily see by inverting with respect to the intersection of PM and K, the angles L_1PM and L_2PM are equal. Further, any h-line through P within the angle L_1PM will cut L_1L_2. Further, if L_1P, MP and L_2P be produced to L'_1, M', L'_2, any h-line through P and within the angle $L_1PL'_2$ will not cut L_1L_2. Thus our new definition of parallels corresponds to that of the hyperbolic plane. The angle L_1PM is the angle of parallelism corresponding to the perpendicular PM.

We need to define the h-length of an h-line AB. Let AB meet K in L_1 and L_2 so that the order of the points is L_1ACBL_2, as in the figure. Then the h-length of AB, which we denote by $\overline{AB}$, is defined by

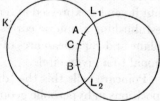

$$\overline{AB} = -R\log\left(\frac{AL_1}{AL_2}\bigg/\frac{BL_1}{BL_2}\right),$$

where R is our previous constant of curvature.

Plainly from this definition $\overline{AL_1}$ is infinite, so that L_1 and L_2 correspond to points at infinity in the hyperbolic plane.

Further, if C lies between A and B on the same h-line, it follows from the definition that $\overline{AC} + \overline{CB} = \overline{AB}$.

Thus our definition satisfies the metrical properties of the hyperbolic plane; and, as we shall shortly shew (§ 42) by evaluating the angle of parallelism, R as just defined is actually the previous constant of curvature.

An example.

As an example of the use of our circular analogue for establishing propositions of the hyperbolic plane we will now prove that, in the analogue, any h-triangle has the sum of its angles less than two right angles.

Such a triangle is made of arcs of three circles C_1, C_2, C_3, orthogonal to K.

Let $C_2 C_3$ meet in P, outside K, and invert the system from P so that K inverts into itself. The angles of the curvilinear triangle are unaltered by inversion; and after inversion we get a triangle within K formed by two straight lines meeting at the centre of K and an arc of a circle orthogonal to K whose centre is therefore outside K. The sum of the angles of this triangle is obviously less than two right angles: and therefore the same fact holds good of the original h-triangle.

§ 41. *The analogue to displacements of a rigid body.*

When first confronted by the circular analogue to the hyperbolic plane we tend to object that the analogue must be imperfect because nothing corresponds to the free movement of a rigid body which is possible in hyperbolic space. But an analogue in two dimensions to such movement can readily be constructed.

Suppose that we have any two h-points A and a. We can in general find one and only one circle α, orthogonal to K, with respect to which A and a are inverse points. Moreover the h-line Aa will then be 'bisected' by the h-line α. In other words a will be the h-reflection of A in the h-line α.

If then we wish in the h-plane to move a rigid lamina so that a point A of the lamina comes to the position a, we merely invert the lamina with respect to α.

Suppose next that we wish to make an h-line AB of the lamina lie in a given h-direction ab'. After the inversion with respect to α the h-line AB will take the position of the h-line ab, let us say. To make it now take the position of the h-line ab', all that is necessary is a second inversion with respect to an h-line β which passes through a and with respect to which ab and ab' are inverse h-lines.

Thus any displacement of a rigid lamina in the hyperbolic plane can be represented by two inversions in the circular analogue. We can, in fact, assert that nothing can happen in the hyperbolic plane for which there is not a circular analogue.

We have limited our 'dictionary' to two dimensions: but we can readily extend it so as to create a complete analogue between hyperbolic space and systems of spheres cutting a fixed sphere orthogonally. The extension is so obvious that it is unnecessary to develop it in detail.

A simple analogy between the French and English languages will now convince us that the hyperbolic geometry of space is a self-consistent system. For the sake of argument we may assume that any idea capable of expression in English can equally well be expressed in French. There would then be no point in describing one language as more perfect or more satisfactory than the other. Similarly, remembering that the geometry of our circular analogue is Euclidean, we are forced to say that it is impossible, as between Lobatchewskyan and Euclidean geometry, to describe one system as more perfect or more satisfactory than the other. Each is self-consistent and, provided R be very large, either can be true within the limits of empirical observation. The Euclidean scheme is much the more simple and so we tend to prefer it. But Nature is not determined by our preferences: there is no reason to believe that the Universe was built on a simple plan that we might understand it. In point of fact, as we shall see later, it is probable that the space of the Universe is neither Euclidean nor Lobatchewskyan: it is more likely to be that which has the geometry which in § 32 we termed Riemannian or spherical.

§ 42. *The utility of the circular analogue. Various examples.*

Many theorems relating to the hyperbolic plane are most easily proved or visualised by their circular analogues.

For instance, we see at once that two straight lines can either meet, be parallel or not meet. In the latter case they have a common perpendicular which does not exist in the two former cases.

Also parallel lines are asymptotic: they continually approach one another but only meet at infinity.

Further, *similar triangles of different sizes cannot exist in the hyperbolic plane.*

If they could exist we could move one of the triangles ABC so that one corner and two sides were coincident with one corner and two sides of the other triangle $A'B'C'$. We should then get a figure, as in the diagram, in which $bB'C'c$ is a quadrilateral the sum of whose angles is four right angles. It is obvious that this is impossible in the h-plane inasmuch as the sum of the angles of each of the triangles bcC' and $bB'C'$ is less than two right angles. In fact similar figures of different sizes only exist in Euclidean space.

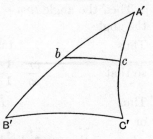

As a final example of the utility of the circular analogue we will use it to find the value of the angle of parallelism.

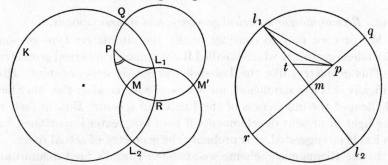

Let P be an h-point not lying on an h-line L_1ML_2, and let PM be the h-line through P perpendicular to L_1L_2.

Then L_1PM is the angle of parallelism corresponding to the perpendicular PM.

Let the circles PM and L_1ML_2, which are each orthogonal to the fundamental circle K, meet again in M'; and invert with respect to M' so that K inverts into itself.

Denote inverse points by small letters.

The h-line L_1ML_2 becomes a straight line l_1l_2 cutting K at right angles, i.e. a diameter. Similarly pm is a diameter and, therefore, m is the centre of K.

The h-parallel PL_1 becomes the arc l_1p of a circle touching l_1m at l_1.

Because h-lengths are defined by an anharmonic ratio they are unaltered by inversion.

Hence
$$\overline{PM} = \overline{pm} = R\log\left(\frac{pr}{pq}\Big/\frac{mr}{mq}\right)$$
$$= R\log\left(\frac{pr}{pq}\right).$$

Let the tangent at p to the arc $l_1 p$ meet $l_1 m$ in t.

Then the angle $tpm = L_1 PM = \theta$, the angle of parallelism. Hence the angle $\qquad tl_1 p = (\pi/4 - \theta/2)$.

Thus $\qquad\qquad\qquad \tan(\pi/4 - \theta/2) = pm/ml_1,$

so that $\qquad \dfrac{pr}{pq} = \dfrac{1 + \tan(\pi/4 - \theta/2)}{1 - \tan(\pi/4 - \theta/2)} = \cot\theta/2.$

Thus $\qquad\qquad\qquad \overline{PM} = R\log(\cot\theta/2),$

or $\qquad\qquad\qquad\qquad \tan\theta/2 = e^{-y/R},$

where y is the perpendicular from P on the line $L_1 M L_2$. We thus obtain with singular elegance our previous result of §38, and shew that the two definitions in which R is involved are consistent.

§43. *Riemannian or spherical geometry, and its assumptions.*

We proceed now to consider briefly the alternative type of non-Euclidean geometry which is called Riemannian or spherical geometry.

This geometry, like the Lobatchewskyan, is self-consistent. Historically it is less significant, for it was discovered after the other had challenged the uniqueness of the Euclidean scheme. But, in fact, in the light of present developments it is of far greater importance for, as has been suggested, it is probably the geometry of actual space.

In the Riemannian scheme we abandon Euclid's tacit assumption that a straight line is of infinite length. It can be proved, if Euclid's assumption be granted, that the angles of a triangle cannot exceed two right angles. Thus, when a complete straight line is infinite in length, we must have either the Euclidean or the Lobatchewskyan scheme of geometry. Of course, when a complete straight line is finite it must be unbounded or endless: thus, in other words, it must return into itself. If this happens, any two straight lines in a plane must intersect*, and, therefore, parallel lines according to Euclid's definition will not exist. Thus at the basis of spherical Riemannian geometry lie two facts. First, any straight line produced indefinitely will return into itself and so be of finite length. Secondly, any two straight lines in a plane will intersect if each be produced sufficiently far.

§44. *The pole of a line in Riemannian geometry.*

We rapidly prove that all perpendiculars to a given line L on the same side of it must meet in a point O, called the pole of L. The per-

---

* We are excluding 'elliptic' geometry (§44) by assuming that the plane is a two-sided surface.

pendiculars when produced on the other side of the line will meet in a point O', which is called the *anti-point* of O. All the perpendiculars from either pole to the line will be of equal length λ. If any perpendicular AO be produced to meet L again in A', we shall have $OA' = \lambda$.

Discrimination between spherical and 'elliptic' geometry.

Two possibilities now arise. There is, in the first place, the case of spherical geometry in which O and O' are different. In this case the line $O'AO$, when produced, will return to O' and be of length 4λ. Thus two straight lines joining O and O' can enclose a space; and the two points O and O' will not determine a straight line.

The second possibility gives rise to the so-called 'elliptic' geometry (the name is unfortunate) in which O and O' coincide. The length of a complete straight line is now 2λ. Moreover, if we have two points P and Q on opposite sides of an endless line L in the same plane as P and Q, we can pass from P to Q without cutting L. An endless straight line in elliptic geometry does not in fact divide the plane into two parts.

The plane in spherical geometry is two-sided: that of elliptic geometry is a one-sided surface. The latter type of surface can be formed from a ribbon by giving one end a twist through two right angles and then sewing it to the other end of the ribbon. We shall not further consider this elliptic geometry.

§45. *Riemannian plane geometry is, in effect, that of a sphere.*

By elementary geometry it may readily be shewn that the sum of the angles of a triangle in the Riemannian plane is greater than two right angles.

Moreover, the area of a triangle is proportional to the excess of this sum above two right angles. Hence similar figures of different sizes do not exist.

In the Riemannian plane let PM be the perpendicular from a point P to a line OX. Put $PM = y$, $OP = r$, $OM = x$. Then, so long as r is less than λ, it is easy to shew that y/r decreases and x/r increases with r.

If OY be perpendicular to OX, and if PN be the perpendicular to Oy from P, we must not assume that $NOMP$ is a parallelogram: it will be a quadrilateral with three right angles and therefore with the angle at P an obtuse angle.

It is hardly worth while to develop Riemannian geometry by elementary methods as, from what has already been said, it is fairly clear that a complete correspondence can be established between plane Riemannian geometry and the Euclidean geometry of the surface of a sphere. Just as such geometry of the surface of a sphere is self-consistent, so is plane Riemannian geometry, and such consistency extends to Riemannian geometry of three dimensions. All the formulae of the Riemannian plane can be reduced to spherical trigonometry.

We shall consider Riemannian geometry in more detail in our next lecture. As we have just remarked, plane Riemannian geometry is, in effect, the geometry of a surface of constant positive curvature, a sphere on which the geodesics or great circles correspond to straight lines in the Riemannian plane. Similarly, as we shall shew in detail in §76, plane Lobatchewskyan geometry is the geometry of a surface of constant negative curvature, called a pseudo-sphere, on which the geodesics also correspond to straight lines in the plane. We may add that the initial propositions of Euclid, which rest on the notion that a rigid lamina can be freely moved without change of size or shape, will apply to all surfaces of constant curvature provided we replace the straight lines of a plane by geodesics of the surface. Euclid's development of geometry obscures this fact; for he first excludes Riemannian geometry by his assumption that the straight line is infinite in length and he then excludes Lobatchewskyan geometry by his postulate as to parallels.

Euclid's scheme and method bear witness to the existence of acute geometrical insight in himself (and also most certainly in his predecessors). Yet we need to emphasise more fully than the consideration is emphasised in his *Elements*, that all our geometries rest on the fact that rigid bodies can be freely moved. This fact would appear to be more certain than subordinate assumptions such as the parallel postulate or the infinite length of the unbounded straight line. These subordinate assumptions cannot be demonstrated by observation or experiment. All we can affirm is that they are very good approximations to the truth.

§ 46. *The theory of groups of displacements of a rigid body as the basis of geometry.*

An alternative method of building up the three possible geometries of the space of our experience is based upon the theory of *continuous groups*. Let capital letters denote positions in space. Then the displacement of a rigid body from A to B followed by its displacement from B to C is, we believe, equivalent to its displacement from A to C.

So also the displacement from A to B is equal and opposite to the displacement from B to A.

Now a set of operations is said to constitute a group when the result of combining any number of the operations is to give a member of the set.

Hence all the displacements of a rigid body constitute an infinite group in which is included the operation of identity. Further, if space be continuous the group is continuous, for the displacements along any line, joining homologous points of two positions A and B, can be so chosen that they form a continuous series whose elements correspond to all commensurable or incommensurable numbers arising from the division of the line.

§ 47. *The idea of space as homogeneous, isotropic and unbounded.*

We say that space is *homogeneous* when it is such that the group of displacements of a rigid body from a position A corresponds exactly to the group of displacements from any position B to which the rigid body can be moved from the position A. Thus our fundamental postulate as to the possibility of freely displacing a rigid body in space, without any change in the size or shape of the body, involves the idea that space is homogeneous.

Similarly this postulate implies that all displacements possible from position A are also possible from position B to which the body can be rotated from A. We express this technically by saying that space is *isotropic*.

If space is homogeneous and isotropic it must be unbounded, for at a point on the boundary of space, did such exist, these properties would fail.

§ 48. *The two sub-groups of rotation which exist for all types of space.*

Sophus Lie (1842–1899), whose investigations into the groups of space are classic, shewed the great importance in the theory of the *sub-groups of rotation*.

When out of all the operations of a group we can separate a class of operations which themselves constitute a group, this is called a sub-group of the complete group.

Evidently all the displacements of a rigid body which correspond to rotations round a fixed point constitute a sub-group. Equally all the displacements of the body which correspond to rotations round an axis joining two points of the body constitute a sub-group. It may be observed that one way of defining a straight line is by saying that a straight line joining two points consists of those points which are motionless in rotations round an axis joining the two points.

Lie gave analytical expression to the theory of continuous groups and shewed that there are three groups of displacements which have the sub-groups just described. These three groups correspond to the space-geometries of Euclid, Lobatchewsky and Riemann respectively.

§49. *Euclidean space and the parallel displacement sub-group.*

What in the theory of groups constitutes the criterion by which we single out Euclidean space? For an answer we need to grasp the idea of 'parallel displacement'.

In Euclidean space we can always, as we believe, freely move a body so that the direction of an axis of the body is invariable: it can be readily shewn that the aggregate of such displacements constitutes a sub-group. For let l be an axis of the body and consider motions in which the direction of l is fixed: let us say, for example, that l always points to the pole star. As a rigid body is thus moved, the motion from A to B followed by the motion from B to C will be equivalent to the motion from A to C. We thus have a series of parallel displacements in which the direction of l is unaltered and they constitute a sub-group. But this is only possible in Euclidean space. In Riemannian space no parallel in position B exists to correspond to the line l in position A; and in Lobatchewskyan space Euclid's idea of a single parallel is abandoned.

We can prove, moreover, that no corresponding sub-group exists in non-Euclidean space.

Suppose for convenience of description that our rigid body consists simply of a directed line l which moves in two-dimensional space. We can in non-Euclidean space of two dimensions move l from A to B and we might define its position at B as that which makes at B the same angle with the straight line (or geodesic) AB produced as it makes with AB at A. In similar fashion we could uniquely specify the position of l at any other point C. Now it might be thought that, although the different positions of l were not parallel in the Euclidean sense, yet they were everywhere definite and so enabled us to build up the sort of sub-group which exists for parallel displacements in Euclidean space.

But this involves the assumption that the direction of the rod at C, when moved from A to C, is the same as its direction at C after it has been moved from A to B and then from B to C. This assumption in non-Euclidean space is untrue. Thus Euclidean space emerges from the theory of groups as that space in which alone a sub-group of parallel displacements exists.

§ 50. "*If there were no solid bodies we should not have geometry.*"

The investigation of space by means of the theory of groups is of value because it shews clearly that our geometry is built on what we imagine to be the behaviour of rigid bodies: it results from the assumption that such bodies can move freely without change of size or shape. Poincaré puts it: "If there were no solid bodies we should not have had geometry". The same writer has also said epigrammatically: "What we call geometry is nothing but the formal properties of certain groups and so we can say 'space is a group'".

When a man, who has been brought up to believe in the absolute truth of Euclidean geometry, is for the first time introduced to the far more complicated possibilities of non-Euclidean geometry, he is inclined to ask somewhat impatiently: "But can this fantastic stuff apply to the Universe of our experience? Is there any chance that our space is thus curved or warped?" When at length he is converted to the possibility that our space may be slightly curved, he goes on to ask whether the fact can have any importance, seeing that the curvature is so slight that we have not yet invented instruments and appropriate experiments sufficiently precise to measure it. We reply that, if space is Riemannian, it will be finite; and there is a vast difference between a Universe which is infinite and one which is finite. If God's Universe is finite, we can hope to begin to understand the range of His activity: if it is infinite any such hope must be abandoned. Suppose, however, that a philosopher comes to us and says: "You have elaborated non-Euclidean forms of geometry, but do you think that you have really discovered the metaphysical character of space?" To him our answer must be a humble negative. All that we actually know, or think that we know, about space is that in it a body can be moved unchanged from one position to another. Of space apart from matter, or from energy which is perceived as radiation and which like matter has inertia, we can say nothing. Matter is so closely bound up with our spatial perception that it seems to create space*. It is true that greater knowledge tells us† that radiant energy equally with matter gives, as it were, actuality to space. But the void, where neither matter nor energy can potentially exist, remains the void, a pure negation.

If we are to give a meaning to such a negation, we must assume that in it ideally solid bodies can be freely moved without change of size or shape. It is this assumption which gives to space a geometry, and such geometry can be Euclidean, Lobatchewskyan or Riemannian. If the geometry be Riemannian, then space is finite and, as we shall see in § 80, there is no space outside it. In other words, a finite Riemannian cosmos embraces the whole of space: it is not a cosmos set in some imaginary product of hazy thinking termed 'empty space'.

* This statement must be considered in conjunction with certain speculative conclusions from the General Theory of Relativity set out at the end of Lecture VI.

† Perhaps we ought merely to say that radiation can be represented by mathematical formulae which seem to imply vibrations in space.

Lecture iv

RIEMANN'S GENERAL THEORY OF SPACE

§ 51. *Introduction.*

In the present lecture we shall consider one of the most brilliant
achievements in the history of human progress: Riemann's General
Theory of Space.

A few words as to its author may not be superfluous. Georg Friedrich
Bernhard Riemann was born in the year 1826 and died in the year 1866
before he had attained the age of 40. He studied under Gauss at Göttingen and subsequently at Berlin. His complete works are contained in
a single, not very large, volume; but, by reason of the fertility of thought
and the mental grasp shewn in the various memoirs which Riemann
wrote, he will rank among the greatest mathematicians of all time. His
great paper* *On the hypotheses which lie at the basis of Geometry* was
written in the year 1854 when he was but 28 years of age. It was not,
however, published until the year 1867, nearly two years after his death.
Its importance was quickly perceived, not least because Helmholtz
(1821–1894) at the height of his fame drew attention to its value. In
the novelty and range of its ideas and in the far-reaching character of
its conclusions, it marks an epoch in the development of our understanding of space and its properties. The nature of the analysis by
which Riemann gave form to his ideas was barely indicated in the
paper; and since his time a group of men, among whom we may mention
Christoffel, Ricci and Levi-Civita, have built up the calculus of tensors as the necessary technique. Riemann did not confine his speculations to three-dimensional space. They were concerned with manifolds
(varieties of space which exist in the mathematician's mind) of any
number of dimensions; and the analysis for the most general case can
be expressed in such a form that it is not more complicated than when
we are dealing with three dimensions.

When we set out to investigate the properties of a generalised space,
each point of which is defined by n numbers, the extreme generality of

---

* Clifford's translation of the paper will be found in W. K. Clifford, *Mathematical Papers*. Macmillan, 1882, pp. 55–71. The paper is available in French
in *Oeuvres Mathématiques de Riemann*. Gauthier-Villars, 1898, pp. 280–99. The
original text is in B. Riemann, *Gesammelte Mathematische Werke*. Teubner,
1876, pp. 254–69.

the undertaking gives us at the outset a sense of impotence. What assumptions must we make, and how can we give mathematical form to such assumptions?

We assume first of all that our generalised space is continuous when continuity is conceived in the following way. A point P of the space is defined by n numbers, which are, of course, not necessarily either integers or rational. If each of these numbers is changed by some small number and all these small numbers are less in absolute magnitude than a definite small number ν, the new set of numbers will define an adjacent point Q of our generalised space. Moreover, if our space is continuous, a point Q will exist however small ν may become and the distance or interval PQ will become as small as we please when we choose ν sufficiently small. At this stage a critic may raise the objection: 'But is space really continuous?' The answer must be a confession of ignorance. Certain quantum phenomena appear to suggest that space may be ultimately discontinuous, and it must be admitted that other speculations point in the same direction. Yet, *per contra*, one may ask whether space has any texture apart from the binding forces, gravitational and electrical, which act within it. It is a reasonable hypothesis that space subjected to such forces is continuous.

Secondly, we assume that we can find some common rule for comparing lengths at different points of our generalised space. We assume, in fact, that if we move a length l from A to B, its measurement at B will not depend on the path by which it is moved and, further, that the length of a small interval at B can be expressed in terms of the numbers defining the ends of the interval exactly in the same way as the length of a small interval at A can be expressed in terms of the numbers defining its ends.

In order to get a satisfactory conception of the way in which we may choose the numbers defining our continuous manifold we must at the outset explain the nature of the intrinsic coordinates introduced by Gauss for the study of surfaces in three-dimensional space.

§52. *Intrinsic geometry of a surface.*

It was Gauss (1777–1855) who first called attention to the *intrinsic* geometry of a surface. Imagine, in the space of our common experience, an ordinary surface represented by a flexible inextensible membrane, this membrane having any natural shape when it is everywhere taut and not necessarily having then the form of a plane. When a surface of this kind is deformed in any way, figures drawn upon it will take different shapes in space; but some at any rate of their properties will be invariant, that is to say unchanged by any deformation. For instance, if two intersecting lines be drawn on the membrane, they will continue to intersect however it be deformed. Further, if we measure *along the surface* the length of the line joining any two points, this measurement will be invariant. In fact, any property which can be investigated without leaving the surface of the membrane will be independent of its deformations and will belong to its intrinsic geometry. It is only after some thought that we convince ourselves that this statement is true: it is surprising that any geometry of a plane should remain invariant when the sheet of paper on which the geometrical figures are drawn is crumpled up into a ball.

§ 53. *Gaussian coordinates.*

Gauss' coordinates were devised for the expression of intrinsic properties. On an ordinary surface in three-dimensional space we can imagine a series of curves drawn. We call these curves $x_1 = $ constant. For varying values of the constant they will cover the whole surface, and we imagine that the functions x_1 are so chosen that through each point of the part of the surface that comes within our consideration one, and only one, x_1-curve passes. Similarly we draw another series of curves, $x_2 = $ constant, which intersect the former system and together with it form a network covering the whole surface. We assume that an x_1-curve and an x_2-curve only intersect in a single point. Any point on the surface will then be given uniquely by the values of x_1 and x_2 at the point. Thus we may say that the coordinates of a point P are x_1, x_2: similarly the coordinates of an adjacent point P' will be $x_1 + dx_1$, $x_2 + dx_2$.

§ 54. *The line-element in Riemann's generalised space.*

The distance $PP' = ds$ will be measured wholly in the surface and will be an intrinsic element of length. If x, y, z are the three-dimensional rectangular Euclidean coordinates of P, $x + dx$, etc., will be similar coordinates of P'; and by Pythagoras' theorem we shall have

$$ds^2 = dx^2 + dy^2 + dz^2.$$

Now x, y, z, the coordinates of P, will each be expressible in terms of x_1 and x_2. Hence we must have

$$ds^2 = g_{11}dx_1{}^2 + 2g_{12}dx_1dx_2 + g_{22}dx_2{}^2,$$

where the g's are magnitudes which depend in a definite way on x_1 and

x_2. Riemann assumed that for manifolds of any number of dimensions the line-element could be similarly expressed. When, in fact, the Gaussian coordinates of an n-dimensional manifold are $x_1, \ldots x_n$, Riemann assumed that

$$ds^2 = g_{11} dx_1{}^2 + \ldots + g_{nn} dx_n{}^2$$
$$+ 2g_{12} dx_1 dx_2 + \ldots 2g_{n-1,\, n} dx_{n-1} dx_n,$$

where $g_{rs} = g_{sr}$. He thus assumed that Pythagoras' theorem is true for infinitesimal triangles in space of any number of dimensions. It is difficult to see exactly what is involved in this assumption: as Riemann himself indicated, we might equally have assumed that a fourth power of ds was a bi-quadratic function of $dx_1, \ldots dx_n$. Pythagoras' theorem, however, suggests that the assumption actually made is satisfactory; and alternatives must wait for further investigation. The expression for ds^2 is said to determine the *metric* of space or of the corresponding n-dimensional manifold. It gives, in fact, the law of measurement at every point; and thus all the intrinsic properties of a two-dimensional surface (or of a more general manifold) are analytically expressible in terms of the quantities g and their differentials.

Why, it may be asked, should it be necessary to introduce infinitesimal quantities, as we do when we define the character of space by a formula of the type

$$ds^2 = g_{11} dx_1{}^2 + \ldots + 2g_{12} dx_1 dx_2 + \ldots ?$$

For an answer we observe that the formula serves to express the way in which we can find the length of a small 'bit' of interval at every point of space. By means of it, therefore, we can pass continuously from point to point through the whole of space; and so, in fact, geometry at a distance can be built up from the geometry of adjacent points. It is well known that Faraday (1791–1867), in exactly the same way, reduced electrical action at a distance to electrical action at adjacent points of what is called the electrical field. The mainspring of Riemann's work, as Weyl has well said*, is "the principle of gaining knowledge of the external world from the behaviour of its infinitesimal parts".

In order completely to characterise the intrinsic geometry of our generalised space we need no knowledge save of ds and therefore of the $n(n+1)/2$ functions g. These functions determine all the properties of our generalised space: any *natural* features of the space can therefore be expressed in terms of them.

* Hermann Weyl, *Space—Time—Matter*. Translated by H. L. Brose. Methuen, 1922, p. 92.

§55. *Geodesics of a manifold.*

It is fairly obvious that we can make no progress with regard to the analysis of space, even after we have obtained Gaussian coordinates to specify its points, unless we can determine some natural structure within it. The natural structure for Euclidean space is made by straight lines: they are the shortest distances between points which they join, and are thus defined by particularly simple properties. In general space we create an analogous structure by determining the *geodesics* of the space. If we have two points P_1, P_2, the length of the line joining them will be

$$L = \int_{P_1}^{P_2} ds.$$

This line will be a geodesic if it is so drawn that L has a stationary value: in other words, it must be as long or as short as possible. Expressed mathematically we say that its variation must vanish, or

$$\delta L = 0.$$

We can immediately by analytical transformations put this condition in the form

$$\int_{P_1}^{P_2} \sum_{1}^{n} {}_k p_k \delta x_k \, ds = 0,$$

where

$$p_k = \sum_{1}^{n} {}_j g_{jk} \frac{d^2 x_j}{ds^2} + \sum_{1}^{n} {}_{jl} [jl, k] \frac{dx_j}{ds} \frac{dx_l}{ds}.$$

In the latter expression $[jl, k]$ is called *Christoffel's symbol of the first kind* and is defined by

$$[jl, k] = \tfrac{1}{2} \left[\frac{\partial g_{jk}}{\partial x_l} + \frac{\partial g_{kl}}{\partial x_j} - \frac{\partial g_{jl}}{\partial x_k} \right].$$

Inasmuch as the condition just written must hold whatever be the arbitrary functions δx_k, we must necessarily have $p_k = 0$, for $k = 1, 2, \ldots n$.

We thus obtain the equations of the geodesics of our manifold and we find that they contain only intrinsic functions, the g's and their differentials, as the nature of geodesics leads us to expect. The geodesics will obviously form a natural system of threads through our manifold which we can use as a basis when we proceed to investigate its curvature.

§56. *Outline of Riemann's investigation.*

We will now, before proceeding farther, give a brief outline* of the method which Riemann suggested for the investigation of the curvature of continuous manifolds of any number of dimensions.

---

* Throughout this investigation I have made use of the exposition of T. Levi-Civita, *The Absolute Differential Calculus.* Translated by M. Long. Blackie, 1927. I have sought to indicate ideas and methods, while of necessity omitting elaborate analysis.

The geodesics of generalised space are clearly the most simple natural constructions within it, for they correspond to straight lines in ordinary Euclidean space. Now, if in such ordinary space we are given a point P and two straight lines PA and PB, we can find one and only one plane containing PA and PB. Similarly, in generalised space, if we are given a point P and two geodesics PA and PB, we can find one and only one *geodesic surface* (doubly-infinite manifold) containing PA and PB. In this way we construct natural two-dimensional surfaces in Riemann's generalised space. Is there now any intrinsic property of these surfaces which will give us knowledge of some intrinsic property of generalised space? Before the time of Riemann's investigation a satisfactory answer to this question had been given by Gauss, who had shewn that what is now called the Gaussian curvature of a surface was an intrinsic property depending solely on the inner measure-relations of the surface or, in other words, on the quantities g which enter into the expression for ds in terms of the intrinsic coordinates of the surface.

If we have a plane curve we define the curvature at any point P to be the rate at which the curve bends. We take a small 'bit' of the curve $ds = PP_1$, joining two adjacent points P and P_1 upon it. From an arbitrary point O we draw radii of unit length, perpendicular to the tangents at P and P_1; and we measure the small angle $d\alpha$ between these lines. Then the curvature of the curve at P is the value of the ratio $d\alpha/ds$ in the limit when $d\alpha$ and ds are both very small.

Gauss shewed that we can find similarly an expression for the curvature of a two-dimensional surface. We take an element of the surface of area dS bounded by a small oval curve on the surface. From an arbitrary point O we draw radii of unit length perpendicular to the tangent-planes to the surface at all points of the small curve. We shall thus get a number of radii of a sphere making a small solid angle $d\omega$ at the centre of the sphere. The Gaussian curvature of the surface at a point P within dS is defined as the value of the ratio $d\omega/dS$ in the limit when $d\omega$ and dS are both very small. Because Gaussian curvature is an intrinsic property of a surface, it is unaltered however the surface be bent provided there is no stretching. In the language of analysis, Gaussian curvature is a function of the g's which is an invariant for all such transformations of the two intrinsic variables x_1 and x_2 as leave

$$ds^2 = g_{11}\,dx_1{}^2 + 2g_{12}\,dx_1\,dx_2 + g_{22}\,dx_2{}^2$$

unaltered.

A geodesic through a point P is completely determined if we know its direction at P. Hence a geodesic surface through P will be completely determined if we have given two directions tangential to it drawn from P, say Pa and Pb.

Riemann, in investigating his generalised space, took at an arbitrary point P the geodesic surface determined by two directions Pa and Pb. He then calculated the Gaussian curvature K of this surface at P. Nowadays we call K *the Riemannian curvature* at the point P of generalised space corresponding to the section of that space determined by the two directions Pa and Pb. Such curvature is an intrinsic property of the space and therefore depends solely on its inherent nature and also, of course, on the directions Pa and Pb. Thus K can be expressed in terms of the quantities g together with expressions which give the directions of Pa and Pb. Moreover, for all transformations of Gaussian coordinates which leave ds invariant, K will itself be an invariant.

Thus, corresponding to any two specified directions Pa and Pb at a point P of our generalised space, we can find a quantity K which is an invariant for general transformations of coordinates.

Now in generalised space of n dimensions a direction Pa is determined by n contravariant components of a vector $u^1, \ldots u^n$.

Suppose that the direction Pb is similarly determined by the components v^i, $i = 1, 2, \ldots n$. Let α be the angle between Pa and Pb. Evidently $K \sin^2 \alpha$ will be symmetrical in the u's and v's. It can, as we shall see in § 66, be put in the form
$$K \sin^2 \alpha = \Sigma \, (ij, hk) \, u^i v^j u^h v^k, \qquad \ldots\ldots(1)$$
where the summation is for all values from 1 to n of i, j, h and k and where (ij, hk) is called Riemann's symbol of the first kind.

The algebra of generalised space is thus the algebra of Riemann's symbols. It was originally developed as the calculus of tensors in order to investigate generalised space: since that time it has been found to be, when $n = 4$, exactly the type of analysis necessary in the theory of general relativity.

In obtaining the expression for $K \sin^2 \alpha$ we shall only have assumed that our generalised space is continuous and with a metric defined by
$$ds^2 = g_{11} dx_1{}^2 + 2 g_{12} dx_1 dx_2 + \ldots + g_{nn} dx_n{}^2.$$
If, now, such space is the space of our experience, it will be, in the language of § 47, homogeneous and isotropic. The formula (1) will enable us to give algebraical form to this characteristic of our space and so to determine the most simple form which ds^2 can take for the kinds of space in which rigid bodies can be freely moved without change of size or shape.

§ 57. *The measurement of angles.*

Before we can begin any investigation of curvature we need to devise expressions by which angles can be measured. Let us at the beginning confine ourselves to ordinary two-dimensional surfaces for which x_1, x_2 are intrinsic (or Gaussian) coordinates. If P be a point x_1, x_2, then clearly dx_1, dx_2 represent a definite tangential direction drawn from P. For the parameters of this direction we take the quantities

$$\lambda^1 = \frac{dx_1}{ds}, \quad \lambda^2 = \frac{dx_2}{ds},$$

where ds is the distance between P and the adjacent point whose coordinates are $x_1 + dx_1$, $x_2 + dx_2$. Remembering the metric of the surface, we see that the parameters are connected by the identity

$$\overset{2}{\underset{1}{\Sigma}}_{i,k} g_{ik} \lambda^i \lambda^k = 1.$$

Corresponding to such parameters (or contravariants) we have a system of moments (or covariants) defined by

$$\lambda_i = \overset{2}{\underset{k=1}{\Sigma}} g_{ik} \lambda^k, \quad \text{for } i = 1, 2.$$

Evidently
$$\overset{2}{\underset{i=1}{\Sigma}} \lambda_i \lambda^i = 1.$$

If we express the rectangular Euclidean coordinates x, y, z in terms of the Gaussian coordinates x_1, x_2, and then use the usual expression in rectangular coordinates for the cosine of the angle between two lines whose direction-cosines are given, we get

$$\cos \theta = \overset{2}{\underset{1}{\Sigma}}_{i,k} g_{ik} \lambda^i \mu^k = \overset{2}{\underset{1}{\Sigma}}_k \lambda_k \mu^k = \overset{2}{\underset{1}{\Sigma}}_i \lambda^i \mu_i,$$

where θ is the angle between the lines whose parameters are λ^1, λ^2 and μ^1, μ^2 respectively. If we take $\lambda^i ds = u^i$ and $\mu^i dS = v^i$, where ds and dS are elements of length on the surface in the directions λ and μ respectively, then the u's and v's are independent. Hence $\underset{ik}{\Sigma} g_{ik} u^i v^k$ is a bilinear form in two sets of arbitrary contravariant variables. Further, the quantities g_{ik} form, as we shall shew in § 63, a tensor of the second rank. Hence, as we shall see later (§ 63), the bilinear form must be an invariant. Its value is actually $\cos \theta \, ds \, dS$.

We may readily prove that

$$\sin^2 \theta = (g_{11} g_{22} - g^2{}_{12}) (\lambda^1 \mu^2 - \lambda^2 \mu^1)^2.$$

§ 58. *Parallelism with respect to a surface.*

We next introduce the very important idea of parallelism with respect to a surface. A little reflection convinces us that we cannot *in general* move a vector (or directed length) from one point P_1 of a surface to another point P_2 without changing its direction, the vector remaining constantly tangential to the surface. In the particular case when the surface is a Euclidean plane there is no trouble: lines at the two points P_1, P_2 are then parallel. For a general two-dimensional surface we can in the following way get a correspondence *which we shall call parallelism.* We join the two points P_1, P_2 of the surface by some definite line l lying, of course, on the surface. We then roll* the surface on a plane so that it begins by touching the plane at the point P_1: as the surface rolls, its point of contact with the plane continually moves along the line l till motion ends when the surface touches the plane at the point P_2.

Corresponding to the vector at P_1 there will be a definite line p_1 on the plane. At the point P_2 on the plane draw the line parallel to p_1: then the vector on the surface which coincides with this parallel after rolling is said, *with respect to the surface and to the line l,* to be *parallel* to the original vector. The parallelism between two vectors defined in this way obviously depends on the line joining the points at which they are placed. If then two points P_1, P_2 are at a finite distance apart, we can only speak of the parallelism of two tangential vectors R_1 at P_1 and R_2 at P_2 if we describe it as being with reference to a definite line l joining P_1 and P_2. But the lengths of the vectors do not enter into the conditions for parallelism.

We can now shew that geodesics are autoparallel curves.

If l be a geodesic on the surface, it will be the shortest distance joining P_1 and P_2 and will therefore be a straight line on the plane. Thus the angle which the vector R_1 makes with the geodesic at P_1 will be equal to the angle which the vector R_2 makes with the geodesic at P_2: in other words, parallel directions on the surface at points of a geodesic make equal angles with the geodesic. If then the vector R_1 be tangential to the geodesic at P_1, the vector R_2 will be tangential at P_2: in short, geodesics are autoparallel curves.

§ 59. *Infinitesimal parallel displacement.*

If there is only an infinitesimal distance between P_1 and P_2, the condition for parallelism between vectors R_1 and R_2 at these two points

* The rolling must be 'pure': there must be no spinning.

will be independent of the arc joining them. Our geometrical construction by which parallelism was defined shews that we must join P_1 and P_2 by the arc of a geodesic on our two-dimensional surface and that the angle which R_1 makes with the geodesic at P_1 must be equal to the angle which R_2 makes with the geodesic at P_2. When, however, P_1 and P_2 are infinitesimally near points any infinitesimal line joining them may be regarded as a geodesic. It is therefore clear that the fact that two vectors at points of a surface infinitesimally distant from one another are parallel is analytically expressed by conditions which involve only the vectors, the two points and the metric of the surface. In other words, infinitesimal parallelism is intrinsic to the surface. Finite parallelism has, of course, no such property.

Suppose now that R^1, R^2 are the contravariant components of a unit-vector R which is, of course, tangential to our two-dimensional surface of which the metric is given by

$$ds^2 = \Sigma g_{jk}\,dx_j\,dx_k.$$

Let R be displaced from the point x_1, x_2 along an infinitesimal path on the surface, the path being defined by dx_1, dx_2. Let dR^1, dR^2 be the changes in R^1, R^2 respectively corresponding to a parallel displacement of R. We proceed to obtain the conditions which connect dR^1, dR^2 with R^1, R^2, and to verify that they depend only upon the quantities g_{jk} which give the metric of the surface.

Let ds be the arc of the geodesic, through x_1, x_2, which is in the direction defined by the elements dx_1, dx_2. If θ be the angle between the unit-vector R and the geodesic, we know by §57 that

$$\cos\theta = \overset{2}{\underset{1}{\Sigma}}_{jk} g_{jk} R^j \frac{dx_k}{ds}.$$

For an infinitesimal parallel displacement of R in the direction dx_1, dx_2 this angle is constant.

Hence along the geodesic we must have

$$\frac{d}{ds}\left(\Sigma g_{jk} R^j \frac{dx_k}{ds}\right) = 0,$$

or
$$\Sigma_{jk}\left\{R^j g_{jk}\frac{d^2 x_k}{ds^2} + \frac{dR^j}{ds}g_{jk}\frac{dx_k}{ds}\right\} + \Sigma_{jkl}\left\{R^j\frac{dx_k}{ds}\frac{\partial g_{jk}}{\partial x_l}\frac{dx_l}{ds}\right\} = 0.$$

Utilise now the value of $\dfrac{d^2 x_k}{ds^2}$ given by the equations of the geodesic which were obtained in §55. We thus eliminate from our parallelism conditions the curvature of the geodesic and obtain an equality which merely involves the direction $\dfrac{dx_1}{ds}$, $\dfrac{dx_2}{ds}$. This equality is

$$\sum_{jk} \frac{dR^j}{ds} g_{jk} \frac{dx_k}{ds} + \sum_{jkl} R^j \frac{dx_k}{ds} \frac{dx_l}{ds} \left\{ \frac{\partial g_{jk}}{\partial x_l} - [kl,j] \right\} = 0.$$

Now, if $[ij, k]$ be Christoffel's symbol of the first kind as defined in § 55, we have

$$\frac{\partial g_{jk}}{\partial x_l} - [kl,j] = [jl,k].$$

Our equality may therefore be written

$$\sum_{k=1}^{2} t_k \frac{dx_k}{ds} = 0, \qquad \text{......(1)}$$

where $\qquad t_k = \sum\limits_{j=1}^{2} g_{jk} dR^j + \sum\limits_{j,\,l=1}^{2} [jl,k] R^j dx_l.$

Now because R_1, R_2 are components of a unit-vector which is tangential to the surface, we have

$$1 = \sum_{jk} g_{jk} R^j R^k.$$

Hence, differentiating,

$$0 = 2 \sum_{jk} g_{jk} R^k dR^j + \sum_{jk} R^j R^k \sum_{l} \frac{\partial g_{jk}}{\partial x_l} dx_l,$$

or $\qquad 0 = 2 \sum\limits_{k} R^k \{ t_k - \sum\limits_{jl} [jl, k] R^j dx_l \} + \sum\limits_{jkl} R^j R^k \dfrac{\partial g_{jk}}{\partial x_l} dx_l.$

Thus $\qquad \sum\limits_{k} t_k R^k = \tfrac{1}{2} \sum\limits_{jkl} R^j R^k \left\{ \dfrac{\partial g_{lk}}{\partial x_j} - \dfrac{\partial g_{jl}}{\partial x_k} \right\} dx_l,$

or $\qquad\qquad \sum\limits_{k=1}^{2} t_k R^k = 0. \qquad \text{......(2)}$

Since the vectors whose components are respectively R^k and dx_k/ds are unconnected, we see from equations (1) and (2) that

$$t_k = 0, \quad (k = 1, 2).$$

These equations give the values of dR^1, dR^2 corresponding to the infinitesimal parallel displacement of the vector whose components are R^1, R^2, in the direction defined by dx_1, dx_2.

An alternative form of the conditions for infinitesimal parallel displacement.

We have obtained the conditions for the infinitesimal parallel displacement of the versor*, whose contravariant components are R^1, R^2, in the form $t_k = 0$,

where $\qquad t_k = \sum\limits_{1}^{2} {}_j g_{jk} dR^j + \sum\limits_{1}^{2} {}_{jl} [jl, k] R^j dx_l \qquad (k = 1, 2).$

* It is convenient to use the term versor to express a vector of unit length.

A different form can readily be given to these equations. We put

$$g = \begin{vmatrix} g_{11} & g_{12} \\ g_{21} & g_{22} \end{vmatrix},$$

and we take $g \times g^{hk}$ to be the minor (with its proper sign) of g_{hk} in g. Then obviously

$$\sum_1^2{}_i g^{hi} g_{ki} = 0, \text{ if } h \neq k,$$

$$= 1, \text{ if } h = k.$$

Take now $$t^i = \sum_1^2{}_k g^{ik} t_k.$$

Then $$t^i = \sum_{kj} g^{ik} g_{jk} dR^j + \sum_{kjl} g^{ik} [jl, k] R^j dx_l,$$

or $$t^i = dR^i + \sum_{jl} \{jl, i\} R^j dx_l,$$

where $$\{jl, i\} = \sum_1^2{}_k g^{ik} [jl, k].$$

The expression $\{jl, i\}$ is called *Christoffel's symbol of the second kind*.

We thus see that the conditions for the infinitesimal parallel displacement in the direction defined by dx_1, dx_2, of the versor whose components are R^1, R^2, may be written in the form

$$dR^i = - \sum_1^2{}_{jl} \{jl, i\} R^j dx_l.$$

These are the intrinsic equations of parallelism for a surface of two dimensions.

§ 60. *Infinitesimal parallel displacements of infinitesimal tangential vectors satisfy the parallelogram rule.*

Suppose now that we have two infinitesimal tangential vectors at a point P of a surface. We may denote these by dP and δP respectively, where dP stands for an infinitesimal element PP_1 on the surface and δP for a similar element PP_2. The (contravariant) components of dP will be dx_1, dx_2, and of δP they will be δx_1, δx_2.

Suppose now that the vector dP be moved by infinitesimal parallel displacement from P to P_2. It will take up the position $P_2 Q_2$, let us say. If now the vector δP be moved by infinitesimal parallel displacement from P to P_1 it will similarly take up the position $P_1 Q_1$, let us say. Our proposition asserts that Q_1 and Q_2 coincide. Thus, if we denote the point of coincidence by Q, $PP_1 Q P_2$ will be an infinitesimal parallelogram.

The increment of dP, when P is moved a distance δP to P_2, may be denoted by δdP, the corresponding increment of a coordinate x_i being δx_i.

Hence, by the result obtained in the previous paragraph, we have

$$\delta dx_i = -\sum_{jl}\{jl, i\}\,dx_j\,\delta x_l.$$

Similarly $$d\delta x_i = -\sum_{jl}\{jl, i\}\,\delta x_j\,dx_l.$$

But, as is readily seen, the symbol $\{jl, i\}$ is unaltered by the interchange of j and l. Hence

$$\delta dx_i = d\delta x_i.$$

But the coordinates of P are x_i; of P_1 they are $x_i + dx_i$, and of P_2 they are $x_i + \delta x_i$, for $i = 1, 2$. Hence the coordinates of Q_1 are

$$x_i + \delta x_i + d(x_i + \delta x_i) \quad \text{or} \quad x_i + \delta x_i + dx_i + d\delta x_i.$$

Similarly those of Q_2 are

$$x_i + dx_i + \delta x_i + \delta dx_i.$$

Thus, because $\delta dx_i = d\delta x_i$, Q_1 and Q_2 will coincide.

The above parallelogram property of infinitesimal parallel displacements of infinitesimal vectors tangential to a surface can be made the basis of the whole theory. We would again emphasise that the infinitesimal vectors can be regarded as infinitesimal arcs of geodesics on the surface.

§ 61. *The extension to n-dimensional manifolds.*

The whole of the previous investigation can be readily extended from two-dimensional surfaces to continuous n-dimensional manifolds. The fundamental metric or inner measure-determination of the manifold is taken to be

$$ds^2 = \sum_{ik}^{n} g_{ik}\,dx_i\,dx_k,$$

where $$g_{ik} = g_{ki}.$$

Sometimes we shall speak of the continuous n-dimensional manifold with such a metric as a V_n. Any vector within it will be determined by n parameters (contravariant components of the vector)

$$\lambda^i = \frac{dx_i}{ds} \qquad (i = 1, \dots n);$$

or, equally, by n moments (covariant components of the vector)

$$\lambda_i = \sum_{k}^{n} g_{ik}\lambda^k \qquad (k = 1, \dots n).$$

The notion of angle.

We may assume that *the angle* θ between two vectors whose parameters are λ and μ is defined by

$$\cos \theta = \overset{n}{\underset{1}{\Sigma}}_{ik} g_{ik} \lambda^i \mu^k = \overset{n}{\underset{1}{\Sigma}}_i \lambda^i \mu_i = \overset{n}{\underset{1}{\Sigma}}_k \lambda_k \mu^k.$$

For, if $\lambda^i ds = u^i$ and $\mu^i dS = v^i$, when ds and dS are elements of length in the directions of the two vectors, the u's and v's will be independent. Hence $\Sigma_{ik} g_{ik} u^i v^k$ will be a bilinear form in two sets of arbitrary contravariant variables. Since the quantities g_{ik} are components of a tensor, the form, as we shall see in §63, will be invariant for all transformations of the coordinates $x_1, \ldots x_n$. Our assumption, being the natural extension of the result previously obtained when $n = 2$, is therefore justified.

The *scalar product* of two vectors R and T is defined to be the product of the lengths of the vectors multiplied by the cosine of the angle between them: this scalar product may therefore be written

$$\overset{n}{\underset{1}{\Sigma}}_i R^i T_i,$$

and in analogous forms.

The definition of infinitesimal parallel displacement in n-dimensional manifolds.

The notion of parallelism corresponding to infinitesimal displacement is easily extended to an n-dimensional manifold V_n. If dR be the change in a vector R, corresponding to an infinitesimal parallel displacement of R from its point P, then the angle between R and the geodesic defined by the direction of the displacement must be unaltered by the displacement.

Further, the vector must belong to the manifold V_n. These conditions correspond exactly to those previously adopted when $n = 2$ and evidently express properties intrinsic to V_n. If now we use the equations of a geodesic in the manifold, already obtained in § 55, we see that we can define the n quantities dR^j by the equations

$$t_k = 0, \quad (k = 1, \ldots n),$$

where $$t_k = \overset{n}{\underset{1}{\Sigma}}_j g_{jk} dR^j + \overset{n}{\underset{1}{\Sigma}}_{jl} [jl, k] R^j dx_l \quad (k = 1, 2, \ldots n).$$

§62. *Parallel displacement round an infinitesimal parallelogram.*

By using the conception of infinitesimal parallel displacement we can determine the curvature properties of a manifold in the vicinity of any assigned point.

Consider an ordinary surface ($n = 2$) which we may imagine to be drawn in three-dimensional space. Take a vector R tangential to the surface at a point P and give to it a parallel displacement round an infinitesimal closed circuit C so that it returns again to P. We shall finally obtain a vector R_1 drawn from P tangentially to the surface but not, in general, coinciding with R. The change in the vector will in general depend on two things: (1) the area of the infinitesimal circuit and (2) the metrical properties of the surface at P, these metrical properties being such as may be expressed by the g's and their derivatives.

For a similar displacement in a general manifold V_n we must also include, in addition to the two conditions enumerated above, the orientation in the manifold of the circuit round which the vector is taken: a circuit on a surface ($n = 2$) has, of course, only a single orientation at any point, namely the tangent plane at the point.

Let us first of all consider, in a general manifold, the parallel displacement of a vector round an elementary parallelogram from the point P through successive corners P_1, Q, P_2 and finally back again to P. As before, we assume that $PP_1 = dP$ and $PP_2 = \delta P$. Let q be any scalar or vector quantity. If dq denotes the change in q as we pass from P to P_1, then its value at P_1 will be $q + dq$. The value of this quantity after passing from P_1 to Q will be

$$q + dq + \delta q + \delta \, dq.$$

Similarly the value of q after passing from P to Q through P_2 will be

$$q + \delta q + dq + d \, \delta q.$$

Hence the change in q on passing from P right round the circuit will be

$$\Delta q = (\delta d - d\delta) \, q.$$

Suppose now that g stands for the determinant

$$\begin{vmatrix} g_{11} & \cdots & g_{1n} \\ g_{n1} & \cdots & g_{nn} \end{vmatrix},$$

where, of course, $g_{rs} = g_{sr}.$

Let gg^{hk} be the minor (with its proper sign) of g_{hk} in g. Then, by the properties of determinants,

$$\sum_i^n g^{hi} g_{ki} = 0, \text{ if } h \neq k;$$
$$= 1, \text{ if } h = k.$$

It is customary to put

$$g_k^h = \sum_i^n g^{hi} g_{ki}.$$

Let now R^r be one of the parameters (contravariant components) of any vector R in V_n. Then, if dR^r be the change in R^r corresponding to an infinitesimal parallel displacement in the direction defined by $dx_1, \ldots dx_n$, we shall have, by § 61,

$$\sum_h^n g_{lh} dR^h = -\sum_{hk}^n [hk, l] R^h dx_k, \quad \text{for } l = 1, 2, \ldots n.$$

Multiply both sides of this equality by g^{rl}, and sum for all values of l from 1 to n. We get, as in § 59,

$$dR^r = -\sum_{hk}^n \{hk, r\} R^h dx_k.$$

The expressions $[hk, l]$ and $\{hk, r\}$ are Christoffel's symbols defined by the identities

$$[hk, l] = \tfrac{1}{2} \left\{ \frac{\partial g_{hl}}{\partial x_k} + \frac{\partial g_{lk}}{\partial x_h} - \frac{\partial g_{hk}}{\partial x_l} \right\},$$

and

$$\{hk, r\} = \sum_l^n g^{rl} [hk, l].$$

We have previously said in § 55 that $[hk, l]$ is usually called Christoffel's symbol of the first kind. Similarly $\{hk, r\}$ is, for general values of n, called *Christoffel's symbol of the second kind*. Comparatively simple algebraical calculations now shew that the change

$$\Delta R^r$$

in the parameter R^r, owing to its parallel displacement round the elementary parallelogram, is given by the equality

$$\Delta R^r = -\sum_{ihk}^n \{ir, hk\} R^i dx_h \delta x_k.$$

§ 63. *The Riemann-Christoffel tensor.*

In this formula $\{ir, hk\}$ is defined by the identity

$$\{ir, hk\} = \frac{\partial}{\partial x_k} \{ih, r\} - \frac{\partial}{\partial x_h} \{ik, r\} - \sum_l^n [\{lh, r\}\{ik, l\} - \{lk, r\}\{ih, l\}]$$

$$(i, r, h, k = 1, 2, \ldots n).$$

This function of the g's and their first and second differentials is sometimes called *Riemann's symbol of the second kind*: by some writers it is denoted by the expression B^r_{ikh}. The aggregate of the set of symbols of the second kind bears the name of the Riemann-Christoffel tensor, the symbols themselves being called the components of the tensor. Connected with it are *Riemann's symbols of the first kind*,

$$(ij, hk) = B_{ikhj} = \sum_r^n g_{jr} \{ir, hk\}.$$

A different form can be given to these symbols of the first kind. We have, by definition,

$$(ij, hk) = \sum_r g_{jr} \left[\frac{\partial}{\partial x_k} \{ih, r\} - \frac{\partial}{\partial x_h} \{ik, r\} \right]$$
$$- \sum_{rl} g_{jr} [\{lh, r\}\{ik, l\} - \{lk, r\}\{ih, l\}],$$

each summation being taken from 1 to n. But

$$\sum_r g_{jr}\{ih, r\} = \sum_{rl} g_{jr} g^{rl} [ih, l] = [ih, j].$$

Thus $(ij, hk) = \dfrac{\partial}{\partial x_k}[ih, j] - \sum_r \{ih, r\} \dfrac{\partial g_{jr}}{\partial x_k} - \dfrac{\partial}{\partial x_h}[ik, j]$

$$+ \sum_r \{ik, r\} \frac{\partial g_{jr}}{\partial x_h} - \sum_l [lh, j]\{ik, l\} + \sum_l [lk, j]\{ih, l\}.$$

Now
$$[ih, j] = \tfrac{1}{2} \left[\frac{\partial g_{ij}}{\partial x_h} + \frac{\partial g_{hj}}{\partial x_i} - \frac{\partial g_{ih}}{\partial x_j} \right].$$

Hence we see that

$$(ij, hk) = \tfrac{1}{2} \left\{ \frac{\partial^2 g_{hj}}{\partial x_k \partial x_i} + \frac{\partial^2 g_{ik}}{\partial x_h \partial x_j} - \frac{\partial^2 g_{ih}}{\partial x_k \partial x_j} - \frac{\partial^2 g_{kj}}{\partial x_h \partial x_i} \right\}$$
$$- \sum_l \{ih, l\}[jk, l] + \sum_l \{ik, l\}[jh, l]. \qquad \text{......(1)}$$

This expression for Riemann symbols of the first kind at once gives us a number of their most important properties.

For instance, the symbols are unaltered in value when we simultaneously interchange i and j and also h and k. Equally there is no alteration in value if we simultaneously interchange i and h, j and k; or i and k, j and h. Thus

$$(ij, hk) = (ji, kh) = (hk, ij) = (kh, ji).$$

Further, the symbols are merely changed in sign if we interchange either i and j or h and k. Thus

$$(ij, hk) = -(ji, hk) = -(ij, kh).$$

Finally we have the cyclic relation

$$(ij, hk) + (ih, kj) + (ik, jh) = 0.$$

Evidently there are, in each kind of Riemann's symbol, 4^n components corresponding to the n values of each of the numbers i, j, h, k. These components are by no means all independent of one another: it may, in fact, be proved that the number which are independent is $n^2(n^2-1)/12$. Thus in two-dimensional space the Riemann-Christoffel tensor has but one component. When $n = 3$ there are six independent components; and, when $n = 4$, there are twenty such components.

From the mode of its origin, it is clear that the Riemann-Christoffel tensor is an analytic expression, derived from the g's, which is closely connected with the intrinsic geometry of our manifold. When the Riemann-Christoffel tensor vanishes, the parallel displacement of any vector round any elementary parallelogram within the manifold will vanish: and this is a property of the manifold independent of the coordinate system in terms of which the g's may be expressed.

The aggregate of functions to which we have given the name 'Riemann-Christoffel tensor' is, in fact, a 'tensor' of the fourth rank; and its discovery opened the way to such a development of the calculus of tensors as made it an effective instrument of analysis alike in hypergeometry and in the general theory of relativity. Naturally the development of the algebra of Riemann's symbols must be assumed in any general discussion of these branches of knowledge. Here we can merely give a few fundamental facts.

Tensor transformation-equations.

When the coordinates $x_1, \ldots x_n$ of our manifold are changed by transformation to $x_1', \ldots x_n'$, Riemann's symbols will satisfy the fundamental transformation-equations of the components of a tensor of the fourth rank. We have, in fact, if we denote by accents expressions in terms of the new coordinates,

$$\{ir, hk\}' = B'^r_{ikh}$$

$$= \sum_{\alpha\beta\gamma\epsilon} \frac{\partial x_\alpha}{\partial x_i'} \frac{\partial x_\beta}{\partial x_k'} \frac{\partial x_\gamma}{\partial x_h'} \frac{\partial x_r'}{\partial x_\epsilon} B^\epsilon_{\alpha\beta\gamma},$$

and

$$(ij, hk)' = B'_{ikhj}$$

$$= \sum_{\alpha\beta\gamma\epsilon} \frac{\partial x_\alpha}{\partial x_i'} \frac{\partial x_\beta}{\partial x_k'} \frac{\partial x_\gamma}{\partial x_h'} \frac{\partial x_\epsilon}{\partial x_j'} B_{\alpha\beta\gamma\epsilon}$$

$$= \sum_{\alpha\beta\gamma\epsilon} \frac{\partial x_\alpha}{\partial x_i'} \frac{\partial x_\beta}{\partial x_k'} \frac{\partial x_\gamma}{\partial x_h'} \frac{\partial x_\epsilon}{\partial x_j'} (\alpha\epsilon, \gamma\beta),$$

where the summations are for all integral values of α, β, γ, ϵ from 1 to n. In each of these relations there will be 256 terms in the summation. Furthermore, each relation typifies 256 different transformation-equations.

We have stated that Riemann's symbols only involve the g's and their first and second differentials. But they are complicated functions of these quantities, and the fact that they satisfy the relatively simple transformation-equations just given is a result that is both surprising and beautiful.

It is usual to say that quantities such as $B_{\alpha\beta\gamma\epsilon}$ are components of a covariant tensor of the fourth rank, while quantities such as $B^\epsilon_{\alpha\beta\gamma}$ are components of a mixed tensor of this rank. The laws of transformation just given for Riemann's symbols are examples of the transformation formulae which all tensors satisfy. For a tensor of rank n there will be, under the sign of summation, n elements, such as $\dfrac{\partial x_\alpha}{\partial x_i'}$ or $\dfrac{\partial x'}{\partial x_\alpha}$, forming a product. The number of elements of the type $\dfrac{\partial x_\alpha}{\partial x_i'}$ will correspond to the covariant indices of the tensor, while those of the type $\dfrac{\partial x_i'}{\partial x_\alpha}$ will correspond to the contravariant indices.

The notion of a tensor.

The notion of a tensor is best reached by first considering a vector in n-dimensional space.

Let $x_1, \ldots x_n$ be the general coordinates of a point in a spatial manifold of n dimensions whose measure-determination is given by

$$ds^2 = \overset{n}{\underset{1}{\Sigma}}_{rs} g_{rs} \, dx_r \, dx_s.$$

Let v be a versor in this manifold. We take the (contravariant) components of the versor to be v^i, $i = 1, \ldots n$, where $v^i = \dfrac{dx_i}{ds}$. Evidently the v's will be connected by the identical relation

$$1 = \underset{rs}{\Sigma} g_{rs} v^r v^s.$$

When we pass from the coordinates x_r, $r = 1, \ldots n$, to new coordinates x_r', we shall have

$$(v^r)' = \frac{dx_r'}{ds'} = \frac{dx_r'}{ds},$$

or

$$(v^r)' = \overset{n}{\underset{\alpha=1}{\Sigma}} \frac{\partial x_r'}{\partial x_\alpha} v^\alpha.$$

This is *the fundamental transformation-equation of the contravariant components of a unit-vector.*

The covariant components of the unit-vector will be v_s, $s = 1, 2, \ldots n$, where

$$v_s = \overset{n}{\underset{t=1}{\Sigma}} g_{st} v^t.$$

Now the g's form a tensor of the second rank. For we have

$$\underset{rs}{\Sigma} g_{rs}' \, dx_r' \, dx_s' = \underset{rs}{\Sigma} g_{rs} \, dx_r \, dx_s,$$

since each side is equal to ds^2. Hence we have

$$\sum_{\alpha\beta} g_{\alpha\beta}' \, dx_\alpha' \, dx_\beta' = \sum_{rs\alpha\beta} g_{rs} \frac{\partial x_r}{\partial x_\alpha'} \frac{\partial x_s}{\partial x_\beta'} \, dx_\alpha' \, dx_\beta'.$$

Since this equality holds good for all values of dx_α', dx_β', we must have

$$g_{\alpha\beta}' = \sum_{rs} \frac{\partial x_r}{\partial x_\alpha'} \frac{\partial x_s}{\partial x_\beta'} g_{rs}.$$

Thus the g's are the covariant components of a tensor of the second rank.

Using this result we have at once

$$v_s' = \sum_{t=1}^n g_{st}' (v^t)' = \sum_{\alpha\beta t\gamma} g_{\alpha\beta} \frac{\partial x_\alpha}{\partial x_s'} \frac{\partial x_\beta}{\partial x_t'} \frac{\partial x_t'}{\partial x_\gamma} v^\gamma$$

$$= \sum_{\alpha\beta} g_{\alpha\beta} \frac{\partial x_\alpha}{\partial x_s'} v^\beta.$$

Thus *the fundamental transformation-equation for the covariant components of a unit-vector* is

$$v_s' = \sum_\alpha \frac{\partial x_\alpha}{\partial x_s'} v_\alpha.$$

The significance of a tensor-equation.

Suppose now that we have some physical fact expressed by the equality of two vectors u and v. Then alike the covariant and the contravariant components of the two sides of the equality will be equal. If either set of equalities exist, the other set will exist also. And, moreover, if either set of equalities exist for any one set of axes, similar equalities will exist for any other set of axes which may be chosen instead of the first set. Such an equality of two vectors is the simplest form of a tensor-equation. A tensor-equation, in fact, embraces a series of equations which are together independent of the coordinate system chosen.

The fundamental property of the components of a tensor of any rank.

If we have any vector v, we may take v_s and v^t to be its covariant and contravariant components. These components for an arbitrary vector will themselves be quite arbitrary. There will be no relation between, say, the various contravariant components, though, of course, such components will be connected with the length l of the vector by a relation

$$\sum_{rs} g_{rs} v^r v^s = l^2.$$

Suppose now that we wish to form a mixed tensor of rank 4, contravariant with regard to one index and covariant with regard to the other three indices. We take $_1v, \ldots {_4}v$ to be four arbitrary vectors, and then we say that such a tensor as we require will have components $T^{\alpha}_{\beta\gamma\epsilon}$, when the T's are such that the expression

$$F = \sum_{\alpha\beta\gamma\epsilon} T^{\alpha}_{\beta\gamma\epsilon} {_1}v_\alpha {_2}v^\beta {_3}v^\gamma {_4}v^\epsilon$$

is an *invariant* for general transformations of the coordinate system.

For suppose that a new set of coordinates be denoted by accented letters. Then, since F is an invariant, we shall have

$$\sum_{\substack{\alpha\beta\gamma\epsilon \\ ikhj}} T'^{\alpha}_{\beta\gamma\epsilon} \frac{\partial x_i}{\partial x_\alpha'} \frac{\partial x_\beta'}{\partial x_k} \frac{\partial x_\gamma'}{\partial x_h} \frac{\partial x_\epsilon'}{\partial x_j} {_1}v_i {_2}v^k {_3}v^h {_4}v^j = \sum_{ikhj} T^{i}_{khj} {_1}v_i {_2}v^k {_3}v^h {_4}v^j.$$

Since this result is an identity and the four vectors are arbitrary, we shall have

$$T'^{i}_{khj} = \sum_{\alpha\beta\gamma\epsilon} \frac{\partial x_i'}{\partial x_\alpha} \frac{\partial x_\beta}{\partial x_k'} \frac{\partial x_\gamma}{\partial x_h'} \frac{\partial x_\epsilon}{\partial x_j'} T^{\alpha}_{\beta\gamma\epsilon},$$

which is the fundamental transformation-equation of such a mixed tensor as we set out to form. Clearly we have also the converse result that, *if the T's satisfy such a transformation-equation, the quantity F will be an invariant.*

We see now that, if (ij, hk) be Riemann's symbols of the first kind, and if, as we have stated, they constitute a tensor of the fourth rank, covariant with regard to all the indices, then the expression

$$\sum_{ijhk} (ij, hk) u^i v^j \xi^h \eta^k$$

will be an invariant, the vectors u, v, ξ, η being arbitrary. We shall shortly give Pérès' theorem which determines the value of this invariant.

Conversely, *if Pérès' theorem is true, the symbols (ij, hk) are the components of a tensor of the fourth rank.* Thus the proof of Pérès' formula, which will be given in § 64, establishes the fact that Riemann's symbols of the first kind are actually components of a tensor of the fourth rank, covariant with regard to all four indices.

We also see that, if T_{rs} be the components of a tensor of the second rank covariant with regard to both indices, the expression

$$\sum_{rs} T_{rs} u^r v^s$$

will be an invariant, u and v being any arbitrary vectors.

Further, we can see at once from the preceding result that we may so define our symbols that

$$T_{\alpha\beta\gamma\epsilon} = \sum_m g_{\alpha m} T^{m}_{\beta\gamma\epsilon}.$$

For clearly, if the v's are arbitrary vectors,

$$\sum_{m\beta\gamma\epsilon} T^m_{\beta\gamma\epsilon} {}_1v_m {}_2v^\beta {}_3v^\gamma {}_4v^\epsilon = \sum_{m\alpha\beta\gamma\epsilon} T^m_{\beta\gamma\epsilon} g_{\alpha m} {}_1v^\alpha {}_2v^\beta {}_3v^\gamma {}_4v^\epsilon.$$

If either side of this equality be an invariant, so is the other. Thus $\sum_m g_{\alpha m} T^m_{\beta\gamma\epsilon}$ may, by the result already obtained, be equated to the tensor-component $T_{\alpha\beta\gamma\epsilon}$.

The laws for the raising and lowering of tensor-suffices are now readily deduced. We cannot, of course, write a treatise on the tensor calculus. But the results, to which we have just drawn attention, indicate the character of those which will be used in subsequent analysis.

Geodesic coordinates.

Suppose that in an n-dimensional manifold we have a general transformation of coordinates from $x, \ldots x_n$ to $x', \ldots x_n'$. We proceed to shew that it is always possible so to choose the transformation that all Christoffel's symbols vanish at any assigned point, which without loss of generality may be taken as the origin of our old coordinates. In this case it is customary to say that we have chosen *geodesic or normal coordinates* at the point.

We know that, if ds be any element of length,

$$\frac{dx_k'}{ds} = \sum_q \frac{\partial x_k'}{\partial x_q} \frac{dx_q}{ds},$$

where the summation is taken from 1 to n. Hence

$$\frac{d^2x_k'}{ds^2} = \sum_{pq} \frac{\partial^2 x_k'}{\partial x_p \partial x_q} \frac{dx_p}{ds} \frac{dx_q}{ds} + \sum_q \frac{\partial x_k'}{\partial x_q} \frac{d^2x_q}{ds^2}.$$

Suppose now that ds is the arc of a geodesic. Then, by §55, we have

$$\frac{d^2x_k'}{ds^2} = -\sum_{jl} \{jl, k\}' \frac{dx_j'}{ds} \frac{dx_l'}{ds},$$

and

$$\sum_t \frac{\partial x_k'}{\partial x_t} \frac{d^2x_t}{ds^2} = -\sum_{pqt} \frac{\partial x_k'}{\partial x_t} \{pq, t\} \frac{dx_p}{ds} \frac{dx_q}{ds},$$

where $\{jl, k\}'$ is formed from the quantities g'_{pq} which correspond to the expression for ds^2 in terms of the accented coordinates.

Hence, when ds is the arc of a geodesic, we have the identity

$$\sum_{pq} \left[\frac{\partial^2 x_k'}{\partial x_p \partial x_q} + \sum_{jl} \{jl, k\}' \frac{\partial x_j'}{\partial x_p} \frac{\partial x_l'}{\partial x_q} - \sum_t \frac{\partial x_k'}{\partial x_t} \{pq, t\} \right] \frac{dx_p}{ds} \frac{dx_q}{ds} = 0.$$

But this is an invariant relation of the form $\sum_{pq} f_{pq}(x_1, \ldots x_n) u^p u^q = 0$,

where $f_{pq} = f_{qp}$ and $u^1, \ldots u^n$ are the contravariant components of a quite arbitrary vector.

Hence $f_{pq} = 0$, for all values of p and q.

We therefore have

$$\frac{\partial^2 x_k{}'}{\partial x_p \partial x_q} - \sum_t \{pq, t\} \frac{\partial x_k{}'}{\partial x_t} = - \sum_{jl} \{jl, k\}' \frac{\partial x_j{}'}{\partial x_p} \frac{\partial x_l{}'}{\partial x_q}. \quad \ldots\ldots(2)$$

We shall now make use of this relation to choose new accented co-ordinates so that at an assigned point the Christoffel functions corresponding to the new coordinates all vanish. By Maclaurin's theorem we may assume that near the assigned point the new coordinates can be expressed as power and product series of the old coordinates in the form

$$x_k{}' = x_k + \tfrac{1}{2} \sum_{pq} \frac{\partial^2 x_k{}'}{\partial x_p \partial x_q} x_p x_q + \text{higher terms},$$

for all values of k from 1 to n, the differentials being taken at the assigned point.

If such relations hold good we shall have at the assigned point

$$\frac{\partial x_k{}'}{\partial x_t} = 0, \quad t \neq k,$$

$$= 1, \quad t = k.$$

Take now at the assigned point, as is always possible, such values of $x_k{}'$ that

$$\frac{\partial^2 x_k{}'}{\partial x_p \partial x_q} = \{pq, k\}.$$

Then by the formula (2) we shall have $\{pq, k\}' = 0$ for all values of p, q and k. The transformation to geodesic coordinates is thus effected.

The fact that by the choice of such coordinates we can make Christoffel's symbols vanish at any assigned point is often of great assistance in symplifying algebraical analysis in the tensor theory. Suppose, for instance, that we wish to establish a tensor equality. Such an equality subsists however the axes be changed. If, then, we establish it when Christoffel's symbols all vanish, it will be true universally. In particular we shall see later (§ 117) how this device enables us easily to establish certain important relations between Riemann's symbols which are known as Bianchi's identities.

World-tensors.

A tensor which only involves the quantities g, which define the metric of space, and also their differentials is sometimes called a *fundamental tensor* or *world-tensor*. It can be proved that all world-tensors which only contain the g's and their first and second differentials are functions of the g's and of the Riemann-Christoffel tensor. This fact accounts for the fundamental importance of the latter tensor. It shews that, in any investigation of those properties of n-dimensional manifolds which are independent of the axes of reference, we must expect to reach the Riemann-Christoffel tensor. We shall see in Lecture VI that the tensor, for the four dimensions of space-time, is fundamental in the general theory of relativity.

§ 64. *The definition of a section of a manifold. The change in the components of a vector after the description of an infinitesimal circuit lying in a given section. Pérès' formula.*

Let ξ^h and η^k be the parameters (contravariant vector-components) of two lines PP_1 and PP_2 at a point P, and let θ be the angle between these lines, the lines being within our manifold V_n and the angle being measured according to the metric of the manifold. A versor defined by

$$\rho\xi^i + \sigma\eta^i, \qquad (i = 1, 2, \dots n),$$

where ρ and σ are constants, will determine a section of the manifold through P. The quantities ρ and σ cannot be independent inasmuch as parameters of the versor must satisfy the fundamental equation of the metric. We therefore have

$$\sum_1^n g_{ik}(\rho\xi^i + \sigma\eta^i)(\rho\xi^k + \sigma\eta^k) = 1,$$

or
$$\rho^2 + \sigma^2 + 2\rho\sigma\cos\theta = 1.$$

Clearly, however, when ρ and σ are connected by this relation they define a simply-infinite aggregate of directions through P, this aggregate including the lines PP_1 and PP_2: such an aggregate we term a *section* of the manifold at P.

Suppose now that ΔS represents the area of an infinitesimal circuit on the section through P thus defined, and further let ΔR^i represent the change in R^i, the contravariant component of a vector R, corresponding to the description of this circuit.

We have already in § 62 obtained a formula which gives the change in the contravariant components of any vector due to its parallel displacement round an infinitesimal parallelogram. This formula shews us that the change can be expressed in terms of (1) the contravariant components R^i of the vector R; (2) the quantities dx_h and δx_k, which give the directions and magnitudes of two adjacent sides of the parallelogram; and (3) the Riemann symbols derived from the fundamental metric of the manifold. We now put $dx_h = \xi^h ds$ and $\delta x_k = \eta^k \delta s$, so that ds and δs are the lengths of the sides of the fundamental parallelogram. If the area of this parallelogram be ΔS and θ be the angle between adjacent sides, we have

$$\Delta S = \sin\theta\, ds\, \delta s.$$

We thus obtain from § 62 the equality

$$\Delta R^r = \pm \frac{\Delta S}{\sin \theta} \sum_{1}^{n} {}_{ihk} \{ir, hk\} R^i \xi^h \eta^k.$$

This result will be true for a parallel displacement round any infinitesimal circuit of area ΔS, which surrounds the point P and is in the section of the manifold through P determined by the versors ξ and η. Riemann's symbol of the second kind is such that $\{ir, hk\} = - \{ir, kh\}$. Therefore the sign of the expression on the right-hand side is changed when ξ and η are interchanged. The sign depends, in fact, on the convention which connects the direction in which the fundamental circuit is traversed with the relative positions of ξ and η.

We thus see that the change in the contravariant components of a vector, due to a parallel displacement round an infinitesimal circuit of any oval shape, depends upon the area of the circuit, the contravariant components of the vector, the components of the two vectors which determine the section of the manifold on which the circuit is drawn, and the metric of the manifold.

The formula giving this connection is of the highest importance, as Schouten and Pérès have shewn in their investigations. From it, as a special case, it is immediately possible to derive

Pérès' formula.

Suppose that u and v are two versors drawn from P, but not necessarily in the section of our n-dimensional manifold determined by the versors ξ and η. Let α be the angle between u and v, just as θ is the angle between ξ and η. Further, let $\Delta\alpha$ be the change in α corresponding to the parallel displacement of either u or v round an infinitesimal circuit of area ΔS in the section determined by ξ and η; then, in the limit when ΔS tends to zero,

$$\frac{\Delta\alpha}{\Delta S} = \frac{\pm 1}{\sin \alpha \sin \theta} \sum_{1}^{n} {}_{ijhk} (ij, hk) u^i v^j \xi^h \eta^k,$$

where (ij, hk) is Riemann's symbol of the first kind.

The proof is immediate.

Let us suppose that the versor u is displaced, v remaining unaltered.

Then since, by § 61, $\qquad \cos \alpha = \sum_{r=1}^{n} u^r v_r,$

we shall have $\qquad - \sin \alpha \, \Delta\alpha = \sum_r v_r \Delta u^r$

$$= \pm \frac{\Delta S}{\sin \theta} \sum_{ihkr} \{ir, hk\} u^i v_r \xi^h \eta^k.$$

But
$$v_r = \sum_j g_{rj} v^j.$$

Hence
$$\frac{\Delta\alpha}{\Delta S} = \frac{\pm 1}{\sin\alpha\sin\theta} \sum_{ijhk} \sum_r g_{rj}\{ir, hk\} u^i v^j \xi^h \eta^k;$$

and this, by the definition of Riemann's symbols of the first kind, is equivalent to the given result.

§65. *The total or Gaussian curvature of a two-dimensional surface.*

We are now nearing the end of what is, when the analysis is set out in full detail, a somewhat long journey. First of all we limit ourselves to the case $n = 2$ and consider the form which Pérès' formula takes when the infinitesimal circuit is drawn on a general two-dimensional surface. If we like*, we may imagine that this surface exists in the three-dimensional Euclidean space in which we appear to live. All Riemann's symbols vanish when $n = 2$ save such as reduce to $(12, 12)$; and, by making u and v coincide with ξ and η, we obtain the formula

$$\underset{\Delta S=0}{Lt} \frac{\Delta\alpha}{\Delta S} = \frac{\pm (12, 12)}{\sin^2\alpha} (u^1 v^2 - u^2 v^1)^2.$$

This, in turn, because of the formula of §57 connecting $\sin\alpha$ with the vectors which define α, reduces to

$$\underset{\Delta S=0}{Lt} \frac{\Delta\alpha}{\Delta S} = K, \quad \text{where} \quad K = \frac{\pm (12, 12)}{g},$$

and, as before,

$$g = \begin{vmatrix} g_{11} & g_{12} \\ g_{12} & g_{22} \end{vmatrix}.$$

The quantity K is an invariant, although neither g nor Riemann's symbol $(12, 12)$ is an invariant. Their quotient, however, is invariant because it is a function of position which is the measure of an intrinsic property of the surface.

We proceed to shew that the limiting value of $\Delta\alpha/\Delta S$ is actually the total or Gaussian curvature of the surface. This curvature is defined as the product of the curvatures of the principal sections through any point. In fact, in the neighbourhood of any ordinary point of a surface we can, by suitable choice of Euclidean rectangular coordinates, write its equation in the form

$$2z = \frac{x^2}{\rho_1} + \frac{y^2}{\rho_2} + (x, y)^3 + \dots;$$

and then the Gaussian curvature is $1/\rho_1\rho_2$.

---

* Any two-dimensional space can be immersed in a three-dimensional Euclidean manifold: but *general* three-dimensional space can only be immersed in a six-dimensional Euclidean manifold.

The proof depends upon ideas which ultimately go back to Gauss and are to be found in textbooks which treat of curves on two-dimensional surfaces in Euclidean space*.

Suppose that we have any oval curve C on such a surface, there being no singularities of the surface in the area under consideration. We can circumscribe the surface by a developable touching the surface along the curve. The normal to the surface at any point P on C will then be perpendicular to the tangent plane to the developable at P and will therefore be perpendicular to the rectifying line of the developable through P.

If we draw from a fixed point O lines of unit length parallel to the normals to the surface at all points on C, they will form a curve c on a sphere of unit radius and c is called the *horograph* of C.

Suppose now that we slit the developable along the rectifying line through a point A of the curve C and then smooth it out into a plane. On this plane the closed curve C becomes an open curve ABA' and the rectifying line through A will become two lines OA and OA' inclined at an angle ϕ, say, one to another.

The tangents at A and A' to ABA' will, of course, make equal angles with OA and OA'. If a line be moved from A by parallel displacement along C to A', it will be, on the flattened developable, parallel to its former position. Thus ϕ will be the change, owing to parallel displacement, of the angle between a fixed and a moving vector consequent on a circuit of the closed curve C from A to A again.

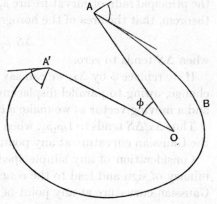

The *integral change of direction* as we pass along any portion of a curve C is defined to be the integral sum of the angles between geodesic tangents at successive points of C. Now, when the developable is flattened out, geodesic tangents to the surface become linear tangents to the developed curve. Hence the integral change of direction along any arc AB of the curve C is measured by the angle between tangents

* See, for example, Thomson and Tait, *Treatise on Natural Philosophy*. Cambridge University Press, 1879, vol. I, part I, pp. 103–14: or P. Frost, *Solid Geometry*. Macmillan, 1886, pp. 310, 311.

at A and B when the developable is flattened into a plane. Thus the integral change of direction as we pass completely round C from A to A again will obviously be

$$2\pi - \phi.$$

Suppose now that we draw a developable to touch the sphere of unit radius at all points of the horograph c. At corresponding points of C and c the tangent planes of the two developables will be parallel. Hence they will have parallel rectifying lines, and the integral change of direction as we pass completely round c will be equal to the integral change of direction as we pass completely round C and each will be equal to $2\pi - \phi$.

But on a sphere of unit radius the area of a triangle formed by geodesics (or arcs of great circles) = 2π − sum of the exterior angles of the triangle. Hence the area bounded by the curve c will be equal to 2π minus the integral change of direction as we pass completely round c; and thus the area of the horograph c is equal to ϕ.

In the previous investigation we have assumed that C is a curve of finite length enclosing a finite area S on our surface. Suppose now that C be a small oval enclosing an area ΔS surrounding a point Q at which the principal radii of curvature are ρ_1 and ρ_2. Then we know, by Gauss' theorem, that the area of the horograph tends to

$$\Delta S / \rho_1 \rho_2,$$

when ΔS tends to zero.

If we replace ϕ by $\Delta \alpha$, we can say that this quantity is equal to the change, owing to parallel displacement, in the angle between a fixed and a moving vector as we make a complete circuit of the curve C.

Thus $\Delta \alpha / \Delta S$ tends to $1/\rho_1 \rho_2$, when the area ΔS tends to zero. Hence the Gaussian curvature at any point of a surface is $\pm (12, 12)/g$.

Consideration of any simple special case will remove the indeterminacy of sign and lead to the conclusion that, if we define K as the Gaussian curvature at any point of a surface, we shall have

$$K = (12, 12)/g,$$

when the formula defining the metric is so chosen that $ds^2 > 0$.

For instance, if we take a sphere of radius a, we have

$$ds^2 = a^2 dx_1{}^2 + a^2 \sin^2 x_1 dx_2{}^2,$$

whence $g = a^4 \sin^2 x_1$ and $(12, 12) = a^2 \sin^2 x_1$, so that $K = 1/a^2$. When, however, we have

$$- ds^2 = a^2 dx_1{}^2 + a^2 \sin^2 x_1 dx_2{}^2,$$

it is obvious that we must put $K = -(12,12)/g$. Thus the sign of K is changed when $ds^2 < 0$.

In relativity-mechanics, as we shall see in Lecture VI, it is usual to define the metric of space-time by the formula

$$ds^2 = c^2 dt^2 - dl^2,$$

where dl^2 is an element of pure space. For such a metric we work with imaginary time $\tau = \sqrt{-1}\, t$ and replace K by $-K$.

The expression which we have thus found for K can, of course, be obtained by direct analysis; but the investigation is somewhat laborious.

§ 66. *Use of geodesic surfaces to determine the curvatures of an n-dimensional manifold at an assigned point.*

We can now use the result of the last section in conjunction with Pérès' formula in order to determine what will be called the Riemannian curvatures of a general manifold at any point P.

We have previously seen that the natural lines of structure of the manifold are the geodesics. Furthermore, from the way in which a geodesic is defined, it will, as we have previously said, be determined by a single point and a single direction at that point. Now if we take at the point P two directions ξ and η in the manifold, they will, as in § 64, determine a section of the manifold which is the aggregate of a simply-infinite number of directions from P. Corresponding to each of these directions we can draw a geodesic. The aggregate of all these geodesics will be a geodesic surface which we call *the geodesic surface with P as pole*. This surface will be a doubly-infinite aggregate of points and will therefore correspond exactly to an ordinary two-dimensional surface in a Euclidean manifold for which $n = 3$. We shall take the Gaussian curvature at P of this geodesic surface to be, by definition, *the Riemannian curvature of the manifold* at P with respect to the particular section.

The idea of using geodesic surfaces in this way to describe the curvatures at any point of a general manifold was one of Riemann's most fertile inventions. It is especially valuable as there is in it nothing artificial: geodesics are natural lines of structure, and geodesic surfaces are the natural analogues to what in Euclidean geometry we should term plane sections through P.

From Pérès' formula, *if K be the Riemannian curvature of the section of the manifold which is given by a point P and the two versors u and v, we have*

$$K = \frac{1}{\sin^2 \alpha} \sum_1^n {}_{ijhk} (ij, hk)\, u^i v^j u^h v^k,$$

where α *is the angle between* u *and* v. The values of u^i, etc., and of Riemann's symbols (ij, hk) are, of course, taken at the point P. This formula* is of surpassing elegance and value. It enables us to relate a type of curvature (of which we can form for simple manifolds a mental picture) to Riemann's symbols which depend solely on the metric of the manifold: we have, in fact, in a very simple though highly condensed form, an analytical expression which serves to measure curvature at any point of the most general n-dimensional space which is continuous and possesses an inner measure-determination of Riemann's type.

§ 67.   *The condition that generalised space should be flat.*

From the preceding formula we can readily deduce one result of great interest.

When the Gaussian curvature of a two-dimensional surface vanishes at every point of the surface, the surface becomes a plane in which we can always choose rectangular coordinates such that the metric is given by

$$ds^2 = dx^2 + dy^2.$$

Our two-dimensional surface is then flat.

Similarly, we can say that three-dimensional space will be *flat*† when all the geodesics within it are the intersections of flat planes or, in other words, straight lines. The Riemannian curvature corresponding to every section through any arbitrary point will then vanish. Our space, moreover, will be Euclidean with a metric which can be, by suitable choice of coordinates, expressed in the simple form

$$ds^2 = dx^2 + dy^2 + dz^2.$$

In general, a continuous manifold of n-dimensions is termed *flat* if the Riemannian curvature corresponding to every geodesic section through every point vanishes. Such a manifold will be hyper-Euclidean and its metric will be expressible in the form

$$ds^2 = dx_1^2 + \ldots + dx_n^2.$$

Evidently, by the formula which we have obtained for K, *a continuous manifold of n-dimensions will be flat if the Riemann-Christoffel tensor vanishes at every point.* The converse theorem is true (*vide* § 69).

In general therefore $n^2(n^2 - 1)/12$ conditions are necessary for *flat* space.

* The formula is substantially due to Riemann. For another method of deducing it, *vide* W. Pauli, jr, "Relativitätstheorie", *Encyklopädie der Mathematischen Wissenschaften*, Bd. v, Theil 2, p. 596.

† The older term, now happily falling into disuse, was homaloidal.

When $n = 2$, we have a single condition (the vanishing of the Gaussian curvature) that space may be flat.

When $n = 3$, six conditions must be fulfilled in order that general three-dimensional space may be Euclidean.

When $n = 4$, as (for example) in the space-time continuum of the general theory of relativity, twenty conditions must be satisfied if the manifold is to be flat.

§ 68. *Application to our three-dimensional space and to similar n-dimensional manifolds.*

We now apply the results which we have obtained to the three-dimensional space of our ordinary experience. That space, as we have previously said, besides being continuous, and therefore unbounded, is homogeneous and isotropic. It has, however, no further properties given to us, as we believe, by experience. We have already seen that it is not necessarily the space postulated by Euclid: we naturally now enquire whether it can possibly be of a more general type than the spaces we have called hyperbolic and spherical. The foregoing analysis enables us to give an answer to this enquiry for n-dimensional manifolds.

If, at any point, n-dimensional space $(n > 2)$ is isotropic, its curvature corresponding to any section through the point must be independent of the orientation of the section. Hence K must be independent of the quantities u and v.

We proceed now to shew that, for the most general manifold whose curvature at any point is independent of the section through the point and equal to a given function of position K, we have the relations

$$(ij, hk) = K(g_{ih}g_{jk} - g_{ik}g_{jh}). \qquad \ldots \ldots (1)$$

Of these relations $n^2(n^2 - 1)/12$ are independent.

In our manifold let u and v be two versors inclined at an angle α, and let a section of the manifold be determined by two versors ξ and η inclined at an angle θ. Then, if $\Delta\alpha$ be the change in α corresponding to the parallel displacement of u or v round an infinitesimal circuit drawn in the section and of area ΔS, we know, by Pérès' theorem, that

$$\frac{\Delta\alpha}{\Delta S} = \frac{\pm 1}{\sin\alpha \sin\theta} \sum_{ijhk} (ij, hk) u^i v^j \xi^h \eta^k.$$

When u and v are in the section made by ξ and η, we have

$$K = \frac{\pm 1}{\sin\alpha \sin\theta} \sum_{ijhk} (ij, hk) u^i v^j \xi^h \eta^k. \qquad \ldots \ldots (2)$$

Substitute now for (ij, hk) the value given by (1). We know that

$$\Sigma g_{ih} u^i \xi^h = \cos(\widehat{u\xi}),$$

where $\widehat{u\xi}$ denotes the angle between u and ξ. Hence, on making the substitution, the relation (2) becomes an identity.

Put now $\phi_{ijhk} = (ij, hk) - K(g_{ih}g_{jk} - g_{ik}g_{jh}).$

Then, since the difference of two tensors is a tensor, ϕ_{ijhk} must be the components of a tensor of the fourth rank, covariant with regard to all four indices. Hence, by the conclusion just reached,

$$\underset{ijhk}{\Sigma} \phi_{ijhk} u^i v^j \xi^h \eta^k$$

is an invariant which vanishes when ξ and η are in the section of the manifold made by u and v. In such a section

$$\xi = \rho_1 u + \sigma_1 v, \qquad \eta = \rho_2 u + \sigma_2 v,$$

the ρ's and σ's being constants. We therefore see that

$$\Sigma \phi_{ijhk} u^i v^j u^h v^k \quad \text{and} \quad \Sigma \phi_{ijhk} u^i v^j u^k v^h$$

are both equal to zero for all values of u and v. From the first result, by making all the u's and v's vanish except u^i, u^h, v^j, v^k, we get

$$\phi_{ijhk} + \phi_{hjik} + \phi_{ikhj} + \phi_{hkij} = 0, \qquad \ldots\ldots(3)$$

for clearly $\phi_{ijij} = 0$, and we can easily shew that $\phi_{ijik} = 0$.

Similarly, from the second result,

$$\phi_{ijhk} + \phi_{kjhi} + \phi_{ihjk} + \phi_{khji} = 0. \qquad \ldots\ldots(4)$$

Now, by the properties of Riemann symbols established in § 63,

$$\phi_{ijhk} = \phi_{hkij} = \phi_{khji}.$$

We therefore have, by (3) and (4),

$$\phi_{ijhk} = -\phi_{ikhj} \quad \text{and} \quad \phi_{ijhk} = -\phi_{ihjk}.$$

Thus $\phi_{ijhk} = \phi_{ihkj} = \phi_{ikjh}.$

Hence, since by § 63 $(ij, hk) + (ih, kj) + (ik, jh) = 0$, we have

$$\phi_{ijhk} + \phi_{ihkj} + \phi_{ikjh} = 0.$$

Finally, therefore, for all values of i, j, h, k we have

$$\phi_{ijhk} = 0.$$

This establishes our result: at any point where n-dimensional space is isotropic and of curvature K, Riemann's symbols take the especially simple form given by the relation (1).

Schur's theorem.

The question now arises as to whether the value of K in space which is everywhere isotropic can be an arbitrarily assigned function of position. An important theorem, obtained by Schur in the year 1886, states that in such space K must be a constant. In other words, *n-dimensional space which is everywhere isotropic is also homogeneous.*

In Lecture VI we shall introduce the idea of covariant differentiation and prove Bianchi's identity (§ 117)

$$(ij, hk)_l + (ij, kl)_h + (ij, lh)_k = 0.$$

Couple this identity with the relation (1) which gives the values of Riemann's symbols in space which is everywhere isotropic. We get

$$(g_{ih}g_{jk} - g_{ik}g_{jh})\frac{\partial K}{\partial x_l} + \text{two similar terms} = 0,$$

the terms being obtained by the cyclical interchange of h, k, l.

Multiply the relation just obtained by $g^{ih}g^{jk}$ and sum for all values of i and j from 1 to n. We get

$$(1 - g_k^h g_h^k)\frac{\partial K}{\partial x_l} + (g_k^h g_l^k - g_l^h)\frac{\partial K}{\partial x_h} + (g_l^h g_h^k - g_l^k)\frac{\partial K}{\partial x_k} = 0.$$

Since our letters denote any numbers from 1 to n, we can assume that h, k, l are all different. Then the relation just written becomes

$$\partial K/\partial x_l = 0.$$

Thus K must be an absolute constant.

Evidently Schur's theorem only applies when $n > 2$; for, when $n = 2$, only one section can be drawn through a point and it is meaningless to speak of the constancy of local curvature. When $n = 3$, Schur's theorem corresponds to our intuitions: it would be difficult to imagine continuous space which at every point had the same curvature corresponding to all sections through the point and yet had different curvatures at different points. Between such an intuition and its proof there is naturally a vast gulf. This gulf the work of Riemann and his followers has enabled us to bridge.

§ 69. *The canonical form for the line-element in generalised space of constant curvature.*

Riemann, in the fundamental paper to which we have so often referred, gave a canonical form for the metric of n-dimensional space of constant curvature K. *For such a space we may always make such a choice of Gaussian coordinates $x_1, \dots x_n$ that the line-element is given by*

$$ds^2 = \left(\sum_{r=1}^{n} dx_r^2\right)\Big/ v^2,$$

where
$$v = 1 + K\left(\sum_{r=1}^{n} x_r^2\right)\Big/ 4.$$

To Beltrami (1835–1900) is due an alternative and more simple canonical form for the metric of a manifold of constant negative curvature. *When K is negative, we may so choose the coordinates $x_1, \ldots x_n$ that the line-element is given by*

$$ds^2 = \left(\sum_{r=1}^{n} dx_r^2 \right) \Big/ (- K x_n^2).$$

We begin with a formula due to Finzi. Suppose that our manifold, or n-dimensional space, is given by

$$ds^2 = \sum_{1}^{n} g_{ij} dx_i dx_j. \qquad \ldots\ldots(1)$$

Let (ij, hk) denote the general Riemann symbol of the first kind for this manifold, and let (IJ, HK) denote the corresponding Riemann symbol for the manifold of which the coefficients are g_{ij}/u^2.

It is not as laborious as might be expected first to calculate Christoffel's symbols corresponding to the latter manifold and then to find the Riemann symbols.

If we put

$$u_i = \frac{\partial u}{\partial x_i}, \qquad u^l = \sum_{k=1}^{n} g^{kl} u_k,$$

and

$$u_{ij} = \frac{\partial^2 u}{\partial x_i \partial x_j} - \sum_{l=1}^{n} [ij, l] u^l,$$

we get

$$u^2 (IJ, HK) = (ij, hk) - \frac{1}{u^2} (g_{ih} g_{jk} - g_{ik} g_{jh}) \sum_{l=1}^{n} u^l u_l$$
$$+ \frac{1}{u} (g_{ih} u_{jk} - g_{hj} u_{ik} + g_{kj} u_{ih} - g_{ki} u_{jh}).$$

This is Finzi's formula.

Now we desire to find the conditions, alike necessary and sufficient, which $u = 1/v$ must satisfy in order that the manifold given by

$$ds^2 = \left(\sum_{ij} g_{ij} dx_i dx_j \right) / u^2$$

may be Euclidean when the original manifold given by (1) is isotropic and of constant curvature K. Clearly it must be possible so to choose u that $(IJ, HK) = 0$, when

$$(ij, hk) = K (g_{ih} g_{jk} - g_{jh} g_{ik}).$$

We must therefore have, by Finzi's formula,

$$u (g_{ih} g_{jk} - g_{jh} g_{ik}) \left(-K + \frac{1}{u^2} \sum_{l=1}^{n} u^l u_l \right)$$
$$= (g_{ih} u_{jk} - g_{hj} u_{ik} + g_{kj} u_{ih} - g_{ki} u_{jh}),$$

where i, j, h, k can take all values from 1 to n inclusive.

These equations will be satisfied provided we can find u such that

$$u_{jk} = g_{jk}(au + b), \qquad \qquad \text{......(2)}$$

while, in addition,

$$au + b = \tfrac{1}{2}u\{-K + \Sigma u^l u_l / u^2\}, \qquad \qquad \text{......(3)}$$

where a and b are arbitrary functions or, in particular, constants. That u can be so found, when $a = -K$ and b is a constant, can be established by means of the theory of systems of total differential equations*.

Now equations (2) and (3) are tensor-equations. In other words, if equations (2) are true for any one system of coordinates they will be true for any transformed system; and, since $\overset{n}{\underset{l=1}{\Sigma}} u^l u_l$ is an invariant, such a transformation will leave equation (3) unaltered.

Furthermore, if the manifold, whose line-element is given by

$$ds^2 = \overset{n}{\underset{1}{\Sigma}}_{jk} \frac{u_{jk}}{u^2(au + b)} dx_j dx_k,$$

be Euclidean, it must be possible to find a system of coordinates such that

$$\left. \begin{aligned} u_{jj} &= u^2(au + b) \\ u_{jk} &= 0, \quad j \neq k \end{aligned} \right\}. \qquad \qquad \text{......(4)}$$

And corresponding to such a system we shall have, by equations (2),

$$g_{jj} = u^2; \qquad g_{jk} = 0, \qquad j \neq k. \qquad \qquad \text{......(5)}$$

We require, therefore, to find a function u which satisfies the equations (4) when the g's are given by equations (5). In addition equation (3) must be satisfied. Now, when $g_{jj} = u^2$ and $g_{jk} = 0$, we clearly have $g^{jj} = 1/u^2$ and $g^{jk} = 0$. Furthermore, if the letters i, j, k stand for different numbers, it may be readily seen that

$$[ii, i] = uu_i, \quad [ii, k] = -uu_k, \quad [ij, i] = uu_j, \quad \text{and} \quad [ij, k] = 0.$$

Also

$$\{ij, l\} = [ij, l]/u^2.$$

Hence from equations (2) and (3) we see that we must find a function u which satisfies the equations

$$\frac{\partial^2 u}{\partial x_s^2} - \frac{2u_s^2}{u} = -\frac{1}{u}\left(\overset{n}{\underset{r=1}{\Sigma}} u_r^2\right) + u^2(au + b), \qquad s = 1, 2, \ldots n;$$

$$\frac{\partial^2 u}{\partial x_r \partial x_s} = \frac{2u_r u_s}{u}, \quad r \neq s, \quad \left. \begin{aligned} r \\ s \end{aligned} \right\} = 1, 2, \ldots n;$$

and

$$(au + b) = \frac{u}{2}\left[-K + \frac{1}{u^4}\overset{n}{\underset{r=1}{\Sigma}} u_r^2\right].$$

* A proof is given in the Appendix (p. 658).

In these equations put $u = 1/v$. Then the equations become

$$\frac{\partial^2 v}{\partial x_s^2} = \frac{1}{v}\left(\sum_{r=1}^{n} v_r^2\right) - \left(\frac{a}{v} + b\right);$$

$$\frac{\partial^2 v}{\partial x_r \, \partial x_s} = 0;$$

and

$$\sum_{r=1}^{n} v_r^2 - K = 2\,(a + bv).$$

Suppose now that v is expanded in a convergent series of powers and products of the n variables $x_1, x_2, \ldots x_n$. Then the second set of equations shews that the expansion can contain no product terms. The first set of equations shews that

$$\frac{\partial^2 v}{\partial x_r^2} = \frac{\partial^2 v}{\partial x_s^2}, \quad \text{when} \quad r \neq s.$$

Hence the expansion for v cannot contain powers of the variables higher than the second. We may then assume that

$$\frac{v}{c} = 1 + \sum_{r=1}^{n} d_r \left(\frac{x_r + a_r}{c}\right)^2,$$

where $a_1, \ldots a_r, d_1, \ldots d_r$, and c are all constants.

If now we put $S = \sum_{r=1}^{n} v_r^2$, we have the equations

$$2d_r/c = S/v - a/v - b;$$

$$S - K = 2\,(a + bv).$$

Hence d_r must be independent of r and equal to d (say). And our equations will then be satisfied provided

$$a = -4d = -K, \quad \text{and} \quad b = 2d/c.$$

Thus we see that for isotropic space of constant curvature K we can obtain a line-element of the canonical form

$$ds^2 = \left(\sum_{r=1}^{n} dx_r^2\right)\Big/v^2,$$

provided

$$\frac{v}{c} = 1 + K \sum_{r=1}^{n} \left(\frac{x_r + a_r}{c}\right)^2\Big/4.$$

This is evidently equivalent to Riemann's result.

In the concluding stages of the investigation just given we assumed that d did not vanish. Let us now see whether a value of v can be found for which $d = 0$. We shall naturally assume

$$v = c + \sum_{r=1}^{n} a_r x_r,$$

where c, a_1, ... a_n are constants. Then the equations to be satisfied become

$$\frac{1}{v}\Sigma a_r^2 = \frac{a}{v} + b;$$

$$\Sigma a_r^2 - K = 2(a + bv).$$

We must therefore have $b = 0$, $a = \Sigma a_r^2 = -K$. Now Σa_r^2 is essentially positive if v be real. Hence our alternative value of v is only possible when K is negative.

Obviously we may, without any essential limitation, put

$$c = 0, \qquad a_1 = ... = a_{n-1} = 0;$$

and then $\qquad\qquad v = \sqrt{-K}\,x_n.$

We thus obtain Beltrami's canonical form.

§70. *Some transformations of the canonical form for three-dimensional space.*

Let us now limit ourselves to three-dimensional space of constant curvature. For such space we may take y_1, y_2, y_3 to be the coordinates for which the metric assumes Riemann's canonical form, so that we have

$$ds^2 = \frac{dy_1^2 + dy_2^2 + dy_3^2}{u^2},$$

where $\qquad u = 1 + \rho^2/4R^2 \quad \text{and} \quad \rho^2 = y_1^2 + y_2^2 + y_3^2.$

We have replaced the curvature K by $1/R^2$, so that R is the Gaussian radius of curvature at any point of our space.

This canonical form naturally admits of a large number of transformations. If we put

$$x_1 = y_1/u, \qquad x_2 = y_2/u,$$
$$x_3 = y_3/u, \qquad x_4 = R(2/u - 1),$$

it can be readily shewn that

$$x_1^2 + x_2^2 + x_3^2 + x_4^2 = R^2.$$

Moreover, the foregoing expression for ds^2 now takes the form

$$ds^2 = dx_1^2 + dx_2^2 + dx_3^2 + dx_4^2.$$

Again, we may put $\qquad y_1 = (2 - u)u_1,$
$$y_2 = (2 - u)u_2,$$
$$y_3 = (2 - u)u_3.$$

Then we shall have

$$\frac{x_1}{u_1} = \frac{x_2}{u_2} = \frac{x_3}{u_3} = \frac{x_4}{R} = \frac{2 - u}{u} = \frac{R}{\sqrt{u_1^2 + u_2^2 + u_3^2 + R^2}}.$$

§71. *A geometrical interpretation of three-dimensional space of constant positive curvature.*

The first of these transformations shews that the surface of a hypersphere of radius R in Euclidean space of four dimensions constitutes a three-dimensional manifold of constant positive curvature $1/R^2$. In other words, *we can represent the most general three-dimensional space of constant positive curvature by a hypersphere in Euclidean space of four dimensions.*

To interpret the second transformation we take the origin of coordinates to be the centre of the hypersphere, the four mutually orthogonal axes being $Ox_1, \dots Ox_4$. Let any radius OP meet in Q the tangent plane at the point where Ox_4 cuts the sphere. Then if the coordinates of P be $x_1, \dots x_4$, the coordinates of Q will be u_1, u_2, u_3, R, where the u's and x's are connected by the relations which have just been written down. Hence the u's of the three-dimensional space in which the four-dimensional space of the x's is cut by the tangent plane may be regarded as parametric coordinates of a point on the four-dimensional sphere. In terms of the u's the line-element of our three-dimensional space of constant curvature $1/R^2$ may be written in the form

$$ds^2 = R^2 \frac{(du_1{}^2 + du_2{}^2 + du_3{}^2)}{(u_1{}^2 + u_2{}^2 + u_3{}^2 + R^2)} - R^2 \frac{(u_1 du_1 + u_2 du_2 + u_3 du_3)^2}{(u_1{}^2 + u_2{}^2 + u_3{}^2 + R^2)^2}.$$

This form can be readily extended to n-dimensional space.

§72. *The canonical forms in quasi-spherical coordinates of the three possible types of homogeneous and isotropic three-dimensional space.*

It is convenient now to make a further transformation. We take

$$u_1 = r \cos \theta,$$
$$u_2 = r \sin \theta \cos \phi,$$
$$u_3 = r \sin \theta \sin \phi.$$

Then we easily see that the line-element, for three-dimensional space of constant curvature $1/R^2$, takes the form

$$ds^2 = \frac{R^4 (dr)^2}{(R^2 + r^2)^2} + \frac{R^2 r^2}{R^2 + r^2} \{(d\theta)^2 + \sin^2 \theta \, (d\phi)^2\}. \qquad \dots\dots(1)$$

This gives us the expression for the metric of the canonical form of general three-dimensional space in what may be regarded as spherical coordinates. Further developments depend upon the sign of R^2.

If K be positive, R will be real and we shall have the case of spherical or Riemannian three-dimensional space. For such space we may put

$$r = R \tan \chi,$$

where χ will be real. Then we get for the *metric of Riemannian three-dimensional space*

$$ds^2 = R^2 (d\chi)^2 + R^2 \sin^2 \chi [(d\theta)^2 + \sin^2 \theta (d\phi)^2].$$

For *Euclidean three-dimensional space* $K = 0$, and therefore R tends to infinity. For such space we have

$$ds^2 = (dr)^2 + r^2 \{(d\theta)^2 + \sin^2 \theta (d\phi)^2\}.$$

When K is negative, R is imaginary and we have *Lobatchewsky's three-dimensional space*. That we may deal with real quantities we now put $K = -1/R^2$, so that in the canonical formula (1) for ds^2, just given, we change the sign of R^2.

Further, we write, after this change, $r = R \tanh \chi$.

This transformation gives us, as the canonical form of Lobatchewskyan space in quasi-spherical coordinates,

$$ds^2 = R^2 (d\chi)^2 + R^2 \sinh^2 \chi [(d\theta)^2 + \sin^2 \theta (d\phi)^2].$$

§73. *The true range and value of Riemann's achievement.*

When one reflects upon the vast amount of labour which has gone merely (as it seems) to demonstrate the existence of the three familiar forms of three-dimensional space, to which we were led by elementary considerations, the result may appear at first sight to be somewhat disappointing.

Weyl comments upon this feeling: "Space", he says*, "is a form of phenomena, and by being so, is necessarily homogeneous". (In saying that space is a form of phenomena Weyl means that the same thing, still remaining what it is, can equally well be at some place in space other than that at which it is actually.) "It would appear from this that, out of the rich abundance of possible geometries included in Riemann's conception, only the three special cases mentioned come into consideration from the outset, and that all the others must be rejected without further examination as being of no account: *parturiunt montes, nascetur ridiculus mus!*"

Weyl goes on to explain that Riemann rightly held a different opinion. The existence of matter constitutes, as Einstein has lately shewn, binding forces in space which alter its metric. Not only so, but space and

* H. Weyl, *Space—Time—Matter*. Translated by H. L. Brose. Methuen, 1922, pp. 96, 97.

time together form a four-dimensional continuum of which the metric depends upon the distribution of the matter within the continuum. It is true that Riemannian hyper-geometry merely demonstrates that for our three-dimensional space three different types of geometry are possible; and it is also true that these, as we have seen in the previous lecture, can be investigated by relatively simple methods. But Riemann also shewed that for a general manifold (and therefore, in particular, for that of space-time) it is possible to create a geometry corresponding precisely to the type of metric which Einstein has found adequate as the expression of the existence of gravitational forces.

§ 74. *The nature of the space of common experience in the light of Riemann's analysis.*

At the risk of some repetition we will now take up again the questions discussed in our previous lecture.

The three-dimensional space of our common experience is the space in which, as we believe, solid bodies can be moved without change of form. Such solid bodies are ideal constructions, perfectly rigid, and unaltered in size or shape by heat or other physical conditions. In consequence of this property of the free motion of solid bodies, we assume that our space is homogeneous and isotropic. Further it has three dimensions. Such space, as we have now realised, can be of three different types.

(1) It may, in the first place, be Euclidean. In this case it is infinite in extent. For it Euclid's postulate as to parallel lines holds good: through any point, outside a given line, one and only one parallel to the given line can be drawn, and this parallel will never meet the line. In Euclidean geometry, therefore, the angles of a triangle together make up two right angles. As was shewn by Wallis (1616–1703) at the end of the seventeenth century, Euclid's postulate is equivalent to the assumption that to every figure there corresponds a similar figure of any size. In fact, if we could accurately demonstrate that we could make two absolutely similar triangles of which the linear dimensions of one are double those of the other, we should prove that Euclidean geometry is the geometry of the space in which we find ourselves. Equally in this geometry the parallax of a very distant star would be zero.

The line-element in Euclidean space takes the well-known form

$$ds^2 = dx^2 + dy^2 + dz^2.$$

(2) Secondly, the geometry of our space may be Lobatchewskyan or (rectangular) hyperbolic. In this geometry Euclid's postulate as to parallels does not hold. In place of it we may take Hilbert's axiom: "If in two-dimensional geometry b be any straight line and A any point outside it, there are always two rays through A, namely a_1 and a_2, which do not form one and the same straight line and do not intersect the line b, while any other ray, which lies in the region bounded by a_1 and a_2 and also passes through A, does intersect the line b". The lines a_1 and a_2 are called the right-handed and left-handed parallels from A to the line b. Parallel lines as thus defined approach one another continually and their distance apart ultimately becomes less than any assigned quantity. In this hyperbolic space the sum of the three angles of a triangle is less than two right angles. If stellar space were hyperbolic the parallax of a star, however distant, would be positive. Three-dimensional Lobatchewskyan space is 'curved' and the Riemannian curvature at any point and in any direction at that point is the same negative quantity: naturally, this quantity must be almost inconceivably small if by any chance the space of our actual experience should be hyperbolic.

(3) As a third possibility space may be spherical or Riemannian. The properties of this space can, as we have seen in the previous lecture, be developed in a simple manner from the assumption that there is no parallel to a given line from any point outside it. In other words, all co-planar straight lines intersect one another. If K be the curvature of this space and if we put $K = 1/R^2$, then R is real and serves to measure the finite dimensions of spherical space. In this space, every straight line is of finite length. In contradiction to the axioms of Euclidean space, two straight lines in Riemannian geometry can enclose a space; and two points, if they happen to be a point and its anti-point, do not determine a straight line. (An analytical definition of the anti-point of a given point will be given shortly: the geometrical definition was given in the last lecture.) The sum of the angles of a triangle is always greater than two right angles; and, if the amount by which they are greater be called the excess, the area of a triangle is proportional to its excess. The parallax of an infinitely distant star would in spherical geometry be negative: in other words there are no infinitely distant stars. Furthermore, in Riemannian geometry similar figures of different sizes do not exist.

§75. *The analytical investigation of plane hyperbolic geometry.*

Hyperbolic geometry of the plane can be investigated *ab ovo* by taking for ds the expression

$$ds^2 = R^2 (d\chi)^2 + R^2 \sinh^2 \chi \, (d\theta)^2.$$

Alternatively, we may take the form, already given in §37,

$$ds^2 = dx^2 \cosh^2 \frac{y}{R} + dy^2,$$

which results from the former by the transformation

$$\cosh \chi = \cosh \frac{x}{R} \cosh \frac{y}{R},$$

$$\tan \theta = \tanh \frac{y}{R} \div \sinh \frac{x}{R}.$$

From the equations of the geodesics, which this expression for the line-element enables us readily to obtain, we may find expressions for the parallels to Ox. If u be a parameter, the lines

$$e^{x/R} = \frac{u}{R} \coth \frac{y}{R}$$

form a right-handed system of parallels to Ox. Similarly, the sheaf of lines

$$e^{-x/R} = \frac{u}{R} \coth \frac{y}{R},$$

forms a left-handed system of parallels to Ox. If the right-handed parallel to Ox through a point P makes an angle θ with the perpendicular PM from P to Ox, then, as in our previous investigation,

$$\tan \theta/2 = e^{-y/R}.$$

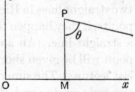

We see that these left-handed and right-handed parallels will not coincide unless $y/R = 0$. In this case, either $y = 0$, and then the parallels coincide with Ox itself: or $R = 0$, and we have Euclidean geometry. We have previously seen that from elementary considerations based on Hilbert's axiom we can build up an entirely self-consistent Lobatchewskyan geometry of space. We now see that equally we may start from the canonical (or from some equivalent) form of the line-element and fashion the same geometry by purely analytical methods.

§76. *Lobatchewskyan geometry of the plane is that of the pseudo-sphere in Euclidean space.*

The geometry of the hyperbolic plane is the same as that of the surface which in Euclidean space is commonly called *the pseudo-sphere*, a surface of revolution obtained by rotating a tractrix round its asymptote. In the figure V is the vertex of the tractrix and Ox is its asymptote.

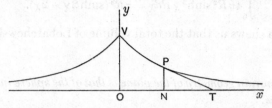

If PT be the tangent at a point P, the tractrix is defined by the condition that $PT = R$, where R is a constant. The tractrix is, in fact, the path of a heavy particle dragged along a rough horizontal plane by a string of length R, of which one end describes a straight line which is the asymptote of the curve. If the arc $VP = \sigma$ and if PN be the perpendicular from P on Ox, we have $dy/d\sigma = -y/R$, and hence $PN = Re^{-\sigma/R}$. Suppose now that ds is an element of length on the pseudo-sphere, and that $d\theta$ is the difference of longitude of the ends of the element. Then we have

$$ds^2 = R^2 e^{-2\sigma/R} (d\theta)^2 + (d\sigma)^2.$$

When this formula is compared with that obtained in the previous lecture for the line-element of the hyperbolic plane (§37), it shews that circles of latitude on the pseudo-sphere correspond to what we have previously called limiting curves in the hyperbolic plane, and that longitudinal tractrices on the pseudo-sphere correspond to the bundle of parallels orthogonal to these limiting curves.

§77. *The volume of Lobatchewskyan space.*

We have seen that in three-dimensional hyperbolic space the line-element can be written

$$ds^2 = R^2 (d\chi)^2 + R^2 \sinh^2 \chi [(d\theta)^2 + \sin^2 \theta (d\phi)^2].$$

This formula shews that, corresponding to any surface for which χ is constant, ds would be an element of length on a sphere which in Euclidean space would have a radius of length $R \sinh \chi$.

Now when θ and ϕ are constants we have $s = R\chi$, if s and χ vanish together: hence $R\chi$ will be the radius of the sphere whose surface is obtained by varying θ and ϕ. Such a sphere will have an area

$$4\pi R^2 \sinh^2 \chi.$$

This area increases indefinitely with χ.

The volume of the sphere will be

$$\int_0^\chi 4\pi R^2 \sinh^2 \chi \, R d\chi = \pi R^3 (\sinh 2\chi - 2\chi).$$

This formula shews us that the total volume of Lobatchewskyan space is not finite.

§78. *Riemannian geometry of the plane is that of the sphere in Euclidean space.*

The plane geometry of Riemannian or spherical space can be derived from that of a sphere in Euclidean three-dimensional space just as the plane geometry of hyperbolic space can be derived from that of a pseudo-sphere. Take a sphere of radius R. Let O be its centre and C its north pole. Take rectangular axes such that OC is the axis of y_0 while the axes of y_1 and y_2 are in the plane of the equator. Let χ be the co-latitude of any point P on the sphere, and let θ be the longitude of P measured from the axis Oy_1. Then we can take

$$y_0 = R\cos\chi,$$
$$y_1 = R\sin\chi\cos\theta,$$
$$y_2 = R\sin\chi\sin\theta.$$

These equations give

$$y_0{}^2 + y_1{}^2 + y_2{}^2 = R^2,$$

and also

$$ds^2 = R^2 (d\chi)^2 + R^2 \sin^2\chi \, (d\theta)^2.$$

But this, as we have seen in §72, is the expression for the element of length in two-dimensional Riemannian or spherical space. Clearly the geometry of such space can easily be worked out in terms of spherical trigonometry.

§79. *The volume of spherical or Riemannian space of three dimensions.*

We have seen that for Riemannian space of three dimensions the line-element is given by

$$ds^2 = R^2 (d\chi)^2 + R^2 \sin^2\chi \, [(d\theta)^2 + \sin^2\theta \, (d\phi)^2].$$

Taking any point in this space as origin, we may assume that θ and ϕ are pseudo-spherical coordinates: as θ and ϕ vary, χ remaining constant, they will trace out the surface of a sphere. The radius of this sphere will be given by putting $\theta = \phi = $ constant, so that for it we shall have $ds = R\,d\chi$, or $s = R\chi$, if s and χ vanish together. We may then take $R\chi$ to be the radius of a sphere whose surface is given by varying θ and ϕ. Points on such a sphere will be obtained by drawing radii of length $R\chi$ in all directions from the origin. Plainly, from the formula which gives ds, the area of the sphere will be

$$4\pi R^2 \sin^2 \chi.$$

If now we put $a = R\chi$, we may say that in Riemannian space the area of a sphere of radius a is

$$4\pi R^2 \sin^2 \frac{a}{R}.$$

This area will be a maximum when a is $\pi R/2$, and its value will then be $4\pi R^2$. As a increases, however, the area of the sphere of radius a will decrease when a has become greater than $\pi R/2$ and will ultimately become zero when $a = \pi R$. Thus any two radii drawn from the origin will meet after the length of each has become πR: the point at which they meet is called the *anti-point* of the origin. It follows that, if a ray of light passes from the origin and continues indefinitely, it will after traversing a distance πR pass through the anti-origin; and then*, after traversing a further distance πR, it will return to the point from which it started.

Thus in Riemannian space there will be, corresponding to any sun, an anti-sun; and, unless light be lost by dispersion or in other ways, it should be possible for an observer to see not only the sun but also the anti-sun by means of rays that have passed right round the Universe. If then our space is Riemannian, as is probable, it may be (apart from physical circumstances unconnected with our present theory) that our astronomers see stars several times over: the light by which the secondary, tertiary, etc. stars are seen will have passed once, twice, etc. round the Universe.

The volume of the whole of three-dimensional Riemannian space of Gaussian curvature $1/R^2$ will be

$$\int_0^{\pi R} 4\pi R^2 \sin^2 \frac{r}{R}\, dr = 2\pi^2 R^3.$$

* We assume that the origin and its anti-point do not coincide. Such coincidence is possible and some would even say that it is probable. If it occurs, space will be 'elliptic' (§ 44).

Thus *Riemannian space is of finite volume*. The larger the curvature of such space, the smaller will be its volume. When the curvature vanishes and space becomes Euclidean, its volume becomes infinite.

§ 80. *Properties of Riemannian space*.

It should be borne in mind that the point which we have chosen for our origin of coordinates in Riemannian or spherical space is quite arbitrary. All that we have said will apply to spheres drawn with any point whatever of Riemannian space as centre. Hence in such space there can be no boundary. *Every point of such space has, in fact, the same relation to the whole space as every other point.* Moreover, although Riemannian space is finite, we must not think of it as in any way immersed in space of four dimensions. Though finite, it is complete in itself; and it exists unaccompanied by any space which wrongly may be thought to be beyond itself.

This feature of Riemannian space is that which is the greatest puzzle to the plain man ignorant of geometrical speculation. He cannot imagine how space can be finite unless it is immersed in some other space that is infinite. So he always enquires what happens at the end of space. The reply that space is unbounded, and that therefore it is impossible to come to the end of it, does not satisfy him. He can conceive that the surface of a sphere in two dimensions is alike finite and unbounded; but he cannot conceive a three-dimensional analogue to this surface unless it be placed in space of four dimensions. It is difficult to see how the mathematician can help him to correct prejudices of his imagination: and it must be admitted that the mathematician himself is not seldom disturbed by what appear to be the paradoxes of Riemannian space.

§ 81. *To which of the three possible types does our space belong?*

The question remains as to which, of the three different types of space which we have described, is in actual fact the space in which we live. Probably our space, as we shall see later at the end of Lecture VI and in § 291, is Riemannian; but we cannot yet pass a final judgment on this point. Evidently our space only differs from that described by Euclid by an extraordinarily small degree of curvature.

Poincaré, in his *Science and Hypothesis*, went so far as to assert that we could not by empirical observations decide for or against the validity of Euclid's geometry*. According to his standpoint, Euclidean geo-

* H. Poincaré, *La Science et l'Hypothèse*. Flammarion, n.d., p. 91.

metry was the more convenient and therefore we should always interpret the physical facts which are at the basis of geometry on the assumption that the Euclidean scheme was valid. The change of outlook due to the general theory of relativity is such that I doubt whether to-day the majority of those who have speculated in this realm would agree with Poincaré; but it is certain that conclusive experiments will only become possible when a complete scheme, alike of geometry and of physics, is worked out for Riemannian space. Obviously we need the great distances of astronomy if we are to make effective observations involving quantities so small as the possible curvature of Riemannian space. These distances are measured by light rays which are a physical phenomenon, and therefore we need to link up physics to our geometrical scheme before final verdicts become possible.

It may well be, however, that in future ages the view that space is finite will become a firmly held dogma, an assumption as universal as the truth of the Copernican view of planetary motions. Men will then regard Euclidean geometry as a convenient approximation to the truth, reprehensible mainly because it tolerates the absurd idea that space can possibly be infinite. Clifford (1845–1879) said*, half-jestingly, "I do not mind confessing that I personally have often found relief from the dreary infinities of homaloidal (Euclidean) space in the consoling hope that, after all, this other (Riemannian space) may be the true state of things".

* W. K. Clifford, *Lectures and Essays*, vol. i, p. 388. Macmillan, 1901.

Lecture v

SPACE-TIME: THE SPECIAL THEORY OF RELATIVITY

§ 82. *The measurement and interconnection of space and time.*

In the two previous lectures we have considered space in separation from time. We have now to consider the remarkable transformation of fundamental concepts which, by developing the consequences of the fact that space and time are always fused together in experience, constitutes theory of relativity*.

Until the present century philosophers and physicists generally assumed that space and time were separate, each existing in its own right and in complete independence of the other. Time is presented to our experience as continuous duration in which there is succession. In space we experience continuous extension without succession. The conception of time as an independent entity presents obvious difficulties. At any instant the past is dead, the 'now' alone exists. How then can we get continuous duration? What is there that binds together successive moments of time? Descartes (1596–1650) assumed, and the idea appears also in earlier Indian philosophy, that the world is perpetually re-created. Conservation, for Descartes, is continuous creation†.

But, if we analyse our experience aright, we reach the conviction that space and time are abstractions made by the mind from a single entity, space-time‡. We do not perceive points of space or instants of time. We perceive point-instants or *events*. The plain man will object that the

* The historical development of the new ideas may be briefly indicated. The Michelson-Morley experiment was first described in the year 1887. Important papers by H. A. Lorentz appeared in the years 1887, 1895 and 1904. A. Einstein's classical paper on the special theory of relativity belongs to the year 1905. H. Minkowski set out his most pregnant ideas in the year 1908. Original papers by Lorentz, Einstein and Minkowski were published together under the title *Das Relativitätsprinzip*. Teubner, 1915. Subsequent editions of this book have included further papers by Einstein. Einstein's fundamental discussion of the General Theory of Relativity appeared in the year 1916.

† *Oeuvres de Descartes*, ed. V. Cousin. Levrault, Paris, 1824, tome i, pp. 381 and 458.

‡ For the present we leave open the question as to whether space-time is other than a necessary form of our perception. This and cognate matters are discussed in Lecture XVII.

end of a lightning-conductor on the Victoria Tower of the Houses of Parliament is a definite point of space which we can perceive. It is, however, only definite with respect to a set of axes in, shall we say, Parliament Square. These axes move with the earth, which is revolving on its own axis and moving roughly in a circle round the sun, while the sun itself is in motion with respect to the so-called fixed stars. A set of axes determined by the stars is as fixed as any set we can choose. But, because the axes in Parliament Square are moving with respect to these axes, we cannot determine the position of the end of the lightning-conductor, even with reference to the stellar axes, without bringing in the notion of *time*.

It might be thought that if we had two clocks identical in all respects, one fixed in Parliament Square and one fixed with reference to the stellar axes, they would go at the same rate and that therefore we could measure absolute time. But the two clocks are moving rapidly with respect to one another. It is a pure assumption that, if a man in Parliament Square could see the clock fixed to the stellar axes, he would find that it appeared to be going at the same rate as the clock by his side. And the theory of relativity says that this assumption is untrue. We need to bring in a knowledge of how the identical clocks are moving with respect to one another in *space* before we can settle their relative rates for our observer.

All physical science is primarily quantitative: it deals with measurements which are expressed by numbers. When the nature of the measurement of space or of time by means of material 'events' is analysed, it is found that considerations of time enter into determinations of space and that considerations of space enter into determinations of time. For instance, an observed distance, like the length AB of a mile of chain stretched out along a straight road, is a system of events. If we stand at one end A of the chain, the light from the other B takes a definite (though very small) time to reach the eye. Thus we actually perceive the two ends A and B at different times. Similarly, actually observed time-intervals are always measured spatially. Our usual measurement uses the coincidence of the hand of a clock with a point on its dial.

§83. *Absolute space.*

We naturally picture space as a vast tenement-house in which different bodies occupy places in its various rooms. We thus fancy that we can define our position in absolute space by saying that we are in a certain position in a certain room. In point of fact we have no means of discovering any such absolutely determined room. All we can do is to find our location with reference to the location of other bodies. We have no knowledge of absolute position or of absolute motion. We cannot, in fact, find out if we are in the same place at two different times. The geometry of space is the study of a network of relations based on observation of the way in which rigid bodies can be moved relatively to one another.

If absolute space, the vast tenement-house of our imagination, exists, we have failed to discover it. There may, or there may not, be an 'ether' filling all space (*vide* § 150), but it is certain that, if an ether exists, we have failed to determine the motion of matter relative to it. The assignment of different bodies to different tenement-rooms in absolute space belongs to the class of distinctions which are not derived from observable phenomena. We can therefore have no use for it. The conception of absolute space we set aside. Geometry is based on the notion of extension and not on the notion of location.

Such a conclusion will, of course, be challenged by those who venerate the name and accept the authority of Newton. Newton's belief in absolute space grew naturally out of the quasi-philosophical, quasi-religious, ideas of the Cambridge Platonism of his age. Henry More (1614–1687) in effect deified space, as when he could write*: "This infinite extent will seem to be something divine. It cannot be nothing as it has so many splendid attributes, such as the following, which are ascribed by metaphysicians to the Supreme Being". Then follows a list which is certainly imposing, "one, simple, motionless, eternal, complete" and so forth. From the atmosphere in which such thought flourished there apparently came Newton's scholium†: "Absolute space by its nature without relation to anything external always remains similar and motionless. Relative space is a measure of this space or a certain movable dimension of it, which is defined by our senses by its position with regard to bodies, and is usually taken for motionless space".

§ 84. *Does absolute rotation exist? The views of Newton and Mach.*

Though neither Newton nor any of his successors could point to any experiment which appeared to give us knowledge of absolute (as

---

* In the metaphysical treatise of 1671, entitled *Enchiridion Metaphysicum: sive, de rebus.* . . .This work was an attack on Cartesian philosophy.

† See, for instance, Thomson and Blackburn's reprint (Maclehose, 1871) of Newton's last edition (1726) of the *Principia*, p. 6.

opposed to relative) motion of translation, yet a number of experiments seem to point to absolute rotation. The earth, for instance, owing to its rotation is flattened at the poles. Foucault's pendulum changes its orientation as the earth rotates and so would prove the existence of such rotation, even though the earth were perpetually covered with clouds so that we were unable to see the so-called fixed stars.

These arguments for the existence of absolute rotation were almost universally accepted as cogent until Ernst Mach (1838–1916) in the second half of the nineteenth century challenged them. He urged that we have no right to claim that the centrifugal forces produced by rotation are due to absolute rotation: they result from rotation relative to the fixed stars. If all the fixed stars had a rotatory motion equal and opposite to that which we ascribe to the earth, and if the earth were at rest, we should not know of the circumstance; and we should be very much surprised if the centrifugal forces of our common experience were not produced. We are thus led to the belief that the law of the inertia of matter must be so formulated that all the masses of the Universe enter into its expression. We are not entitled to say that there is a distinction between rotation and translation, the former being absolute and the latter relative. Both are relative: the fixed stars are the origin of the centrifugal forces which arise where a body is rotated with respect to them. Though this conclusion cannot be proved by experiment, it can be provisionally accepted because we do not then assume the equally undemonstrable belief that we can discover, as regards rotations, the existence of absolute space.

Mach, in the year 1866, wrote: "Physical space such as I have in view (it also includes time) is nothing but the interdependence of phenomena. Modern physics which would recognise this interdependence would have no further need of special views on time and space since they would have been already exhausted". Forty years after these words were written Einstein fused together space and time in the special theory of relativity and shewed that geometry is, in essence, a branch of physics.

§85. *The belief in absolute chronometric time.*

But is there not absolute time? We have an intuitive belief that time is absolute: and Newton* formulated this belief in the *Principia*. He said: "Absolute true mathematical time of itself and from its nature

* This scholium immediately precedes that, relating to space, which has just been quoted.

without relation to anything external flows equally; and its other name is duration".

Newton is here speaking of mathematical time, such as is measured by a perfect chronometer, and not of psychological time, which is measured by our sensations. It is the public time of a community, which different individuals fill with varying intensities of feeling. Belief in the absolute nature of such time, a conviction that it would be the same for ourselves as for beings on a star moving quickly relatively to the earth, was until recently universal. But such belief and conviction cannot be maintained.

We have previously reached the conclusion that we cannot find out what is the same place at two different times: we pass now to the correlative fact that we cannot find out what is the same time at two different places. "But that is obvious nonsense", says the plain man when first introduced to this region of enquiry. "I can move my clock from A to B and discover whether it tells the same time as an exactly similar clock at B. If the two clocks are perfect and synchronised accurately, I have done what you say is impossible."

Let us grant that we can construct perfect chronometers, accurately synchronised, just as we grant the existence of rigid measuring rods. The reply to the objection of the plain man has nothing to do with such mechanical difficulties as are due to imperfections of chronometers. It rests upon the less obvious fact that we do not know whether the rate of our clock A has not altered in going to B. The plain man replies that, if the clocks were a mile apart and sufficiently large and clear, he could by a telescope see that they went at the same rate. "Yes," we answer, "but have you allowed for the fact that light is not instantaneous. It travels at the rate of 186,000 miles a second*, if we may assume that its velocity is unchanged when its direction is reversed." If he replies that one hundred and eighty-six thousandth of a second is so small a period of time as to be negligible, we ask him to imagine the second clock of the sun, whence light will take eight minutes to reach the earth.

The point which I wish to emphasise by this imaginary conversation is that at great distances our measures of time depend upon light-signals, and that the pre-relativity physicist had but a hazy notion of what he meant by the same time at two different places.

* The fact that light travels with a finite though large velocity was first determined by the Danish astronomer Römer (1644–1710) in the year 1676, as a result of observations of Jupiter's moons.

§86. *The belief in absolute simultaneity.*

Light travels so fast that its speed baffles imagination. Sound, how-ever, travels slowly. Let us therefore imagine that we determined time by sound-signals. We have, say, on a still day two soundless motor boats, side by side and each a mile from the ends of a straight canal two miles long. Though they happen to be side by side at a given moment, we postulate that one is at rest and the other moving rapidly. At the given moment shrill whistles are blown at each end of the canal. For an observer on the stationary boat the whistles are simultaneous. Are they simultaneous for an observer in the moving boat? No. He travels to meet sound coming from one of them and away from sound coming from the other. He hears the former whistle first. The whistles, in fact, are not simultaneous for each of the two observers. Simultaneity of sounds depends on the velocity of the observer.

Exactly in the same way simultaneity of events conveyed by light-signals is not absolute but dependent on the motion of the observer. The plain man replies: "I know that I only see things which happen on the sun some eight minutes after they have happened. But an astro-nomer, knowing distances and velocities, can always make the neces-sary corrections. All this talk does not upset my belief in absolute time". To which we answer: "The whole point is whether the astro-nomer has such knowledge based on conclusive physical experiment as to give us absolute time throughout the Universe. In point of fact he has no such knowledge".

§87. *Two fundamental enquiries.*

At the basis of the special theory of relativity are two questions. In the first place, how can we determine the same moment at two different points A and B? Secondly, how can the length of a moving rod be accurately measured by a stationary observer (or, say, the length of a moving railway train by a man on the embankment of the line)? In answer to the first question we have to admit that *the definition of simultaneity rests upon a convention.* Suppose that M is the middle point of the straight line AB. When flashes at A and B reach an observer at M at the same instant we say that the flashes were simultaneous: they occurred at what we define to be the same time at A and B. In this definition we assume (what we cannot prove) that light travels from A to M in the same time that it travels from B to M.

Suppose now that an observer S is at M when the flashes occur, but that he is moving along AB towards B. The flash from B will clearly meet him before the flash from A. Hence for the moving observer the flashes were not simultaneous. In short, events which by the most natural and convenient definition are judged to be simultaneous for one observer will not usually be simultaneous for an observer moving relatively to him. Moreover, as we shall see shortly, we cannot discover which observer is moving relatively to the medium in which it is natural to assume that the light is moving.

It may be objected that a more natural definition of simultaneity would be found by having two synchronised identical clocks, one of which was left at A and the other slowly moved to B. When the clocks indicated the same time we should have simultaneity at the two places. In this definition, however, there is an assumption which cannot be demonstrated to be a physical fact. In slowly going from A to B the clock might gain exactly the time which it lost in its slow return journey from B to A; and then an observer at A would think that it had continuously kept perfect time. To define simultaneity by a moving clock we assume that the clock does not alter its rate when it is slowly moved. It can be proved that this assumption is equivalent to the former.

How, in the second place, can we measure the length of a railway train AB from the embankment with respect to which it is rapidly moving? For the embankment we can find, by our previous definition or convention, simultaneity at all points. We take then an instant of embankment-time t_0; and we suppose that, at that particular instant, the ends A and B of the train are opposite to points A' and B' of the embankment. The measure of $A'B'$ by a man on the embankment will then be the measure of the length of the train from the embankment. It must be carefully noticed, however, that, at the instant of embankment-time when A and B are opposite A' and B' respectively, the time at A as measured by a man on the train will differ from this man's measurement of the time at B.

§88. *The Michelson-Morley experiment.*

What knowledge of light-signals have we? We do not know that light travels backwards and forwards with equal velocities: but we make this very natural assumption. We have seen that it is at the basis of our conventional definition of simultaneity. If the assumption be granted, a famous experiment, the Michelson-Morley experiment, has shewn that *the measured velocity of light is independent of the velocity of the man who measures it.* Not only so, but the astronomer de Sitter, from observations of double stars, has demonstrated the congruous fact that *the measured velocity of light is independent of the velocity of its source.*

We may add that the velocity of light is the same for all colours, besides being independent of the velocity of its source. This conclusion follows from the observed fact that the minimum of emission is observed simultaneously for all colours when a fixed star is eclipsed by a dark neighbour.

We must then assume that light always travels *in vacuo* with constant velocity c relative to all bodies in space, however they may be moving. Its velocity, of course, changes when the light travels through a medium such as air or water. But we can make corrections for such change: moreover, the intervals between astronomical bodies are, save near the bodies, free from such media.

Now the constancy of the measured velocity of light is the puzzle which led to the theory of relativity. If light moves with velocity c relative to A, and if A moves with velocity v in the same direction relative to B, the principles of classical Newtonian kinematics would lead us to assert that the velocity of the light relative to B would be $c + v$. Yet we learn from the Michelson-Morley experiment that the velocity of light relative to B is not $c + v$ but c. Obviously, then, a radical revision of one of the foundations of classical kinematics, the law of composition of velocities, becomes necessary. This revision turns out to be so drastic that in it we give up both the idea of absolute measurement of length and also the idea of absolute simultaneity in time.

§89. *The fundamental result of the special theory of relativity.*

We proceed now to consider bodies moving relatively to one another with constant velocity or, as it is sometimes described, in uniform relative motion. For such bodies we shall shew how to formulate measurements of length and time that will be in agreement with the Michelson-Morley experiment. We assume that, if the direction of light be reversed, its velocity will be unaltered. We further accept the experimental result that this velocity c is a constant, whatever be the velocity of the observer who measures it. We measure a distance by the time which it takes light to travel along it: if light takes time t to travel from A to B, then the length of AB is ct. But we make no assumption that the measurement of distances or times is independent of the velocity of the observer.

Suppose that we have a 'fixed' rod OA, of length l, with two identical synchronised clocks fixed at O and A. We must, of course, synchronise our clocks by flashing a signal from O to A and back again: and we make the assumption that the 'to and fro' velocities of light as measured by an observer at O are the same. If now light flashed from O takes time t to get to A, we have

$$l = ct.$$

Suppose further that we have an exactly similar rod $O'A'$, instantaneously coinciding with OA but moving with velocity v relative to OA. Let there be an observer S at O and a 'moving' observer S' at O'. Let S' have at O' and A' clocks which are duplicates of the clocks at O and A. (The two rods are separated in the diagram, although they are coincident for a moment in actual fact.)

We do not assume that the length of OA as measured by S' would be l. We call it l', so that l' is the apparent length of the rod as measured by the 'moving' observer.

Neither do we assume that the time which the flash takes to go from O to A would be t when measured by S'. We assume that according to his measurement it is t'; and he, in this measurement, will act on the belief that the 'to and fro' velocities of light are the same. Thus both S and S' will respectively assume that they are at rest relatively to the luminiferous ether, if such exists.

S' will then see a flash start from O, a point where he momentarily is; it will go a distance which he measures as l' in time which he measures as t'. It will go from him with velocity c and therefore according to his calculation will have passed over a distance ct' on arriving at A. But the point A appears to him to be travelling towards the origin of the flash with velocity v.

Thus he will compute that the light has passed over a distance $l' - vt'$.

Hence $ct' = l' - vt', \quad \text{or} \quad t' = l'/(c + v).$

Hence the time which S measures as l/c, S' will measure as

$$l'/(c + v). \qquad \qquad \dots\dots(\text{I})$$

Now no physical experiment enables us to detect absolute motion. Hence we may repeat the preceding argument after we have impressed a velocity $-v$ on the whole system. Then S' will be 'at rest' and S with his rod and clock will be moving with velocity $-v$ relatively to S'.

Assume now that the length of $O'A'$ as measured by S is the same as the length of OA as measured by S'.

Then, as before, the time which S' measures as l/c, S will measure as

$$l'/(c-v). \qquad \qquad \cdots\cdots(\text{II})$$

By (I), unit measure of time by S corresponds to a measure $cl'/l(c+v)$ by S'.

By (II), unit measure of time by S corresponds to a measure $l(c-v)/cl'$ by S'.

Hence $\qquad \qquad \qquad c^2 l'^2 = l^2(c^2 - v^2);$

or $\qquad \qquad l = l'h, \quad \text{where} \quad h = 1/\sqrt{1 - v^2/c^2}.$

§ 90. The restricted principle of relativity.

In the previous investigation we have assumed:

(1) that, if the direction of light be reversed, its velocity will be unaltered;

(2) that the measured velocity of light is the same constant quantity c for both observers S and S', notwithstanding that they are in uniform motion relative to one another;

(3) that the length of the rod $O'A'$ as measured by S is the same as the length of the rod OA as measured by S'.

The second assumption is the result of the Michelson-Morley experiment.

The third assumption is an illustration of the *special or restricted principle of relativity*. This principle may be stated in Einstein's words* as follows: "If, relative to S, S' is a system moving with uniform velocity of translation, then natural phenomena run their course with respect to S' according to exactly the same general laws as with respect to S". Alternatively we may state the principle in the form†: "It is impossible by any experiment to detect uniform motion relative to the ether".

The principle is justified by the fact that we cannot detect an absolute movement of uniform translation in space.

The restricted principle of relativity gives rise to Einstein's special theory of relativity. The more general extension of this principle gives rise, as we shall see later, to the general theory of relativity.

* A. Einstein, *Relativity, the special and the general Theory*. Translated by R. W. Lawson. Methuen, 1924, p. 13.

† A. S. Eddington, *Space, Time and Gravitation*. Cambridge University Press, 1923, p. 20.

§91. *The Fitzgerald-Lorentz contraction.*

What is the meaning of our result

$$l' = l\sqrt{1 - v^2/c^2}, \quad \text{or} \quad l = l'h?$$

When c is infinite, this equality becomes $l = l'$, so that Newtonian dynamics rests on the assumption that $c = \infty$. Usually v/c is very small. Except in some modern experiments concerned with the motions of electrons we have no knowledge of velocities approximating to that of light. Thus Newtonian dynamics did not, until recent times, conflict with experimental results.

Evidently $1 - v^2/c^2$ is a positive quantity less than unity, so long as v is less than c. Hence h is greater than unity; and thus l' is less than l. Hence the length of a rod moving with uniform velocity v along its length is, as measured by a stationary observer, contracted in the ratio $1/h$. This is the famous Fitzgerald-Lorentz contraction.

The intelligent but puzzled citizen asks at once: "Does the rod *really* grow smaller?" We must answer "No"; because the rod, for an observer moving with it, keeps the same length. But the only way, in which an observer with respect to whom the rod is moving can measure it, makes it appear shorter. We cannot get behind our measurements and we must be content to repeat ascertained truths. Two observers with respect to whom the rod is respectively stationary and moving, when they measure it by the only methods available, get different results. For an observer S at O the length of the rod OA is l. For an observer S', momentarily at O, but moving along OA with velocity v, its length is l/h.

Can we say what its 'real' length is? We can only do so if we make the convention that the 'real' length is the length as measured by an observer at rest relatively to the rod. We call a length so measured the *proper* length.

If v becomes equal to c, h becomes infinite and l' becomes zero. Thus *the length of a rod moving with the velocity of light is zero.*

If v were greater than c, h would be imaginary. Hence, unless we pass to conditions not contemplated by the special theory of relativity, there can be no speeds in nature greater than c. Thus *the velocity of light is not only an absolute constant of the Universe: it is the greatest velocity possible in that Universe.* It must be remembered that this is the conclusion reached for the special theory of relativity, in which we ignore gravitational fields and their effect on the motion of light.

§92. *The equations of the Lorentz transformation.*

Suppose that we have two axes Ox and $O'x'$, such that $O'x'$ moves along Ox with velocity v. (For convenience of drawing the axes are separated in the figure. In this figure the points P' and P are actually coincident.)

Suppose further that we have identical synchronised clocks at O and P and that the time t given by them vanishes when O' is at O.

Let there be an observer S at O and another observer S' at O'.

Let S's measure of OP be x; and, when t is the time measured by the clock at O, let $O'P'$ as measured by S' be of length x'.

Then $x - vt$ is the distance $O'P'$ as computed by S

and x' is the distance $O'P'$ as computed by S'.

These computations are measures of the same 'moving' length as seen by 'fixed' and 'moving' observers. Hence

$$\frac{x - vt}{l'} = \frac{x'}{l}, \quad \text{or} \quad x' = (x - vt)\,h.$$

Take the point P' on $O'x'$ which instantaneously coincides with P. Suppose further that we have identical synchronised clocks at O' and P' and that the time t' given by them vanishes when O' is at O.

If now we give a velocity $-v$ to the whole system and repeat our previous argument we shall get

$$x = (x' + vt')\,h.$$

Hence, eliminating x', we have

$$t' = \left(t - \frac{vx}{c^2}\right)h.$$

Thus for two systems of rectangular axes moving uniformly with regard to one another, with velocity v in the direction Ox, we shall have

$$\left.\begin{aligned}
x' &= h\,(x - vt), \\
y' &= y, \\
z' &= z, \\
t' &= h\left(t - \frac{vx}{c^2}\right),
\end{aligned}\right\} \qquad \ldots\ldots(\text{L})$$

and conversely

$$\left.\begin{aligned}
x &= (x' + vt')\,h, \\
y &= y', \\
z &= z', \\
t &= \left(t' + \frac{vx'}{c^2}\right)h.
\end{aligned}\right\}$$

These equations constitute the Lorentz transformation. They connect the measurements of space and time made by two observers with regard to whom the two systems are respectively at rest.

The hypothesis that the length of a moving body contracts in the direction of motion in the ratio $(1 - v^2/c^2)^{\frac{1}{2}} : 1$ was first suggested in the year 1892 by G. F. Fitzgerald (1851–1901), the Irish physicist. It was immediately adopted by the Dutch physicist H. A. Lorentz (1853–1928), who made it an element in his general electrical theory. Lorentz' discovery that the time must be changed as in the last of equations (L) was published in the year 1895.

§93.   Einstein's deduction of the Lorentz transformation.

Einstein[*] obtains the previous results in the following manner. We reproduce his argument because it serves to bring out equally clearly, though in conjunction with a different proof, the underlying assumptions of the theory.

Suppose that we have two parallel sets of rectangular axes Ox, Oy, Oz and $O'x'$, $O'y'$, $O'z'$, and that O' is moving with velocity v along Ox so that $O'x'$ and Ox are in the same straight line.

Let an event whose coordinates are x, y, z, t in the one system have accented coordinates in the other. Further, let us assume that t and t' are so measured that both vanish when O and O' coincide. Clearly $y = y'$ and $z = z'$.

Since the two systems are moving uniformly with respect to one another, *linear* relations will connect accented and unaccented coordinates. Moreover, a light-signal (x, t) will be transmitted according to the equation $x - ct = 0$. Hence, since a ray of light travels in both directions with the same velocity c in the two systems, we must have

$$x' - ct' = \lambda (x - ct),$$

and

$$x' + ct' = \mu (x + ct),$$

where λ and μ are constants.

Hence we must have

$$x' = hx + kct,$$
$$ct' = kx + hct,$$

where h and k are constants.

Now O' $(x' = 0)$ moves with velocity v along Ox; and therefore $x = vt$ when $hx + kct = 0$. Thus $k = -hv/c$.

---

[*] See his popular exposition, to which reference has just been made, pp. 115–20.

Hence
$$x' = h(x - vt),$$
$$t' = h\left(t - \frac{vx}{c^2}\right),$$

where h is a constant still to be determined.

Eliminating t we have
$$hx\{1 - v^2/c^2\} = x' + vt'.$$

If we have a rod $A'B'$, fixed relatively to $O'x'$, we can measure its

length in the 'moving' system (just as we should measure its length in a railway carriage) by using a foot-rule that moves with the rod.

But how can we measure the length of the rod as it appears to an observer S in the 'fixed' system? We have seen that we take the points A and B of Ox, which *coincide with A' and B' at the same instant of S's time*, and then measure AB. This is what Einstein calls taking a snapshot of $A'B'$ from the fixed system.

Let l be the length $A'B'$ as measured by S'; and let l' be the length AB as measured by S.

Then, since $x' = h(x - vt)$, we have $l = hl'$. Evidently l is the length of the rod at rest and l' its length when measured by an observer with respect to whom it is moving with velocity v.

Put now the rod of length l in Ox and take a snapshot of it from the moving system. For this snapshot t' must be constant.

Hence, from the equation
$$hx\{1 - v^2/c^2\} = x' + vt',$$
we see that the length of the rod as measured from the moving system is
$$hl\{1 - v^2/c^2\}.$$

But this length is l', since the measure of a 'fixed' rod as seen from a 'moving' system is the same as the measure of the same 'moving' rod as seen from a 'fixed' system.

Hence
$$l' = hl\{1 - v^2/c^2\}.$$

Combine this with $l = hl'$ and we have $h = 1/\sqrt{1 - v^2/c^2}$. Thus the Lorentz equations are, as before,

$$\left.\begin{array}{l} x' = h(x - vt), \\ y' = y, \\ z' = z, \\ t' = h(t - vx/c^2). \end{array}\right\} \qquad \dots\dots(L)$$

§ 94.   *The Lorentz transformation for infinitesimals.*

Obviously the equations just obtained lead at once to

$$dx' = (dx - v\,dt)\,h,$$
$$dy' = dy,$$
$$dz' = dz,$$
$$dt' = \left(dt - \frac{v}{c^2}\,dx\right)h.$$

If then we put $-ds^2 = dx^2 + dy^2 + dz^2 - c^2 dt^2,$
the quantity *ds* will be invariant.

We call *ds the interval between the two adjacent events*

$$(x, y, z, t) \qquad \text{and} \qquad (x + dx, \quad y + dy, \quad z + dz, \quad t + dt).$$

Our result tells us that the Lorentz transformation leaves *ds*, the element of interval, unaltered. In other words, the element of interval is an invariant for the Lorentz transformation.

It can further be proved that the Lorentz transformation is, in effect, the most general linear transformation between two sets of four-dimensional rectangular coordinates for which *ds* is an invariant.

§ 95.   *Time-measurements in the special theory of relativity.*

The Lorentz equations enable us to consider the relation of the different measures of time made by two observers S and S' moving uniformly with respect to one another.

We have assumed that the observer S is with his clock at the origin O of the (x, t) coordinates, and that S' with his clock is at the point O' of the axis $O'x'$ which is moving with velocity v along Ox. The clocks are exactly similar and measure the same zero time when O and O' instantaneously coincide. Let us suppose that an event happens in the moving system of S'. According to the clock at O which measures the common time of the 'fixed' system the event has taken place at time t; but according to the clock at O' which measures the common time of the moving system it has happened at a time t'.

The equation $t = \left(t' + \dfrac{vx'}{c^2}\right)h$

connects the two times.

The difference between the times t_1' and t_2' of two events which happen at O' will be $t_1' - t_2'$ and for them $x' = 0$. Let $t_1 - t_2$ be the corresponding difference between the times of the two events as measured by S at O. Then we have the relation

$$t_1 - t_2 = h\,(t_1' - t_2').$$

Now h is greater than unity. Hence $t_1' - t_2'$ is less than $t_1 - t_2$. In other words time in the moving system seems to the observer S to go more slowly: it is retarded in the ratio $1/h$.

At this statement all our prejudices rise in revolt. So ingrained is our belief in absolute time that we cannot accept the idea that time on a body moving rapidly with respect to ourselves goes more slowly than our time. It should, moreover, be noticed that an observer on the moving body finds that our time goes more slowly than his, for we are moving with respect to himself.

The paradox seems intolerable; but it is the only conclusion we can derive from such measurements as we can make. It results, of course, from the fact that each observer assumes that he himself is at rest relatively to the ether (or to whatever be the medium in which light travels) and makes his calculations accordingly.

The paradox gives rise to a very pretty conundrum. An observer, say, shoots away on a ball moving with nearly the velocity of light. He returns, having made a vast circuit of the heavens, after a century of our time. Measured by himself this time is only a year. What is the *true* time? We must, as Eddington* says, draw a distinction between the time of consciousness and time as used in physical or astronomical measurements. Suppose that we define *proper time* as the time of an observer moving with the system in which the time is measured. Then proper time will be time of consciousness, and its element du will be definite in amount. Physical time, the element of which we can take to be dt, changes (as we have seen) for different observers. On the other hand, dt is a perfect differential, so that the sum of its values over a track will only depend on the end points of the track. But du is not a perfect differential and the sum of its values will depend not only on the end points of the track but also on the particular track along which it is summed.

In the language of the integral calculus $\int du$, taken from point of departure to point of return, will be the time lived by the two men, one on the earth and the other on the ball, and will differ according to the tracks along which they move. But $\int dt$ will be the common time for each as objects observed by some super-observer and will be independent of their tracks.

Why the time of consciousness for the man on the ball should go so much more slowly than for ourselves on the earth has not, I think, been satisfactorily explained.

* A. S. Eddington, *The Mathematical Theory of Relativity*. Cambridge University Press, 1924, p. 241.

Critics of relativity have sometimes contended that, since the motion of the ball is merely relative to the earth, we might equally well argue that the man on the ball is at rest and we in motion, so that our year would be equal to a century of his time. But in the case postulated the ball is, by hypothesis, moving in a strong gravitational field, while in the second case we should be so moving. Relativity does not assert that physically different processes are the same. For the case when the ball moves first directly away from, and then backwards again to, the earth, Einstein has shewn that the right use of the principle of relativity does not lead to contradictions*.

§ 96.   *The space-time continuum and the interval.*

Let us take a system of coordinates x, y, z, t. We take the quantities x, y, z to fix the position of a point in space with respect to three mutually perpendicular planes. We take t to be a fourth dimension so that Ot is perpendicular to Ox, Oy and Oz.

"It cannot be done", you will say. Quite true. Imagination fails to picture a fourth dimension. But any event in space needs four numbers to describe it. Three of these, x, y, z, fix its relative position. The fourth, t, fixes its time relative to an observer whom we may suppose to be at the origin of the x, y, z coordinates.

We have knowledge only of *events*; that is to say, of relative positions at relative times. So we need four numbers to describe the results of our observations. We do not observe points in space but events in space-time. The Universe of our observation is thus a four-dimensional space-time continuum. We call it a continuum because near to any event there are as many events, either actual or conceivable, as we care to choose.

Now we have to make a way of picturing this continuum. Just as for linear motion we can take Ox and Ot to be axes at right angles with respect to which x and t are measured, so for general motion in space we take four mutually perpendicular axes, Ox, Oy, Oz and Ot, which serve for similar measurements. *We are safe in using such imaginative geometry provided we avoid internal contradictions.*

Suppose now that we have two sets of mutually perpendicular reference-axes Ox, Oy, Oz, Ot and $O'x'$, $O'y'$, $O'z'$, $O't'$; and that $O'x'$ moves with velocity v along Ox. Then, by what we have already learned,

$$\left. \begin{aligned} x' &= h\,(x - vt), \\ y' &= y, \\ z' &= z, \\ t' &= h\left(t - \frac{vx}{c^2}\right). \end{aligned} \right\} \qquad \ldots\ldots(\mathrm{L})$$

* *Vide Die Naturwissenschaften*, vol. VI, 1918, p. 697.

The equations (L) constitute the Lorentz transformation.

Newtonian dynamics was built upon the system in which $c = \infty$, $h = 1$. That system is

$$\left.\begin{aligned} x' &= x - vt, \\ y' &= y, \\ z' &= z, \\ t' &= t. \end{aligned}\right\} \qquad \ldots\ldots\text{(N)}$$

Thus, in Newtonian dynamics, the time is absolute.

Suppose now that we have the events P_1 and P_2 whose coordinates in the 'fixed' system of axes are x_1, y_1, z_1, t_1 and x_2, y_2, z_2, t_2.

Let accented letters denote their coordinates for the moving axes. Then

$$x_1' - x_2' = [x_1 - x_2 - v(t_1 - t_2)]\, h,$$
$$y_1' - y_2' = y_1 - y_2,$$
$$z_1' - z_2' = z_1 - z_2,$$
$$t_1' - t_2' = \left[t_1 - t_2 - \frac{v}{c^2}(x_1 - x_2)\right] h.$$

Hence $\quad (x_1 - x_2)^2 + (y_1 - y_2)^2 + (z_1 - z_2)^2 - c^2(t_1 - t_2)^2$
$$= (x_1' - x_2')^2 + (y_1' - y_2')^2 + (z_1' - z_2')^2 - c^2(t_1' - t_2')^2.$$

Thus the expression

$$c^2(t_1 - t_2)^2 - [(x_1 - x_2)^2 + (y_1 - y_2)^2 + (z_1 - z_2)^2]$$

is unaltered by the Lorentz transformation.

Calling this, by a natural extension of our previous definition of ds, *the square of the interval between the two events*, and denoting it by s^2, we have

$$s^2 = c^2(t_1 - t_2)^2 - (x_1 - x_2)^2 - (y_1 - y_2)^2 - (z_1 - z_2)^2.$$

When the events take place at the same point of space as judged by our fixed reference system, s/c is the time between them.

If the two events are observed at the same moment of time, the space-distance between them is $\sqrt{-1}\, s$.

Hence the interval is a generalisation of space-differences and time-differences; and, because it is unaltered by the Lorentz transformation, it is the same for all observers moving with a uniform velocity of translation relative to one another. Thus, though measures of length and measures of time differ for different observers, the interval is the same for all.

Introduce now a new measure of time, given by

$$\tau = \sqrt{-1}\, ct.$$

8-2

Then $\qquad -s^2 = (x_1 - x_2)^2 + (y_1 - y_2)^2 + (z_1 - z_2)^2 + (\tau_1 - \tau_2)^2.$

The expression for s^2 is now symmetrical in x, y, z and τ. In the expression for the interval the part played by τ is exactly that played by x or y or z. Space and time have thus been put on the same footing, so far as analysis is concerned. Are they actually on the same footing in Nature? The answer is in the negative. We have put $\tau = \sqrt{-1}\,ct$; and the existence of the imaginary quantity $\sqrt{-1}$ expresses the fundamental difference between space and time. Analytically the difference is slight: practically it has a profound significance.

We know that the square of the distance between two points in three-dimensional space is

$$(x_1 - x_2)^2 + (y_1 - y_2)^2 + (z_1 - z_2)^2.$$

Hence the interval is $\sqrt{-1}$ times the distance between two points in the four-dimensional continuum measured by the coordinates x, y, z, τ. The latter continuum we call *Minkowski's world*.

In view of the elegance of the contribution made by Hermann Minkowski (1864–1909) to the special theory of relativity, his death at the height of his powers was a grave loss.

§97. *Minkowski's world and its stratification*[*].

Take a two-dimensional section of Minkowski's world given by $y = 0, z = 0$. In accordance with the common notation we put $\iota = \sqrt{-1}$. Then, since $t = \tau/\iota c$, the Lorentz transformation becomes

$$x' = \left(x + \frac{\iota v}{c}\,\tau\right) h,$$

$$\frac{\tau'}{\iota c} = \left(\frac{\tau}{\iota c} - \frac{vx}{c^2}\right) h.$$

If $h = \cos\theta$, we have

$$1 - v^2/c^2 = 1/\cos^2\theta,$$

so that $\qquad v = \iota c \tan\theta \quad$ and $\quad \iota v/c = -\sin\theta.$

Thus the Lorentz transformation becomes, for our two-dimensional section of Minkowski's world,

$$x' = x\cos\theta - \tau\sin\theta,$$
$$\tau' = \tau\cos\theta + x\sin\theta.$$

These are the usual equations of transformation with respect to two sets of rectangular axes having a common origin and inclined at an

---

[*] An admirable discussion of Minkowski's world will be found in Chapter III of A. S. Eddington's book, *Space, Time and Gravitation*. Cambridge University Press, 1920 and subsequently.

angle θ. As a generalisation of this result to four dimensions we can state that, in Minkowski's world, the Lorentz transformation is exactly equivalent to rotation of axes. Thus in the special theory of relativity different observers break up the space-time continuum by taking different stratifications within it. *All their different measurements are merely the result of taking, with a common origin, different sets of mutually orthogonal axes of reference in Minkowski's world.*

§98. *Geometrical illustration of the way in which different observers break up the space-time continuum.*

A simple mechanism, for illustrating the way in which two observers S and S', moving uniformly relatively to one another, break up the space-time continuum, can be constructed when we limit ourselves to one dimension in space.

Let us choose our units of space and time so that the velocity of light is unity. In this system of units let v be the velocity of S' relative to S along the space dimension under consideration.

Our former equations now become

$$x' = (x - vt)\,h,$$
$$t' = (t - vx)\,h,$$

where $1/h = \sqrt{1 - v^2}$.

Put $v = \tan \theta$. Then $h = \dfrac{\cos \theta}{\sqrt{\cos 2\theta}}$ and $vh = \dfrac{\sin \theta}{\sqrt{\cos 2\theta}}$.

Our equations now become

$$\sqrt{\cos 2\theta}\,x' = x \cos \theta - t \sin \theta,$$
$$\sqrt{\cos 2\theta}\,t' = t \cos \theta - x \sin \theta;$$

whence conversely

$$\sqrt{\cos 2\theta}\,x = x' \cos \theta + t' \sin \theta,$$
$$\sqrt{\cos 2\theta}\,t = t' \cos \theta + x' \sin \theta.$$

Take axes Ox and Ot at right angles, and on them make a meshwork in which each square has sides of unit length. This meshwork will, of course, be symmetrical with respect to the diagonal OP whose equation will be $x = t$.

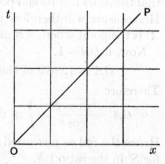

The lines $t' = $ cons. will be given by

$$t \cos \theta - x \sin \theta = \text{cons.}$$

They are thus a series of lines making an angle θ with Ox.

Similarly the lines $x' = $ cons. are a series making an angle θ with Ot. Hence a meshwork for x', t' consists of a series of diamond shapes (equilateral parallelograms) symmetrical with respect to OP. But

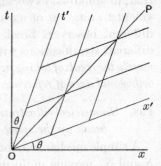

$$x^2 + t^2 = \frac{x'^2 + t'^2 + 2x't'\sin 2\theta}{\cos 2\theta}.$$

Hence the scale of S' is enlarged in the ratio $1/\sqrt{\cos 2\theta}$. In other words unit length for S' is a length $1/\sqrt{\cos 2\theta}$ in S's measurement. Hence we get from S's meshwork to S''s by squeezing Ox and Ot each through an angle θ towards OP and then enlarging the resulting diamond-shaped network in the ratio $1/\sqrt{\cos 2\theta}$.

We have only to lay one network over the other to get the two ways of breaking up space and time adopted by our two observers S and S'.

The Fitzgerald-Lorentz contractions.

The fact that a rod as measured by S is contracted for S', and *vicê versâ*, is easily deduced by use of the networks.

Let OA be a rod which for S is of unit length.

He will measure it on the assumption that time at O and A is the same. He will thus put it along Ox (or along some parallel to Ox). Moreover, as t varies, the end O of the rod will occupy different positions along Ot and the end A will occupy different positions along the line AB parallel to Ot.

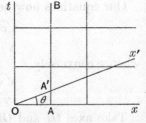

S' will measure the rod on the assumption that the times t' of its end points are the same. His measure will therefore be the value *in his own scale* of OA', where A' is the point where AB meets Ox'.

Now, if $OA = 1$,

$$OA' = 1/\cos\theta \text{ in the scale of } S.$$

Therefore

$$OA' = \frac{\sqrt{\cos 2\theta}}{\cos\theta} = \frac{1}{h} \text{ in the scale of } S'.$$

Hence the rod as measured by S is contracted for S' in the ratio $1/h$.

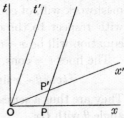

Next let OP' be a unit rod as measured by S'. In his measurement he assumes that t' is constant for the rod. He thus puts it along Ox' (or along some parallel line). As t' varies, the end O of the rod will occupy different positions along Ot' and the end P will occupy different positions along the line PP' parallel to Ot'.

S will measure the rod at his time $t = 0$ by the length OP.

If $OP' = 1$ in the measure of S', it will be $1/\sqrt{\cos 2\theta}$ in the measure of S.

From the triangle $OP'P$ we have

$$\frac{OP}{OP'} = \frac{\cos 2\theta}{\cos \theta}.$$

Hence, in S's measure,

$$OP = \frac{\sqrt{\cos 2\theta}}{\cos \theta} = \frac{1}{h}.$$

Hence the rod, as measured by S', is contracted for S in the ratio $1/h$.

Now in our figure there is complete symmetry when times and lengths are interchanged. Hence a measure of time made by S will be contracted for S' in the ratio $1/h$, and vicê versâ. Hence S' will think that S's clocks go slow in this ratio, and vicê versâ.

The two networks which we have constructed give for time and one-dimensional space a concrete picture of the way in which different observers break up the space-time continuum.

Minkowski's general transformation cannot be given the same physical interpretation since four-dimensional space has no actual existence. For the mathematician, however, it is equally valuable as an analytical picture which includes the whole of the space-time continuum. In it both time and the three dimensions of space enter symmetrically. It is the analytical expression of the method in the madness of simple relativity.

§ 99. *The order of events in the world.*

In Minkowski's picture of the world the whole of space and time is spread before us. Furthermore, space and time have ceased to be independent of one another. Time has become a conventional something which depends upon the axes we may choose. Now man has an incurable propensity for imagining himself at rest when he is undisturbed with reference to his surroundings. Hence observers instinctively break up space and time on the assumption that they are at rest; and this they are encouraged and apparently ordered to do by the result of the Michelson-Morley experiment. So observers moving relatively to one another, and each of them satisfied to make measurements as though he himself were at rest, choose different axes in the space-time continuum. They break it up in different ways.

Again there comes the revolt of the common sense of the plain man. "It is", he affirms, "nonsense to say that space and time are interwoven in a single continuum. We can go backwards and forwards in space: we cannot go backwards in time. Here is a distinction which no sophistry of physicists, with their talk about methods of measurement, can overcome."

It may be answered that relativity does not, in fact, deny this fundamental distinction.

In Minkowski's picture any point of the four-dimensional continuum corresponds to an event, a point-instant. Any track through the continuum is a string of events. All events of the track might happen to the same particle in its life-history, but only if the track were such that the particle in following it did not have to move at any time with a velocity greater than that of light.

For simplicity let us consider time as associated with one-dimension of space. As before, we choose co-ordinate measures such that c, the velocity of light, is unity. We picture x and t by rectangular coordinates. Let UOU' and VOV' bisect the angles between Ox and Ot. Then, if $U'OU$ be the world-line of a particle, that particle will move so that it passes over unit distance in unit time. Thus $U'OU$ is the path of a light-signal, or if we prefer

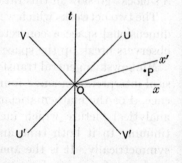

to say so, of a wireless-signal, since wireless waves travel with the velocity of light. Similarly $V'OV$ corresponds to a wireless-signal sent in the reverse direction.

Any event Q in the sector UOV takes place after the event O inasmuch as a particle could travel from O to Q with a velocity less than that of light. This moreover will be true for all observers, for we get S'''s network by squeezing S's network symmetrically with respect to OU. Similarly any event in the sector $V'OU'$ will be before the event O.

What about an event P in the sector UOV'? The same particle can never be at the event O and also at the event P because to do so it would have to travel with a velocity greater than that of light.

For our observer S the event P is after the event O when, as in the diagram, P is above Ox. But for an observer S'', for whom P is below Ox', the event P is after the event O. In other words events in the sector UOV' cannot be said to be either before or after the event O: and the same is true of events in the sector VOU'.

The plain man with his belief in absolute time is naturally indignant at this statement. To persuade him that it is reasonable let us take a concrete example.

Consider an event, say a violently brilliant explosion, on a star which is 150 light-years distant. Light-signals telling us of this event take a century and a half to reach us.

Suppose that astronomers on the earth in the twenty-first century calculate, when they have knowledge of the event, that it happened in the year 1927. Could we say, at the moment when this lecture was being given, in the year 1928, that the event was already in the past? We have no knowledge of it and all of us will be dead before knowledge of it can reach the earth. Thus it does not exist for us here and, though the fact is irrelevant, never will exist for us. Moreover, the astronomers of the future will only be able to say that the event had happened before the year 1928 provided they then make the *assumption* that their time-measurements are satisfactory. Astronomers elsewhere in space on some planet of a solar system which moves rapidly in relation to the earth will make other time-measurements, and some will reach the conclusion that it happened in the year 1929. There will be a difference of opinion which only a super-observer with a knowledge of absolute time could authoritatively settle. May we not fairly say, as regards ourselves and that explosion, that the terms before and after have ceased to have any meaning?

The upshot of the discussion is clear. For two events which are so related that a particle travelling with a velocity not exceeding that of a wireless-signal could experience both, there is a clear difference between 'before' and 'after' as regards time. And this difference persists for all observers. For all observers one such event is before the other, if it is before it for any one observer.

But when the events are not so related, a particle to experience both would have to travel with a velocity greater than that of light, which is physically impossible in non-gravitational fields. In this case 'before' and 'after' have no meaning.

§ 100. *Weyl's picture of 'the scene of reality'.*

Weyl, in a striking paragraph*, sums up the change in our thought which has resulted from Einstein's union of space and time.

"The scene of action of reality is not a three-dimensional Euclidean space but rather a four-dimensional world in which space and time are linked together indissolubly. However deep the chasm may be that separates the intuitive nature of space from that of time in our experience, nothing of this qualitative difference enters into the objective world which physics endeavours to crystallise out of direct experience. It is a four-dimensional continuum, which is neither 'time' nor 'space'. Only the consciousness that passes on in one portion of this world experiences the detached piece which comes to meet it and passes behind it, as *history*, that is, as a process that is going forward in time and takes place in space."

§ 101. *Composition of velocities according to the special theory of relativity.*

With the notation which we used in obtaining the Lorentz transformation let (x, t) be the space and time-coordinates of an event P relative to an observer S at the origin O. Let S' move along the axis Ox with velocity v relative to S, and let (x', t') be the coordinates of P relative to the observer S' who is at the origin O' of his own coordinates. Further, let O' coincide with O when $t = 0$; and let t' be measured from this instant.

Then we have seen that, by Lorentz' equations of § 92,
$$x' = h(x - vt), \qquad t' = h(t - vx/c^2).$$
Now u, the velocity of P relative to S, is dx/dt; and the velocity of P relative to S' is dx'/dt'. But
$$\frac{dx'}{dt'} = \frac{dx - v\,dt}{dt - v\,dx/c^2}, \quad \text{or} \quad \frac{dx'}{dt'} = \frac{u - v}{1 - uv/c^2}.$$

If we change the sign of v, we obtain the following law of composition of velocities: If P be a point moving with velocity u relative to the observer S and if S move in the direction of u with velocity v with reference to an observer S', then the velocity of P with reference to S' will be
$$w = \frac{u + v}{1 + uv/c^2}. \qquad \qquad \dots \dots (1)$$

The 'plain man' objects that, if the velocity of P relative to S is u and

---

* H. Weyl, *Space—Time—Matter*. Translated by H. L. Brose. Methuen, 1922, p. 217.

of S relative to S' is v, then the velocity of P relative to S' is 'obviously'

$$w = u + v. \qquad\qquad \ldots\ldots(2)$$

What the 'plain man' has to realise is that in calculating u we assume that S is 'at rest', while in calculating v and w we assume that S' is 'at rest'. Thus in obtaining the formula (2) two contradictory assumptions are made. Evidently the Einsteinian formula (1) coincides with the Newtonian formula (2) when $c = \infty$.

§102. *Fizeau's experiment.*

The result of an experiment performed by A. H. L. Fizeau (1819–1896) in the middle of the nineteenth century elegantly confirms the Einsteinian law of composition of velocities.

Suppose that light travels through a motionless liquid with velocity u, then its velocity with respect to the liquid will be u when the latter is in motion in any manner. Suppose that the liquid is moving with velocity v relative to a straight tube along which the light travels in the direction of v.

Then the velocity of the light relative to the tube will, by Einsteinian kinematics, be

$$U = \frac{u + v}{1 + uv/c^2}.$$

Thus

$$U = (u + v)\left(1 - \frac{uv}{c^2}\right) = u + v\left(1 - \frac{u^2}{c^2}\right),$$

approximately, if we remember that u and c are large compared with v and both of the same order of magnitude.

Fizeau proved that

$$U = u + v\left(1 - 1/\mu^2\right),$$

where $\mu = c/u$ is the index of refraction of the liquid. The agreement of this result with that reached by the kinematics of the special theory of relativity is obviously most satisfactory.

§103. *The fundamental definitions of the mechanics of the special theory of relativity.*

We now proceed to investigate the manner in which the fundamental definitions and formulae of mechanics must be changed when Einstein's assumptions of the special theory of relativity replace the postulates of Newton.

The numerical differences between Einsteinian and classical mechanics will, as we have seen, be slight, for they will involve at most terms of the order of $1/c^2$, where c is the velocity of light. On the other hand, the formula for the composition of velocities, just given, shews that in form the changes may be such as deserve to be described as revolutionary.

Volume and statical volume.

We proceed first of all to find the formula which connects the measure of an element of volume dV', measured with respect to axes with respect to which it is itself fixed, with its measure dV measured with respect to axes in regard to which it is moving with uniform velocity v.

Let the coordinates of a point P with respect to a set of rectangular axes, fixed relatively to an observer S at the origin O, be x, y, z. Let accented letters denote similar coordinates relative to an observer S', moving with velocity v relative to S.

Suppose that the element of volume is at the point P and that it is rigidly attached to the x', y', z' system.

We will assume that the axes of x and x' are measured in the same direction, and that $O'x'$ is moving with velocity v relative to Ox.

Then, by the Lorentz equations,

$$x' = h(x - vt); \qquad z' = z;$$
$$y' = y; \qquad t' = h(t - vx/c^2).$$

Now an elementary volume at P will, with respect to axes $O'x', O'y', O'z'$, with respect to which it is fixed, be

$$dV' = dx' \, dy' \, dz'.$$

The same element will be measured in the unaccented system by

$$dV = dx \, dy \, dz.$$

But dx' is the measure of an element of length at P made by the observer S' who uses a foot-rule moving with the element; and dx will be the measure of the same element made by the observer S. S, however, measures by taking a snap-shot of this element of length: that is to say, he measures the distance between two points which at the same moment of his own time t instantaneously coincide with the ends of dx'. Thus we have, from the first of the Lorentz equations, $dx' = h \, dx$. Also $dy' = dy$, $dz' = dz$. Hence

$$dV' = h \, dV.$$

It is convenient to term an element of volume, measured with respect to axes with respect to which it is itself at rest, the *statical* element of volume and to denote it by dV_0. Similarly we call dV the moving element of volume. We therefore have

$$dV = dV_0/h, \quad \text{where} \quad h = 1/\sqrt{1 - v^2/c^2}.$$

Sometimes dV_0 is called the *proper-measure* of the element of volume: it is the measure made by an observer moving with the element.

The formula just obtained connects the statical and moving elements of volume. Evidently the final result is quite general, and independent of our preliminary assumption that the axis of x should be measured in the direction of v.

Mass and invariant mass.

According to Newton's second law of motion we can, as we have seen in Lecture II, attach to every body some number, which we call its *inertial mass*; and this number, in classical mechanics, is fundamental in the dynamics of the body.

There is always the possibility that M, the mass of a body as the term is commonly used in classical dynamics, will prove to vary as the body moves with respect to the axes with respect to which it is measured. There must, however, be some invariant number attachable to the body: let us call this m, its *invariant mass*. We shall usually term M the 'physical' mass of a body.

Density: statical invariant-mass density.

Consider an infinitesimal body of invariant mass dm. Let dV and ρ be the volume and density of this body calculated with reference to axes with respect to which the element is moving with velocity v.

Let dV_0 and ρ_0 be the volume and density of the same infinitesimal body calculated with respect to axes moving with the element. We call ρ_0 the *statical*, or *proper*, invariant-mass density of the body.

Clearly we shall have, since dm is by its definition an invariant number attached to the infinitesimal body,

$$\rho\, dV = dm, \quad \text{and} \quad \rho_0\, dV_0 = dm.$$

But we have just seen that $dV_0 = h\, dV$. Hence

$$\rho = h\rho_0.$$

This result connects the invariant-mass density of a moving infinitesimal body with its statical invariant-mass density.

Before we proceed farther we must make a simple yet highly important observation.

It is clear that the use of the conception of *density* enables us to deal with what is happening *at* a point and therefore to obtain microscopic equations. Even a single particle of matter, according to our modern knowledge, consists of a discontinuous arrangement of nuclei and electrons; and, therefore, equations for the motion of a particle are macroscopic equations which may only be statistical averages of more accurate results. *Consequently we use the ideas of force-density and mass-density when we wish to build up the Einsteinian modification of the fundamental classical equations of the dynamics of a particle.*

§104. *The fundamental law of kinetics, and its transformation in the special theory of relativity.*

If P be the force acting on a particle of mass M and if α be its consequent acceleration, then by Newton's law of motion in classical mechanics, α is in the same direction as P. Further, if the units be suitably chosen,

$$P = M\alpha.$$

If u be the velocity of the particle we may put $\alpha = du/dt$ and write the fundamental equation in the form

$$P = M\frac{du}{dt}. \qquad \qquad \text{......(1)}$$

We wish to modify this result so as to obtain a formula which shall be valid when the assumptions of the special theory of relativity replace those of classical mechanics. Any such formula must reduce to the form (1) when $c = \infty$; and it must only differ from (1) by terms of at most the order $(v/c)^2$, where v is the order of a planetary velocity and c is the velocity of light. The formula will thus be such that we cannot, save in certain rare and exceptional cases, experimentally distinguish between it and (1). Further, by the fundamental postulate of the special theory of relativity, since the formula expresses a physical law it should assume a form which is invariant for any linear transformation, corresponding to the Lorentz equations, which leaves ds unaltered. In particular, therefore, the time must no longer have in the formula the privileged position which it occupies in the classical theory.

§105. *Minkowski's world. Time and proper-time. The 'four-velocity' and 'four-acceleration' vectors.*

Minkowski's world, as we have seen, is one in which the Lorentz transformation equations of the special theory of relativity assume a symmetrical and singularly elegant form. It is of four dimensions; and the axes in it, which we may take to be $Oy_1, \ldots Oy_4$, are mutually orthogonal. Any Lorentz transformation is equivalent to the choice of a new set of mutually orthogonal axes with the same origin, say $Oy_1', \ldots Oy_4'$.

When a particle is represented in Minkowski's world, its successive positions will be a string of 'events', each represented by four co-ordinates y_1, y_2, y_3, y_4. The interval between two successive events will be given by

$$- ds^2 = dy_1{}^2 + \ldots + dy_4{}^2;$$

and this interval is invariant for any possible change of axes consistent with the Lorentz transformations. In three-dimensional space we think of the particle as moving on a curve, the coordinates of each point of which are functions of the time t. Similarly in four-dimensional space-time we can picture the particle as moving on a world-line s, the coordinates of each point of which are functions of s.

In Minkowski's world the time has no privileged position. We proceed to relate that world to a world in which space and time are separated. To this end we suppose that an observer splits up Minkowski's world by taking his time-axis along the axis of y_4. We shall then have

$$dy_4 = \iota c\, dt,$$

where $\iota = \sqrt{-1}$, and c is the velocity of light; and also

$$ds^2 = c^2 dt^2 - dy_1{}^2 - dy_2{}^2 - dy_3{}^2.$$

Put now $\qquad \dfrac{dy_1}{dt} = \dot{y}_1, \quad$ and $\quad v^2 = \dot{y}_1{}^2 + \dot{y}_2{}^2 + \dot{y}_3{}^2.$

Then obviously v will be the velocity of the particle and we shall have

$$ds = c\,dt\{1 - v^2/c^2\}^{\frac{1}{2}},$$

or $\qquad\qquad ds = c\,dt/h, \quad$ where $\quad h = 1/\sqrt{1 - v^2/c^2}.$

Proper-time.

When an observer moves with the particle, dy_1, dy_2 and dy_3 will all vanish for him; and his time t will be given by $ds^2 = c^2 dt^2$. Thus we can take s/c to be the *proper-time* of the particle, that is to say, time as measured by an observer moving with the particle.

The 'four-velocity' vector.

Consider now the 'four-velocity' vector U, of which the (contra-variant) components along the axes in Minkowski's world are

$$u^1 = \frac{dy_1}{ds}, \quad \ldots \quad u^4 = \frac{dy_4}{ds}.$$

Evidently U is a vector in space-time for which time has no privileged position; and for Minkowski's world it is a sort of generalisation of the notion of velocity.

When we split up Minkowski's world, by taking the time-axis along Oy_4 as in the last paragraph, we get, for the components of U,

$$u^1 = \frac{h}{c}\dot{y}_1, \quad u^2 = \frac{h}{c}\dot{y}_2, \quad u^3 = \frac{h}{c}\dot{y}_3, \quad u^4 = \iota h.$$

Thus the space-components of U will be h/c times the classical velocities $\dot{y}_1, \dot{y}_2, \dot{y}_3$.

If the coordinates $y_1, \ldots y_4$ are altered into accented letters by the Lorentz transformation it is evident, since $ds' = ds$, that the velocity-components $u^1, \ldots u^4$ will obey the same Lorentz law of transformation.

The 'four-acceleration' vector.

We can now similarly construct in space-time a vector F, 'the four-acceleration vector', whose components are

$$f^1 = \frac{du^1}{ds}, \quad \ldots f^4 = \frac{du^4}{ds}.$$

These components represent the rate of increase of the components of the four-velocity vector with respect to s. Evidently time has no privileged position for F. If we split up Minkowski's world by taking Oy_4 for the time-axis, we shall get

$$f^k = \frac{h}{c^2}\frac{d}{dt}(h\dot{y}_k), \quad \text{for} \quad k = 1, 2, 3;$$

and

$$f^4 = \frac{\iota h}{c}\frac{dh}{dt}, \quad \text{where} \quad h = 1/\sqrt{1 - v^2/c^2}.$$

We may write these results at length in the form

$$f^k = \frac{\ddot{y}_k}{c^2 - v^2} + \frac{\dot{y}_k}{(c^2 - v^2)^2}\{\dot{y}_1\ddot{y}_1 + \dot{y}_2\ddot{y}_2 + \dot{y}_3\ddot{y}_3\}, \quad \text{for} \quad k = 1, 2, 3;$$

and

$$f^4 = \iota c\frac{\dot{y}_1\ddot{y}_1 + \dot{y}_2\ddot{y}_2 + \dot{y}_3\ddot{y}_3}{(c^2 - v^2)^2}.$$

Thus when we take Oy_4 for the time-axis, the space-components of $c^2 F$ will become Newtonian components of acceleration when $c = \infty$. Clearly the components of F obey the same Lorentz law of linear transformation as $y_1, \ldots y_4$ satisfy.

§ 106. *The fundamental dynamical equations of the special theory of relativity.*

We have seen that, in Minkowski's world, the Lorentz transformations are equivalent to a change from one set of mutually orthogonal axes to a similar set with the same origin. Moreover, by Einstein's fundamental postulate of the special theory of relativity, physical laws must be such that their expression is unaltered by any Lorentz transformation.

Suppose now that P be a force acting on a particle of physical mass M and producing in it acceleration α, P and α being vectors. We have seen that, according to classical Newtonian mechanics, $P = M\alpha$; and we seek to generalise this result for Minkowski's world.

Let Π be a four-vector in this world representing force-density. Further, let F be the four-acceleration vector representing the acceleration of the element dV, of invariant-mass density ρ, at which Π acts. If F results from the action of Π, the two vectors must coincide in direction. By definition, the element dV has $\rho \, dV$ for its invariant mass, and the components of force acting on the element are components of $\Pi \, dV$.

It is natural to assume for our required generalisation the formula

$$\Pi = c^2 \rho F, \qquad \qquad \text{......(1)}$$

the number c^2 being inserted that we may have the ordinary formula when Minkowski's world is split up into space and time.

By Einstein's principle, however, the assumed equation cannot express a physical law unless it is a vector equation. In it, therefore, ρ must not be a quantity which changes with the change of axes Oy_k to Oy_k' $(k = 1, \ldots 4)$. But we have seen that, if ρ be the invariant-mass density at a point, it will be connected with the statical invariant-mass density ρ_0 by the relation $\rho = h\rho_0$. Now ρ_0 is a constant, while h is a quantity which by §97 depends upon the way in which the axes are rotated in Minkowski's world. Thus ρ changes with the change from the axes Oy_k to the axes Oy_k'. Hence such an equation as (1) cannot be a satisfactory generalisation of the fundamental law of kinetics given by the second law of motion.

Such a generalisation, however, may be given by

$$\Pi = c^2 \rho_0 F.$$

This vector-equation may be written, if we use the four-velocity vector U,

$$\Pi = c^2 \rho_0 \frac{dU}{ds}. \qquad \qquad \text{......(A)}$$

To see whether it is adequate as the generalisation which we seek, we will see what it becomes when we first integrate it so as to apply to a particle of matter and then split up Minkowski's world into space and time. Let π^k $(k = 1, \ldots 4)$ be the components of the space-time-vector Π. Then, remembering that the components of U are u^k, $k = 1, \ldots 4$, we see that the equation (A) will take the form

$$\pi^k = c^2 \rho_0 \frac{du^k}{ds}, \quad k = 1, \ldots 4. \qquad \ldots\ldots\text{(A)}$$

It is worth while noticing that, if these equations are valid,

$$\sum_{k=1}^{4} \pi^k u^k = \frac{c^2}{2} \rho_0 \frac{d}{ds} \{ \Sigma (u^k)^2 \} = 0,$$

since
$$\Sigma (u^k)^2 = \frac{\Sigma dy_k{}^2}{ds^2} = 1.$$

Suppose now that we integrate equation (A) so that it applies to an infinitesimal material element of volume dV and proper-mass m. We thus change from density *at* a point to an actual particle of matter.

Then
$$m = \rho_0 dV_0 = \rho dV,$$
where dV_0 is the proper-volume of the element.

Equations (A) will now take the form

$$\pi^k dV_0 = mc^2 \frac{du^k}{ds}, \qquad k = 1, \ldots 4. \qquad \ldots\ldots\text{(B)}$$

Suppose now that we put $P_k = \pi^k dV$, so that the quantities P_k are the components of the total force acting on the infinitesimal material element. Then, if we remember that $dV_0 = h\, dV$, our equations may be written

$$hP_k = mc^2 \frac{du^k}{ds}, \qquad k = 1, \ldots 4. \qquad \ldots\ldots\text{(C)}$$

Let us now split up Minkowski's world by taking Oy_4 as the time-axis as in previous paragraphs.

Then, as we have seen,

$$\frac{du^k}{ds} = \frac{h}{c^2} \frac{d}{dt} (h\dot{y}_k), \qquad k = 1, 2, 3;$$

and
$$\frac{du^4}{ds} = \frac{\iota h}{c} \frac{dh}{dt}.$$

Suppose now that M be the 'physical' mass of the element; *and let us assume that it is connected with the invariant mass by the equality*

$$M = mh.$$

Then equations (C) may be written

$$P_k = \frac{d}{dt} (M\dot{y}_k), \qquad k = 1, 2, 3, \qquad \ldots\ldots\text{(1)}$$

and
$$P_4 = \iota c \frac{dM}{dt}. \qquad \ldots\ldots\text{(2)}$$

Obviously equations (1) are the usual equations expressing the connection between force and rate of change of momentum in classical mechanics.

Hence *the vector-equation* $\Pi = c^2 \rho_0 \dfrac{dU}{ds}$ *is a satisfactory generalisation of the fundamental law of kinetics.* This generalisation assumes that Newtonian mechanics is only an approximation to the truth, inasmuch as the 'physical' mass M is not an invariant associated with the material element since it is connected with the invariant number m by the relation $M = mh$.

§107. *The equivalence of mass and energy.*

What now is the meaning of the equation

$$P_4 = \iota c \frac{dM}{dt}? \qquad \qquad \dots\dots(2)$$

We recall that, as we have established,

$$\sum_{k=1}^{4} \pi^k u^k = 0.$$

Hence, when Minkowski's world is split up into space and time in the usual manner,

$$\sum_{k=1}^{3} P_k h \dot{y}_k + P_4 c \iota h = 0.$$

Thus equation (2) may be written

$$\sum_{k=1}^{3} P_k \frac{dy_k}{dt} = \frac{d(Mc^2)}{dt},$$

or

$$\sum_{k=1}^{3} P_k \delta y_k = \delta(Mc^2).$$

Thus the equation asserts that the work done by the forces on the element when it undergoes an infinitesimal displacement is equivalent to the increase of the physical mass multiplied by c^2. In other words, the increase of energy of the element is measured by the increase of

$$\frac{mc^2}{\sqrt{1 - v^2/c^2}}.$$

We have just stated that the generalisation of the fundamental equation of kinetics in classical mechanics, that is to say, of $P = M\alpha$, is the four-vector density equation

$$\Pi = c^2 \rho_0 F$$

in Minkowski's world. We now see that the latter equation is equivalent to four equations. Three of these, when integrated so as to apply to an isolated particle, are equations of momentum; and in a world split up into space and time they may be written

$$P_k = \frac{d}{dt}(M\dot{y}_k), \qquad k = 1, 2, 3.$$

The fourth is an energy equation which asserts that the increase of the energy of the particle is measured by the increase of

$$Mc^2 = \frac{mc^2}{\sqrt{1 - v^2/c^2}}.$$

We notice that, in the equations of momentum, M is a quantity which we have called the 'physical' mass. It is related to the invariant mass of the element whose motion we are considering by the identity

$$M = \frac{m}{\sqrt{1 - v^2/c^2}}.$$

Thus M varies with v, the velocity of the element; and, in so far as classical mechanics assumes that M is an absolute constant, it is in error. The error, however, only involves a quantity of order v^2/c^2 and is thus inappreciable when we are dealing with the velocities of ordinary experience.

That the special relativity theory should lead to such a modification of the measure of mass in the fundamental equations of dynamics is alike surprising and interesting. But of still greater interest is the fact which has emerged that the increase of the energy of a particle of 'physical' mass M is measured by the increase of Mc^2. This suggests that the measure of the whole intrinsic energy of the particle is simply the measure of its mass. For, if E be the kinetic energy of the particle, we have

$$E = \text{cons.} + Mc^2.$$

Thus
$$E = \text{cons.} + \frac{mc^2}{\sqrt{1 - v^2/c^2}}$$
$$= \text{cons.} + mc^2 + \tfrac{1}{2}mv^2 + \text{terms in } 1/c^2.$$

This result shews that, for a particle of invariant mass m moving with velocity v, the part of the kinetic energy which depends upon v is $\tfrac{1}{2}mv^2$, if we neglect terms of order $1/c^2$. We thus have the ordinary formula of classical mechanics.

Presumably E and m will vanish together, inasmuch as it seems right to assume that a particle of zero invariant mass cannot have energy. The constant of integration previously introduced is therefore zero; and we have the remarkable conclusion that the measure of the kinetic energy of a particle of invariant mass m, referred to axes with respect to which the particle is at rest, is

$$E = mc^2.$$

It would thus appear that *kinetic energy, like mass, has inertia,* and that *the inertia of matter is due solely to its internal energy.* This conclusion is one of Einstein's most significant discoveries.

Can we go further and say that matter is simply congealed energy? The idea is attractive. We cannot, however, prove it. As we have several times insisted, our knowledge of matter is almost exclusively a knowledge of its inertia. Inertia is the measurable property on which we naturally seize. By arguing as to inertia we have reached the conclusion that the inertia of matter is due solely to its internal energy. Now there can be little doubt that, in so far as we investigate inertial properties of matter, it will be satisfactory to regard matter as congealed energy. But matter may have other properties, qualities or attributes which energy has not; and, *vicê versâ*, energy may have characteristics which are not those of matter. It may even be that, although energy can congeal into matter under conditions of which we are at present ignorant, yet in the very process some type of creative activity may be manifested which will lead to the matter being possessed of qualities or attributes which apparently had no existence in the energy from which it was derived.

In the transformations which are common in our experience, the regular sequences of Nature, there may continually be the emergence of that which is new; and equally such a change as that by which energy congeals into matter is quite possibly a creative process. So also if, as Jeans was the first to suggest, the reverse process can take place in the stars with the result that in their depths matter can dissolve into radiation, this process may actually be a process of destruction, a reversal of the first stages of that creative development which has led to ourselves. We may then allow it to be just possible that energy can turn into matter: it is also possible, and (as we shall see in § 300) at present much more probable, that matter can turn into radiant energy: but our knowledge alike of matter and of energy is so limited that we must beware of the assumption that the two for all purposes can be regarded as identical. In the change of one into the other some imponderable, something which has no inertia and cannot be weighed, may be lost or gained. When a man dies, such an imponderable vanishes; but not even the most hardened physicist would dare to say that its vanishing could be disregarded.

Lecture vi

GENERAL RELATIVITY

§ 108. *The fundamental limitation of the special theory of relativity.*

The special theory of relativity makes it clear that we must abandon not only belief in absolute position but also belief in absolute time. As Eddington has well expressed it*: "The denial of absolute simultaneity is a natural complement to the denial of absolute motion. The latter asserts that we cannot find out what is the same place at two different times; the former that we cannot find out what is the same time at two different places". The special theory, however, was based on a modification of the equations of Newtonian dynamics which led to equations invariant for *axes moving uniformly and rectilinearly with respect to one another*. It naturally suggested the question as to whether extensions could not be made to meet the case of axes whose relative motion was variable or, if uniform, at any rate not rectilinear.

§ 109. *The 'reality' of centrifugal forces.*

Everyone knows that, if a stone be whirled round at the end of a string, a force is produced by the motion which is measured by the tension of the string. The more rapidly the stone moves, the greater the force. This force thus appears to take its origin in the motion of the body. It is certainly an actual force, as will be admitted by anyone who has felt the pull of the string experimentally. In classical dynamics, however, it has always been regarded as but 'partially real': it has been thought of as the sort of apparent force which arises owing to changing axes. Einstein was led to ask whether such pseudo-forces are not as real as, *and analogous to*, gravitation.

§ 110. *Does absolute rotation exist?*

Can we think of such forces as having an actual existence because we must attribute an absolute meaning to uniform rotation whereas we attribute no such meaning to uniform motion in a straight line? In the last lecture, in a brief discussion of this matter, we referred to Newton's belief in absolute rotation, which was based on the experiment of a

---

* A. S. Eddington, *Space, Time and Gravitation*. Cambridge University Press, 1923, p. 51.

rotating vessel filled with water. Bishop Berkeley (1685–1753), in his essay *De Motu** printed in the year 1721, gave an acute criticism of the derivation of the belief from the experiment. His views, however, had little influence on thought until revived by Ernst Mach. As we have indicated in § 84, Mach became the protagonist of the idea that all spatial motion is relative. In the year 1883, for instance, he said: "For me only relative motions exist; and I can see, in this regard, no distinction between rotation and translation. When a body moves relatively to the fixed stars, centrifugal forces are produced; when it moves relatively to some different body and not related to the fixed stars, no centrifugal forces are produced. I have no objection to calling the first rotation so long as it be remembered that nothing is meant except relative rotation with respect to the fixed stars".

It is, in fact, plain that any body with which we can experiment is surrounded by the vast mass of so-called fixed stars and spiral nebulae which constitutes, as it were, a firm background against which all our experiments take place. Mach suggests that these distant masses are the cause of the centrifugal forces developed in rotation. We have, of course, no means of determining whether Mach's belief is true, or whether we must alternatively accept the Newtonian hypothesis of absolute rotational motion.

Einstein, in the year 1921, set forth his own opinion with characteristic wisdom: "With Mach I feel that an affirmative answer is imperative, but for the time being nothing can be proved. Not until a dynamical investigation of the large systems of fixed stars has been performed from the point of view of the limits of validity of the Newtonian law of gravitation for immense regions of space will it perhaps be possible to obtain eventually an exact basis for the solution of this fascinating question".

§ 111. *The equality of inertial and gravitational mass.*

In classical dynamics we know that the forces which arise from non-uniform motion are always proportional to the mass of the particle in which they arise. This, however, as we have seen in § 21, is exactly true of gravitation. A body moving under the influence of a field of gravitation receives an acceleration which is entirely independent of any physical property of the body save its inertial mass. In other words, one and the same quality of a body shews itself under some circumstances as

* *The Works of George Berkeley*, ed. A. C. Fraser. 3 vols. Clarendon Press, 1871, vol. III, pp. 95, 96. [*De Motu*, §§ 60–2.]

inertia and under others as weight. Eötvös, in the year 1890, used an exceedingly sensitive apparatus known as a torsion balance. This apparatus enables the inertial mass of a body to be measured with as great a degree of accuracy as that with which its weight may be determined by the most sensitive balance. More recently, in the year 1919, Pekár repeated these experiments. The result is to shew that, in measurements of the greatest refinement, no difference between inertial and gravitational mass can be detected.

§112. *The likeness between gravitational and uniformly accelerated regions.*

Consider now the experiment imagined by Einstein, which by him is made to serve as the starting-point of the general theory of relativity. We imagine a large chest equipped like a room in which there is an observer with the necessary instruments. If this chest were not in a gravitational field, the slightest impact between the man and the floor would cause him slowly to rise to the ceiling. But suppose now that, the observer being on the floor, some external being attaches a rope to the top of the chest and begins to pull it upward with constant force. The chest will then move upwards with uniform acceleration. How will the man in the chest regard this process? Most certainly if he were one of ourselves, and therefore accustomed to gravitation, he would assume that he had suddenly been placed in a gravitational field similar to that which, on the earth, conditions human existence. Every experiment which he could make would, moreover, confirm his belief that the chest was at rest in a gravitational field whereas, in fact, it would be moving with uniform acceleration. Gravitational force can thus be regarded as emerging from an acceleration in exactly the same way as the centrifugal forces, which arise when a stone is swung at the end of a string, emerge from the acceleration of the stone.

§113. *The passage from the special to the general theory of relativity.*

The special theory of relativity was based on the assumption that space and time form a single four-dimensional continuum, and that the laws of nature are invariant for any Galilean mesh-system within this continuum. By Galilean mesh-system we mean a set of axes of reference corresponding to which the element of interval ds is given by an equality which can be put into the form

$$ds^2 = c^2 dt^2 - dx^2 - dy^2 - dz^2,$$

where dt is the element of time and c is the velocity of light. For any such mesh-system ds is an invariant; and the most general transformation by which two such mesh-systems can be connected with one another is effectively that of Lorentz.

In the general theory of relativity we retain the idea that space and time form a four-dimensional continuum, but we assume that our mesh-system of reference has the most general character possible. Any 'event' in the world, that is to say any occurrence at a point of space and an instant in time, is signified by four numbers determined with respect to this general mesh-system of reference. These numbers we may term x_0, x_1, x_2, x_3. We do not assume that one of them is temporal and the other three spatial; but, when it is necessary to make comparisons with classical dynamics, from which our new equations will only differ slightly, we shall assume that x_0 is some multiple of the time-coordinate. In the new general mesh-system the interval will be denoted by ds; and we shall assume that the square of this interval is the most general possible quadratic function of the coordinate differentials

$$dx_0, \dots dx_3.$$

This is equivalent to the assumption that space-time is a continuous manifold of four dimensions of the type investigated by Riemann. We shall thus have

$$ds^2 = g_{00} dx_0{}^2 + \dots + g_{33} dx_3{}^2 + 2g_{01} dx_0 dx_1 + \dots + 2g_{23} dx_2 dx_3.$$

In this expression the g's are, in general, continuous functions of $x_0, \dots x_3$. Altogether there are ten g's and they are known as *coefficients of potential*. As in any general transformation ds will be invariant, the condition for such invariance will connect the expressions for the g's in terms of the new coordinates with their expressions in terms of the old. *The general principle of relativity asserts that it is possible to express the laws of any physical phenomenon whatever in a form which is invariant for the most general possible transformation of space-time coordinates.*

§ 114. *The type of mathematical analysis needed in the general theory of relativity.*

It is obvious that if we are to apply the general principle of relativity to formulate a new type of mechanics we need a calculus which shall provide us with forms (in other words expressions involving coordinates, potentials and their differentials) which are invariant for the most general change in the mesh-system of reference which leaves ds invariant. These forms are provided by the calculus of tensors which, as we saw earlier, was developed by Christoffel, Ricci, Levi-Civita, and others in order to build up, on Riemann's foundations, the geometry of many-dimensional space.

In this calculus, as we have seen in Lecture IV, invariants are tensors of zero rank: they are functions of the coordinates which are absolutely unchanged when the coordinates are transformed. Vectors are tensors of the first rank. The vanishing of a vector in the four-dimensional manifold which we call space-time is equivalent to four equations. Although the components of a vector are not individually unchanged by the transformation of coordinates, yet all components are similarly changed so that, if a vector vanishes in one system of coordinates, it will vanish in any other. Similarly, a tensor of the second rank has sixteen components. If all these vanish for any one system of co-ordinates, they will all vanish for any other. We thus see that *according to the general principle of relativity the laws of nature must be expressible as tensor-equations.*

§115. *Riemann's symbols.*

It is by no means easy to build up tensors of the type which we require for the general theory of relativity. There is, however, as we have seen in our discussion of generalised space of n dimensions, a tensor of the fourth rank called the Riemann-Christoffel tensor (§ 63), the discovery of which is one of the triumphs of the tensor calculus. It is the aggregate of the set of symbols which are variously denoted by

$$B^j_{ikh} \quad \text{and} \quad \{ij, hk\}; \quad \left.\begin{matrix} i \\ j \\ h \\ k \end{matrix}\right\} = 1, 2, \dots n.$$

These symbols are, we have said, known as Riemann's symbols of the second kind.

We recall that in § 55 Christoffel's symbol of the first kind was defined by

$$[jl, k] = \tfrac{1}{2}\left[\frac{\partial g_{jk}}{\partial x_l} + \frac{\partial g_{kl}}{\partial x_j} - \frac{\partial g_{jl}}{\partial x_k}\right].$$

In § 62 Christoffel's symbol of the second kind was defined by

$$\{jl, i\} = \sum_k g^{ik}[jl, k],$$

the summation being taken for all values of k from 1 to n.

In §63 Riemann's symbols of the second kind, which are the components of the Riemann-Christoffel tensor, were defined by

$$\{ij, hk\} = \frac{\partial}{\partial x_k}\{ih, j\} - \frac{\partial}{\partial x_h}\{ik, j\} - \sum_l [\{lh, j\}\{ik, l\} - \{lk, j\}\{ih, l\}].$$

Finally Riemann's symbol of the first kind is

$$B_{ikhj} = (ij, hk) = \sum_l g_{jl}\{il, hk\},$$

the summation being taken for all values of l from 1 to n.

The Riemann-Christoffel tensor for four-dimensional space-time is of the fourth rank and contains in consequence 256 components. Many of these, however, are repetitions of one another, inasmuch as Riemann's symbol of the first kind (ij, hk) is anti-symmetrical in h and k and also in i and j, while it is symmetrical for the double interchange of i and k, h and j. We are thus left with twenty-one different components between which there is one further relation which was given in §63. In short, when $n = 4$, the Riemann-Christoffel tensor has twenty independent components.

When, then, the Riemann-Christoffel tensor vanishes for space-time, twenty equations must be satisfied. In order that these equations may be satisfied, there must be imposed on the g's a very rigorous set of restrictions. It has, in fact, been proved in our discussion of continuous manifolds (§ 67), that such vanishing of the Riemann-Christoffel tensor is a necessary and sufficient condition that space-time should be Galilean. In Galilean space-time, it will be recalled, the element of interval is reducible to the form

$$ds^2 = dx_0{}^2 - dx_1{}^2 - dx_2{}^2 - dx_3{}^2,$$

by a suitable transformation of coordinates.

The Einstein world-tensor.

From the Riemann-Christoffel tensor we can, by the practice known as 'contraction', deduce the Einstein world-tensor G_{ik} defined by the relation

$$G_{ik} = \sum_{jh} g^{jh}(ij, hk), \qquad \begin{Bmatrix} j \\ h \end{Bmatrix} = 0, 1, 2, 3.$$

Evidently we have

$$\sum_{jh} g^{jh}(ij, hk) = \sum_{jh}\sum_l g^{jh} g_{jl}\{il, hk\} = \sum_h \{ih, hk\}.$$

Hence we may put

or

$$G_{ik} = \sum_h \{ih, hk\} = \sum_h B^h_{ikh},$$

$$G_{ik} = \sum_{l=0}^{3}\left[\frac{\partial}{\partial x_k}\{il, l\} - \frac{\partial}{\partial x_l}\{ik, l\}\right] + \sum_{lm}^{3}[\{il, m\}\{km, l\} - \{ik, l\}\{lm, m\}].$$

The Einstein world-tensor of which the components are G_{ik} is symmetrical (in other words its value is unaltered when i and k are interchanged), and hence it has ten components. From the Einstein tensor we can deduce the Einstein invariant G, which is defined by the relation

$$G = \sum_{ik} g^{ik} G_{ik}, \qquad \left.\begin{matrix} i \\ k \end{matrix}\right\} = 0, 1, 2, 3.$$

The Einstein tensor for a general type of space-time.

We often need to know the values of the components G_{ik} of the Einstein world-tensor for various types of space-time. A general type, which includes most of those connected with problems which we shall consider, is given by

$$ds^2 = f^2 dx_0{}^2 - \sum_{1}^{3} {}_{ik} a_{ik} dx_i dx_k, \qquad \ldots\ldots(1)$$

where $x_0 = ct$, and f is a function of x_1, x_2, x_3, but is independent of the time. The quantities a_{ik} belong to a space, variable with the time,

$$dl^2 = \Sigma \, a_{ik} dx_i dx_k.$$

Furthermore, these quantities a_{ik} are supposed to be functions of x_1, x_2, x_3 which only depend on x_0 owing to the presence of a factor r^2 common to them all, r being a function of x_0 only.

We suppose that A_{ik} is a tensor-component formed from the three-dimensional a_{ik}'s just as the Einstein tensor-component G_{ik} is formed from the four-dimensional coefficients of potential g_{ik} given by

$$ds^2 = \sum_{0}^{3} g_{ik} dx_i dx_k.$$

Further, we put $\qquad f_m = \dfrac{\partial f}{\partial x_m}, \qquad f^l = \sum_{m=1}^{3} a^{lm} f_m,$

and $\qquad\qquad f_{ik} = \dfrac{\partial^2 f}{\partial x_i \partial x_k} - \sum_{l=1}^{3} \{ik, l\}' f_l,$

where $\{ik, l\}'$ is Christoffel's symbol of the second kind formed from the coefficients a_{ik}. We also use a to denote the determinant of the a_{ik}'s.

Naturally it is laborious to write down first all Christoffel's symbols of the first kind corresponding to the form of ds^2 given by (1), then to calculate all the symbols of the second kind, and finally to use the long formula which expresses G_{ik} in terms of Christoffel's symbols of the second kind. But, laborious though this proceeding is, it rapidly becomes almost purely mechanical. We will content ourselves with giving results which can be easily verified.

If $i > 0$, $k > 0$, we have

$$G_{00} = \frac{3}{c^2 r}\frac{d^2 r}{dt^2} - \frac{f}{\sqrt{a}}\sum_{l=1}^{3}\frac{\partial}{\partial x_l}(\sqrt{a}f^l),$$

$$G_{0k} = -\frac{2f_k}{fcr}\frac{dr}{dt},$$

and
$$G_{ik} = A_{ik} + f_{ik}/f - \frac{a_{ik}}{c^2 f^2}\left\{\frac{1}{r}\frac{d^2 r}{dt^2} + \frac{2}{r^2}\left(\frac{dr}{dt}\right)^2\right\}.$$

Further, the Einstein invariant G is given by

$$G = -A - \frac{1}{\sqrt{af}}\sum_{l=1}^{3}\frac{\partial}{\partial x_l}(\sqrt{a}f^l) - \frac{1}{f}\Sigma_{ik}^{3} a^{ik}f_{ik} + \frac{6}{c^2 f^2}\left\{\frac{1}{r}\frac{d^2 r}{dt^2} + \frac{1}{r^2}\left(\frac{dr}{dt}\right)^2\right\},$$

where A is formed from the coefficients a_{ik} just as G is formed from the coefficients g_{ik}.

The Einstein tensor for spherical space.

When we are dealing with a problem in which space is of a three-dimensional Riemannian type which has spherical symmetry round the origin it is, by §72, convenient and legitimate to assume that the line-element for space has the form

$$dl^2 = r^2\{dx_1{}^2 + \sin^2 x_1\, dx_2{}^2 + \sin^2 x_1 \sin^2 x_2\, dx_3{}^2\},$$

when r is independent of x_1, x_2, x_3, but is possibly a function of $x_0 = ct$, the time.

As before, let A_{ik} be a world tensor-component for this space, so that A_{ik} is formed from the coefficients

$$a_{11} = r^2, \qquad a_{22} = r^2 \sin^2 x_1, \qquad a_{33} = r^2 \sin^2 x_1 \sin^2 x_2,$$

just as the coefficients G_{ik} of the Einstein tensor are formed from the coefficients of potential

$$g_{ik}, \qquad \left.\begin{matrix}i\\k\end{matrix}\right\} = 0, 1, 2, 3.$$

Then we readily find
$$A_{11} = -2,$$
$$A_{22} = -2\sin^2 x_1,$$
$$A_{33} = -2\sin^2 x_1 \sin^2 x_2,$$
and
$$A_{ik} = 0, \qquad i \neq k.$$

The invariant $A = \sum_i a^{ii}A_{ii}$ is readily seen to be equal to $-6/r^2$.

We now see that, corresponding to space-time for which the line-element is

$$ds^2 = f^2 dx_0{}^2 - r^2\{dx_1{}^2 + \sin^2 x_1\, dx_2{}^2 + \sin^2 x_1 \sin^2 x_2\, dx_3{}^2\},$$

where f is independent of x_0, and r is a function of x_0 only, we can write down the coefficients of the Einstein world-tensor.

We have

$$G_{00} = \frac{3}{c^2 r}\frac{d^2 r}{dt^2} - \frac{f}{r^2 \sin^2 x_1 \sin^2 x_2}\left\{\sin^2 x_2 \frac{\partial}{\partial x_1}\left(\sin^2 x_1 \frac{\partial f}{\partial x_1}\right)\right.$$
$$\left. + \sin x_2 \frac{\partial}{\partial x_2}\left(\sin x_2 \frac{\partial f}{\partial x_2}\right) + \frac{\partial^2 f}{\partial x_3^2}\right\}.$$

When $k > 0$, we have

$$G_{0k} = -\frac{2}{f}\frac{\partial f}{\partial x_k}\frac{dr}{cr\,dt}.$$

Also we have the set of six components

$$G_{11} = -2 + \frac{1}{f}\frac{\partial^2 f}{\partial x_1^2} - \frac{1}{c^2 f^2}\left\{r\frac{d^2 r}{dt^2} + 2\left(\frac{dr}{dt}\right)^2\right\};$$

$$G_{22} = -2\sin^2 x_1 + \frac{1}{f}\frac{\partial^2 f}{\partial x_2^2} + \frac{\sin x_1 \cos x_1}{f}\frac{\partial f}{\partial x_1} - \frac{\sin^2 x_1}{c^2 f^2}\left\{r\frac{d^2 r}{dt^2} + 2\left(\frac{dr}{dt}\right)^2\right\},$$

$$G_{33} = -2\sin^2 x_1 \sin^2 x_2 + \frac{1}{f}\frac{\partial^2 f}{\partial x_3^2} + \frac{\sin x_1 \cos x_1 \sin^2 x_2}{f}\frac{\partial f}{\partial x_1}$$
$$+ \frac{\sin x_2 \cos x_2}{f}\frac{\partial f}{\partial x_2} - \frac{\sin^2 x_1 \sin^2 x_2}{c^2 f^2}\left\{r\frac{d^2 r}{dt^2} + 2\left(\frac{dr}{dt}\right)^2\right\};$$

$$G_{12} = \frac{1}{f}\frac{\partial^2 f}{\partial x_1 \partial x_2} - \frac{\cot x_1}{f}\frac{\partial f}{\partial x_2},$$

$$G_{23} = \frac{1}{f}\frac{\partial^2 f}{\partial x_2 \partial x_3} - \frac{\cot x_2}{f}\frac{\partial f}{\partial x_3},$$

$$G_{13} = \frac{1}{f}\frac{\partial^2 f}{\partial x_1 \partial x_3} - \frac{\cot x_1}{f}\frac{\partial f}{\partial x_3}.$$

Finally the invariant G will be given by

$$G = \frac{6}{r^2} - \frac{2}{r^2 f}\left[\frac{\partial^2 f}{\partial x_1^2} + \frac{1}{\sin^2 x_1}\frac{\partial^2 f}{\partial x_2^2} + \frac{1}{\sin^2 x_1 \sin^2 x_2}\frac{\partial^2 f}{\partial x_3^2}\right.$$
$$\left. + 2\cot x_1 \frac{\partial f}{\partial x_1} + \frac{\cot x_2}{\sin^2 x_1}\frac{\partial f}{\partial x_2}\right] + \frac{6}{c^2 f^2}\left\{\frac{1}{r}\frac{d^2 r}{dt^2} + \frac{1}{r^2}\left(\frac{dr}{dt}\right)^2\right\}.$$

Though these formulae are lengthy and cumbrous, they are worth placing on record, as they supply the algebra requisite to obtain the forms of the cosmos which are associated respectively with the names of Einstein (§ 139), de Sitter (§ 140) and Friedman-Lemaître (§§ 285–90).

§ 116. Divergence.

In tensor analysis one of the most important operations is that of divergence. This takes its rise in classical mechanics as the operation by which we analytically express the fact of conservation.

Suppose that ρ is the density of a fluid at any point, and that v_1, v_2, v_3 are the components of velocity of the fluid at the point in the direction of rectangular axes Ox_1, Ox_2, Ox_3; then the equation

$$\frac{\partial}{\partial x_1}(\rho v_1) + \dots + \dots = -\frac{\partial \rho}{\partial t}$$

expresses the fact that the decrease of mass in any element of volume is equal to the mass of the matter which flows out of the element. The expression on the left-hand side is termed the *divergence* of the vector representing the momentum-density at the point.

Now in tensor analysis we naturally take such an extension of this primitive notion of divergence as shall lead to equations independent of the axes of coordinates.

Covariant differentiation.

To this end we first introduce the conception of *covariant differentiation*. The partial derivatives of an invariant with respect to the co-ordinates can be proved to form a covariant vector, for they will satisfy the fundamental relations of § 63. But the derivatives of a vector do not form a tensor; and covariant derivatives of vectors and tensors are such operations as form tensors while at the same time they can be regarded as extensions of the notion of partial differentiation. The definitions and formulae of the present section are applicable to the general case of n variables.

In the first place, the covariant derivatives of an *invariant I* are denoted by $I_{|k}$ and defined by

$$I_{|k} = \frac{\partial I}{\partial x_k}.$$

We often write them in the more simple form I_k.

In the second place, if V be a *vector* whose covariant components are V_i, then the covariant derivatives of V are defined by

$$V_{i|k} = \frac{\partial V_i}{\partial x_k} - \sum_l \{ik, l\} V_l,$$

where $\{ik, l\}$ is Christoffel's symbol of the second kind, and the summation is taken for all values of l from 1 to n.

The aggregate of such covariant derivatives of a vector can be proved to form a tensor of the second rank. These covariant derivatives reduce to ordinary derivatives in Galilean space-time for which $n = 4$ and the g's are constants. If $V^i = \sum_k g^{ik} V_k$, the quantities V^i are the contravariant components of the vector V. The covariant derivatives of these contravariant components can be shewn to be given by

$$V^i_{|k} = \frac{\partial V^i}{\partial x_k} + \sum_m \{mk, i\} V^m.$$

The *divergence of the vector V* is now defined to be $\sum_l V^l_{|l}$ and may equally be written $\sum_{ik} g^{ik} V_{i|k}$, the summation being taken for all values of i and k from 1 to n. It will be noticed that the divergence reduces for hyper-Euclidean coordinates to $\sum_i \frac{\partial V_i}{\partial x_i}$: our definition is therefore a legitimate extension of that previously given.

In the third place we consider *tensors of the second rank*. Such a tensor can be written in the three forms T_{ik}, T^k_i, T^{ik}. They are connected by the identities $T^k_i = \sum_m g^{mk} T_{im}$, $T^{ik} = \sum_m g^{km} T^i_m$. Equally $T_{ik} = \sum_m g_{mk} T^m_i$, and $T^k_i = \sum_m g_{mi} T^{km}$. The corresponding covariant derivatives are defined by

$$T_{ik|l} = \frac{\partial T_{ik}}{\partial x_l} - \sum_j \{il, j\} T_{jk} - \sum_j \{kl, j\} T_{ij};$$

$$T^k_{i|l} = \frac{\partial T^k_i}{\partial x_l} - \sum_h \{il, h\} T^k_h + \sum_h \{hl, k\} T^h_i;$$

$$T^{ik}_{|l} = \frac{\partial T^{ik}}{\partial x_l} + \sum_j \{jl, i\} T^{jk} + \sum_j \{jl, k\} T^{ij}.$$

The aggregate of each set of covariant derivatives can be proved to form a tensor of the third rank.

Ricci's lemma.

There is an important theorem, often called *Ricci's lemma*, that the covariant derivatives of the quantities g_{ik} and g^{ik} all vanish. If, in fact, we substitute in the formulae just given and remember the definition of Christoffel's symbols of the second kind, we get $g_{ik|l} = 0$ and $g^{ik}_{|l} = 0$.

There is a further important proposition that the covariant differentiation of a product of two tensors is formed by the rule for the ordinary differentiation of a product. Thus, if A and B be two tensors,

$$(AB)_{|l} = A_{|l}.B + A.B_{|l}.$$

It follows from this rule, combined with Ricci's lemma, that *in covariant differentiation the g's can be treated as constants*.

This fact enables us readily to prove that the definitions of $T_{ik|l}$, $T_{i|l}^k$ and $T_{|l}^{ik}$ are consistent. We can, for example, deduce the second from the first by means of the formula

$$T_{i|l}^k = \sum_m (g^{mk} T_{im})_{|l} = \sum_m g^{mk} T_{im|l}.$$

The components of the divergence of the tensor T^{ik} are now defined to be $\sum_k T_{|k}^{ik}$, where, as usual, the summation is taken for $k = 1, 2, \ldots n$.

Since $T_{|l}^{ik}$ is a tensor, we have the transformation equations (*vide* § 63)

$$T_{|l}^{\prime ik} = \sum_{pqr} \frac{\partial x_r}{\partial x_l{}'} \frac{\partial x_i{}'}{\partial x_p} \frac{\partial x_k{}'}{\partial x_q} T_{|r}^{pq}.$$

If now we put $l = k$, we get

$$\sum_k T_{|k}^{\prime ik} = \sum_{pq} \frac{\partial x_i{}'}{\partial x_p} T_{|q}^{pq}.$$

Hence the components of the divergence of the tensor T^{ik} are the contravariant components Y^i of a vector Y; and we have $Y^i = \sum_k T_{|k}^{ik}$.

In all the applications of the tensor calculus which we shall make, we shall deal with symmetrical coefficients of potential for which $g_{ik} = g_{ki}$, and with *symmetrical tensors* of the second rank for which $T^{ik} = T^{ki}$. If $T^{ik} = T^{ki}$ it may be at once proved that $T_{ik} = T_{ki}$, since each will be equal to $\sum_{hm} g_{mk} g_{hi} T^{mh}$. Thus T_{ik} will also be a symmetrical tensor. But it must be observed that T_i^k is not necessarily, or usually, equal to T_k^i.

The vector Y, which represents the divergence of the symmetrical tensor of the second rank T^{ik}, can be expressed in terms of the allied tensors T_i^k and T_{ik} respectively.

We proceed to shew, in the first place, that the covariant components Y_i of Y are such that $Y_i = \sum_k T_{i|k}^k$.

We have, by definition, $Y_i = \sum_l g_{il} Y^l$. Hence, since $Y^l = \sum_k T_{|k}^{lk}$, we have

$$Y_i = \sum_{lk} g_{il} T_{|k}^{lk} = \sum_{lk} (g_{il} T^{lk})_{|k} = \sum_k T_{i|k}^k,$$

provided T^{lk} is a symmetrical tensor.

Thus, when T_{ik} is a symmetrical tensor, the covariant components of its divergence may be written $\sum_k T_{i|k}^{\ k}$.

In the second place, we will shew that, when T_{ik} is a symmetrical tensor, the covariant components of its divergence are

$$\sum_{kl} g^{kl} T_{ik|l}.$$

The expression just written down

$$= \sum_{klm} g^{kl}(g_{km}T_i^m)_{|l} = \sum_{klm} g^{kl}g_{km}T_{i|l}^m = \sum_{lm} g_m^l T_{i|l}^m = \sum_l T_{i|l}^l = Y_i.$$

Let us now introduce the symbol of *contravariant differentiation*. We define $T_{ik}^{|m}$ by the equality

$$T_{ik}^{|m} = \sum_l g^{ml} T_{ik|l}.$$

We now see that, *when T_{ik} is a symmetrical tensor of the second rank, the covariant components of its divergence are the expressions*

$$Y_i = \sum_k T_{ik}^{|k}.$$

We can now prove that the covariant components of the divergence of the symmetrical tensor T_{ik} can be written in the form

$$\sum_k \frac{1}{\sqrt{-g}} \frac{\partial}{\partial x_k}\{T_i^k \sqrt{-g}\} - \sum_{kl}\{ik, l\} T_l^k,$$

where g is the determinant of the coefficients g_{ik}.

We have seen that the components of the divergence may be written $\sum_k T_{i|k}^k$.

But $$T_{i|l}^k = \frac{\partial T_i^k}{\partial x_l} - \sum_h \{il, h\} T_h^k + \sum_h \{hl, k\} T_i^h.$$

Hence the i-th component of the divergence is equal to

$$\sum_k \frac{\partial T_i^k}{\partial x_k} - \sum_{hk}\{ik, h\} T_h^k + \sum_{hk}\{hk, k\} T_i^h.$$

Now $$\sum_k \{hk, k\} = \sum_{km} \tfrac{1}{2}g^{km}\left[\frac{\partial g_{hm}}{\partial x_k} + \frac{\partial g_{mk}}{\partial x_h} - \frac{\partial g_{hk}}{\partial x_m}\right]$$

$$= \tfrac{1}{2}\sum_{km} g^{km}\frac{\partial g_{mk}}{\partial x_h}.$$

Further, $\frac{\partial g}{\partial x_h} = \sum_{km} g g^{km}\frac{\partial g_{km}}{\partial x_h}$, by the ordinary rule for the differentiation of a determinant; and thus $\sum_k \{hk, k\} = \frac{1}{2g}\frac{\partial g}{\partial x_h}$. Finally, therefore, we have the given result.

It is customary to insert the minus sign in $\sqrt{-g}$, so that for the Galilean ground-form, for which $ds^2 = c^2dt^2 - dx^2 - dy^2 - dz^2$, we may work with a real quantity.

Throughout the previous analysis we have assumed that we were working with n coordinates. When T_{ik} is a tensor in space-time, we have four coordinates. In this case the divergence of T_{ik} has four components, and hence the vanishing of this divergence implies four equations. We shall see shortly that when T_{ik} is a certain tensor, known as the energy-momentum-stress tensor, the vanishing of its divergence gives the four fundamental equations of dynamics.

§117. *The fundamental identities of the general theory of relativity.*

We have previously defined the Einstein world-tensor G_{ik}. In connection with it there is a remarkable and most important fact: the divergence of the expression

$$G_{ik} - \tfrac{1}{2}g_{ik}G + \lambda g_{ik}$$

vanishes when λ is any constant.

The expression thus formed from the Einstein world-tensor is sometimes called the *gravitational tensor*: it is obviously a tensor of the second rank. The vanishing of its divergence means that there can be formed four identities connecting the quantities g_{ik} and their first and second differentials. These identities are of fundamental importance in general relativity-mechanics, and they are surprising consequences of the way in which G_{ik} is constructed from the g_{ik}'s and their differentials. Naturally the identities cannot, on account of their complexity, be readily obtained by direct algebra. An elegant proof can be obtained by using

Bianchi's identities.

We first of all shew that, if $(ij, hk)_l$ denotes the covariant derivative with respect to x_l of Riemann's symbol (ij, hk), then

$$(ij, hk)_l + (ij, kl)_h + (ij, lh)_k = 0.$$

We take the formula, established in §63,

$$(ij, hk) = \tfrac{1}{2}\left\{ \frac{\partial^2 g_{hj}}{\partial x_k \partial x_i} + \frac{\partial^2 g_{ik}}{\partial x_h \partial x_j} - \frac{\partial^2 g_{ih}}{\partial x_k \partial x_j} - \frac{\partial^2 g_{kj}}{\partial x_h \partial x_i} \right\}$$
$$- \sum_m \{ih, m\}[jk, m] + \sum_m \{ik, m\}[jh, m].$$

On differentiating with regard to x_l, we get

$$\frac{\partial}{\partial x_l}(ij, hk) = \tfrac{1}{2}\left\{ \frac{\partial^3 g_{hj}}{\partial x_k \partial x_i \partial x_l} + \frac{\partial^3 g_{ik}}{\partial x_h \partial x_j \partial x_l} - \frac{\partial^3 g_{ih}}{\partial x_k \partial x_j \partial x_l} - \frac{\partial^3 g_{kj}}{\partial x_h \partial x_i \partial x_l} \right\},$$

together with terms which vanish when Christoffel's symbols all vanish. If then we put

$$Q = (ij, hk)_l + (ij, kl)_h + (ij, lh)_k,$$

we see that Q is a tensor of the fifth rank, covariant with regard to all five indices, which vanishes at any point when geodesic coordinates (§63) are taken. Q is therefore zero.

We thus have Bianchi's first identity. Similarly we can shew that

$$\{ij, hk\}_l + \{ij, kl\}_h + \{ij, lh\}_k = 0.$$

Now we have seen that the Einstein tensor G_{ik} is symmetrical in i and k. Hence the components of the divergence of G_{ik} will be components of a vector Y. We shall, in fact, have, by § 115,

$$Y_i = \sum_k G_{ik}^{|k} = \sum_{kl} g^{kl} G_{ik|l} = \sum_{kljh} g^{kl} g^{jh} (ij, hk)_l.$$

Now $(ij, hk) = (hk, ij)$; and we know from Bianchi's identity that

$$(hk, ij)_l + (hk, jl)_i + (hk, li)_j = 0.$$

Thus $$Y_i = - \sum_{kljh} g^{kl} g^{jh} [(jl, hk)_i + (li, hk)_j].$$

But, by definition, $$G = \sum_{jklh} g^{jk} g^{lh} (jl, hk).$$

Therefore $$\frac{\partial G}{\partial x_i} = - \sum_{lkjh} g^{lk} g^{jh} (jl, hk)_i.$$

Hence $$Y_i = \frac{\partial G}{\partial x_i} - Y_i \quad \text{or} \quad Y_i = \tfrac{1}{2} \frac{\partial G}{\partial x_i}.$$

But equally the components of the divergence of $(\lambda - \tfrac{1}{2} G) g_{ik}$ will be given by

$$\sum_k [(\lambda - \tfrac{1}{2} G) g_{ik}]^{|k} = \sum_{kl} g^{kl} [(\lambda - \tfrac{1}{2} G) g_{ik}]_{|l}$$
$$= \sum_{kl} g^{kl} g_{ik} \left(-\tfrac{1}{2} \frac{\partial G}{\partial x_l} \right) = -\tfrac{1}{2} \frac{\partial G}{\partial x_i}.$$

We thus see that the divergence of $G_{ik} - \tfrac{1}{2} G g_{ik} + \lambda g_{ik}$ vanishes when λ is any constant.

Evidently the gravitational tensor is a world-tensor, for it involves merely the quantities g_{rs}, which define the metric of space-time, and their differentials. The vanishing of its divergence implies, as we have said, four identities. Now the vanishing of the divergence of the vector representing momentum-density at a point of a fluid expresses permanence of density of matter. We can therefore anticipate that the four fundamental identities of the general theory of relativity, summed up in the statement that the divergence of the gravitational tensor vanishes, will express certain relations of the nature of inherent permanence connected with the physical world. It is thus to be expected that they will prove to be of great importance in mechanics.

§ 118. *The stress-tensor at a point in a continuous material medium.*

Let us now pass from algebra to some physical considerations. Such will enable us to use the very complicated algebraical results just mentioned which the calculus of tensors has made it possible to obtain.

The idea of a tensor, as the word suggests, originally arose from the consideration of the stresses which exist in a continuous material medium. This medium is assumed to be of a general type in which shearing stresses occur. Suppose that we take rectangular axes, then the components of stress per unit area, at any point in such a medium, across three planes perpendicular to the coordinate axes, can be expressed by π_1, π_2, π_3, where the π's are vectors having both length and direction. (The component of stress across any plane is, of course, not necessarily perpendicular to that plane.)

The components of these stresses parallel to the axes can be written

$$p_{11}, p_{12}, p_{13}, \text{ and so on.}$$

Altogether there are nine such components; but in them, as we see by considering the couples on an elementary cube with its faces perpendicular to the coordinates axes,

$$p_{ik} = p_{ki}, \qquad i, k = 1, 2, 3.$$

Hence only six of the stress-components are independent.

Consider now a section of the medium at a point at which the stress-components are p_{ik} $(i, k = 1, 2, 3)$. Let the direction-cosines of the normal to the section be λ^i, and let the vector P represent the stress per unit area across it. We can prove that the component of P in the direction μ^k $(k = 1, 2, 3)$, which we shall denote by $P(\lambda, \mu)$, will be

$$\overset{3}{\underset{1}{\Sigma}}_{ik}\, p_{ik}\lambda^i\mu^k.$$

For, let us consider the equilibrium of a small tetrahedron $OABC$, formed by the section under consideration and by planes parallel to the axial planes through an adjacent point O. If dS be the area of the base ABC of this tetrahedron, the areas of the axial faces will be $\lambda^i dS$ $(i = 1, 2, 3)$. Let now the vector π_i represent, as we have previously said, the stress per unit area across the axial face perpendicular to Ox_i. Then the condition of equilibrium of the tetrahedron gives us the vector-equation

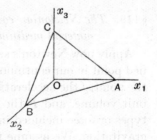

$$P = \overset{3}{\underset{1}{\Sigma}}_i\, \pi_i\lambda^i.$$

Now the components of π_i are p_{ik} $(k = 1, 2, 3)$. If then p_k $(k = 1, 2, 3)$ be the components in the directions of the axes of the vector P, the last equation is equivalent to the three equations

$$p_k = \underset{i}{\Sigma}\, p_{ik}\lambda^i, \qquad k = 1, 2, 3.$$

Hence the component, in the direction μ, of the stress per unit area across a section normal to λ, is

$$P(\lambda, \mu) = \sum_{1}^{3} {}_{k}\, p_{k}\mu^{k} = \sum_{1}^{3} {}_{ik}\, p_{ik}\lambda^{i}\mu^{k}.$$

Now obviously $P(\lambda, \mu)$ is an invariant when the directions λ and μ are invariant: it will be unchanged however the axes be changed.

Hence, by §63, the quantities p_{ik} are the components of a symmetrical tensor of the second rank.

The divergence of this stress-tensor has an important interpretation, inasmuch as the components of this divergence are the components of a vector $- \varpi$, where ϖ is the resultant of the molecular forces per unit volume at the point under consideration. We can readily prove this result for Cartesian coordinates by considering the equilibrium of an elementary rectangular parallelepiped with its edges parallel to the coordinate axes and of lengths δx_1, δx_2, δx_3. For Cartesian coordinates we thus get

$$\varpi_i = - \sum_{k=1}^{3} \frac{\partial p_{ik}}{\partial x_k}, \quad i = 1, 2, 3.$$

For the most general axes we have therefore

$$\varpi_i = - \sum_{1}^{3} {}_{kl}\, g^{kl} p_{ik|l}, \quad \text{or} \quad \varpi_i = - \sum_{k} p_{ik}^{|k}.$$

Thus the components of the divergence of the stress-tensor are the components of $- \varpi$.

§119. *The Newtonian equations of motion at a point in a continuous material medium.*

Apply now Newton's second law of motion to an element at a specified point in our continuous material medium. Let ρ be the density at the point, f the acceleration of the element, ϖ the molecular force per unit volume, and F the 'external' force per unit mass. Among the types of force included in F, the most important will be the force of gravitation. We assume that the medium is continuous in the sense that ρ, though it may become zero, is never infinite.

If Newton's second law of motion in classical mechanics be true, the resultant of the forces acting on an element of our medium are in the direction of its acceleration and equal to its acceleration multiplied by its mass. We therefore have the vector-equation

$$\rho f = \rho F + \varpi,$$

in which f, F and ϖ are all vectors. We have also the 'equation of continuity', which expresses the fact that there is no creation of matter in any element of volume. If our coordinates be rectangular in Euclidean space, this equation may be written, as we have seen in §116,

$$\frac{\partial \rho}{\partial t} + \frac{\partial}{\partial x_1}(\rho v_1) + \frac{\partial}{\partial x_2}(\rho v_2) + \frac{\partial}{\partial x_3}(\rho v_3) = 0$$

or

$$\frac{\partial \rho}{\partial t} + \operatorname{div}(\rho v) = 0,$$

where v is the velocity-vector with components v_1, v_2, v_3. When the vectors involved are resolved parallel to the axes of coordinates, the equation $\rho f = \rho F + \varpi$ gives us three equations. Altogether, therefore, we have four equations. If now we *assume that F can be absorbed* into the stress-actions, we may write the equations in the form

$$\rho \frac{dv}{dt} = \varpi \quad \text{and} \quad \frac{\partial \rho}{\partial t} + \operatorname{div}(\rho v) = 0.$$

Now dv/dt is the 'proper' derivative for the element under consideration: as t varies, v must refer to one and the same particle of matter. The derivative thus depends directly on t, and also on the variation of x_1, x_2, x_3 with t. The first of our equations may therefore be written

$$\rho \left\{ \frac{\partial v_i}{\partial t} + \sum_{k=1}^{3} v_k \frac{\partial v_i}{\partial x_k} \right\} = - \sum_{k=1}^{3} \frac{\partial p_{ik}}{\partial x_k}, \qquad i = 1, 2, 3.$$

The four equations may therefore be put in the form

$$\frac{\partial (\rho v_i)}{\partial t} + \sum_{1}^{3} \frac{\partial}{\partial x_k}(\rho v_i v_k + p_{ik}) = 0,$$

and

$$\frac{\partial \rho}{\partial t} + \sum_{1}^{3} \frac{\partial}{\partial x_k}(\rho v_k) = 0.$$

§120. *A symmetrical form for the fundamental Newtonian equations of motion of a continuous medium.*

We wish gradually to change these fundamental equations of motion into a form where the time does not occupy an apparently privileged position. As the first stage of this transformation we put $x_0 = ct$; and we form a symmetrical group of expressions T_{ik} defined by

$$\begin{aligned} T_{00} &= c^2 \rho, \\ T_{i0} &= T_{0i} = -c\rho v_i, \\ T_{ki} &= T_{ik} = \rho v_i v_k + p_{ik}, \end{aligned}$$

where i and k can take all values 1, 2, 3.

It is important to notice that T_{ik}, as thus defined, is not a tensor. The four equations can all be now written in the inclusive form

$$\frac{\partial T_{i0}}{\partial x_0} - \sum_{1}^{3} k \frac{\partial T_{ik}}{\partial x_k} = 0, \quad \text{where } i = 0, 1, 2, 3.$$

In the special theory of relativity we have realised the connection between mass and energy; and we see that the expression T_{00} represents simple energy-density. The expression T_{i0} represents in absolute value the i-th component of the momentum-density, calculated with regard to what is sometimes called the Römerian time $x_0 = ct$.

§ 121. *A modified form of the Newtonian equations in which the time no longer has a privileged position.*

The Newtonian equations in the form to which we have reduced them are not invariant when the axes of reference undergo a Lorentz transformation. But we can make a slight change in them whereby they assume a form which is invariant. In making such a change *we implicitly assert that the fundamental equations of Newtonian dynamics are only an approximation to the truth* and that this approximation has been obtained by neglecting terms involving $1/c$.

We have, for the expression of the line-element in the special theory of relativity,

$$ds^2 = dx_0{}^2 - dx_1{}^2 - dx_2{}^2 - dx_3{}^2, \qquad \text{where } x_0 = ct.$$

The components of velocity will be given by

$$v_i = c \frac{dx_i}{dx_0}.$$

Suppose now that we introduce the contravariant parameters

$$\lambda^i = \frac{dx_i}{ds}, \quad \text{where } i = 0, 1, 2, 3.$$

Then we have $\quad \lambda^0 = \dfrac{dx_0}{ds} = \dfrac{1}{\sqrt{1 - \beta^2}};$

and $\quad \lambda^i = \dfrac{dx_i}{ds} = \dfrac{v_i}{c \sqrt{1 - \beta^2}}, \quad \text{for } i = 1, 2, 3;$

where $\quad \beta^2 = \dfrac{dx_1{}^2 + dx_2{}^2 + dx_3{}^2}{dx_0{}^2}.$

Corresponding to these contravariant parameters we have the covariant components

$$\lambda_0 = \frac{1}{\sqrt{1 - \beta^2}}; \quad \lambda_i = -\frac{v_i}{c \sqrt{1 - \beta^2}}, \qquad i = 1, 2, 3.$$

We will now utilise these covariant components to define anew the components of the group of expressions T_{ik}. We take, in fact,

$$T_{00} = c^2\rho\lambda_0{}^2,$$
$$T_{i0} = T_{0i} = c^2\rho\lambda_i\lambda_0,$$
$$T_{ki} = T_{ik} = c^2\rho\lambda_i\lambda_k + p_{ik}, \qquad i, k = 1, 2, 3.$$

It is most important to notice that, as a result of this change, *the new values of the T's will differ from the old only by quantities of the order of β^2.*

So far we have merely termed ρ the 'density' at any point of our medium. But, if we refer back to the more simple investigation of §§ 103, 106, we see that we must take ρ to be an invariant for transformations of our space-time coordinates: it will, in fact, be ρ_0, the statical invariant-mass density at any point, when the medium consists of discrete particles so that the stresses p_{ik} do not exist. In the general case, also, ρ must be an invariant: we shall shortly discuss its physical meaning when our medium is a perfect fluid. Obviously, if ρ be an invariant, and if the terms p_{ik} do not exist, the quantities T_{ik} will be the components of a symmetrical tensor of the second rank for the most general system of space-time coordinates.

We have seen that the p_{ik}'s are components of a tensor for such general transformations of the three-dimensional space-coordinates as do not involve the time-coordinate x_0. When, however, we consider general transformations in the four dimensions of space-time, the p_{ik}'s are no longer components of a tensor. We must, therefore, introduce new terms π_{ik}. These new terms must be components of a tensor in space-time and must reduce to values which at most only differ by terms of order $1/c$ from the given p_{ik}'s (or from zero when $k = 0$) for the Galilean space-time which is defined by

$$ds^2 = dx_0{}^2 - dx_1{}^2 - dx_2{}^2 - dx_3{}^2, \qquad x_0 = ct.$$

We shall assume that the discovery of such modified terms is possible and we shall write

$$T_{ik} = c^2\rho\lambda_i\lambda_k + \pi_{ik}, \qquad \left.\begin{array}{c} i \\ k \end{array}\right\} = 0, 1, 2, 3,$$

where the quantities T_{ik} are now components of a symmetrical tensor.

When a tensor of this nature has been formed, our four fundamental equations of motion take the form

$$\frac{\partial T_{i0}}{\partial x_0} - \sum_1^3{}_k \frac{\partial T_{ik}}{\partial x_k} = 0, \quad \text{for } i = 0, 1, 2, 3.$$

Now, in the Galilean coordinates with which we are dealing,

$$g^{00} = 1; \quad g^{kk} = -1, \quad \text{for } k = 1, 2, 3; \text{ and } g^{kl} = 0, \quad \text{for } k \neq l.$$

Our equations may therefore be written

$$\sum_{kl} g^{kl} \frac{\partial T_{ik}}{\partial x_l} = 0, \qquad i = 0, 1, 2, 3.$$

They can therefore be put into the form

$$\sum_{kl} g^{kl} T_{ik\,|\,l} = 0,$$

since Christoffel's symbols of the second kind all vanish for Galilean coordinates.

Finally, therefore, by § 116 we can write our equations in the form

$$\sum_0^3{}_k T_{ik}^{|k} = 0, \qquad \text{where } i = 0, 1, 2, 3;$$

and in them *the time has no longer a privileged position.*

These equations can be summed up by stating that the divergence of the tensor T_{ik} vanishes. This is a property which is invariant for all changes of space-time coordinates. We thus express the general conditions of equilibrium at any point of a continuous material medium in a form which is invariant for all transformations of space-time coordinates. *The general conditions of equilibrium are thus expressed by a law which satisfies the general principle of relativity.*

§ 122.   *The energy-momentum-stress tensor.*

The tensor T_{ik} is known as the energy-momentum-stress tensor or, more briefly, as the energy-tensor. The vanishing of its divergence is equivalent to four equations; and these equations, on the assumption that our previous modification of Newtonian dynamics is valid, will be an accurate expression of the fundamental dynamical laws of the continuous material medium associated with T_{ik}. But these fundamental equations are in classical mechanics given by the laws of conservation of energy and conservation of momentum. We thus see that these dynamical laws, in so far as they are valid, are of exactly equal importance: in fact, they are different expressions of the statement that the divergence of the energy-tensor vanishes.

We repeat that the fundamental principle of relativity-mechanics is that it is possible to express the laws of any physical phenomenon in a form which is a tensor-equation valid for every possible transformation of space-time coordinates. We now see that, if our modification of Newtonian mechanics and the assumption with regard to the quantities π_{ik} are alike correct, we have expressed as a single tensor-equation the laws of conservation of energy and momentum by making a change from the formulae of classical mechanics, which only involves quantities so small as to be inappreciable in experiments in which we are concerned with the velocities of common experience or of planetary motions. We may therefore say with some confidence that, for the dynamics of a continuous material medium in the most general space-time coordinates, the equations of motion are satisfactorily expressed by the fact that the divergence of the energy-stress tensor vanishes.

It may be objected that we have ignored the 'external' forces initially represented by the vector F. But such forces will be absorbed into the stresses within the medium if we abolish the idea of action at a distance. Such action at a distance belongs to the Newtonian theory of gravitation as commonly presented, although Newton himself found it repugnant*. In Einstein's relativity-mechanics, however, all actions of gravitational origin are supposed to result from the particular space-time metric which exists when they appear. They are, in fact, exactly analogous to centrifugal forces which arise when we take a metric corresponding to rotating axes. By these considerations we can adequately justify our neglect of so-called 'external' forces.

It may be further objected that we have yet to justify the assumption that the tensor π_{ik} can be formed, of which the components for Galilean space-time only differ at most by terms in $1/c$ from the components of shearing-stress p_{ik}. Now if such a tensor exists it is alike necessary and sufficient that $\sum_{ik} \pi_{ik} u^i v^k$ should be an invariant, where u^i and v^k are the contravariant components of two arbitrary vectors.

We may put
$$u^i = \frac{dx_i}{ds}, \qquad u^k = \frac{dy_k}{d\sigma}.$$

Then, if accented letters correspond to transformed coordinates, the expression in question will be an invariant provided

$$\sum_{0}^{3}{}_{ik} \left\{ \pi_{ik}' \frac{dx_i'}{ds} \frac{dy_k'}{d\sigma} = \pi_{ik} \frac{dx_i}{ds} \frac{dy_k}{d\sigma} \right\},$$

or
$$\pi_{00}' dx_0' dy_0' + \sum_{1}^{3}{}_i \pi_{i0}' dx_i' dy_0' + \sum_{1}^{3}{}_k \pi_{0k}' dx_0' dy_k' + \sum_{1}^{3}{}_{ik} \pi_{ik}' dx_i' dy_k'$$
$$= \pi_{00} dx_0 dy_0 + \sum_{1}^{3}{}_i \pi_{i0} dx_i dy_0 + \sum_{1}^{3}{}_k \pi_{0k} dx_0 dy_k + \sum_{1}^{3}{}_{ik} \pi_{ik} dx_i dy_k.$$

Now, if the time be unchanged, $dx_0 = dx_0'$ and $dy_0 = dy_0'$; and, since these quantities are arbitrary, we must therefore have the three identities

$$\pi_{00}' = \pi_{00}; \qquad \sum_i \pi_{i0}' dx_i' = \sum_i \pi_{i0} dx_i;$$

and
$$\sum_{ik} \pi_{ik}' dx_i' dy_k' = \sum_{ik} \pi_{ik} dx_i dy_k.$$

* Newton's words are quoted in § 133 *infra*.

The last identity shews that, for transformations which leave the time unaltered, the π_{ik}'s must be components of a tensor for space; and this is the known property of the p_{ik}'s. What we therefore need is that, when $x_0 = ct$ and x_1, x_2, x_3 are Euclidean space-coordinates, the difference $\pi_{ik} - p_{ik}$ $(i > 0, k > 0)$, shall be at most of order $1/c$. It must also be possible to find the tensor-components π_{00} and π_{0i} $(i = 1, 2, 3)$, such that π_{00} and $\sum\limits_{i=0}^{3} \pi_{i0} dx_i$ only involve terms of order $1/c$ when $x_0 = ct$ and x_1, x_2, x_3 are Euclidean space-coordinates.

The stress-tensor for a perfect fluid.

Consider the case of a perfect fluid, that is to say, one with no shearing-stresses, in which the pressure at every point is p. For it we have, in Euclidean space,

$$p_{ii} = -p, \quad i = 1, 2, 3; \qquad p_{ik} = 0, \quad i \neq k.$$

Suppose now that we take, for values of i and k which include zero,

$$\pi_{ik} = p(\lambda_i \lambda_k - g_{ik}).$$

Then clearly for Galilean space-time, for which $g_{00} = 1$, $g_{ii} = -1$ $(i > 0)$, $g_{ik} = 0$ $(i \neq k)$ and $x_0 = ct$, π_{00} is of order $1/c^2$; π_{0i} is of order $1/c$; and $\pi_{ik} - p_{ik}$ is of order $1/c^2$.

Thus π_{ik} satisfies the required conditions, and therefore the *energy-stress tensor for a perfect fluid is*

$$T_{ik} = (c^2\rho + p)\lambda_i \lambda_k - pg_{ik},$$

where p is the pressure per unit area at any point and ρ is an invariant representing 'density', of which the exact physical meaning must be found. We shall shortly prove that ρ is the total density at any point of the fluid. This density is made up of the proper density ρ_0 together with the contributions to density due to energy at the point, whether the latter is energy of radiation (if such exists) or of relative motions. We shall, in fact, shew that

$$c^2\rho = c^2\rho_0 + 3p.$$

We notice that any combination of ρ and p will be an invariant, since each is an invariant separately.

Corresponding to the tensor just obtained, the invariant $T = \sum\limits_{ik} g^{ik} T_{ik}$ is given by

$$T = (c^2\rho + p) \Sigma g^{ik} \lambda_i \lambda_k - p \Sigma g^{ik} g_{ik}.$$

Now
$$\lambda_i \lambda_k = \Sigma_{\alpha\beta} g_{i\alpha} g_{k\beta} \lambda^\alpha \lambda^\beta.$$

Hence
$$\sum_{ik} g^{ik}\lambda_i\lambda_k = \sum_{ik\alpha\beta} g^{ik}g_{i\alpha}g_{k\beta}\lambda^\alpha\lambda^\beta$$
$$= \sum_{k\alpha\beta} g^k_\alpha g_{k\beta}\lambda^\alpha\lambda^\beta$$
$$= \sum_{\alpha\beta} g_{\alpha\beta}\lambda^\alpha\lambda^\beta = 1.$$

Thus
$$T = c^2\rho + p - 4p = c^2\rho - 3p.$$

Further the invariant $\sum_{ik}\lambda^i\lambda^k T_{ik}$ is equal to $c^2\rho$. We see still further that, since the stress-tensor is symmetrical,

$$T^\alpha_k = \sum_i g^{i\alpha}T_{ik}$$
$$= \sum_i g^{i\alpha}(c^2\rho + p)\lambda_i\lambda_k - \sum_i g^{i\alpha}pg_{ik}$$
$$= (c^2\rho + p)\lambda^\alpha\lambda_k - pg^\alpha_k.$$

Thus, for general space-time coordinates, the stress-tensor corresponding to a perfect fluid is such that

$$T^\alpha_\alpha = (c^2\rho + p)\lambda^\alpha\lambda_\alpha - p,$$
and
$$T^\alpha_\beta = (c^2\rho + p)\lambda^\alpha\lambda_\beta, \qquad \alpha \neq \beta.$$

From these results we readily see that

$$T^{ik} = (c^2\rho + p)\lambda^i\lambda^k - pg^{ik}.$$

The stress-tensor for a perfect fluid at rest in space-time of the type $ds^2 = g_{00}dx_0{}^2 - dl^2$, where dl is purely spatial.

Suppose now that we have a form of space-time for which $g_{0i} = 0$ ($i = 1, 2, 3$), where $x_0 = ct$. Then, if our perfect fluid be at rest, $\lambda^i = 0$, and therefore $\lambda^0 = 1/\sqrt{g_{00}}$. Hence $\lambda_0 = \sqrt{g_{00}}$, and $\lambda_i = 0$.

Thus we shall have $T^0_0 = c^2\rho$; $T^i_i = -p$; and $T^k_i = 0$, $i \neq k$.

Similarly $\qquad T_{00} = c^2\rho g_{00}$; $T_{ik} = -pg_{ik}$.

These results will be useful in subsequent investigations.

The determination of the stress-tensor under general conditions.

We have just seen how, in the particular case of a perfect fluid, it is possible to find the quantities π_{ik}, and so to determine the energy-stress tensor T_{ik}.

Such a tensor, moreover, if the general principle of relativity be true, must always exist. In any medium, dynamical conditions at a given point and instant will be theoretically determined if we know at the particular point-instant

(1) the density of the matter or, what is the same thing, of the energy;
(2) the velocity of the matter; and
(3) the distribution of the stress.

But these determine the energy-stress tensor; and, conversely, if the energy-stress tensor be known at every point-instant, we know the world history of the aggregate of matter under consideration.

Of course the final test of the truth of our assumptions must be the fact that conclusions drawn from them are verified by observation. Such verification, as we shall see shortly, proves that in certain crucial cases Einstein's relativity-mechanics gives more accurate results than the classical dynamics of Newton.

When in thought we pass behind material elements to the ultimate particles of which matter is composed, we may regard our continuous medium as an aggregate of discrete particles between which gravitational forces act; and we assume that such forces may be absorbed into the metric of space-time*.

We have seen that the energy-stress tensor for a perfect fluid is given by

$$T_{ik} = (c^2\rho + p)\lambda_i\lambda_k - pg_{ik},$$

where p is the pressure at any point of the fluid and ρ is an invariant quantity representing 'density', of which the exact physical meaning remains to be discovered.

Put $p = 0$ in this result. Then we see that for an aggregate of discrete particles the energy-stress tensor takes the form

$$T_{ik} = c^2\rho\lambda_i\lambda_k.$$

Corresponding to this value of the energy-tensor the invariant T is equal to $c^2\rho$. Now for an aggregate of discrete particles the only quantity which can be regarded as density, and is also invariant, is the 'proper' or, as we called it in § 103, the statical invariant-mass density. Denote this 'proper' density by the symbol ρ_0. Then we see that for an aggregate of discrete particles the energy-tensor is given by

$$T_{ik} = c^2\rho_0\lambda_i\lambda_k,$$

and the invariant T is equal to $c^2\rho_0$.

We may conveniently think of formulae, in which components of shearing-stress enter into the expression for T_{ik}, as macroscopic formulae obtained after the aggregation of ultimate particles into the matter of our ordinary experience. When we pass from an aggregate of discrete particles to a continuous medium, pressures and stresses arise owing to relative motions. Even in a fluid 'at rest', the pressure has its

---

* The argument cannot be regarded as finally satisfactory or complete until the possible existence of forces of electro-magnetic origin has been admitted and such forces have been absorbed into the metric. (*Vide* § 141.)

origin in small random motions of molecules of the fluid. In a solid 'at rest', heat, as we know from Joule's experiments, is a form of motion.

Now we have seen that, for a perfect fluid of pressure p and 'density' ρ, $T = c^2\rho - 3p$. Hence, since T is an invariant unaffected by the introduction of relative motions, this 'density' ρ must be connected with the 'proper' density ρ_0 by the relation

$$c^2\rho_0 = c^2\rho - 3p,$$

the term $3p$ arising from relative motions within the medium. The pressure p thus has its origin in random motions and the energy due to them contributes nothing to 'proper' or invariant-mass density. The same fact is true of a more general continuous medium in which $T_{ik} = c^2\rho\lambda_i\lambda_k + \pi_{ik}$ and shearing-stresses similarly arise from the relative motions of molecules.

It remains to be said that, as we have already indicated, energy of radiation can contribute to pressure. We shall see in §192 that the pressure per unit area due to isotropic radiation of energy-density E is $E/3$. We know that radiation, since it travels with the velocity of light, has no 'proper' mass and therefore its existence in our medium will contribute nothing to the 'proper' density ρ_0.

§123. *The connection between mechanics and geometry.*

We will now recall a statement of Clifford, which shews that he contemplated the fusion of mechanics and geometry. It* runs:

We may conceive our space to have everywhere a nearly uniform curvature, but that slight variations of the curvature may occur from point to point, and themselves vary with the time. These variations of the curvature with the time may produce effects which we not unnaturally attribute to physical causes independent of the geometry of our space. We might even go so far as to assign to this variation of the curvature of space 'what really happens in that phenomenon which we term the motion of matter'.

With such speculations in his mind Clifford imagined a Universe in which matter and force are mere manifestations of the curvature of space.

Riemann had previously approached the same range of ideas when he said:

If in the case of a discrete (discontinuous) manifold the basis for its metrical determination is comprised in the very idea of this manifold, then for a con-

---

* W. K. Clifford, *Common Sense of the Exact Sciences.* Kegan Paul, 1885, p. 225. The words are due to Karl Pearson, as Clifford did not live to complete the book. But we learn from Pearson's preface that "whatever there is in them of value I owe to Clifford".

tinuous one it ought to come from without. Therefore the reality which lies at the basis of space either constitutes a discrete manifold, or the basis of metrical definition must be sought outside the manifold in the forces which act on it and hold it together.

This passage is somewhat obscure*; but it clearly affirms that Riemann saw a connection between the metric of space and the forces within it.

Einstein took up these ideas and applied them not merely to space but to space-time. He conceived that the metric of space-time is intimately connected with physical phenomena. Put out more precisely, the suggestion is that at every point of the space-time continuum there must be some connection between the energy-tensor T_{ik} and the Einstein world-tensor G_{ik}. The latter tensor is derived from the g's which determine the metric of space-time, and by its mode of formation is, as we have seen, closely associated with the measures of the curvatures of space-time.

§ 124. *Einstein's gravitational equations of the general theory of relativity.*

As soon as speculative enquiry brings us to this point, we are led to put side by side two remarkable facts. On the one hand the fundamental dynamical laws of a material medium are expressed by the statement that the divergence of the energy-stress tensor vanishes. On the other hand the divergence of the world-tensor

$$G_{ik} - \tfrac{1}{2}Gg_{ik} + \lambda g_{ik}$$

also vanishes. Is it not possible that there is an intimate connection between these two facts, one of which expresses the fundamental laws of mechanics while the other is solely a consequence of the structure of space-time? May it not be, in fact, that we have some relation of the type

$$G_{ik} - \tfrac{1}{2}Gg_{ik} + \lambda g_{ik} + \vartheta T_{ik} = 0, \qquad i, k = 0, 1, 2, 3,$$

where ϑ is some definite constant? And is it not possible that among the sixteen equations which this relation apparently implies are equations which express gravitational action in the most general space-time coordinates? Such is the assumption which Einstein was finally led to make.

At the beginning of his speculations Einstein assumed that the quantities G_{ik} were proportional to the quantities T_{ik}. He quickly reflected, however, that the fundamental equations of mechanics must not impose on the metrical properties of space-time any *à priori*

---

* Clifford's slightly different translation conveys the same sense. *Vide Mathematical Papers.* Macmillan, 1882, p. 69.

limitation. There would have been such a restriction on the g's had G_{ik} been proportional to T_{ik}, because the equations of dynamics imply that the divergence of T_{ik} vanishes. Einstein was therefore led to put

$$G_{ik} - \tfrac{1}{2}Gg_{ik} = -\vartheta T_{ik}, \qquad i, k = 0, 1, 2, 3.$$

This set of sixteen equations, equally with the slightly more general equations for which λ is not zero, reduces to ten because each is symmetrical for an interchange of i and k. Further, between the ten equations there are four relations which result from the vanishing of the divergence. We are then left with six independent equations, which are usually regarded as *the fundamental equations of gravitation in general relativity*. Such equations are thus included in the system

$$G_{ik} - \tfrac{1}{2}Gg_{ik} + \lambda g_{ik} = -\vartheta T_{ik}, \qquad i, k = 0, 1, 2, 3, \ \ \dots\dots(E)$$

where ϑ is a definite constant, of which the value will be found at the close of § 126.

§ 125. *The curvature of a region of space-time containing neither matter nor energy.*

From the tensor T_{ik} we construct the invariant T exactly as from the tensor G_{ik} we constructed the invariant G. In fact, as we have already seen in § 122, $T = \overset{3}{\underset{0}{\Sigma}}_{ik} g^{ik} T_{ik}$. Multiply now by g^{ik} the fundamental gravitation-relation (E) which expresses T_{ik} in terms of the gravitational tensor. Then we get, on summing for all values of i and k,

$$G - 2G + 4\lambda = -\vartheta T,$$

or

$$G - 4\lambda = \vartheta T.$$

If Einstein's assumed gravitational equations are correct, then clearly, for a region of space-time where there is neither matter nor energy, we shall have $T_{ik} = 0$. Hence we shall have for such a region $T = 0$; and therefore we have $G = 4\lambda$ and $G_{ik} = \lambda g_{ik}$. Thus the six independent conditions expressed by the tensor-equation $G_{ik} = \lambda g_{ik}$ serve to define the state of space-time in a region which contains neither matter nor energy. Inasmuch as light is a form of radiant energy and, further, inasmuch as on Faraday's principles energy is stored in the electromagnetic field, there must also be, in any region where $G_{ik} = \lambda g_{ik}$, neither light nor an electro-magnetic field.

Einstein's gravitational equations in empty space-time are thus

$$G_{ik} = \lambda g_{ik}, \qquad i, k = 0, 1, 2, 3.$$

In the year 1916 Herglotz shewed that a geometrical interpretation could be given to these equations when, as in Minkowski's world, imaginary time is represented by a real direction. His results are conveniently deduced from a study of the behaviour of the parameters of a set of n concurrent mutually orthogonal lines in general n-dimensional space defined by

$$ds^2 = \sum_1^n g_{ik} dx_i dx_k.$$

Let $_\lambda u^i$ be the parameters of the lines, the associated unit-vectors being $_\lambda u$, $\lambda = 1, 2, \ldots n$. Because the lines are mutually orthogonal we shall have, by § 61,

$$\sum_{ik} g_{ik}\, _\lambda u^i\, _\mu u^k = g_\mu^\lambda,$$

where
$$g_\mu^\lambda = 0, \qquad \lambda \neq \mu,$$
$$= 1, \qquad \lambda = \mu.$$

If now $_\lambda u_i$ be the moments which correspond to the parameters $_\lambda u^i$, we have by definition

$$_\mu u_i = \sum_k g_{ik}\, _\mu u^k.$$

Therefore
$$\sum_i\, _\lambda u^i\, _\mu u_i = g_\lambda^\mu. \qquad \ldots\ldots(1)$$

Now it is well known that reciprocal relations hold good for the parameters and moments of such a set of mutually orthogonal lines. We have, in fact, by (1), $_\lambda u^i = {_\lambda U_i}/u$, where $_\lambda U_i$ is the minor, with its proper sign, of $_\lambda u_i$ in the determinant

$$u = \begin{vmatrix} _1u_1 & \cdots & _1u_n \\ \vdots & & \vdots \\ _nu_1 & \cdots & _nu_n \end{vmatrix}.$$

Therefore
$$\sum_1^n {_\lambda}\, _\lambda u^i\, _\lambda u_k = g_k^i.$$

Hence
$$\sum_\lambda\, _\lambda u_i\, _\lambda u_k = \sum_{\lambda h} g_{ih}\, _\lambda u^h\, _\lambda u_k$$
$$= \sum_h g_{ih}\, g_k^h = g_{ik};$$

and also
$$\sum_\lambda\, _\lambda u^i\, _\lambda u^k = \sum_\lambda\, _\lambda u^i \sum_h g^{hk}\, _\lambda u_h$$
$$= \sum_h g^{hk} g_h^i = g^{ik}.$$

Moreover, by the fundamental theorem of § 66 we know that, if $K_{(\lambda\mu)}$ be the Riemannian curvature of that section of our n-dimensional manifold which is given by a point P and by two vectors through P which we may call $_\lambda u$ and $_\mu u$, then

$$K_{(\lambda\mu)} = -\frac{1}{\sin^2 \alpha} \sum_{ijhk} (ij, hk)\, _\lambda u^i\, _\mu u^j\, _\lambda u^h\, _\mu u^k,$$

where α is the angle between the vectors. In virtue of the remark made at the end of § 65, we introduce the negative sign on the assumption that $ds^2 < 0$.

When the vectors $_\lambda u$ and $_\mu u$ are orthogonal, $\sin \alpha = 1$.

Further, by the properties of Riemann's symbols of the first kind,

$$(ij, hk) = -(ji, hk) = -(ij, kh) = (ji, kh).$$

We therefore see that, when $\lambda = \mu$, the expression just given for $K_{(\lambda \mu)}$ vanishes.

Denote now by $\overset{n(n-1)/2}{\underset{1}{\Sigma_{(\lambda \mu)}}} K_{(\lambda \mu)}$ the sum of the Riemannian curvatures of all possible sections of the manifold which are defined by the lines $_\lambda u$ ($\lambda = 1, 2, \dots n$), taken two by two. We shall have, by reason of the identities just given,

$$2 \overset{n(n-1)/2}{\underset{1}{\Sigma_{(\lambda \mu)}}} K_{(\lambda \mu)} = \underset{ijhk}{\Sigma} (ij, hk) \overset{n}{\underset{1}{\Sigma_{\lambda \mu}}} {}_\lambda u^i {}_\lambda u^k {}_\mu u^j {}_\mu u^h$$

$$= \underset{ijhk}{\Sigma} (ij, hk) g^{ik} g^{jh}.$$

If, then, for n-dimensional space we take the definitions already given in § 115 when $n = 4$, namely

$$G_{ik} = \underset{jh}{\Sigma} g^{jh} (ij, hk) \qquad \text{and} \qquad G = \underset{ik}{\Sigma} g^{ik} G_{ik},$$

we shall have

$$\underset{(\lambda \mu)}{\Sigma} K_{(\lambda \mu)} = \tfrac{1}{2} G.$$

Thus $\underset{(\lambda \mu)}{\Sigma} K_{(\lambda \mu)}$ is an invariant: it is independent of the particular set of mutually orthogonal straight lines with which we started.

Let us now form the sum of the Riemannian curvatures of the $(n-1)$ sections of the manifold which are defined by a definite vector $_\rho u$ in combination with a perpendicular vector $_\lambda u$, where λ has any value $1, 2, \dots n$, except ρ. Such a sum will be

$$\overset{n}{\underset{\substack{\lambda = 1 \\ \lambda \neq \rho}}{\Sigma}} K_{(\rho \lambda)} = \underset{ijhk}{\Sigma} (ij, hk) \overset{n}{\underset{\substack{\lambda = 1 \\ \lambda \neq \rho}}{\Sigma}} {}_\rho u^i {}_\rho u^k {}_\lambda u^j {}_\lambda u^h.$$

Since the expression on the right-hand side vanishes when $\lambda = \rho$, we have

$$\overset{n}{\underset{\substack{\lambda = 1 \\ \lambda \neq \rho}}{\Sigma}} K_{(\rho \lambda)} = \underset{ijhk}{\Sigma} (ij, hk) {}_\rho u^i {}_\rho u^k g^{jh}$$

$$= \underset{ik}{\Sigma} G_{ik} {}_\rho u^i {}_\rho u^k.$$

Hence the sum of the Riemannian curvatures corresponding to those sections which are formed by $(n-1)$ mutually orthogonal straight lines, in the $(n-1)$-dimensional space orthogonal to the line u^i $(i = 1, 2, \ldots n)$, will be

$$\tfrac{1}{2}G - \sum_{ik} G_{ik}u^i u^k,$$

or

$$- \sum_{ik} (G_{ik} - \tfrac{1}{2}Gg_{ik})u^i u^k.$$

This expression is the sum of the Riemannian curvatures of sections formed by mutually orthogonal lines in the $(n-1)$-dimensional section of the world at right angles to the direction of the vector u. It is equal to $\tfrac{1}{2}G_{(n-1)}$, where $G_{(n-1)}$ is the invariant G of the $(n-1)$-dimensional section, and is consequently independent of the particular orthogonal system drawn in that world.

Let us take, in an n-ple manifold for which $ds^2 < 0$, $G_{(n)} = n(n-1)/R^2_n$; and further let us call R_n *the radius of spherical curvature* of the manifold. Then the radius of spherical curvature of an $(n-1)$-ple manifold will be a quantity R defined by

$$G_{(n-1)} = (n-1)(n-2)/R^2,$$

where $G_{(n-1)}$ is the invariant of the manifold. When the $(n-1)$-ple manifold takes the special form of a hypersphere in n-dimensional Euclidean space

$$x_1^2 + \ldots + x_n^2 = \rho^2,$$

it is readily seen, by an extension of the results obtained in §§ 70, 71, that for it

$$G_{(n-1)} = (n-1)(n-2)/\rho^2.$$

We therefore have $\rho = R$. This fact explains the origin of the term 'radius of spherical curvature'.

We can directly prove that $\rho = R$ from our knowledge that the line-element of the hypersphere is given by

$$- ds^2 = dx_1^2 + \ldots + dx^2_{n-1} - \frac{(x_1 dx_1 + \ldots + x_{n-1}dx_{n-1})^2}{x_1^2 + \ldots + x^2_{n-1} - R^2}.$$

With such a definition we can say that the radius of spherical curvature of the $(n-1)$-dimensional space orthogonal to the vector u will be a quantity R given by

$$\frac{(n-1)(n-2)}{2R^2} = - \sum_{ik} (G_{ik} - \tfrac{1}{2}Gg_{ik})u^i u^k.$$

This $(n-1)$-dimensional space is a section of the n-ple manifold made by a plane perpendicular to the vector u; and, if we like, we may speak of R as the radius of spherical curvature in the direction of u. Take now the quadric

$$-\sum_{1}^{n}{}_{ik}(G_{ik} - \tfrac{1}{2}Gg_{ik})x_ix_k = \frac{(n-1)(n-2)}{2}, \qquad \ldots\ldots(Q)$$

and imagine it to exist in Euclidean space of n dimensions. The radius of the quadric in a direction from the origin to the point $(x_1, \ldots x_n)$ will be given by putting $Ru^i = x_i$. Consequently the radius of the quadric in any direction is equal to the radius of spherical curvature of the manifold in that direction.

We can immediately apply this result to interpret in terms of curvature Einstein's gravitational equations at a point of space-time where there is neither matter nor energy nor an electro-magnetic field.

We have at such a point, as we have seen,

$$n = 4, \qquad G = 4\lambda, \qquad G_{ik} = \lambda g_{ik}.$$

Hence the quadric (Q) becomes

$$\sum_{1}^{4}{}_{ik}g_{ik}\lambda u^i u^k = 3/R^2.$$

But $u^i = \dfrac{dx_i}{ds}$, and therefore $R = \sqrt{3/\lambda}$.

Thus Einstein's gravitational equations lead to the conclusion that, *at any particular point where space-time is empty, the radius of spherical curvature of any three-dimensional section of space-time is of constant length* $\sqrt{3/\lambda}$. In obtaining this result we have assumed that $ds^2 < 0$, so that, as in Minkowski's world, imaginary time is represented by a real axis.

It must not, of course, be thought that the result just obtained shews that the Riemannian curvature is the same in all directions at any point of the space-time continuum for which $T_{ik} = 0$. Were this true, empty space-time in the vicinity of matter would be homogeneous and isotropic. It is, in fact, curved; and the effects of its curvature appear as gravitation.

But in empty space-time the curvature is of a limited type. At any point we can take four mutually orthogonal directions. What we have shewn is that, if we take a section of space-time perpendicular to any one of these axes, the sum of the three curvatures within it made by sections defined by the other three axes taken two by two will be a constant. Let the four mutually orthogonal directions be denoted by

1, 2, 3, 4; and let (rs) denote the Riemannian curvature of the section of space-time made by the directions r and s. Then

$$(12) + (13) + (23) = 3/R^2,$$
$$(21) + (41) + (24) = 3/R^2,$$
$$(31) + (41) + (34) = 3/R^2,$$
$$(23) + (42) + (43) = 3/R^2.$$

Hence $\qquad (12) = (34), \qquad (13) = (24), \qquad (14) = (23),$

and $\qquad \dfrac{(12) + (13) + (14)}{3} = 1/R^2.$

Thus at any point of empty space-time, for which imaginary time is represented by a real axis, the Riemannian curvatures, corresponding to opposite pairs of any set of four mutually orthogonal directions, are equal; and the mean of the three curvatures which thus arise is $1/R^2$, where R is the radius of spherical curvature of any three-dimensional section of the manifold.

de Sitter's cosmos.

Suppose that at any particular point of empty space-time the Riemannian curvature K is the same in all directions. At the point space will be homogeneous and isotropic; and therefore matter, radiation and the origin of any possible electro-magnetic field must be infinitely distant.

By the fundamental equation of § 68 we shall have at such a point

$$- (ij, hk) = K (g_{ih}g_{jk} - g_{ik}g_{jh}),$$

the minus sign being inserted since $ds^2 < 0$ if t be a purely imaginary quantity. Hence, by the definition of the Einstein world-tensor (§ 115), we have $\qquad G_{ik} = - \sum_{jh} g^{jh} K (g_{ih}g_{jk} - g_{ik}g_{jh})$

$$= - K \sum_{j} (g_i^j g_{jk} - g_{ik}g_j^j) = 3g_{ik}K.$$

We shall therefore have $G_{ik} = \lambda g_{ik}$, provided $K = \lambda/3$. Thus, as de Sitter was the first to shew, Einstein's gravitational equations are satisfied by an isotropic space-time cosmos which is everywhere empty, and the Riemannian curvature of this cosmos will be $\lambda/3$ or $G/12$.

We shall give further consideration to de Sitter's cosmos in § 140.

§ 126. *The justification of Einstein's gravitational equations.*

Although the considerations by which we have been led to formulate Einstein's gravitational equations are more than merely plausible, yet they are not absolutely cogent; and the actual justification of the equations must be sought for in the correspondence between physical observation and the conclusions to which the equations lead. As is well known, Einstein pointed out three physical phenomena in which minute differences might serve to determine whether his gravitational scheme or that of Newton was the more accurate. The divergent consequences of the two theories differ so little that it must be admitted that there is still some slight doubt as to whether the superiority of the Einstein approximation has been proved in all three cases. There are, however, few men of science who doubt its ultimate experimental vindication.

A statical gravitational field in Euclidean space.

We will first of all shew that, for a statical gravitational field of potential ϕ in flat space of three dimensions, the space-time equations of a particle moving freely take, where terms in $1/c^2$ are ignored, the usual form of classical mechanics

$$\frac{d^2x_l}{dt^2} = \frac{\partial\phi}{\partial x_l}, \qquad l = 1, 2, 3;$$

and that Einstein's gravitational equations lead to Poisson's equation

$$\sum_{l=1}^{3} \frac{\partial^2\phi}{\partial x_l^2} = -4\pi\gamma\rho,$$

provided $\vartheta = 8\pi\gamma/c^4$, where c is the velocity of light, and γ is the Newtonian gravitational constant.

We assume, in the first place, that the metric of our space-time is given by

$$ds^2 = f^2 dx_0^2 - dx_1^2 - dx_2^2 - dx_3^2,$$

where f is a function of x_1, x_2 and x_3, but not of x_0, and where $x_0 = ct$.

A particle moving freely in such space-time will traverse a geodesic. Hence the equations of its path will be, by § 55,

$$\frac{d^2x_l}{ds^2} + \sum_{0}^{3}\{ik, l\}\frac{dx_i}{ds}\frac{dx_k}{ds} = 0, \qquad l = 0, 1, 2, 3.$$

We can readily calculate Christoffel's symbols $\{ik, l\}$ for space with the given metric, and the equations of the path become

$$\frac{d^2x_l}{ds^2} + ff_l\left(\frac{dx_0}{ds}\right)^2 = 0, \qquad \text{when } l > 0, \qquad \dots\dots(1)$$

and

$$\frac{d^2x_0}{ds^2} + 2\sum_{k=1}^{3}\frac{f_k}{f}\frac{dx_0}{ds}\frac{dx_k}{ds} = 0, \qquad \dots\dots(2)$$

where

$$f_l = \frac{\partial f}{\partial x_l}.$$

Put now $f = 1 - \phi/c^2$, where ϕ is independent of x_0; and assume that c is a very large quantity such that terms in $1/c^2$ will ultimately be ignored. Then equation (1) becomes

$$\frac{d^2 x_l}{ds^2} = \frac{1}{c^2} \frac{\partial \phi}{\partial x_l} \left(\frac{dx_0}{ds}\right)^2 + \text{smaller terms};$$

or, in the limit, $\qquad \dfrac{d^2 x_l}{dt^2} = \dfrac{\partial \phi}{\partial x_l}, \qquad l = 1, 2, 3.$

Equation (2) may be written

$$f \frac{d}{ds}\left(\frac{dx_0}{ds}\right) + 2 \frac{df}{ds}\frac{dx_0}{ds} = 0,$$

so that $f^2 \dfrac{dx_0}{ds} = $ a constant, $1/k$ (say).

If now v be the velocity of the particle

$$\frac{v^2}{c^2} = \frac{dx_1{}^2 + dx_2{}^2 + dx_3{}^2}{dx_0{}^2}.$$

We have, therefore, accurately,

$$k^2 f^4 = f^2 - v^2/c^2.$$

Put now $f^2 = 1 - 2\phi/c^2$ and $k = 1 - a/c^2$ and we obtain, in the limit when terms of order $1/c^2$ are ignored,

$$\tfrac{1}{2}v^2 = \phi + a,$$

the equation of *vis viva*. This result, combined with that just reached, shews that ϕ is the potential of the field of force in which the particle moves.

We proceed next to shew that, for pseudo-Euclidean space-time of a metric approximating to

$$ds^2 = f^2 dx_0{}^2 - dx_1{}^2 - dx_2{}^2 - dx_3{}^2,$$

where $x_0 = ct$ and $f^2 = 1 - 2\phi/c^2$, Einstein's gravitational equations lead to Poisson's equation.

For space which is rigidly Euclidean at infinity λ must vanish by §125. Moreover, Poisson's equation applies to a medium in which material stresses are ignored, so that, as has been seen in §122, T/c^2 is equal to the 'proper' density, or statical invariant-mass density, at any point for which it is calculated. If ρ be this proper density, $T = c^2 \rho$.

Einstein's gravitational equations, if we use the formula $G - 4\lambda = \vartheta T$ of §125, and then put $\lambda = 0$, may be written

$$G_{ik} = -\vartheta\{T_{ik} - \tfrac{1}{2}g_{ik}T\}, \qquad\qquad \ldots\ldots(3)$$

where $i, k = 0, 1, 2, 3$.

Now in § 122 we obtained the stress-tensor for a perfect fluid, at rest in space-time of a type including that now under consideration. It yields $T_{00} = c^2 \rho f^2$. Moreover, by the algebraical results obtained in § 115, we have approximately

$$G_{00} = -f \sum_{l=1}^{3} \frac{\partial^2 f}{\partial x_l^2}.$$

Thus the identity (3) leads, for $i = k = 0$, to

$$\sum_{l=1}^{3} \frac{2}{f} \frac{\partial^2 f}{\partial x_l^2} = \vartheta c^2 \rho. \qquad \ldots\ldots(4)$$

Put now $f = 1 - \phi/c^2$ and ignore all but primary terms. We deduce from equation (4) that

$$\sum_{l=1}^{3} \frac{\partial^2 \phi}{\partial x_l^2} = -\frac{\vartheta c^4 \rho}{2}.$$

We thus obtain Poisson's equation

$$\sum_{l=1}^{3} \frac{\partial^2 \phi}{\partial x_l^2} = -4\pi\rho\gamma, \text{ provided } \vartheta = 8\pi\gamma/c^4.$$

The use of G_{00} just adopted enables us to escape the consequences of the fact that, in the expression for ds^2, our space-coefficients, owing to the presence of matter, may differ from -1 by quantities of order $1/c^2$. Product terms of the same order may also occur.

In having thus obtained the value of ϑ we have completed Einstein's gravitational equations: we have further shewn that, when terms in $1/c^2$ are ignored, these equations reduce to those of the Newtonian theory. It was to have been expected that ϑ would be a very small quantity when measured in our ordinary units. When these are the centimetre, gramme and second, we have (as we shall see in § 234)

$$\gamma = 6\cdot 7 \times 10^{-8}; \text{ and we know that } c = 3 \times 10^{10}.$$

Thus $\vartheta = 2 \times 10^{-48}$, approximately.

§ 127. *The problem of two bodies is insoluble in Einsteinian dynamics.*

The difficulty of working with the Einstein equations in the general case when the g's involve the time-coordinate is very great. Hence applications of them must be limited to cases where the analysis assumes a relatively simple form. We cannot, for instance, use Einstein's equations to obtain the relative motions of two approximately equal bodies influencing one another. In fact, in Einsteinian dynamics the problem of two bodies is as difficult as the problem of three bodies in classical mechanics.

We can, however, obtain from Einstein's equations the metric of space under the sole influence of a symmetrical particle. Then, somewhat paradoxically, we treat the sun as though it were this particle and regard a planet moving round the sun as of negligible mass. We can thus obtain a modified form of the familiar ellipse of planetary motion given by classical mechanics. The analysis may be briefly indicated.

§128. *The gravitational field of an isolated particle.*

We first of all consider what form ds^2 must take under statical conditions when we have spherical symmetry in space-time, the isolated particle being at the origin of our spatial coordinates. We begin by proving, as in Lecture IV, that for three-dimensional space symmetrical round a point the most general expression for the line-element is given by

$$dl^2 = g^2 dx_1^2 + x_1^2 dx_2^2 + x_1^2 \sin^2 x_2 dx_3^2,$$

where g is a function of x_1 only, and where x_1, x_2, x_3 are coordinates which reduce to polar coordinates for Euclidean space. We then make the assumption that the interval-element in the space-time surrounding the isolated particle is of the form

$$ds^2 = f^2 dx_0^2 - dl^2,$$

where f is a function of x_1 only. The assumption is justified by the fact that we are dealing with a *statical* phenomenon which has spherical symmetry in space.

Clearly the gravitational field, that is to say the disturbance of Galilean space-time due to a particle, diminishes indefinitely as we pass away from the particle. We may therefore conclude that f and g both tend to unity as x_1 tends to infinity, if we so choose x_0, our unit of time, in such a way that $c = 1$. We shall, of course, have $x_0 = ct$, when t is expressed in seconds.

Now, in a region of space-time containing neither matter nor energy, we have seen in §125 that Einstein's gravitational equations take the form $G_{ik} = \lambda g_{ik}$. If then we assume that λ vanishes (so that space-time is flat at infinity), Einstein's equations will take the form $G_{ik} = 0$.

Suppose now that

$$dl^2 = g^2 dx_1^2 + x_1^2 dx_2^2 + x_1^2 \sin^2 x_2 dx_3^2$$

is the form taken by the general line-element of three-dimensional space

$$ds^2 = \Sigma a_{ik} dx_i dx_k.$$

Then, as in §115, we can readily prove that the world tensor-components of this space all vanish except

$$A_{11} = -\frac{2}{x_1} g'/g; \qquad A_{22} = 1/g^2 - x_1 g'/g^3 - 1; \qquad A_{33} = \sin^2 x_2 A_{22},$$

where $g' = \dfrac{dg}{dx_1}$, g being a function of x_1 only. Hence, by the general result of §115, the Einstein tensor-components for

$$ds^2 = f^2 dx_0{}^2 - g^2 dx_1{}^2 - x_1{}^2 dx_2{}^2 - x_1{}^2 \sin^2 x_2 dx_3{}^2,$$

when f and g are functions of x_1 only, all vanish except

$$G_{00} = \frac{-f}{g x_1{}^2} \frac{d}{dx_1}\left(\frac{x_1{}^2}{g} f'\right),$$

$$G_{11} = f''/f - f'g'/fg - 2g'/x_1 g,$$

$$G_{22} = x_1 f'/fg^2 + 1/g^2 - x_1 g'/g^3 - 1,$$

$$G_{33} = \sin^2 x_2 G_{22}.$$

The equations $G_{ik} = 0$, for $i, k = 0, 1, 2, 3$, therefore reduce to

$$\frac{d}{dx_1}(x_1{}^2 f'/g) = 0 \qquad \text{or} \qquad f'' + \frac{2}{x_1} f' - \frac{g'f'}{g} = 0; \quad \text{......(1)}$$

$$f'' - \frac{2fg'}{x_1 g} - \frac{g'f'}{g} = 0; \qquad\qquad \text{......(2)}$$

and

$$f'/f = g'/g + (g^2 - 1)/x_1. \qquad\qquad \text{......(3)}$$

From (1) and (2) $\qquad\qquad f'/f + g'/g = 0,$

or, integrating, $\qquad fg = l$, where l is a constant.

Now $f \to 1$ and $g \to 1$ when $x_1 \to \infty$. Therefore $l = 1$ and $f = 1/g$. Hence by equation (3)

$$2g'/g = -(g^2 - 1)/x_1.$$

Whence, integrating, if m be a constant of integration,

$$f^2 = 1/g^2 = 1 - 2m/x_1.$$

Thus we finally obtain, as the line-element of our gravitational field,

$$ds^2 = \mu\, dx_0{}^2 - \mu^{-1} dr^2 - r^2 d\theta^2 - r^2 \sin^2\theta\, d\phi^2,$$

where $\mu = 1 - 2m/r$, m being a constant of integration. This is the well-known metric of the gravitational field of an isolated particle which was first given by Schwarzschild in the year 1916.

It is clear that when $\mu = 1$, ds^2 becomes Galilean. In general, however, when m does not vanish, the flatness of space-time is modified in two ways: first, by the fact that μ is the coefficient of $x_0{}^2 = c^2 dt^2$; and in the second place, because $-1/\mu$ is the coefficient of dr^2. Inasmuch as c is large, it is fairly obvious that the main deviation from flat space-time arises from the presence of μ as the coefficient of $c^2 dt^2$.

§129.　*Einstein's equations for the orbit of a planet moving round the sun.*

　　The motion of a particle of negligible mass round the gravitational particle which we have been considering will be determined by finding the equations of a geodesic in space-time which has Schwarzschild's metric. These equations can be written

$$\frac{d^2 x_l}{ds^2} + \sum_{0}^{3}{}_{ik}\{ik, l\}\frac{dx_i}{ds}\frac{dx_k}{ds} = 0,$$

where $l = 0, 1, 2, 3$.

　　Straightforward algebra leads to the equations

$$\frac{d^2 x_0}{ds^2} + 2\frac{f'}{f}\frac{dx_0}{ds}\frac{dx_1}{ds} = 0, \qquad\qquad\qquad\qquad \text{......(1)}$$

$$\frac{d^2 x_1}{ds^2} + \frac{ff'}{g^2}\left(\frac{dx_0}{ds}\right)^2 + \frac{g'}{g}\left(\frac{dx_1}{ds}\right)^2 - \frac{x_1}{g^2}\left(\frac{dx_2}{ds}\right)^2 - \frac{x_1 \sin^2 x_2}{g^2}\left(\frac{dx_3}{ds}\right)^2 = 0, \text{......(2)}$$

$$\frac{d^2 x_2}{ds^2} + \frac{2}{x_1}\frac{dx_1}{ds}\frac{dx_2}{ds} - \sin x_2 \cos x_2 \left(\frac{dx_3}{ds}\right)^2 = 0, \qquad\qquad \text{......(3)}$$

$$\frac{d^2 x_3}{ds^2} + \frac{2}{x_1}\frac{dx_1}{ds}\frac{dx_3}{ds} + 2\cot x_2 \frac{dx_2}{ds}\frac{dx_3}{ds} = 0. \qquad\qquad \text{......(4)}$$

Without limiting our problem we can assume that the particle starts from rest in the plane $x_2 = \pi/2$. Then the third equation just written shews that it will remain continually in this plane. Assume then that $x_2 = \pi/2$, continually. Integrating equations (1) and (4) we get

$$f^2 \frac{dx_0}{ds} = k \qquad \text{and} \qquad x_1{}^2 \frac{dx_3}{ds} = h,$$

where h and k are constants. Substituting in equation (2) we have, after an obvious reduction,

$$\frac{d^2 x_1}{ds^2} + \frac{m}{x_1{}^2} = \frac{h^2}{x_1{}^3}\left\{1 - 3\frac{m}{x_1}\right\}.$$

Put now $x_1 = 1/u$ and $x_3 = \phi$. Then the equations of our geodesic are

$$\frac{d^2 u}{d\phi^2} + u = \frac{m}{h^2} + 3mu^2, \qquad \frac{d\phi}{ds} = hu^2.$$

These, then, are the equations which determine the motion round the sun of a planet of negligible mass on the assumption that Einstein's gravitational theory is true. They may be compared with the usual equations of an orbit in classical Newtonian dynamics, namely

$$\frac{d^2u}{d\phi^2} + u = \frac{m}{h^2}, \qquad \text{coupled with} \qquad \frac{d\phi}{dt} = hu^2.$$

§130. *The justification of Einstein's gravitational equations. The motion of the perihelion of Mercury.*

It will be seen that the differences between the two sets of equations just given are small. We first of all deduce from the comparison of the two equations that m, which originally arose as a constant of integration, is actually the expression of the mass of the attracting sun when the gravitational constant is unity and the unit of time is so chosen that $c = 1$.

Now to a first approximation $ds = c\,dt$. If, then, M be the mass of the sun in ordinary units, γ the measure of the Newtonian constant of gravitation (§126), and c the velocity of light, we shall have

$$m = \gamma M / c^2.$$

In the next place we notice that the addition of $3mu^2$ to m/h^2 in the first equation is an alteration of ratio

$$3h^2u^2 = 3\left(r\frac{d\phi}{ds}\right)^2.$$

For normal planetary speeds this is an extremely small quantity of the order of the inverse square of the velocity of light. The only other difference between the two pairs of equations is that ds is replaced by dt. The meaning of this is difficult to define, as we do not know exactly what dt means in Newtonian dynamics. In fact, Newton's law of the inverse square, when the refinements of relativity-mechanics are introduced, becomes elusive: we need to know more accurately how mass and interval are defined than was contemplated by Newton. Clearly, however, the Einstein gravitational equations lead in the case of planetary motion to results which differ only infinitesimally from those consequent on Newton's law of the inverse square.

So infinitesimal is the discrepancy that it is difficult to find an observation which will decide between the two systems. Such an observation is, however, given by the motion of the perihelion of Mercury, the perihelion being the point on the orbit of the planet nearest to the sun. According to Newton's law, Mercury, if undisturbed, would move round the sun in an ellipse so that, if no other planets were to disturb its motion, it would repeat the same path *ad infinitum*. According to

Einstein's law, the path is an ellipse which fails to close up: as a result its axis slowly revolves. When account is taken of all disturbing influences, there was on the classical theory a motion in longitude of the perihelion of Mercury of 42 seconds of arc per century which could not be accounted for. If calculations be made according to Einstein's law, this discrepancy is almost accurately eliminated.

§ 131. *The bending of rays of light near the sun.*

A second test of the truth of Einstein's assumption is furnished by the passage of light near the sun. Light consists of the transference of energy through space: it, therefore, has momentum and, in fact, its pressure can, as we shall see in a subsequent lecture, be measured by sufficiently delicate instruments. Light must therefore, like any material body, be subject to gravitation. In Schwarzschild's metric it will travel along a geodesic for which $ds = 0$. We can, therefore, obtain on Einstein's assumptions the equations giving the path of a ray of light which passes near the sun. Since $ds = 0$, we shall have in the previous investigation $1/h = 0$. Hence the path of a ray of light is given by the equation

$$\frac{d^2u}{d\phi^2} + u = 3mu^2, \qquad \text{where} \qquad u = 1/r.$$

We recall that, if M be the measure of the sun's mass in ordinary units, $m = \gamma M/c^2$. We shall then treat the term $3mu^2$ as small, this being in accordance with the fact that, because of the very rapid velocity of light, its path is approximately a straight line.

If we ignore the term $3mu^2$ we obtain, as a solution of the differential equation which has been obtained,

$$u = a \cos(\phi - \epsilon),$$

where a and ϵ are constants of integration. The constant a will be the maximum value of u; and, if the ray of light just graze the sun, it will, to a first approximation, be equal to $1/R$, where R is the radius of the sun.

Substituting the value of u just found, we obtain as a further approximation the solution

$$u/a = \cos(\phi - \epsilon) + ma\{1 + \sin^2(\phi - \epsilon)\},$$

in which terms involving $(ma)^2$ and higher powers are neglected.

If now we put

$$x = r\cos(\phi - \epsilon), \qquad y = r\sin(\phi - \epsilon),$$

and remember that $r = 1/u$, we shall obtain

$$x = 1/a - ma\{r + y^2/r\}$$

as an approximation to the curve in which a ray of light is bent as it passes round the sun.

The asymptotes to this curve are the lines

$$x = 1/a - 2may, \qquad y > 0,$$
$$x = 1/a + 2may, \qquad y < 0.$$

The angle between these lines is

$$2\tan^{-1} 2ma,$$

or approximately $4ma$.

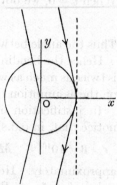

Hence the deflection of a ray of light which just grazes the sun's disc is, in ordinary units, if we accept the conclusions of the general theory of relativity, $\qquad 4\gamma M/c^2 R,$

where R, which to a first approximation is equal to $1/a$, is the radius of the sun.

Suppose now that we consider, according to the rules of classical mechanics, the deflection of a light-particle moving, with initial velocity c from infinity, in a curve round the sun.

The particle will describe a hyperbola whose equations will be given by

$$\frac{d^2u}{d\phi^2} + u = \frac{\gamma M}{h^2}, \qquad \phi = hu^2.$$

Integrating, we have $\left(\dfrac{du}{d\phi}\right)^2 + u^2 = 2\gamma M u/h^2 + K$, where K is a constant. The velocity at any point will be v, where $v^2/h^2 = \left(\dfrac{du}{d\phi}\right)^2 + u^2$. When $u = 0$, $v = c$; and therefore $K = c^2/h^2$. Hence

$$\left\{\left(\frac{du}{d\phi}\right)^2 + u^2\right\} h^2 = 2u\gamma M + c^2.$$

If then the orbit be

$$u = a\cos(\phi - \epsilon) + \gamma M/h^2,$$

we shall get, on substitution,

$$a^2 = \gamma^2 M^2/h^4 + c^2/h^2.$$

When $1/a$ is the radius of the sun, $m = \gamma M/c^2$ will be small compared with $1/a$. Moreover, $(c/h)^2$ must be positive. We may thus neglect the first term on the right-hand side of this equation for h and, to a first approximation, we may put $a = c/h$.

Thus, approximately, the hyperbola, of which a branch is described by the particle of light, has for its equation

$$u = a \cos(\phi - \epsilon) + \gamma M a^2/c^2.$$

When $u = 0$, we obtain

$$\cos(\phi - \epsilon) = -\gamma M a/c^2.$$

Thus the angle between the asymptotes of this hyperbola is $2\gamma M a/c^2$.

Hence the bending of a ray of light, according to Einstein's theory, is twice as much as would be predicted by Newton's classical mechanics on the assumption that light, being a form of energy, has mass.

In justification of the approximations which we have made, we notice that, in c.g.s. units,

$$c = 3 \times 10^{10}, \qquad M = 2 \times 10^{33}, \qquad R = 7 \times 10^{10}, \qquad \gamma = 6 \cdot 7 \times 10^{-8},$$

approximately. Hence $m = \gamma M/c^2 = 1 \cdot 5 \times 10^5$, and the maximum value of $mu^2 = m/R^2 = 3 \times 10^{-17}$.

Einstein's value of the angle of bending of a ray of light which just grazes the sun

$$= 4\gamma M/c^2 R \text{ radians}$$
$$= 8 \cdot 5 \times 10^{-6} \text{ radians.}$$

The numerical value of this angle is $1 \cdot 7$ in seconds of arc. It is evident that to measure such a small angle we need exceptional circumstances and, in particular, the sun must be obscured as at a total eclipse. Measurements made by British astronomers at the total eclipse of the year 1919 gave results in fairly close agreement with expectation.

§132. *The spectrum-shift due to a strong gravitational field.*

The third discrimination between Newtonian and modern gravitational assumptions is provided by the displacement of the lines in the spectrum which correspond to definite vibrations of assigned atoms. An atom may be regarded as a little clock; and an atom on the sun is a clock placed in a strong gravitational field. For the space-time interval corresponding to a single, complete and very short vibration of such a clock at rest at a point P, we must put

$$dr = d\theta = d\phi = 0$$

in Schwarzschild's metric, since r, θ and ϕ are unchanged as a result of the particular vibration. We thus get $ds_P^2 = \gamma_P dt_P^2$, where dt_P and ds_P are elements of time and of interval respectively at the point P, and where γ_P is the value of $1 - 2m/r$ at P.

Similarly, for a vibration of an atom, chemically alike to the former and in a similar physical state, at another point Q, we should have

$$ds_Q{}^2 = \gamma_Q dt_Q{}^2.$$

Suppose now that the atoms are in different fields of force, one being, for example, on the earth and the other on the sun. We may legitimately assume that the space-time interval would be the same for both*, so that

$$ds_P = ds_Q.$$

We should therefore have

$$\sqrt{\gamma_P}\,dt_P = \sqrt{\gamma_Q}\,dt_Q.$$

This result means that the times of vibration of the differently placed atoms vary inversely as $\sqrt{\gamma}$. Corresponding to the varying times of vibration we must have a small displacement in the spectrum. This displacement will be the same wherever it is seen (provided there is no Doppler effect†) inasmuch as the time-interval between two successive light-rays does not change as they pass through Schwarzschild's metric, of which the coefficients do not contain t. But, unfortunately, the displacement is very small when we compare an atom on the sun with a corresponding atom on the earth, and experimental results from such comparison are so far not decisive. A shift, however, has been measured for the 'white dwarf' companion to Sirius: and the result agrees satisfactorily with expectation (*vide* § 259 *infra*).

§ 133. *Gravitation is due to the warping of space-time.*

Enough, however, has now been said to shew that Einstein's law of gravitation must replace that of Newton. The result is highly significant. Apart from the fact that Newton's law required more adequate definition before it could be deemed satisfactory, it was a law of action at a distance and, as such, a scandal to reflective thought. Newton felt this: and, in the third of his *Four Letters to Bentley*, which was written in February of the year 1693, said‡ "that gravity should be innate, inherent, and essential to matter, so that one body may act upon another at a distance through a *vacuum*, without the mediation of anything else, by and through which their action and force may be conveyed from one to another, is to me so great an absurdity, that I

---

* A. S. Eddington considers in detail the possibility that this assumption is untrue. See *Space, Time and Gravitation*, pp. 131, 132.

† The Doppler effect is discussed in § 191 *infra*.

‡ Richard Bentley, *Works*, vol. III, Sermons preached at Boyle's Lecture; etc. Edited by Dyce. Macpherson, 1838, p. 212. Newton's *Four Letters to Bentley* were first published in the year 1756.

believe no man, who has in philosophical matters a competent faculty of thinking, can ever fall into it. Gravity must be caused by an agent acting constantly according to certain laws; but whether this agent be material or immaterial, I have left to the consideration of my readers ".

Newton so far as we know, never indicated what, in his opinion, was the nature of the agent causing gravity. Einstein has made it clear that this 'agent' is none other than the warping of space-time. In the neighbourhood of matter space-time deviates from its normal flatness (or, if λ be not zero, from its normal constant curvature) and becomes warped. Matter, as it were, thus gives rise to little hummocks on the smooth surface of space-time. It is these hummocks which cause the phenomena interpreted by us as gravitation. Particles moving in warped space-time take the shortest (or longest) path possible, when account is taken of the warping, and thus appear to move subject to gravitational influences.

§134. *The law of gravitation is a disguised identity.*

The astonishing thing about Einstein's equations is that they appear to have come out of nothing. In deducing them we have, first of all, assumed that the interval-element ds is such that its square is a quadratic function of the differentials of the space-time coordinates. We have further assumed that the laws of nature must be capable of expression in a form which is invariant for all possible transformations of the space-time coordinates. But, so far as can be seen, no other assumption has been made; and yet *from this exiguous basis we deduce formulae of gravitation more accurate than those given by Newton's law of the inverse square.*

The conclusion seems to be irresistible that such laws of nature as the principle of conservation of energy, the principle of conservation of momentum and the law of gravitation *are necessary consequences of our modes of measurement.* They are, in fact, elaborately disguised identities which could have been predicted *à priori* by a being of sufficiently powerful analytical insight who fully understood all that is implied in the way in which we measure space-time intervals.

§135. *Our measures of matter and momentum are determined by the warping of space-time.*

A further conclusion is equally significant. In forming the quantity T_{ik} we took, at the beginning of §121,

$$T_{00} = c^2 \rho \lambda_0{}^2,$$

and
$$T_{0i} = c^2 \rho \lambda_i \lambda_0, \qquad i = 1, 2, 3.$$

Thus these T's are expressions for energy-density and components of momentum-density. The modified forms of T_{ik}, which arise from the introduction of terms π_{ik}, will only differ, for Galilean space-time, from those just written down by terms involving $1/c$. They may be regarded as more accurate expressions for energy-density and components of momentum-density in media where shearing-stresses exist. But Einstein's equations (E) of § 124 give

$$- \vartheta T_{ik} = G_{ik} - \tfrac{1}{2} G g_{ik} + \lambda g_{ik}, \qquad i, k = 0, 1, 2, 3;$$

and, assuming that ϑ and λ are known constants, we thus express matter and momentum in terms of the g's. That is to say, *our measures of matter and momentum can be derived from the coefficients of potential which express the nature of the warping of space-time.* We do not say that matter and momentum themselves can be thus derived: in fact, we do not know what matter and momentum are in themselves apart from the measurements of them which we make. Our measures, it would appear, leave reality elusive.

We can seize on some of the aspects of matter in motion. These aspects are those to which the mind of man appears to attach especial importance: they are such as inertia, momentum and stress. Such consequences of the warping of space-time as have relative permanence, and can therefore be expressed by conservation theorems, seem to us especially significant. But why other aspects of energy in motion, equally amenable to mathematical representation, are not singled out in the same way is obscure. Einstein's triumph has, in short, revealed to us the extent of our ignorance.

Until comparatively recently there was a feeling, among those men of science who accepted the idea of the Divine ordering of the Universe, that we could see a manifestation of God's will in the great laws of physics. In the law of gravitation and in the great conservation laws of energy and momentum we could see how*

> Worlds His mighty voice obeyed:
> Laws which never shall be broken,
> For their guidance He hath made.

Then came Einstein. He led us forward and upward till 'silent upon a peak in Darien' we thought to gaze upon some new ocean which more fully should reflect the will of God. But all such hopes have been disappointed. It is true that from our new vantage ground we see more

---

* The lines come from a hymn which was apparently written at the end of the eighteenth century, when it is known to have been in use at the Foundling Hospital in London.

clearly; but, whereas we had thought to know less imperfectly the mind of God, we have apparently discovered that all the while we have merely been gazing into the mind of man.

The law of gravitation is, it would seem, a mere consequence of our mode of measurement. The law is of human origin, made by our minds, just in so far as we make the way in which we measure intervals. Possibly, of course, our very modes of measurement reflect the Divine will in the physical realm; but most certainly any knowledge of God we may thus get is very indirect and obscure. Thus, as regards some laws where we had thought that we saw God's will in the physical order, the general theory of relativity now shews us that we were mistaken. To many this will be a perturbing conclusion; but we of the new era who are pledged to put the search for truth above all else must not seek to evade a result of our search, even though it be a source alike of surprise and perplexity.

Let me again insist that possibly unsuspected assumptions have crept into the general theory, so that the part played by the mind of man is less than we at present feel forced to postulate. And, whatever the truth, let us not forget that the only foundations for any belief in God worth preserving must be discovered, not in inanimate nature, but in that moral order, emergent through animate nature, from which man's spiritual longings have been derived.

§ 136. *The position of the law of conservation of energy in Einsteinian mechanics.*

In general relativity-dynamics the position of the great conservation theorems of energy and momentum becomes of much interest. These theorems, when generalised so as to assume an invariant form, were written (§ 121)

$$\sum_{0}^{3}{}_k T_{ik}^{|k} = 0, \qquad i = 0, 1, 2, 3;$$

or, alternatively by § 116, we have the equations

$$\sum_{0}^{3}{}_k T_{i|k}^{k} = 0.$$

By algebraical manipulation these equations can, as we have seen at the end of § 116, be changed so as to assume the form

$$\sum_{0}^{3}{}_k \frac{1}{\sqrt{-g}} \frac{\partial}{\partial x_k} (T_i^k \sqrt{-g}) = \sum_{kl}^{3} \{ik, l\} T_l^k, \qquad \text{for } i = 0, 1, 2, 3,$$

where g is the fundamental determinant of the coefficients of potential. Put now
$$T_i^k \sqrt{-g} = \overline{T}_i^k.$$
Then the four equations which express the conservation of energy and momentum in Newtonian dynamics take, according to the theory of general relativity, the form

$$\sum_{0}^{3}{}_k \frac{\partial}{\partial x_k} \overline{T}_i^k = \sum_{0}^{3}{}_{kl} \{ik, l\} \overline{T}_l^k, \quad \text{where } i = 0, 1, 2, 3. \quad \ldots\ldots(A)$$

Now, if x_0, x_1, x_2, x_3 be general space-time coordinates, the expression
$$\sqrt{-g}\, dx_0 \ldots dx_3$$
behaves as if it were invariant in volume integration. By this we mean that, if the coordinates x_0, x_1, x_2, x_3 be changed in any way to new accented coordinates, the expression in volume integration becomes $\sqrt{-g'}\, dx_0' \ldots dx_3'$. The reason is that g'/g is proportional to the square of the Jacobian of transformation. Hence, if we wish to integrate a tensor component T_i^k through any volume of space-time, we must use the formula
$$\int T_i^k \sqrt{-g}\, dx_0 \ldots dx_3, \quad \text{or} \quad \int \overline{T}_i^k \, dx_0 \ldots dx_3.$$

Thus in Gaussian coordinates we can deal with the energy-tensor throughout a volume just as if our coordinates were Galilean provided we replace the components T_i^k by $\overline{T}_i^k$. Such quantities as $\overline{T}_i^k$ are called *tensor-densities*, because $\overline{T}_i^k dx_0 \ldots dx_3$ represents the quantity of the tensor T_i^k in the natural unit of volume $\sqrt{-g}\, dx_0 \ldots dx_3$.

Suppose now that instead of the equations (A) we had the more simple system
$$\sum_{0}^{3}{}_k \frac{\partial \overline{T}_i^k}{\partial x_k} = 0, \qquad i = 0, 1, 2, 3.$$

Let x_0 be the time-coordinate. Multiply the left-hand side of the foregoing equation by $dx_1 dx_2 dx_3$, and integrate through a definite region of three-dimensional space. The first term due to the integration will be
$$\frac{\partial}{\partial x_0} \int \overline{T}_i^0 \, dx_1 dx_2 dx_3,$$
and the other three terms will give surface integrals over the boundary of the region. Our equation thus tells us that time-changes in the integral
$$\int \overline{T}_i^0 \, dx_1 dx_2 dx_3,$$
taken throughout a region of three-dimensional space, can only result

from changes of $\overline{T}_i^k$ at the boundary of the region. In other words, the integral remains unaltered so long as there is no transmission across the boundary of the region for which it has been calculated. This is what we mean by the conservation of the integral. We thus see that, strictly speaking, *the theorems of conservation of energy and momentum are only true in generalised space-time when the expressions*

$$\overset{3}{\underset{0}{\Sigma}}_{kl}\{ik, l\}\,\overline{T}_l^k$$

vanish. In general, however, they only vanish when we have Galilean coordinates. These expressions are, in fact, pseudo-forces introduced by gravitational metrics and they are exactly analogous to the centrifugal forces which similarly arise from the choice of rotating axes.

That the law of conservation of energy would cease to have a satisfactory generalisation in Einsteinian mechanics could have been predicted at the start. In classical mechanics we preserved the law for gravitational forces by introducing the conception of potential energy, which is supposed to be energy stored up in the gravitational field. But such energy has no place as a physical quantity in a scheme in which gravitational forces result from the curvature of space-time and therefore vary as the coordinate system is changed.

A formal law of conservation can, however, be obtained from our equations

$$\overset{3}{\underset{0}{\Sigma}}_k T_{ik}^{|k} = 0, \qquad i = 0, 1, 2, 3.$$

It is possible to discover expressions $\bar{t}_i^k$ such that

$$\overset{3}{\underset{0}{\Sigma}}_{kl}\{ik, l\}\,\overline{T}_l^k = -\overset{3}{\underset{0}{\Sigma}}_k \frac{\partial}{\partial x_k}(\bar{t}_i^k), \qquad i = 0, 1, 2, 3.$$

If now we put $\overline{S}_i^k = \overline{T}_i^k + \bar{t}_i^k,$

we get $\overset{3}{\underset{0}{\Sigma}}_k \frac{\partial}{\partial x_k}(\overline{S}_i^k) = 0, \qquad i = 0, 1, 2, 3.$

This is a conservation equation and we may say that in it $\bar{t}_i^k$ represents a pseudo-tensor-density for *potential* energy, momentum and stress. In other words $t_i^k = \bar{t}_i^k / \sqrt{-g}$ represents the pseudo-energy, pseudo-momentum and pseudo-stress, due to the metric of space out of which the so-called gravitational forces arise. But the quantity $\bar{t}_i^k$ is not of the nature of a tensor, or of a tensor which has been multiplied by $\sqrt{-g}$, inasmuch as it can be made to vanish at any point by suitable choice of the coordinate system. We need, in fact, only take *geodesic* coordinates at the point, inasmuch as then, by § 63, we shall have $\{ik, l\} = 0$ at the point; and therefore $\bar{t}_i^k$ will vanish there.

The conclusion that $\bar{t}_i^k$ cannot be a tensor, or a tensor which has been multiplied by $\sqrt{-g}$, is confirmed by another fact. By means of the equations which express the quantities T_{ik} in terms of G_{ik} and g_{ik}, we can express $\bar{t}_i^k$ in terms of the coefficients of potential and their derivatives. From such expressions it can be shewn that, if we take curvilinear coordinates even in a world containing no gravitating matter, $\bar{t}_i^k$ will not vanish.

Thus the pseudo-energy-tensor t_i^k does not correspond to any physical entity: it is not truly analogous to the actual energy-tensor T_i^k.

. We see then that the law of conservation of energy can only be made to apply to gravitational fields by introducing the fiction of potential energy. If we wish to avoid such a fiction we shall begin with Joule's discovery and admit, in the first place, that energy includes not only kinetic energy of visible motion but also heat and molecular kinetic energy. Then from such energy and from matter in visible motion we shall construct the energy-tensor T_{ik}. Finally we shall generalise the law of conservation of energy for gravitational fields by saying that the divergence of this energy-tensor must everywhere vanish. Unfortunately, we thus get an abstraction which cannot in general be represented by concrete imagery; but such is the final outcome of many physical developments.

§ 137. *Is space finite?*

One of the most interesting enquiries which can engage the speculative thought of man is concerned with the extent of space. Is the Universe finite or indefinitely extended? Everyone would agree with Riemann that we must regard it as unbounded. But quite possibly space is slightly curved and so, though its total content is very great, that content is nevertheless finite. We have previously seen that Riemannian space is both possible and of this character.

It has been lately discovered that our own galactic universe—we shall describe its nature and extent in Lecture XI—is but one of many others which we see as spiral nebulae, and it may be that the whole aggregate of these universes constitutes, as it were, a finite island in infinite space. This is the natural assumption to make if we believe that space is Euclidean and therefore infinite in extent. Such an assumption, however, is most unsatisfactory, because we must then conclude that the radiation constantly emitted from the stars is as constantly passing away into the depths of space, where it is lost.

On any such assumption the whole Universe or cosmos*, as we shall call it, is either slowly losing all its heat or, if radiation results from the actual destruction of matter, it is slowly vanishing away. If, however, our space is Riemannian and finite, the energy lost as radiation will be contained within a finite region. It then becomes possible to speculate that within this region, at distances very remote from ourselves, radiation is being reformed into matter: at all events the matter of the cosmos is not being hopelessly dissipated.

§ 138. *The objection to a Newtonian-Euclidean cosmos.*

It might be urged that space is Euclidean, and that in it the distribution of matter is roughly uniform, so that, however far we could with our telescopes plumb the depths of space, we should find there aggregations of stars comparable to the distribution which exists in and near our galactic universe. But according to Newton's theory of gravitation, as the German astronomer Seeliger (1849–1924) emphasised, such a uniform distribution is impossible. On this theory, as is well known, the number of lines of force which come from infinity and end in a mass m is proportional to m.

Suppose, now, that we have a uniform mass-density ρ distributed throughout the cosmos. Then a sphere of volume V, with any centre whatsoever, will enclose a mass ρV. Hence the number of lines of force passing through the surface of the sphere to the mass within it will be proportional to ρV. Now the area of the sphere is proportional to R^2 and its volume is proportional to R^3. Therefore the number of lines of force which pass through a unit area of the sphere will be proportional to ρR. Thus the intensity of the gravitational field at the surface of the sphere must increase indefinitely as the sphere expands; and this is, since the sphere may have any centre, impossible.

§ 139. *Einstein's time-cylindrical cosmos.*

We thus reach the conclusion that our own space is probably finite and Riemannian. Einstein was led to apply his general law of gravita-

---

* The discovery that the spiral nebulae constitute 'island universes' which correspond to our own 'galactic universe' makes it awkward to describe the whole by the term 'Universe'. We shall, consequently, often use the term 'cosmos' when we speak of the whole of space and its content. Humboldt, in the year 1848, used the word cosmos as "the assemblage of all things in heaven and earth, the universality of created things, constituting the perceptible world".

tion to such a space on the assumption that within it there is a uniform distribution of matter moving with velocities that are negligible. If matter is so distributed, we also assume that space is homogeneous and isotropic, that is to say that its Riemannian curvatures at every point and in every direction are the same. Objection may, of course, be raised to these assumptions. It is undeniable that, when matter is aggregated into suns and planets, it is not uniformly distributed; nor do suns and planets move with absolutely negligible velocity. In fact, if Doppler's principle (§ 191) can be applied to interpret the reddening of light from distant spiral nebulae, it would appear (as we shall see in § 284) that the speeds of recession of the spiral nebulae are proportional to their distances and that a nebula at a distance of a million light years has a velocity of recession of some 150 kilometres per second. Our assumptions, therefore, are certainly unsatisfactory. But possibly they will not lead us hopelessly astray.

In § 72 we obtained a form for the metric of Riemannian three-dimensional space. By this result we may assume that the metric of our space-time is given by

$$ds^2 = dx_0{}^2 - r^2 \{dx_1{}^2 + \sin^2 x_1 \, dx_2{}^2 + \sin^2 x_1 \sin^2 x_2 \, dx_3{}^2\},$$

when $x_0 = ct$, and r is a constant.

We thus assume that our space-time is cylindrical with regard to time and that time-sections of it (i.e. sections which are purely spatial as they are given by $t = $ constant) are homogeneous, isotropic and of constant positive Riemannian curvature $1/r^2$.

Now the metric which we have chosen is a particular case of that previously discussed in § 115. In our former investigation we need only put $f = 1$ and $dr/dt = 0$. Then all the coefficients G_{ik} of the Einstein world-tensor vanish except

$$G_{11} = -2; \qquad G_{22} = -2\sin^2 x_1; \qquad G_{33} = -2\sin^2 x_1 \sin^2 x_2.$$

Also, we see at once that the Einstein-invariant G is equal to $6/r^2$.

The fundamental gravitational equations (E) of § 124 are now

$$G_{ik} - \tfrac{1}{2} G g_{ik} + \lambda g_{ik} = -\vartheta T_{ik}, \qquad \text{where } \vartheta = \frac{8\pi\gamma}{c^4}.$$

Further, by § 122,

$$T_{ik} = (c^2\rho + p)\lambda_i\lambda_k - p g_{ik},$$

when $c^2\rho$ and p are the total energy-density and pressure respectively at any point.

When the velocities of the matter in space are negligible, we may put

$$\lambda_0 = 1 \qquad \text{and} \qquad \lambda_i = 0, \qquad i > 0.$$

It is readily seen that the fundamental gravitational equations, for the metric which we have chosen, then become

$$\lambda - 3/r^2 = -\vartheta c^2 \rho,$$

and
$$1 - \lambda r^2 = -\vartheta r^2 p,$$

the latter equation being repeated three times over. From these equations we have

$$2/r^2 = \vartheta (c^2 \rho + p).$$

Thus if an Einstein cosmos could exist in static equilibrium, with a uniform energy-density $c^2 \rho$ and a uniform pressure p at every point, material velocities being negligible, we see that for it space would be spherical and therefore finite and the Riemannian curvature at every point would be

$$\tfrac{1}{2}\vartheta (c^2 \rho + p).$$

It is worth while briefly to examine the results of two further assumptions.

(1) The existence of the 'cosmological' term λ is not wholly satisfactory as its meaning is obscure. Suppose that $\lambda = 0$. Then our assumed form of space will be satisfactory for matter, uniformly distributed with energy-density $c^2 \rho$ moving with negligible velocities, provided at every point there be a *pull* of magnitude $1/\vartheta r^2$. If this pull be p it will be connected with the energy-density by the relation $p = c^2 \rho/3$. Thus the space corresponding to a homogeneous medium of energy-density $c^2 \rho$, subjected everywhere to a uniform pull $c^2 \rho/3$, would have, were it stable, the constant positive curvature $\vartheta c^2 \rho/3$.

(2) Alternatively let us assume that the pressure p is zero. Then $\lambda = 1/r^2 = \vartheta c^2 \rho/2$. Thus in a cosmos in which matter is distributed with uniform energy-density $c^2 \rho$ moving with negligible velocities, the pressure everywhere being also negligible, space will be spherical of Riemannian curvature $\vartheta c^2 \rho/2$.

The total volume of such space is known (§ 79) to be $2\pi^2 r^3$. Hence if such an Einstein cosmos could exist, the total mass in it would be

$$M = 2\pi^2 r^3 \rho = \frac{4\pi^2}{c^2 \vartheta} r.$$

Thus the radius of the cosmos would be proportional to the total amount of matter in it. This surprising fact was made the basis of interesting speculations shortly after its discovery. But these speculations have lost their value since Eddington, on the basis of work of Friedman and Lemaître, shewed that this Einstein cosmos must be unstable. We shall reproduce the investigation in Lecture XI.

§140. *de Sitter's cosmos.*

As we have previously seen at the end of §125, a cosmos corresponding to which the *space-time* continuum is everywhere homogeneous and isotropic (§47) (real time being represented by an imaginary axis), so that all Riemannian curvatures that can be formed within such space-time are equal, is a possible form of empty space. The Dutch astronomer de Sitter was the first to point out this possibility and to examine the features of such space.

Obviously two-dimensional space of constant positive curvature $1/r^2$ is the sphere given by

$$- ds^2 = r^2 (dx_0^2 + \sin^2 x_0 \, dx_1^2).$$

(We take a negative sign before ds^2 according to the usual convention of the general theory of relativity.)

Three-dimensional space which is everywhere of constant positive curvature is, as we have seen in §72, given by

$$- ds^2 = r^2 (dx_0^2 + \sin^2 x_0 \, dx_1^2 + \sin^2 x_0 \sin^2 x_1 dx_2^2).$$

It may readily be shewn that four-dimensional homogeneous space which is everywhere of constant positive curvature $1/r^2$ is similarly given by the analogous formula

$$- ds^2 = r^2 (dx_0^2 + \sin^2 x_0 \, dx_1^2 + \sin^2 x_0 \sin^2 x_1 \, dx_2^2$$
$$+ \sin^2 x_0 \sin^2 x_1 \sin^2 x_2 \, dx_3^2). \quad \ldots\ldots(1)$$

This then is the expression of the space-time continuum of de Sitter's cosmos when imaginary time, as in Minkowski's world, corresponds to a real coordinate.

The formula (1) gives us a completely homogeneous continuum, in which space and imaginary time are indistinguishable one from another. To break up the continuum we put

$$\sin \chi = \sin x_0 \sin x_1,$$
$$\tan \tau = \tan x_0 \cos x_1, \quad \text{where } \tau = \sqrt{-1} \, ct.$$

Then we readily see that, reciprocally,

$$\cos x_0 = \cos \chi \cos \tau,$$
$$\cot x_1 = \cot \chi \sin \tau;$$

and our metric now becomes

$$ds^2 = r^2 \cos^2 x_1 dx_0^2 - r^2 (dx_1^2 + \sin^2 x_1 dx_2^2 + \sin^2 x_1 \sin^2 x_2 dx_3^2), \ldots(2)$$

where now $x_0 = ct$ and χ has been replaced by x_1.

It can be readily verified that the cosmos given by this metric is a possible form of empty space-time. To this end we take the formulae of p. 142 and in them put

$$r = \text{constant} \qquad \text{and} \qquad f = r \cos x_1.$$

Then all the coefficients of the Einstein world-tensor vanish except

$$G_{00} = 3 \cos^2 x_1, \quad G_{11} = -3, \quad G_{22} = -3 \sin^2 x_1, \quad G_{33} = -3 \sin^2 x_1 \sin^2 x_2;$$

and the Einstein-invariant G is given by $G = 12/r^2$.

The gravitational equations

$$G_{ik} + (\lambda - \tfrac{1}{2}G) g_{ik} = -\vartheta T_{ik},$$

since $T_{ik} = 0$ for empty space, become $\lambda r^2 = 3$, this equation being repeated four times over.

Thus, as before, we see that the Riemannian curvature of our empty space-time is everywhere equal to

$$1/r^2 = \lambda/3 = G/12.$$

We see then afresh that de Sitter's cosmos is a possible form of empty space-time. Inasmuch as the density of matter in our actual Universe is very small, possibly to be measured by 10^{-30} in c.g.s. units (*vide* § 290 *infra*), it is arguable that de Sitter's cosmos resembles in its general form that in which we live.

When this cosmos was first discovered by de Sitter certain paradoxical features of it gave rise to much perplexity. For instance, a vibrating atom is, as we have previously said in § 132, a natural clock. If such a clock is at a fixed point in the cosmos given by the metric (2), the coordinates x_1, x_2 and x_3 will all be constant; and we shall have

$$ds^2 = r^2 \cos^2 x_1 \, c^2 dt^2.$$

Thus the time of vibration of the atom will vary as $\sec x_1$. In other words, the atomic clock will go more slowly the farther it is from the origin. When it is at a distance corresponding to $x_1 = \pi/2$, the time of vibration will become infinite. In fact, nothing will then happen, so far as an observer at the origin will be able to observe.

Other surprising conclusions can similarly be reached. But it is now clear that they result from the way in which space-time is broken up in passing from the metric (1) to that numbered (2). It is true that in (2) *space* is homogeneous. But in (1) *space-time* is homogeneous, so that all events are equivalent one to another. In (2), however, the homogeneity of space-time is not preserved. We have introduced a centre, which is a fiction of our mathematical analysis. In fact, by our choice of coordinates we have broken the space-time homogeneity which is fundamental.

It remains to be said, however, that the form of metric (2) is satisfactory in that plane sections of the cosmos which contain real time are hyperbolas, so that we do not make any assumption contradictory to our belief that time 'goes on for ever'. Further, the spatial part of this form of the metric of de Sitter's cosmos is spherical or Riemannian. Thus in this cosmos the time-dimension is infinite, but the three space-dimensions are finite.

When it was first brought to the notice of astronomers, de Sitter's cosmos was welcomed because the slowing down of an atomic clock means a displacement towards the red in the spectrum. Thus in this cosmos distant objects give out light which, as we shall see in § 191, will, by Doppler's principle, be interpreted as a motion of recession. Now the immensely distant spiral nebulae, as we shall see in Lecture XI, appear, by such use of Doppler's principle, to be travelling away from us with very large velocities. Of such apparent motion de Sitter's equations seemed to offer the hint of an explanation. Further and more satisfying possibilities of a solution, of the problem presented by the large apparent velocities of recession of the distant spiral nebulae, will be indicated in Lecture XI when the Friedman-Lemaître 'expanding' cosmos is discussed.

§ 141. *General relativity and the Maxwell field-equations.*

The general theory of relativity as developed by Einstein gives a satisfactory description of the metrical structure of space-time which contains matter. In other words, it successfully unites geometry and gravitation. But there is no evident place in it for electro-magnetic phenomena. Now such phenomena are a singularly important part of the realm of physics; and they cannot be separated from the investigation of the motion of matter inasmuch as a material body carrying an electric charge experiences a mechanical force in an electrostatic field. Hence the general theory of relativity cannot be considered to be complete until the metrical structure of space-time is modified so as to contain terms which will correspond to, or account for, electromagnetic phenomena.

By the work successively of Faraday (1791–1867) and Clerk Maxwell (1831–1879) all electro-magnetic phenomena can be expressed by means of a set of eight equations (of which two may be regarded as resulting from the other six) giving the behaviour of vectors in the electro-magnetic field. These equations can be reduced to two tensor-equations. Many efforts have been made by Einstein and others to find such a metrical structure for space-time that these equations result naturally from it. Einstein* has given a system of sixteen unified field-equations which include both Maxwell's field-equations and his own gravitational equations. But the problem is not yet finally solved. The direction of Einstein's thought is indicated by his idea that, whereas in the gravitational equations elements in space are compared only as regards size, such elements must also be compared as regards direction if those additional terms in the fundamental metric are to be found which will enable geometry, gravitation and electro-magnetic phenomena to be fused together. Out of such a fusion we may hope that it will be possible to find the relation of electrons and protons to the metrical structure of space.

Because the very important developments here indicated are not yet completed, we have not in these lectures set out the Faraday-Maxwell theory of the electro-magnetic field. It ought, however, to be explicitly stated that that theory was the most brilliant advance made in mathematical physics during the nineteenth century.

§ 142. *Conclusions and speculations.*

It must be admitted that, just as we are ignorant of the metrical structure of space-time which contains electro-magnetic phenomena, so we do not know with absolute certainty whether the actual space of our experience is Riemannian. Yet, though we still lack certainty as to these important matters, the understanding gained thus far, which has united geometry and gravitation, ought probably to be regarded as the most remarkable intellectual achievement of mankind. How great has been the progress since Kant (1724–1804) claimed that the axioms of Euclidean geometry were *à priori* principles, antecedent to all experience, given by transcendental† intuition.

We are still in doubt as to whether 'the reality which underlies space' forms a discrete manifold. Observational results in regard to the absorption and emission of radiation by material atoms constitute the so-called quantum phenomena which we shall discuss in Lecture IX. These seem to shew that energy is atomic; and possibly, therefore, space may present itself to our investigation as a manifold which is

---

* A. Einstein, *Berliner Berichte*, vol. I, 1929, pp. 1–8. Einstein's work has been modified and simplified by T. Levi-Civita. A translation of Levi-Civita's exposition, entitled *A Simplified Presentation of Einstein's Unified Field Equations*, has been made by J. Dougall. Blackie, 1929.

† With Kant, knowledge is transcendental "which is occupied not with objects, but with our mode of knowing objects so far as that is possible *à priori*".

ultimately discrete and not continuous. Even so, we shall but vindicate Riemann's idea that space in itself is merely a three-dimensional manifold devoid of all form. We can, in fact, conclude that, in the absence of electro-magnetic phenomena, space only acquires a definite form* as a consequence of what we term its material content. This, as has been made clear by Einstein's genius, determines the metrical structure, not of space alone, but of space-time. The structure of space was formerly thought to be 'fixed and independent of the physical phenomena for which it serves as a background'. It was conceived as a barrack-like building, ready for occupation, of which energy and matter took possession. Now we understand that the binding forces which give to space its character are due to its material content. These binding forces are, in fact, what we call gravitation. If we could suitably modify the distribution of matter and energy in space we could give to it any form that we please: and this form would be visual, for we should alter the path taken by rays of light.

It would seem, then, that the reality underlying space-time, and giving to it its metrical structure, is matter or energy. But there is another and probably more satisfactory way of interpreting our observations and conclusions. It is possible that what we call the material content of space is but the manifestation of the warping of space-time. Einstein's researches have, in fact, fused together geometry and physics as they have united space and time. The presence of what we call matter is revealed by the metrical structure of space-time, and we have no reason to think of matter as more than a symptom of singularities or acute warpings in space-time.

When a wave moves over the sea the form travels on, but the particles of water of which it consists are always changing. In the wave as such there is no substance. So also when a particle of matter travels through space we probably have the motion of pure form. In space-time the particle is a line of singularity of metrical structure: and such structure is apparently the origin of what we term matter and of what erroneously we imagine to be composed of substance.

Old traditions, embedded in Christian thought, describe a time when "the earth was without form and void": and probably most Christian philosophers in the past have believed in a process of creation by God, in time and 'out of nothing'. We seem, in the analysis of matter to

---

* We refer, of course, to geometrical form. Kant uses the word 'form' in quite a different sense. For him space and time are forms inasmuch as they arise from mind as factors in experience.

which Einstein's general relativity leads, to see 'in the beginning' a process by which form or structure was given to the void of space-time. As the many complex forms which then arose assumed an ever greater complexity, the material world took shape. It is natural to ask whether, in such development, there was creative activity, the emergence of something new. I feel constrained to answer in the affirmative. Things were other and more diverse at the end than at the beginning. Even though the process of assuming greater complexity may be exhibited as a mechanical sequence, it may none the less conceal or embody genuine creative activity. In such processes, moreover, as we can reverse, there may be a genuine destruction of the results of such activity.

He who has seen a boy play with a young dog must have reflected upon the extraordinary likenesses between the two young specimens of highly developed mammals. One differs from the other primarily in what we call a greater complexity of brain structure. Did not such complexity involve in its making a series of acts rightly to be called creative, or at least a series of changes which led to the creation of something that did not previously exist?

In such a region of speculative thought we have not yet reached a stage when questions can be replaced by statements. And I would reiterate that at the basis of our speculations is the measurement of matter by its inertia. Energy, momentum and stress have been, in Einstein's scheme, exhibited as consequences of the metrical structure of space-time. But most certainly, apart altogether from electro-magnetic phenomena, the Universe contains much that cannot be classified under these attributes of matter. Do such other realities result from nothing but, as it were, the mechanical concretion of space-time? I cannot feel that an affirmative answer to such a question is satisfactory.

Moreover, we must bear in mind the even more fundamental fact that the union of space and time *may* be a necessity to the physicist because he can only observe point-instants and measure intervals between them. The qualitative distinction between space and time which is always present in common thought may correspond to something in the character of the Universe which eludes the physicist's measurements. In fact, the limitations of purely quantitative analysis must never be forgotten.

Lecture vii

THE ELECTRICAL THEORY OF MATTER

§ 143. *Electricity and magnetism: the original discoveries.*

It was known to the ancients that amber (ἤλεκτρον), when rubbed with a dry cloth, has the power of attracting certain light substances. They also knew that magnetic iron-ore can attract small pieces of iron. The use of the magnetic needle in navigation appears to have been a Chinese discovery which passed to Europe about the time of the Crusades. Modern investigation of magnetism began in the latter half of the sixteenth century with William Gilbert of Colchester*, who died in the year 1603. Progress was rapid during the hundred years which ended in the year 1871 when Clerk Maxwell's great treatise on *Magnetism and Electricity* was published.

§ 144. *Maxwell's achievement.*

Maxwell succeeded in uniting magnetism, electricity and light into one theory. He obtained a series of equations, alike simple and comprehensive, which give a satisfactory representation of electro-magnetic phenomena. Their efficiency for the purpose is undoubted, for Maxwell's vectors specify what is happening at every point of the 'field' in which electrical phenomena are taking place. The mathematical scheme is, however, highly abstract and no attempts to make a 'concrete' explanation of it have been wholly satisfactory. Yet ought we to expect to be able to construct an adequate mechanical model? Physics consists of descriptions of behaviour; and when we have a scheme which describes how electricity, at rest and in motion, behaves, we presumably know all there is to be known about it.

§ 145. *Electricity and matter.*

During the sixty years which have passed since Maxwell established his system of laws, a remarkable insight has been obtained into the relations between electricity and matter. The new knowledge began, a few years before the end of the nineteenth century, with experiments

---

* Sir J. J. Thomson, commenting on Gilbert's work *De Magnete* published in the year 1600, writes that he "laid down in an admirable manner the cardinal principles of the science".

on electric sparks sent through tubes containing highly rarefied gases. It was developed by researches into the spontaneous disintegration of certain radio-active substances. The result has been the construction of 'the electrical theory of matter', according to which every atom of a material element consists of a central core or nucleus round which there is a system of satellite electrons in rotation or, at any rate, in existence. The main outlines of this theory will probably be little changed by subsequent research. But it has led to a scheme of sub-atomic dynamics which implies concepts at variance with those fundamental in that Newtonian-Maxwellian scheme which a quarter of a century ago seemed wholly adequate to explain the phenomena of matter and motion embraced in mechanics.

§ 146. *Coulomb's law.*

According to a law, first enunciated by Coulomb (1736–1806) about the year 1784, two particles, similarly electrified and of negligible mass, repel one another with a force which varies directly as the product of the electric charges and inversely as the square of the distance between them. This experimental result, save that attraction is replaced by repulsion, corresponds exactly to the Newtonian law of gravitation. We have seen in § 134 that Newton's law seems to be merely the result of our mode of measurement. Though the subject is highly speculative, we naturally tend to assume that Coulomb's law has the same character. The suggestion has been put forward that the law is a consequence of the fact that our space is three-dimensional. An influence proceeding from an origin in such space will naturally be at any point inversely proportional to the area of a sphere through the point with its centre at the origin. The influence will thus be measured by the 'inverse square' law. Such an argument, however, needs further development if it is to explain the relativity-modification of the law of gravitation.

Suppose that we have two very small bodies, of negligible mass, with equal charges of negative electricity at unit distance from one another in dry air of standard pressure and temperature. If they repel one another with unit mechanical force, each is said to be charged with *an electrostatic unit of electricity.*

What is electricity?

In answer to this question, we must confess that electricity is one of Nature's fundamental entities and, as such, is incapable of satisfactory definition. We can, however, say (as a result of researches in which

J. J. Thomson did the most important pioneer work) that electricity is atomic. The atom of electricity is the *electron*: in other words, the smallest particle of electricity which can exist is a minute charge of definite amount. This is a charge of what is usually termed negative electricity: when the units of length, mass and time are centimetre, gramme and second, it consists of 4.77×10^{-10} 'electrostatic units'. No similar electron of positive electricity has been isolated, and it is believed that positive electricity is always associated with the nuclei of material atoms. Normally an atom of matter is electrically neutral because its nuclear positive charge is neutralised by the presence of satellite electrons, that is to say, of atoms of negative electricity.

Charges and electrons.

As a result of the researches of Faraday and Maxwell we regard the properties of charged bodies as due to lines of force which spread out from the bodies into the surrounding medium. Thus we may think of an electric charge as creating round itself an electrostatic field in every part of which there is energy. When the charge is at rest, there is at every point of the field an electric but not a magnetic force. When the charge is in motion, there will also be a magnetic force at every point of the field. When we speak of a charged body being at rest or in motion, we mean, of course, at rest or in motion with regard to the earth. We do not know, and cannot discover, what its motion may be in 'the ether', if such a thing exists, or in absolute space. Most physicists regard the electro-magnetic energy of a charged body as wholly contained in the external field. When the velocity of a moving charge is changed, the distribution of electro-magnetic energy in the surrounding field changes. This causes an electro-magnetic disturbance which, as Maxwell shewed, travels with the speed of light. Light is, in fact, a special kind of such disturbance.

A moving charge produces a magnetic field. But in unit volume of a field at a point where the magnetic force is H, μ being the magnetic permeability of the medium, there are $\mu H^2/8\pi$ units of energy. If now we have a charged sphere, of mass m and radius a, moving in such a medium with uniform velocity v, the total kinetic energy of the system is

$$\tfrac{1}{2}(m + 2\mu e^2/3a)\,v^2,$$

e being the charge on the sphere. Thus there is an apparent increase in the mass of the sphere—an increase due to the charge—which is, in appropriate units,

$$2\mu e^2/3a.$$

It is thus clear that to put an electric charge into motion work must be done, inasmuch as magnetic energy must be distributed throughout the field. To stop the motion of the charge, such energy must be removed. Thus, by virtue of its charge alone, a charged body has inertia or mass. The mass of an immaterial sphere, if such could be imagined, of charge e and radius a in a field of magnetic permeability μ is thus, in appropriate units,

$$2\mu e^2/3a.$$

The electron, as we have said, is an atom of electric charge. It is usually assumed that a single moving electron will give rise to an electromagnetic field; but experiments are always made with a large number of electrons. It is generally assumed, also, that the whole mass of an electron is due to its charge. If the assumptions be justified, and if, further, the electron consists of a charge e contained within a sphere of radius a, its 'proper' mass m will be given by

$$m = 2e^2/3c^2a,$$

where c is the velocity of light, and e is measured in electrostatic units.

We shall explain in §149 how m and e are determined. Using their values, it appears that a should be of the order of 2×10^{-13} cm. This estimate, of course, will be valueless if the postulates made in reaching it are unsound. It used to be thought that the assumption that the whole mass of an electron is due to its charge was established by the experimental fact that the mass of an electron increases with its velocity v in the ratio $1/\sqrt{1 - v^2/c^2}$. But we now know (§107) that such increase is true for all kinds of mass.

It is well to state further that, though it is an undoubted experimental fact that an accelerated electric charge gives rise to an electro-magnetic disturbance analogous to light, there is no evidence that a single electron can, when its speed is changed, produce such an effect. It is, however, natural to assume the fact.

Ions.

Theoretically we can deprive any atom of matter of some of its satellite electrons. The atom then becomes positively charged and we term it a positive ion.

Hydrogen has a more simple constitution than any other element. In its neutral state it consists of a single electron rotating round (or associated with) a nucleus on which there is a single equal and opposite charge of electricity. If the electron be removed there is left the nucleus, the positive hydrogen-ion. Hydrogen is usually denoted by the letter

H, and ionised hydrogen by the symbol H+. We shall see later that the nuclei of all atoms can be built up from electrons and hydrogen-nuclei. For this reason the hydrogen-nucleus is usually called a *proton*.

The electrical theory of matter is, in essence, the assertion that the material universe is built out of protons and electrons. They and the energy which results from their interaction are the fundamentals of the world of sense-observation. Possibly, indeed, protons and electrons are merely manifestations of energy, built out of space-time as right-handed and left-handed vortices might be created in a fluid. But such a reduction of the universe to the forms taken by a single fundamental entity remains a speculative possibility.

We shall shortly describe the electrical structure of helium, which after hydrogen is the most simple element. It has two electrons rotating round a nucleus which has a double positive charge. From the atom of helium we can remove one electron and get a helium-ion with a single positive charge. If we remove both electrons from an atom of helium we get a helium-ion with a double positive charge. Helium is usually denoted by the abbreviation He; and, by an obvious symbolism, He++ is the symbol for doubly ionised helium.

The forces between electrons.

Electrons repel one another and attract ions with forces which are colossal, vastly in excess of those which we can produce in chemical explosives. Such forces are unperceived by us because equal amounts of positive and negative electricity are usually conjoined. We only perceive slight residual inequalities. But the forces resulting from such residual effects are the cause of chemical affinity and of most of the ordinary physical properties of matter.

§ 147. *The nature of an electron.*

An electron, we have said, is an indivisible unit, a definite amount of negative electricity. Before the year 1927 it was, for the reasons given in § 146, usually supposed to be a sphere whose radius was of the order of 10^{-13} cm. If there is some measure of truth in such a statement the electron must be, in its linear dimensions, about one thirty-thousandth of the average atom.

Speculations as to the nature of electrons have, however, taken a radically different form in recent years owing to experiments which shew that electrons can be diffracted like light or, more accurately, like the X-rays which differ from light in that their 'wave-length' is much shorter. (A detailed account of the diffraction of X-rays will be given (§ 225) towards the close of Lecture IX.)

The first successful experiments in the diffraction of free electrons were made by Davisson and Germer. They shewed that a nickel surface, which had been crystallised by heat, scattered electrons in certain definite directions: the electrons were, in fact, diffracted by the regular arrangement of the molecules in the crystal of nickel. G. P. Thomson made further developments. He took a narrow pencil of high-speed electrons and passed it through an excessively thin film of gold, probably not more than a thousand atoms thick. After its passage the pencil fell upon a photographic plate. The pencil spread out into a cone, as might have been expected, owing to the deflection of the electrons by the atoms of the gold film. But it was found that the photographic plate did not shew a general blur, a smudge without pattern. On the contrary, a series of bright rings appeared with radii bearing definite ratios to one another. Further, these rings could not have been due to X-rays excited by electrons, inasmuch as the cone could be deflected by a magnet. A cone of electrons would exhibit such deflection and one of X-rays would not. The result seemed to shew conclusively, either that the electron was accompanied by a train of waves which were a part of itself, or that it was itself a group of waves.

More recently Rupp in Göttingen has confirmed the apparent wave character of electrons by shewing that a beam of them could be diffracted at grazing incidence on an ordinary ruled grating, such as is described later in § 217.

On the other hand, if a sheet of glass is powdered by crystals of zinc sulphide and exposed to a shower of electrons, it will emit scintillations, sparks which can be seen in the dark by the help of a magnifying glass. This fact seems to shew conclusively that the electrons are particles, bits of electricity which produce sparks when they hit the screen. Yet G. P. Thomson's experiments go to shew that, if a stream of electrons was sent through two holes close enough together, we should find that the scintillations occurred in bands separated by darkness. If, however, one hole was blocked up, the scintillations would appear everywhere on the portion of the screen beyond the other hole.

The facts are puzzling beyond belief and yet are not in doubt. It is *as though an electron became a wave for the purpose of passing through a diffraction grating and then transformed itself into a particle to produce the scintillation effect.*

Sir J. J. Thomson*, arguing from the experimental results obtained by his son, concluded that the electron has a dual structure. In one part of the structure, he suggested, the energy is located and that part is built up of a number of lines of electric force; the other part, however, consists of a train of waves which determine the path along which the electron travels. These suggestions have not won general acceptance. The usual attitude† of physicists at the present time is that the electron has a wave aspect and also a particle aspect. "An electron is a particle 'and/or' a wave. We must be ready all the time to think of it as either or both, but we must not mix the ideas." Nature has so arranged matters that we can see either the one or the other aspect. "There is nothing of the same kind elsewhere in scientific thought." However ingeniously this point of view may be defended, those critics are surely right who regard it as a confession of bewilderment rather than an explanation.

The wave mechanics of de Broglie‡ and Schrödinger has had much success in an attempt to bridge the gulf between particles (including electrons) and waves. In this theory, as will be explained in § 209, the particle corresponds to a group of waves, its velocity being the 'group-velocity', as distinguished from the velocity of the waves. Up to a certain point this attempt to represent a particle by a special 'wave packet' works satisfactorily. But in the end it has to be allowed that the waves give, not particles, but probabilities that particles will be in particular positions.

Bohr and Heisenberg have endeavoured to interpret the dualism of waves and particles; and at the basis of their ideas lie Heisenberg's *uncertainty-relations*, formulated in the year 1927. According to these relations any method of observing such a particle as an electron affects its circumstances. The act of observing the position of an electron will cause a change in its momentum. Similarly the act of observing the time-coordinate will give rise to a change of energy. We will later (§ 210) take up the question of these uncertainty-relations. For the present we must content ourselves by saying that, in Bohr's words, electrons are "unsharply defined individuals within finite space-time regions". In

* J. J. Thomson, *Beyond the Electron. A Lecture.* Cambridge University Press, 1928.

† See, for instance, C. G. Darwin, *The New Conceptions of Matter.* Bell, 1931, p. 82 and elsewhere.

‡ An authoritative account of this recent development will be found in Louis de Broglie, *An Introduction to the Study of Wave Mechanics.* Translated by H. T. Flint. Methuen, 1930.

fact, it appears that the space-time framework is inadequate to describe natural phenomena when we apply it to ultimates such as the electron. Lindemann* concludes that "no reality is to be attached to the wave aspect: it is a makeshift to get over the failure of space-time description".

Even though the 'wave v. particle' controversy could be satisfactorily settled—and obscurity still clouds the issue—we should not know how an electron holds together without exploding. Were this problem solved, others would undoubtedly present themselves. It may be that, beyond the limits of our understanding, unknown regions will for ever lie.

This brief statement as to the nature of an electron is incomplete unless we add that, when an electron is a satellite within an atom of matter, it appears to behave like a small magnet. This behaviour is thought to be due to its rotation and hence 'the spinning electron' is important in recent physical theory. It has been found that the spin of an electron is such that its angular momentum is a constant quantity $\frac{1}{2}h$, where h is Planck's constant (§ 202). Some consequences of electron spin will be considered in § 208.

§ 148. *Radiation.*

An electric current consists of a stream of electrons moving (usually in a metal wire) in the opposite direction to that which in common speech we term the direction of the current. Such a current, wherever it exists, is, as we have said, surrounded by an electro-magnetic field, a field of energy which can influence other electrical charges and magnets placed in the field. The energy of the space surrounding a stream of moving electrons changes as the stream changes its velocity. Such changes are transmitted with the speed of light.

When the changes of motion of electrons are rhythmical they send out waves of energy. Such waves can be several miles in length, as they are when produced by the to and fro motion of electrons in a wireless transmitting aerial. When energy of electrical origin comes from within an atom it can appear as light and heat waves, as the shorter X-rays or as the even shorter waves termed γ-rays. All these waves are included in the term 'radiation' and travel with the same velocity as light. Radiation is the transfer through space of the energy which arises from changes in the velocity or potential energy of electrons: it is a transfer unaccompanied by the motion of material particles.

* F. A. Lindemann, *The Physical Significance of the Quantum Theory.* Clarendon Press, 1932, p. 144.

It is convenient to gather together, for future reference, a brief description of the various forms of radiation:

Type of radiation	Wave-length in centimetres	How produced
Wireless waves	2,000,000	Oscillating electric
	10	circuits
Heat radiation	·03	Ordinary fires at
	·00,008	dull heat
Visible light	·00,008	Ordinary methods
	·00,004	of lighting
Ultra-violet radiation	·00,004	Ordinary methods
	·00,000,5	of lighting
X-rays	·00,000,1	Crookes' tubes
	·00,000,000,8	
γ-rays	·00,000,000,5	Break-up of radio-
	·00,000,000,005	active atoms

The so-called 'cosmic radiation', which of late has attracted the keen interest of astronomers, is even shorter in wave-length than the shortest γ-rays. Its origin, as we shall see in § 300, is still the subject of enquiry and debate.

Such phenomena of light as interference and diffraction—we shall discuss them in §§ 216 *et seq.*—have led to the conclusion that visible light, and, by analogy, all other forms of radiation, consist of transverse waves similar to the waves on a still pond into which a stone is thrown. Newton (1642–1727) had previously suggested that light consists of corpuscles. The undulatory theory, however, seemed to be firmly established by Fresnel (1788–1827): it was subsequently developed by Maxwell (1831–1879) in his electro-magnetic theory of light. But, as we shall see later (§ 203), what is known as the photo-electric effect led Einstein to suggest in the year 1905 that all radiation is emitted in small parcels or quanta. A quantum of light is called a *photon*. The problem of how an electron can be both a particle and a wave meets us in a slightly different form when we seek to reconcile the wave theory of light with the existence of light-quanta. We shall consider it later in connection with the discussion of the quantum theory in Lecture IX. Meanwhile, in accordance with prevailing custom, we shall usually assume the truth of the wave theory of radiation. But, though we shall speak of wave-length and frequency, it must always be understood that the numerical values of these quantities will serve to differentiate different kinds of radiation even though the wave theory be abandoned.

§ 149. *The inertia of an electron.*

To accelerate an electron we must give it the energy which it will send out as radiation: we must do work upon it. Thus, as we said in § 146, an electron has inertia. In other words it has mass.

The ratio of the charge e to the mass m of an electron has been accurately determined by measuring deflections produced by electric and magnetic fields. As will be described in § 154, a stream of electrons proceeds from the cathode of a Crookes' tube. The velocity of this stream varies with the potential of the cathode; but the ratio e/m is independent of the metal of the cathode and of the chemical nature of the exhausted gas in the tube. The electrons can be deflected both by electric and by magnetic forces. The measurement of such deflections gives $e/m = 5 \cdot 31 \times 10^{17}$ in electrostatic gramme units. The value of e can be obtained independently. R. A. Millikan determined it by observing the motion through the air of small electrified oil-drops in an electric field. He found $e = 4 \cdot 77 \times 10^{-10}$, whence $m = 9 \times 10^{-28}$ grammes. From this value it follows that the weight of an electron is about 1/1840th of that of an hydrogen atom. This weight corresponds, of course, to the 'proper mass', that is to say it is the weight as measured by an observer moving with the electron. Electrons can be experimentally observed which move with velocities which reach 99 per cent. of the velocity of light. The measured mass of such an electron, according to the special theory of relativity, is very much greater than the normal: it is, in fact, about seven times as great.

For, let M be the measured mass when an electron is moving with velocity v, and let m be its proper mass. Then, as we have seen in § 107, we must have $M = m / \sqrt{1 - v^2/c^2}$, where c is the velocity of light.

Hence $M = 100m / \sqrt{199} = 7m$ approximately.

§ 150. *The ether.*

Are we to regard the 'field' of an electron as having a substantial basis? We have seen that the space round a set of moving electrons is the seat of electro-magnetic forces. Through it rhythmic vibrations of groups of electrons send out waves of radiation moving with the speed of light at 186,000 miles a second. These waves consist of energy unaccompanied either by atoms or molecules of matter, or by protons or electrons. Light, as we have said, may consist of transverse waves similar to the waves on a still pond into which a stone is thrown. Now, when light reaches us from a far-distant star, years must have elapsed between the time when it left the star and the time when it reaches our eyes; and we have the feeling that there must have been a something material or quasi-material to support it during the interval.

Such considerations led in the nineteenth century to the assumption of the existence of an ether filling the void and affording a sort of substantial basis for the waves of radiation. But is not such a conjectured ether the result of our desire for concrete symbols? All attempts, in Poincaré's phrase, to "touch the ether with one's finger" have failed. In order to understand what goes on in 'empty space', it is rather absurd to fill it with a something which has some of the properties of matter but which, nevertheless, we cannot perceive. The Michelson-Morley experiment, no less than a similarly decisive experiment concerning the behaviour of a charged condenser and associated with the names of Trouton and Noble, shewed that motion relative to an hypothetical ether could not be established: on the basis of such experimental results, as we have seen, the special theory of relativity was erected. In short, the idea of the ether, as an all pervasive substance filling the Universe, has no foundation in perceptual experience.

We saw at the close of the previous lecture that increasingly modern physicists accept Berkeley's conclusion that space is the subjective result of sensations of sight, touch and movement. They regard geometry as a branch of physics, or *vicê versâ*; and under the influence of Einstein there is a growing conviction that not only material but also electro-magnetic phenomena may be regarded as consequences of the geometry of space. Dynamics thus becomes a sort of kinematics. Clifford*, in the year 1870, when little more than an undergraduate, threw out speculations which no longer seem fantastic. He suggested

(1) That small portions of space *are* in fact of a nature analogous to little hills on a surface which is on the average flat; namely, that the ordinary laws of geometry are not valid in them.

(2) That this property of being curved or distorted is continually being passed on from one portion of space to another after the manner of a wave.

(3) That this variation of the curvature of space is what really happens in that phenomenon which we call the *motion of matter*, whether ponderable or etherial.

(4) That in the physical world nothing else takes place but this variation, subject (possibly) to the law of continuity.

We shall briefly describe the electro-magnetic phenomena associated with radiation in § 188. At present we will only say that the ether, as a basis of such phenomena, satisfies our desire for concrete imagery.

* *Proceedings of the Cambridge Philosophical Society*, vol. II, 1876, pp. 157, 158. See also W. K. Clifford, *Mathematical Papers*. Macmillan, 1882, pp. 21, 22.

But, if such speculation as Clifford reached is valid, there is no need to postulate an ether in order to explain why certain aspects of radiation can be expressed by the same mathematical forms as are useful to describe the motion of waves in water. We must be content with the fact that such forms express in an abstract manner (and, as we are beginning to realise, somewhat inadequately) what happens in space-time.

§ 151. *The inertia of light.*

We have indicated in § 146 that, although we can only experiment with aggregates of electrons, yet it is reasonable to hold that an electron possesses mass in virtue of its inertia. Thus we must do work upon it to alter its velocity; and such work passes as radiation into the surrounding field. Light, which is a form of radiation, that is to say of electro-magnetic energy, also possesses inertia. We shall later give a measure of the pressure which a beam of light exerts upon a material disc which stops the beam by being held normal to its direction. The force is, of course, excessively small; but it has been detected by delicate experiments. Because light possesses inertia, it also possesses mass, and we have as much right to speak of a pound of light as of a pound of butter. Calculations shew that about 160 tons of sunlight fall upon the earth in 24 hours.

We have previously said that there is apparently no matter in an electron. All its mass is probably due to its electro-magnetic reactions. The question therefore arises as to whether the mass of an atom is due in part to something other than what we may regard as the congealed energy of its nucleus. We have, when discussing the consequences of the special theory of relativity in Lecture V, given the reasons which led Einstein to the conclusion that the whole inertial mass of an atom is due to the inertia of its energy. If m be the inertial mass of the atom, E its energy and c the velocity of light, we have, in suitable units, the equation (§ 107)

$$E = c^2 m.$$

§ 152. *The energy of matter.*

Since the velocity of light is enormous, a small quantity of matter must contain a vast store of energy. In one gramme of water there must be a store of energy sufficient to raise a load of one million tons to the top of Mt Everest.

It is obvious that if we could release such energy we should have discovered a source of available power incomparably greater than any which we have at present tapped. The first man to make the discovery would probably destroy himself and his neighbours for miles round. Inasmuch as the use of such enormous stores of energy in warfare would rapidly depopulate the earth, it is probably well that the discovery should not be made until the human race has become more civilised. It is almost certain, as will be seen later, that the vast amounts of energy of radiation emitted by the stars are drawn from within the nucleus of the atom. So much energy is given out by our own sun that it would (as astronomers measure time) rapidly become dark if its source were limited to known mechanical and chemical changes, such as contraction and combustion.

We shall see in Lecture XI (§ 265) that the vast stores of energy, which seem required to explain the enormous amounts of radiation emitted by the bright stars, must result either from the radio-active disintegration of highly complex atoms, or from the synthesis of helium, or from the actual destruction of matter. If matter is actually destroyed to produce radiation, atoms must vanish when their protons and electrons unite to disappear as radiant energy. Needless to say, we have no positive knowledge of the existence of such a process as the destruction of matter. Yet astrophysicists of high standing regard it as a probable inference from facts of observation.

§ 153. *Can we create electrons?*

At first sight the answer would appear to be in the affirmative. The ordinary cell used in our houses for an electric bell creates a current of electricity which consists of electrons moving along the wires. The motion of the electrons begins as soon as we close the circuit by 'pressing the knob'. Similarly in a dynamo a rotating magnet produces an alternating current. But in each case we supply energy to make the current. The energy of the cell comes from chemical decomposition: that of the dynamo comes from the engine which drives it. So, as Sir William Bragg* has said, "we must think of the battery or the dynamo, not as manufacturing electricity, but as sending round a circuit a stream of electrons that are already there and are more or less free to move. Just so the engine in a factory makes a leather belt continually travel round a certain circuit: but the engine does not manufacture leather". In short, we cannot create electrons; and, so far as we know, there is no place or process in the Universe where or by which they are

* W. H. Bragg, *Concerning the Nature of Things.* Bell, 1925, p. 220.

created. It might be urged that, if it is true that they can be destroyed in the stars to produce radiation, a counterbalancing production of them must take place elsewhere. Possibly, however, the destruction of protons and electrons is a one-sided process which shews that the material of the Universe is disappearing, just as the second law of thermodynamics (§ 178) apparently shews that its heat is "running down".

The reason why metals are good conductors is that their atoms have outer electrons that are easily detachable. But we still lack a complete understanding of what happens when an electric current is produced and travels round a circuit.

§ 154. *X-rays*.

X-rays were discovered by Röntgen in the year 1895. In the following year Becquerel (1852–1908) discovered that the element uranium is radio-active. These two discoveries led to that continuously increasing knowledge of the constitution of matter which has been so characteristic of scientific progress in the twentieth century.

Everyone who has been radiographed knows what a Crookes' tube is like. It consists of a glass tube in which there is almost a complete vacuum. Through its walls two wires are passed; and one of them ends in a metal disc, the cathode, inside the tube. Outside the tube the wires are connected to a generator of electricity. When a current passes through the wires its direction, according to the common convention, is from anode to cathode. If the current be of several hundred volts, 'rays' emanate from the cathode disc and produce a characteristic fluorescence where they strike the glass walls at the other end of the tube. These 'rays' proceed in straight lines. They can be deflected by magnets. They are, as Crookes (1832–1919) discovered, streams of electrons. When they impinge on the glass walls they are stopped; but in being stopped they excite a form of radiation so penetrating that it can pass through the wooden shutter protecting a photographic plate and actually affect the plate. This form of radiation constitutes the famous X-rays of Röntgen. X-rays thus result from the impact of swiftly moving electrons on ordinary matter.

Ten years after their discovery Barkla shewed that X-rays are transverse waves like those of light. They are, in fact, of the same nature as light-waves save that, as we have already indicated, they are some 10,000 times smaller in wave-length than those of light. Their smaller wave-length gives them their greater penetrative power, their greater 'hardness'.

Photography by X-rays.

The capacity of matter for stopping X-rays varies roughly as the fourth power of the atomic number of the element of which the matter is made. Flesh consists mainly of carbon, oxygen, nitrogen and hydrogen: their atomic numbers are 6, 8, 7, and 1. Calcium, of which the bones are mainly made, has an atomic number 20. Hence it is 160,000 times as effective as hydrogen in stopping X-rays. Lead has 82 for its atomic number, so that it is about 280 times as effective in resisting power as calcium. Consequently the bones of animals come out as dark shadows in X-ray photographs, but bullets are shewn completely black.

X-ray spectra.

Instead of allowing the electrons in a Crookes' tube to strike the glass we can insert a metal plate which they shall strike. It is then found that, when they are stopped by the plate, two kinds of X-rays are produced. One kind is a mixture which has no particular relation to the metal of which the plate is made. The other kind consists of rays characteristic of the substance which emits them. These latter characteristic X-rays must manifest some property which is connected with the structure of the atoms of the element from which they arise. We shall explain later, in Lecture IX, how the study of the X-ray spectra of substances has become an important branch of modern physical research.

§ 155. *The radio-active process*.*

In the year 1896 Becquerel discovered that certain uranium salts spontaneously emitted a radiation which could to some extent pass through matter, could affect a photographic plate and could make air a conductor of electricity. Shortly afterwards it was found that another element radium, which is excessively rare, possessed similar properties in a still higher degree. Continuous investigation has now revealed that uranium, protactinium and thorium, which are three of the heaviest elements known to us, spontaneously disintegrate. Each produces a series of other radio-active elements, and radium belongs to the uranium series. The final products of the disintegration of each are

* An authoritative and comprehensive account of radio-active transformations is given by F. Soddy, *The Interpretation of the Atom.* Murray, 1932. Professor Soddy kindly allowed me to see the proof-sheets of his book before it was published and in several instances I used them to correct or amplify statements in the present lectures.

electrons, helium and a form of lead. In each case there is a series of complicated transformations before the end of the process is reached. In the course of the transformations some 40 radio-active substances make their appearance. This process is a veritable change of one element into another: in fact, the alchemists' dream of the transmutation of the elements has come true. Unfortunately, we do not get gold from lead. From radium, which is infinitely more precious than gold, we get lead.

The law of radio-active decomposition.

We do not know the cause of the disintegration of radio-active elements. All we can say is that the atoms of certain heavy elements are unstable. We cannot prevent radio-activity, neither can we in the laboratory hasten or retard the rate at which decomposition proceeds. Einstein has deduced from the quantum theory a formula for *negative absorption* which indicates the effect which temperature has in stimulating radio-activity. According to his formula even a temperature of a million degrees Centigrade would have little effect in accelerating the emission of the so-called γ-rays, the radiation of extremely short wavelength which is one product of radio-active disintegration.

The law of decomposition for every radio-active element is believed to be simple. In a given time a certain proportion of the atoms die. The rate of decomposition is usually measured by the time in which half of a given collection decomposes. For uranium this time is computed to be about 4000 or 5000 million years. For radium the period is known within one or two per cent. to be 1600 years*. For the inert gas radon, an isotope of niton, the period is about 3·83 days. We may put what happens in mathematical form by saying that of N atoms of any radio-active substance, kN will disintegrate in any given time, where k is a fixed *radio-active constant* depending only on the substance.

The law of radio-active disintegration admits of simple mathematical expression.

Suppose that Q atoms of a radio-active substance exist. Then $-\Delta Q$ may be taken to be the number which break up in time Δt. This number is proportional to Q. Hence we may write

$$-\frac{\Delta Q}{\Delta t} = kQ,$$

or
$$\frac{dQ}{dt} = -kQ.$$

* Soddy, *loc. cit.* p. 61.

Therefore on integration we have $Q = Q_0 e^{-kt}$, where Q_0 is the number of atoms existing when $t = 0$. Thus, of Q atoms, the number left after time t is Qe^{-kt}. Experimental observations give, when plotted, a curve exactly agreeing with this exponential law.

The number of atoms which will break up in an interval dt at time t is

$$Q\{e^{-kt} - e^{-k\{t+dt\}}\} = Qe^{-kt}k\,dt, \text{ approximately.}$$

Thus the average life of the atoms of the radio-active substance is

$$\int_0^\infty Qe^{-kt}kt\,dt \Big/ \int_0^\infty Qe^{-kt}k\,dt = 1/k.$$

In other words, the average life of a radio-active substance is measured by the inverse of the radio-active constant.

Let us now investigate the relation after a long period of time between, on the one hand, the number of atoms in existence of a long-lived radio-active substance and, on the other hand, the number of its relatively short-lived child. We will assume that the average life of the parent is $1/k$ and that of the child $1/l$, where k is very small compared with l.

Then, of Q atoms of the parent, Qe^{-kt} are left after a time t. Now $Qe^{-kt_1}k\,dt_1$ atoms will break up to produce the child in an interval dt_1 at time t_1. Each will produce an atom of the child; and of such atoms we shall have

$$Qe^{-kt_1}k\,dt_1\,e^{-l(t-t_1)}$$

left at time t, where $t > t_1$.

Thus the total number of atoms of the child which remain in existence at time t will be

$$\int_0^t Qe^{-lt}e^{(l-k)t_1}k\,dt_1 = \frac{k}{l-k}Q\{e^{-kt} - e^{-lt}\}.$$

Thus after a time t the proportion of the number of atoms of the parent to the number of atoms of the child will be

$$\frac{l-k}{k}\Big/\{1 - e^{(k-l)t}\}.$$

When t is large this ratio $= (l-k)/k$. If, moreover, k is small compared with l, this ratio $= l/k$ approximately. In other words the proportion between the elements is in the ratio of their respective average lives.

§ 156. *The age of the earth.*

It is clear, from the kind of investigation just given, that if we can find the ratio between the uranium in any lump of rock and the lead which has resulted from its decomposition we can estimate the age of the rock, provided we may assume that all the lead present has resulted from the decomposition of an original mass of uranium.

In this way estimates have been made of the age of various rocks in the earth's surface. They are necessarily dependent on the accuracy of the assumption made. But they have led to the conclusion that rocks of the Carboniferous period have an age of some 280 million years, while certain pre-Cambrian rocks are some 1300 million years old. Such conclusions are naturally important, especially because we know of no better way of discovering the ages of the different geological strata of the earth. A fuller account of the results reached will be given subsequently in Lecture XI (§ 318). We will merely observe now that, if k be the radio-active constant for uranium and if one-half of a collection of uranium decomposes in $4 \cdot 5 \times 10^9$ years, then

$$4 \cdot 5 \times 10^9 = (\log_e 2)/k,$$

so that $1/k = 6 \cdot 6 \times 10^9$ years is the average life of a uranium atom. This is probably as good an estimate as can be obtained at the present time.

§ 157. *The puzzle of uranium.*

It appears to be a matter of pure chance as to which atoms of a radio-active substance explode. The half of any given quantity of radium will have exploded in 1600 years: but of the remainder only one-half will explode in the next 1600 years. Age does not alter the proportion of the atoms of a substance which die in a given time. Why radio-active elements should thus behave is inexplicable. We only know statistical averages.

Moreover, we know of no converse process of the building up of atoms. The process of decomposition of atoms of high atomic number liberates immense quantities of energy, so that for the reverse process equally large amounts of energy would have to be supplied. Such energy is doubtless available in the suns which are scattered through space; though, as we shall see, physicists feel it necessary to invoke the possible annihilation of matter to supply sufficient energy for the radiation actually emitted by such suns. There is, in fact, no evidence whatever of the building up of heavy atoms in the fixed stars. "Our universe", as Bertrand, Earl Russell, acutely says, "*seems* like a clock running down with no mechanism for winding it up again." "All the uranium in the world is breaking down and we know of no source from which new uranium can come. Under these circumstances it seems strange that there should be any uranium."

There is, it would appear, no other reason for the continued existence on the earth of uranium than the fact that all which now survives was in the earth when the latter was ejected from the sun. If it be true that the sun has existed for a time measured by millions of millions of years (*vide* § 273 *infra*), and if the earth was torn out of the sun in the great disruption which produced the planets some 2000–4000 million years ago, then presumably there must have been some machinery for preserving uranium from radio-active disintegration while it was in the sun. It may be that in the sun's interior the heat is so great that all atoms are there deprived of most of their rings of electrons and that in such a condition radio-activity ceases. It may also be that elements, unknown on earth, of higher atomic number than 92, can exist in the sun's interior and that uranium results from their almost incredibly slow disintegration. At present speculation is necessarily indecisive.

§ 158. *The products of radio-active disintegration.*

When the radio-active elements disintegrate the process is accompanied by the expulsion of 'rays'. Of these rays three types can be observed in different cases: they are usually called α-, β- and γ-rays.

The α-rays consist of atoms of helium, each with a double positive charge. The discovery of this fact is due to Lord Rutherford. He found that α-rays could be deflected from their paths by strong electrostatic and electro-magnetic fields. They therefore consisted of charged particles. He further shewed that it was possible to make numerical estimates of the atomic weights of the particles. It thus became clear that an α-particle is a doubly ionised atom of helium, that is, an atom which has lost two electrons. These particles are ejected with great velocities. Such velocities vary with the nature of the radio-active substance which emits them, but they are of the order of 2×10^9 centimetres per second: in fact, they vary roughly from one-fifteenth to one-twentieth of the velocity of light. (It will be recollected that the velocity of light is 3×10^{10} centimetres per second.)

The α-particles have little penetrating power and can be stopped by a sheet of paper. When they pass through a rarefied gas or a very thin plate of metal they go through its atoms as if the latter were not present, save that in rare circumstances they are sharply deflected. Now it must be remembered that the helium-nucleus is so much heavier than an electron that, when it hits an electron, it will not be deflected from its path. Hence, as Sir W. H. Bragg convincingly argued, the observed phenomenon suggests that each atom of the gas or metal consists of a solar system of electrons rotating round a central nucleus and that there is so much empty space within the atom that the helium-nucleus can pass freely through it unless it happens to hit the nucleus of the atom. By a most ingenious experiment due to C. T. R. Wilson the paths of the helium-nuclei under such conditions can be actually photographed.

The β-rays consist of electrons. They are similar to the cathode rays of a Crookes' tube save that the velocity of the electron is greater. Velocities which are within one-half of one per cent. of the velocity of light have been observed. It is, as we have previously said, at such large speeds that Einstein's law of the increase of mass with velocity can be experimentally verified. The penetrating power of the β-rays is naturally much greater than that of the α-rays: they can, however, usually be stopped by a sheet of aluminium of a quarter of an inch in thickness.

The γ-rays are true radiation: that is to say, they consist of waves of energy which travel with the velocity of light and are not accompanied in their motion by electrical or material particles. They are in all respects similar to X-rays save that their wave-length is only a fraction of the hardest X-rays (those of shortest wave-length) produced by a Crookes' tube. They are the most penetrative rays known to physicists, with the exception of 'cosmic radiation' (§ 300). The X-rays are produced when swiftly moving electrons strike atoms: and it is surmised that the γ-rays are produced when an α-particle, excited to a higher level by β-ray emission, jumps again to its normal or ground level, the whole process taking place within the nucleus of the atom*.

What happens when an atom of radio-active element breaks up?

Detailed research has led to the conclusion that the atom consists of a nucleus round which a number of electrons form a satellite system and that the α-rays and β-rays result from the break-up of the nucleus. The α-rays can have no other origin: we must assume that helium-nuclei are constituents of the nucleus of the radio-active element. Since, moreover, some radio-active elements change into others merely by shooting out β-rays, there is high probability that these latter rays must similarly come from the nucleus, and this conclusion is confirmed by other experimental results.

§ 159. *The electrical constitution of matter.*

We can now give a brief description of what is believed to be the electrical constitution of matter.

* Soddy, *loc. cit.* p. 298.

Every atom of every element normally consists of a nucleus round which a number of electrons are revolving. (The question as to how far a space-time description is applicable within the atom must be left over for the present: some discussion of the question is given later in § 211.) The number of satellite electrons, when the atom is electrically neutral, is the *atomic number* of the element. It is equal to the net positive charge on the nucleus, which itself consists of a number of protons (or hydrogen-nuclei) and electrons united by forces whose nature is at present a puzzle. Since the mass of an electron is only about 1/1840th of the mass of a proton, the mass of the nucleus of an atom determines its *atomic weight*.

The hydrogen atom is in structure the most simple of all. It consists of a positively charged proton round which one electron is revolving. If the electron be removed we are left with the nucleus or, as it is sometimes termed, the hydrogen-ion with a single positive charge.

The next most simple atom is that of helium, which consists of a nucleus round which two electrons are revolving. If the atomic weight of hydrogen is 1·008, that of helium is 4. We must therefore assume that in the helium-nucleus there are four protons. There must also be two electrons in it; for, if there be, the positive charge on the nucleus is 2 and this allows two electrons to form the planetary system of helium.

Inasmuch as radio-active disintegration leads to helium-nuclei and not to hydrogen-nuclei, it is clear that the helium-nucleus must be extremely stable. Much energy must therefore be needed for its disintegration. This suggests that when four hydrogen-nuclei and two electrons unite to form a helium-nucleus, there is a great loss of energy and that the mass of this energy represents the difference between $4 \times 1·008$ and 4. In other words, the energy set free when a helium-nucleus is made out of protons and electrons is the difference between the masses of four hydrogen-nuclei and one helium-nucleus. If this surmise is true, an enormous amount of energy is produced by the formation of a helium-nucleus. It has been calculated that there is thus produced some 60,000,000 times as much energy as we get in ordinary chemical combinations of atoms.

Hydrogen has thus atomic weight 1·008 and atomic number 1. Helium has atomic weight 4 and atomic number 2.

§ 160. *The ordering of the elements.*

The modern theory of atomic structure is founded on the work of the Danish physicist Niels Bohr, which in its most significant features appeared in the year 1913. But it was Moseley who, about the same time, finally reduced the chemical elements to order. His classification of the elements by atomic *number*, and not by atomic *weight*, leads to a periodic table which is completely the ideal sought by Mendeléev. All the elements, as we have already stated in § 26, can be arranged in a series of which the atomic numbers differ by unity. That the whole of the elements should thus correspond to a numerical sequence is a result as surprising as it is beautiful.

Moseley's investigations shewed that in the list of chemical elements ordered by their atomic numbers we may expect 92 entries. We have no reason to expect more entries inasmuch as the elements corresponding to the highest numbers are radio-active: they continuously disintegrate without external stimuli. In the opinion of Sommerfeld*, "the facts of radio-active decay encourage the view that elements heavier than uranium are possible in themselves although they cannot exist under the conditions of our earth". But, to illustrate the perplexity which surrounds the question, we may point out that potassium, which has the low atomic number 19, is believed to be faintly radio-active.

When Moseley's investigations were first published, there were six empty places in his list. Four of these, numbered 43, 61, 72 and 75, have since been filled by elements which have been discovered; and there now remain only the places numbered 85 and 87. Bohr's theory of atomic structure gave such an arrangement of the electrons of the unknown elements as made it possible to predict what their chemical properties and spectra would be when they were found. Belief in the substantial accuracy of Bohr's theory has naturally been strengthened by the correctness of the predictions.

One example of the success of such predictions is most striking. Before the element with atomic number 72 had been discovered, Bohr's theory was used to shew that it must in its chemical properties differ markedly from the trivalent rare earths and shew a considerable resemblance to zirconium, which is a tetravalent element of atomic number 40. Zirconium is a fairly common, though useless, element. When some of its ores were examined in Copenhagen a few years after the end of the Great War, two physicists, Hevesy and Coster, found that they contained up to as much as 10 per cent. (more recent investigators have found 30 per cent.) of the new element. By its discoverers it was

* A. Sommerfeld, *Atomic Structure and Spectral Lines*. Translated by H. L. Brose. Methuen, 1928, p. 58.

named hafnium, Hafnia being the equivalent of Copenhagen. Thus, owing to a similarity of properties, hafnium was successfully hidden by zirconium. Though the new element so long eluded discovery, there is said to be a greater proportion of it in the earth's crust as a whole than of gold in the quartz reefs from which the precious metal is crushed.

The first two elements of Moseley's list are, as we have said, hydrogen and helium. Then follows lithium of atomic number 3. Then, in order, we have beryllium, boron, carbon,... up to uranium of atomic number 92. Presumably the undiscovered elements, of atomic numbers 85 and 87 respectively, are rare and will before long be found.

We have said that the atomic number defines an element by specifying alike its nuclear charge and the number of its satellite electrons. For instance, carbon of atomic number 6 has, when electrically neutral, six satellite electrons. Corresponding to these electrons its nucleus has a sixfold positive charge. But, it is important to observe, the charge on the nucleus of an atom does *not* determine its weight. Atoms of the same atomic number can have different atomic weights. We can, in fact, build out of protons and electrons nuclei of different weights which have the same residual positive charge. With these different nuclei we can construct atoms with a similar arrangement of electron satellites. All such atoms, notwithstanding their different weights, will have the same chemical properties, since these latter are determined by the system of satellite electrons. Such atoms of similar chemical properties and of different atomic weights are termed *isotopes* of one another. We shall discuss them further in § 164.

§ 161. *The sizes of atoms, electrons and protons.*

We have previously seen in § 147 that there is much controversy as to the nature of the electron. In particular, its shape and size are undetermined, if indeed they can be said to exist. It may be that spatio-temporal descriptions fail when we reach objects as small as the electron. None the less such descriptions are practically adequate, as has already been indicated in § 24, when the sizes of atoms are in question. There exists at present the curious situation that, while the mathematicians and those interested in the philosophy of physics are expressing the utmost scepticism as to the size and shape of protons and electrons, the practical physicists are bombarding atoms of various elements with helium-nuclei and obtaining facts on which to base conclusions as to the size of protons and the structure of nuclei. Ultimately, of course, theoretical speculations must conform to experimental results.

In extension of the statement made in § 24, it may be now said that the diameter of the average atom under normal terrestrial conditions is about one hundred-millionth of an inch: for instance, according to Bohr's theory, the diameter of the hydrogen atom in its normal (un-excited) state is $1 \cdot 056 \times 10^{-8}$ cm. or $4 \cdot 15 \times 10^{-9}$ in. The lighter atoms have smaller domains than 10^{-8} in. and the heavier somewhat larger. But a factor of three or four will take us from the smallest to the largest. Within such a minute space the electrons of an undisturbed atom will exist as satellites. When an atom is disturbed or 'excited' by radiation impinging upon it, its satellite electrons either fly away, when it be-comes ionised, or they may jump to orbital regions of existence larger than the normal: in the latter case we must assume that the 'size' of the atom increases.

If an electron can be regarded as a small sphere of electricity and if all its mass be due to its charge then, as we have said in § 146, its diameter must be about 4×10^{-13} cm. Thus its linear dimensions will be some thirty-thousandth of those of the average atom.

If the proton, or hydrogen-nucleus, be also a small sphere, and if all its mass be due to its (positive) charge, its diameter should be 1/1840th of the diameter of the electron. For, as we have seen in § 146, the mass of the proton must under the assumptions made be inversely pro-portional to its radius; and there is no doubt that the mass of the proton is about 1840 times that of the electron. We should thus conclude that the proton has a diameter of order 10^{-16} cm. On the other hand, ex-periments on collisions between helium-nuclei and atoms of the two most simple elements seem to shew that a proton behaves as an elastic sphere of radius 2×10^{-13} cm., while a helium-nucleus is an elastic oblate spheroid with semi-minor axis of 2×10^{-13} cm., and semi-major axis between three and four times as great*. If such results are accurate, the assumed size of the electron will be approximately that of the proton. But that one estimate of the size of a proton can be nearly 2000 times as great as the other shews the uncertainty of our present knowledge. Whatever conclusion be accepted, it remains true that by far the greater part of the interior of the atom of even one of the heaviest elements is empty space. Even in a solid not more than a millionth of a millionth of the volume is occupied by protons and electrons.

* Soddy, *loc. cit.* p. 293.

§162. *Bohr's model of the atom.*

The problem of the arrangement of the orbits (if, indeed, they be orbits) of the electrons in an atom is difficult: but an ingenious solution, propounded by Bohr and developed by Sommerfeld, has won general acceptance.

It must be clearly understood that Bohr has suggested a *model* to represent by concrete imagery the structure of a typical atom. In it the electron is assumed to be the little billiard-ball to which we always turn lovingly when we attempt to picture material reality. Such a conception of the electron is certainly inadequate; and, in consequence, *the whole Bohr model is not ultimate truth but a convenient aid to the imagination.* To a surprising degree the model corresponds to the results of observation; and, as we have just said, it has been shewn to have a certain predictive power. Unfortunately, it is inadequate because Bohr is forced to postulate that satellite electrons rotate in orbits within the atom but do not emit radiation in their undisturbed motion. According to the Newtonian-Maxwellian scheme of electro-dynamics, such behaviour is impossible.

Hydrogen can naturally be described by the most simple model. According to Bohr and Sommerfeld, whose investigations we shall sketch in §§ 206, 207, the single electron of the hydrogen atom may move in any one of a certain definite set of orbits, infinite in number, relatively large and small, circular and elliptic. When the atom is unexcited, that is to say when its internal energy is a minimum, its electron moves in the smallest of the possible circular orbits. This has a radius of 5×10^{-9} cm. Its velocity in this orbit is one hundred and thirty-seventh part of that of light, which is 300,000 kilometres a second. Thus the electron covers nearly 1400 miles in a second! Bohr assumes that, when the electron moves in any of the permissible orbits, it sends out no radiation as a result of its motion: radiation is only emitted when the electron jumps from one orbit to another. Moreover, the satellite electron cannot move in stable equilibrium in a series of orbits intervening between those of the permissible set, nor can it pass *gradually* from one of these permissible orbits to another. It will be seen later that, though we still await the complete elucidation of these surprising facts, it is probable that their strange character is connected with the inadequacy within the atom of our usual space-time concepts.

Helium has two electrons as satellites of its doubly charged nucleus. Each can move in one of a definite set of orbits, infinite in number. When the helium atom is unexcited, corresponding orbits of the two electrons are believed to be of the same size and shape; but according to the Pauli exclusion principle (§ 208) the electrons must be spinning in opposite directions. The two electrons, as is said, belong to the same *ring* or *shell*.

After helium Bohr suggests that the form of the structure of the unexcited atom changes and that we begin an outer ring or shell of electrons. The eight elements from lithium to neon have respectively from one to eight electrons in this outer shell. Thus unelectrified neon has two electrons in an inner ring and eight in an outer shell. The eight forming the outer shell make a complete and self-satisfied system. Thus neon, like helium, does not enter into chemical combination with other elements: it is inert. The Germans call such inert elements 'noble': they refuse to associate with the rest of their kind.

With unexcited sodium begins the formation of a third shell of electrons. This type of structure ends, after eight electrons have been added, with the inert gas argon of atomic number 18. With potassium of atomic number 19 we begin a fourth group of elements. This group contains 18 elements: we do not reach an inert element until we get krypton of atomic number 36. The result is surprising, for we should have expected another group of eight elements. But the evidence afforded by the chemical and spectroscopic properties of members of the group is decisive. Bohr supposes that the added electrons are not all in the new outermost shell, but that some of them are in the previous shell, which becomes able to hold more electrons when it has others outside it. Thus krypton in its successively larger shells has 2, 8, 18 and 8 electrons. The fifth group similarly consists of 18 elements, ranging from rubidium of atomic number 37 to the inert xenon of atomic number 54. In the successive shells of xenon there are in order 2, 8, 18, 18 and 8 electrons.

In the sixth group there are 32 elements of which one remains to be discovered. The group contains heavy metals with highly complex nuclei, like gold and lead. All the atoms of the group have six shells of electrons. In the outer shell, as always, there will be from one to eight electrons. Thus niton*, atomic number 86, the inert atom with which the group concludes, will have eight electrons in its sixth shell, the numbers in successive shells being, in order, 2, 8, 18, 32, 18 and 8.

After the sixth group of the Periodic Table there remain only six

---

* The inert element niton consists of at least three highly radio-active isotopes, radion, thoron, actinion, which may be distinguished by their differing radio-active constants.

elements, one of which is still to be discovered. All the known elements of this set, of which uranium (atomic number 92) is the last, are breaking down through their radio-activity. Presumably no more complex elements can exist because their atoms would be even more unstable than those of the radio-active series. But it may be, as we have already suggested, that under other conditions of pressure and temperature than those of the earth's surface, for example in the sun and other stars, more complex atoms, or the nuclei of such, can exist. We must not assume that terrestrial chemistry holds all the secrets of the Universe.

§ 163. *Chemical combination.*

Bohr's theory is, in part, built upon the assumption, confirmed by much experimental evidence, that the chemical properties of an element depend almost entirely on its outer shell of electrons. According to the theory there are, in the outer shell or ring of every element, from one to eight electrons. When atoms combine chemically they will, if possible, form a molecule with a full number of electrons in an outer shell. Thus chlorine with seven electrons in an outer shell combines readily with sodium, which has but one such electron, to make common salt. Without entering into further detail it suffices to say that chemical combination is an electrical phenomenon.

§ 164. *Isotopes.*

Suppose that a radio-active substance expels a helium-particle from its nucleus. Its atomic weight will be reduced by 4: and, because the helium-nucleus has a double positive charge, the atomic number will be reduced by 2. Let now the new element expel two electrons from its nucleus: by such action its atomic number will be increased by 2 and its atomic weight will be practically unaltered. Thus as a result of the two changes we shall get a new element of the same atomic number as that with which we began, but with its atomic weight reduced by 4.

The original and final elements will be alike as regards their chemical properties. The same is true of what are called their ordinary spectra and of their X-ray spectra; for all these phenomena depend solely on the structure of the planetary system of the atom and each element will have the same type of planetary system. But, as we have seen, the elements will differ in the structure of their nuclei and in their atomic weights. They are the isotopes already mentioned in § 26; and their discovery by Aston has made us realise that the same chemical element can be a mixture of substances of different atomic weights. Chlorine consists of two isotopes of atomic weights 35 and 37 respectively. Mercury appears to be a mixture of no less than seven isotopes. Tin, so far as is known, is the most complex element with eleven isotopes.

It appears that, with the exception of hydrogen, all the elements have atomic weights which are whole numbers, the fractions given in the older chemical tables being due to the extent to which, in ordinary specimens of the elements, the isotopes are mixed together. The fact that in all such ordinary specimens the mixture is in definite proportions suggests that it arose very far back in the history of the Universe.

The investigation of isotopes has proceeded rapidly of recent years. Much progress has been achieved by means of the mass-spectrograph of Aston. In this instrument ions of the different elements are passed through a highly exhausted Crookes' tube, under the influence of known co-planar electric and magnetic fields which deviate the ions in different directions. The arrangement is such that the beam of ions is made convergent, so that it can be brought to a focus on a photographic plate. Needless to say, the interpretation of the photographs demands experience and knowledge. For instance, hydrocarbons, from the vapour of the grease used to lubricate the taps, are always present in the tube and represented in the photographs.

It is found that isotopes of the elements of even atomic number are much more common than isotopes of odd atomic number. There appear, in fact, so far as present investigations go, to be only four homogeneous elements of even atomic number. Thirty elements of odd atomic number have been examined. Of them seventeen are homogeneous and the remaining thirteen possess only two isotopes each.

The investigations have also led to the discovery of *isobars*, which are chemically different elements having the same atomic weight. For instance, copper and zinc each possess an isotope of atomic weight 65. Isobars only appear with the more complex elements, chromium of atomic number 24 being the first to have an isobar of which the atomic weight is 54. The existence of isobars indicates that stable nuclei of the more complex elements can be formed in a number of different ways out of the same number of protons, though by incorporating a different number of electrons. Whether elements whose nuclei are formed from the same number of protons and electrons always have the same nuclear structure is unknown.

§ 165. *The spectrum of an element.*

It is well known that, when a pinch of salt is dropped into the colour-less flame of a Bunsen burner, a bright yellow light is produced. What is the cause?

The first step in the investigation is to split up the light into its component parts by means of a spectroscope. The essential part of the spectroscope is, of course, a prism which bends light of different wave-lengths at different angles. Now the eye is a curious product of human evolution which can recognise different wave-lengths of visible light as different colours. The spectroscope thus produces a series of lines, of different colours and intensities, which correspond to the different wave-lengths contained in the composite light which is being investigated. These lines, which thus result from strongly heating a substance, constitute its spectrum.

It is found that each element produces a characteristic series of lines. The yellow flame of common salt is due to the fact that the spectrum of sodium has two yellow lines of especial intensity. But there are other lines in the spectrum of sodium: and the chlorine of common salt itself gives rise to a series of lines characteristic of the element chlorine. Such facts enable us by spectrum-analysis to discover the presence of various elements in compounds which we investigate. The eye can only recognise such parts of the spectrum as correspond to visible wave-lengths of radiation. But the photographic plate is sensitive to light of shorter wave-lengths and various heat-measuring electrical instruments can detect light of longer wave-lengths.

How a spectrum originates.

We are led, by the foregoing facts of observation, to believe that the spectrum characteristic of an element is due to changes inside the atom. When light is emitted by a small portion of an element, a number of the atoms in this portion are sending out energy in the form of radiation. Different atoms are doubtless sending out radiant energy of different wave-lengths. But if a large number of the atoms are sending out energy of a particular wave-length, the corresponding line of the spectrum will have a special intensity. In spectroscopic work, in fact, we observe a statistical phenomenon. It is, however, important to emphasise that the atoms of a particular element cannot send out radiation of continuously varying wave-lengths. Only a certain discontinuous series of wave-lengths is produced by the atoms of any particular element, and thus we get the discontinuous lines of the spectrum.

When we put sodium into a flame to make it send out its character-istic waves of energy, the energy emitted must come ultimately from the heat of the flame. Hence we believe that the energy of the flame causes the atoms of the sodium to absorb energy. In thus absorbing energy the electrons in the atom must pass, in the Bohr model, from their old orbits near the nucleus to others more distant. When the electrons subsequently return to their old orbits they will send out, as light, the energy which had been absorbed.

§ 166. *A comparison with the solar system.*

Let us imagine that the Bohr model of the atom is satisfactory and that it is so magnified that with regard to it we can use the familiar imagery of the solar system. Then we say that, when the atom is put into a Bunsen burner, the flame causes the earth to move round the sun in a larger orbit than the normal. When the earth gives up its acquired energy, it passes back to the orbit from which it started. But because the light emitted by the atom gives a discontinuous spectrum the earth must jump from one orbit to another. It can only move in some one of a definite series of orbits: and, in jumping from one to another of these, it emits different kinds of light-rays. Moreover, the other planets be-have in the same way. No planet can pass *continuously* from a larger to a smaller orbit or *vice versâ*.

Such a description of what happens inside an excited atom is, of course, inexplicable if Newtonian dynamics be true within the atom. But, by assuming the truth of such a picture, Bohr gave for the hydrogen atom an astonishingly satisfactory explanation of its spectral lines.

§ 167. *The spectrum of hydrogen.*

Hydrogen, because of the great simplicity of its atomic structure, is naturally the element whose spectrum is most easily investigated. The number of its spectral lines is very large. But Ritz in the year 1908, developing a discovery made by Balmer in the year 1885, shewed empirically that the wave-numbers of these lines are given by the formula

$$R \left(\frac{1}{n^2} - \frac{1}{k^2} \right),$$

where R is a certain constant (Rydberg's constant) and n and k are any whole numbers, k being greater than n. (The wave-number is the number of waves of a ray of light in a centimetre: it is the reciprocal of the wave-length.) It was clear that there must be some reason why the wave-lengths should all correspond to this remarkably simple formula. But that reason was not given until Bohr published his description of the atom in the year 1913. He then shewed that the Balmer-Ritz series could be explained on Newtonian principles if we assume that the electron of hydrogen normally moves in its smallest possible circle with a radius of approximately 5×10^{-9} cm., and if its only other possible orbits have radii n^2 times as large, where n is anyone of the numbers 2, 3, 4, ... With these assumptions it follows that, when the electron jumps from an orbit of radius proportional to k^2 to one of radius proportional to n^2 ($k > n$), the wave-number of its corresponding spectral line will be

$$R\left(\frac{1}{n^2} - \frac{1}{k^2}\right).$$

In the above concise statement we have, of course, only given a rough description of the spectral theory of the hydrogen atom. We would add that the observed values of the wave-length can also be deduced if it is allowed that the orbits of the electron can be, not circular, but elliptic with a discontinuous series of eccentricities. Further refinements, due to Sommerfeld, follow from the fact that the mass of the electron varies with its velocity so that the axes of the possible elliptic orbits revolve in their own plane. In this way the 'fine structure' of each of the hydrogen lines of the Balmer-Ritz series was explained. Bohr and Sommerfeld thus shewed how on Newtonian principles, modified when necessary by Einstein's development of them, they could make a model which accounted for normal features of the hydrogen spectrum.

§ 168. *Perplexities due to the Bohr model.*

Yet we must reiterate that the fundamental assumption of the discontinuity of possible orbits within the atom is wholly incompatible with Newtonian dynamics.

The electron ought gradually to pass from one orbit to another. It does nothing of the kind. It proceeds by a finite jump without apparently passing over the intermediate space. The constitution of the atom thus changes by a revolution, which we may liken to that which ended the Czarist *régime* in Russia: it does not change by the evolutionary process characteristic of our own political development. By the success of the Bohr model physicists were obviously brought into the presence of facts likely to cause a fundamental revolution in their ideas of the nature of the electron and its relation to space. In § 147 we have already hinted at the new speculations. Any further discussion must be postponed until the quantum theory has been described in Lecture IX.

But there is a further perplexity. When an electron jumps from, say, the orbit of radius 3^2, it may jump to the orbit of radius 2^2 or it may jump at once to the orbit of radius 1^2. And it seems to know at the beginning which jump it is going to take and arranges things accordingly. As Kramers and Holst say*: "We can no more give the reason why one given electron at a given time determines to make a double jump while another decides to make a single jump or not to jump at all, than we can say why a certain radium nucleus among many explodes at a given moment".

Why should an inanimate object like an electron appear to anticipate the end of a movement before it is begun? Is there foresight in the electron and therefore nascent mind at the very basis of creation? The possibility suggests a Universe of monads (§ 438) such as Leibniz imagined and James Ward felt worthy of acceptance.

§ 169.　Is free-will possible in inanimate nature?

Poincaré found a somewhat similar suggestiveness in the dynamical principle of least action. He said†:

The very enunciation of the principle of least action somewhat shocks us. A material molecule, under the action of no forces but constrained to move on a surface, will take, in going from one point to another, a geodesic path, that is to say the shortest possible path. This molecule seems to know the point to which it wishes to go, to foresee the time which it will take to follow such or such a path, and to choose in consequence the most convenient. The enunciation presents it, so to say, as an animated and free being. It is clear that it would be better to replace the formulation of the principle by a form less shocking; by one in which, as the philosophers say, final causes do not seem to be substituted for efficient causes.

It is certainly strange that modern physics should present us with apparent examples of spontaneity and foresight. In human affairs, statistical averages mask the operation of free-will and supply arguments in favour of a rigid determinism which is relatively easy to justify by plausible argument, though it is contrary to our constant and invariable experience. Statistical averages might similarly mask individual initiative in the case of the atoms of a radio-active element. An atom might resolve to set out on an 'adventure brave and new', as an Irish peasant might have resolved to emigrate to the United States

* H. A. Kramers and H. Holst, The Atom and the Bohr Theory of its Structure. Gyldendal, 1923, p. 137.

† H. Poincaré, La Science et l'Hypothèse. Flammarion, n.d., p. 154.

in days before America imposed restrictions on the number of immigrants she admitted. There are far more atoms in a fragment of radio-active matter than people in Ireland: and we should therefore expect statistical averages to be more constant. But we can only, in the present state of knowledge, hint at possibilities and leave open a set of enquiries of fundamental importance.

What surprises us most in connection with Bohr's theory of the atom is that, though the fundamental assumptions are so contrary to any possible in the scheme of Newtonian dynamics, yet all details follow from Newtonian analysis. In the same connection Einstein's modification of Newton's theory of gravitation is, as Bertrand, Earl Russell, has well said, "the crown of the old dynamics and not the beginning of the new". "Thus the old principles, though incomplete, must be true up to a point."

§ 170. *Some further enquiries.*

The brief sketch of the electrical theory of matter given in the present lecture need only be compared with the ideas and knowledge of the year 1890 to shew how vast has been the progress of our understanding as to the nature of the stuff of which the material world is composed. But, as always, progress has only served to reveal the extent of our ignorance and to disclose a vast number of perplexities and problems. Fundamental is the problem of the nature of the electron, which carries enquiries into the validity of our concepts of space and time But almost equally difficult is the question of the proton, its nature and relation to such ultimates. Then, when we leave enquiries which thus tend to carry us to the region of metaphysics, there remain problems connected with those aggregates of protons and electrons which constitute the nuclei of the different elements. How are the nuclei formed? Why are helium-nuclei apparently common constituents of the nuclei of the radio-active elements? Are there, as we should expect, nuclear constituents formed by the close union of a single proton and a single electron, particles which are electrically neutral though their mass is that of a proton? Why are some elements stable and others highly unstable? Is artificial disintegration of elements possible?

Such questions indicate some of the enquiries with regard to which experimental research is at present active. Two recent results are of great interest. Chadwick, bombarding beryllium by α-rays, has found a type of radiation, more penetrating than γ-rays, which he suggests consists of *neutrons*, formed of a single proton and electron in intimate union. Again, in the early part of the year 1932, Cockcroft and Walton bombarded lithium with protons of a few hundred thousand volts and discovered that the lithium nucleus can absorb the protons and break up into two α-particles. If Li^7 denotes lithium of atomic weight 7, the process of disintegration seems to be represented by

$$Li^7 + H^1 = 2He^4.$$

Thus lithium in its bombardment by hydrogen is transformed into helium.

We shall expect that similarly fluorine will be decomposed into oxygen and helium according to the formula

$$Fl^{19} + H^1 = He^4 + O^{16}.$$

There is thus evidence that a beginning is being made with that transmutation of the elements which was the dream of the medieval alchemists. Possibly the artificial synthesis of gold will some day be effected. It belongs to a region of experiment where no-one can predict the limits of success.

Lecture viii

HEAT AND LIGHT

§ 171. *Heat and change of state of bodies.*

The sensations of heat and cold are some of the most familiar in our experience: they are so fundamental as to be practically incapable of definition. When we touch a cold body we have the feeling that heat is passing out of us: we are losing something. Thus, as we have previously said, it was for long believed that heat was an element; and the idea was subsequently transformed into the belief (§ 16) that in combustion there was an escape of the element phlogiston. We now know that heat is a mode of motion or, in other words, a form of energy. When a man touches a cold object energy escapes from his body to the object.

Probably the most significant property of heat is its power to change the state of substances. Exactly the same substance exists as ice, water and steam. Its differing states are due to the fact that heat-energy applied to ice relaxes the rigid cohesion of its molecules so that they move freely as in water, while further heat-energy will dissociate the molecules of water from one another so that they fly apart as steam. The familiar changes of state of water appear to be an example of a universal phenomenon. Under suitable conditions of pressure and temperature so-called permanent gases, such as air, can be liquefied and even solidified, while the most intractable solids can be liquefied.

§ 172. *Pressure and temperature.*

Usually solids and liquids expand when heated: but this is not an invariable law for, as we know, ice floats upon water. The expansion of solids and liquids under changing conditions of temperature and pressure is irregular; but the expansion of gases, especially when they are not near their liquefying point, is very approximately governed by simple laws of great utility.

Every gas exerts a *pressure* on the walls of the vessel which contains it. Such pressure, as on a piston, can be measured as a force per unit area. As was stated in Lecture II, the pressure is due to the velocity of the molecules of the gas which normally (*vide* § 196) are perfectly elastic and bombard the sides of the vessel with high velocities. If the amount of the gas in the vessel be kept constant while heat is put into it, the velocities of its molecules will become greater and hence its pressure will increase.

Temperature is such a familiar notion that we do not make the idea clearer by taking Clerk Maxwell's definition*: "the temperature of a body is its thermal state considered with reference to its power of communicating heat to other bodies". More simply a body A is at a higher temperature than a body B if A gives heat to B when they are in contact. The fundamental law of temperature is that if A and B are at the same temperature and if also B and C are at the same temperature, then A and C are at the same temperature. In other words the temperature of a body does not depend on the substance of which the body is composed.

§ 173.　*Boyle's law.*

In the year 1662, Robert Boyle, and some fourteen years later Mariotte, enunciated the law that, when the temperature is kept constant, the volume of a gas varies inversely as its pressure. This so-called law of Boyle and Mariotte is not accurately true for any gas. But it is a very good approximation to the truth for many gases, and it represents the ideal which we ascribe to a 'perfect' gas. It is equivalent to the statement that every portion of a gas exerts, on the sides of a vessel in which it is contained, the same pressure as if the other portions of the gas were not present. Dalton discovered that this fact also holds good when different gases at the same temperature are put into the same vessel: each exerts the same pressure as if the others were not present.

If p be the pressure and v the volume of a perfect gas, then, for changes of state in which the temperature is kept constant,

$$pv = \text{cons.}$$

Charles' law.

In the year 1801, Dalton published a law still sometimes called by his name. Gay-Lussac, a year later, gave the same law but stated that it had been communicated to him by Charles (1746–1823) fifteen years earlier. This law states that when the pressure of a gas is kept constant its volume, when it is raised from 0° C. to 100° C., increases by the same fraction of itself, *whatever be the substance of which the gas is made.* Our limits of temperature in this statement are the boiling and freezing points of water, but the same statement is true whatever limits of temperature be chosen.

---

* J. Clerk Maxwell, *Theory of Heat.* Longmans, 1891, p. 32.

§ 174. *The graduation of an air thermometer.*

Charles' law enables us to make an ideal thermometer. Throughout our experiment we assume that the pressure is kept constant and equal to some standard pressure.

We take a narrow uniform tube and place in it a volume of air separated from the outer air by a thread of mercury of negligible mass. We can readily graduate the tube for $0°$ C. and $100°$ C., since these temperatures are the freezing and boiling points of water. We then arbitrarily divide the tube between these two marks into 100 equal parts. Each will furnish one degree: but we do *not* say that the heat required to raise the air in the tube by $1°$ C. will be the same at different temperatures: the degrees obtained by our graduation are purely conventional. We next extend our graduation below $0°$ C. Naturally, corresponding to each degree below zero, we mark a length on our uniform tube equal to that already obtained for a degree above zero.

§ 175. *Absolute zero.*

On the air thermometer as thus graduated we can pass upwards almost indefinitely. Temperatures of several thousand degrees can be obtained in our furnaces and the temperatures within the fixed stars must run up to millions of degress on the Centigrade scale. But we cannot in the same manner pass downwards indefinitely. Experimental research points to the existence of a limit, an absolute zero, below which temperature cannot fall. This limit has never been actually reached, so that we cannot say what would happen there: but, near it, even the permanent gases are frozen.

Let us suppose that absolute zero is, on the Centigrade scale, $x°$ below $0°$ C. To find x, we shall assume that when temperature is measured from absolute zero, the volume of the air in the thermometer tube is proportional to its temperature. (By the kinetic theory of gases the assumption which we have made ought to be true for a perfect gas.)

We shall then have

$$\frac{\text{Volume at } 100° \text{ C.}}{\text{Volume at } 0° \text{ C.}} = \frac{x + 100}{x}.$$

But we know by Charles' law that the ratio on the left-hand side is constant for *all* gases: it is, in fact, $1\cdot3665$. Hence, if x is given by

$$x + 100 = 1\cdot3665x, \qquad\qquad \ldots\ldots(\text{I})$$

the volume of *any gas whatever* will be proportional to its temperature as measured from the new zero. The equation (I) gives

$$x = 273.$$

Hence on the Centigrade scale $-273°$ is called the absolute zero and temperatures measured from it are called absolute temperatures.

If now p, v and T be the pressure, volume and absolute temperature of a perfect gas, it will obey the law $\dfrac{pv}{T} = $ cons.

An alternative way of graduating a thermometer would be to estimate the temperature of a substance by the heat which it gives out as it cools to a standard temperature. But the amount of heat required to raise unit mass of a body by unit temperature varies with the temperature and the variation differs for different bodies. This method would not therefore give us a more satisfactory graduation than that of the air thermometer which we have just described.

The general theory of thermodynamics, as we shall see shortly, enables us to make a temperature scale which shall be independent of the properties of any particular substance. This scale, however, as was first established experimentally by Joule and Lord Kelvin (1824–1907), is almost exactly that of our air thermometer.

§176. *Work done by an expanding gas.*

When a gas expands it does work, for its pressure moves through a certain distance.

If we imagine that the expansion moves a piston of area A through a small distance ds the work done will be $pA\,ds$, where p is the pressure of the gas per unit area.

But the volume of the gas will be increased by the small amount $dv = A\,ds$.

Hence the work done will be $p\,dv$.

Thus the total work done in the expansion of a gas from volume v_1 to volume v_2 is

$$\int_{v_1}^{v_2} p\,dv,$$

where p is the pressure when the volume is v.

Suppose now that we draw a diagram in which the pressure is measured vertically and the volume horizontally. Let $OM = v_1$ and $ON = v_2$. Then, as the gas changes from the state indicated by the point A to that indicated by the point B, the work done by it will be represented by the area $AMNB$.

§ 177. *The first law of thermodynamics.*

The investigations of Joule in the middle of the nineteenth century finally established, as was stated in § 20, that heat is a form of energy. In any closed system, that is to say in any system theoretically isolated from the rest of the Universe, the total quantity of energy is invariable. In other words, the quantity of heat which disappears in the system is equivalent to the quantity of other kinds of energy that appears and *vicê versâ*. This result is sometimes called the first law of thermodynamics: it is the principle of conservation of energy coupled with the fact that heat is a form of energy.

§ 178. *The character and origin of the second law of thermodynamics.*

The second law of thermodynamics involves much more difficult conceptions. It relates to the *quality* of energy, as opposed to the *quantity* of energy which the first law pronounces to be invariable in a closed system. Its basis is the experimental fact that there is a continuous running down of the utility of the energy of the Universe. The ultimate effect of this process in any isolated system would be such a distribution of the energy of the system that none could be used as work.

The fundamental investigation which laid the foundations of the second law of thermodynamics was made by Carnot*, who published his *Reflections on the Motive Power of Heat* in the year 1824. He considered what happens in an ideal engine which absorbs heat and does work. The ratio of W, the work done, to H, the heat absorbed, may be termed the efficiency of the engine, and Carnot investigated the conditions for maximum efficiency. He observed that for such maximum efficiency there must not be any direct interchange of heat between bodies of different temperature, for, whenever such direct interchange takes place, a difference of temperature is wasted which might have been used to produce mechanical work. In practice, of course, there is always some slight loss of efficiency by heat thus passing 'of itself' from a higher to a lower temperature, but such loss may in theory be indefinitely reduced.

§ 179. *Carnot's reversible engine.*

Assume now that a perfect engine exists in which there is no loss of efficiency due to heat passing 'of itself', and let us imaginatively

---

* Sady Carnot (1796–1832) was the eldest son of the famous 'organiser of victory' of the French Republic.

describe what happens when the engine performs a single cycle of operations, after which it returns to its initial state. We shall need two bodies A and B, each of which is maintained at a constant temperature, the temperature of A being higher than that of B. These bodies are the source and condenser of the engine. We can imagine that, first of all, the air or steam in the cylinder of the engine is at the temperature of the body A and receives heat from that body while remaining at its constant temperature: the piston will thus be raised; and the air or steam in the cylinder will thus take from the body A a quantity of heat H_1. Then we can imagine that the air or steam ceases to receive any heat while the piston continues nevertheless to rise: this will necessarily be accompanied by a fall in the temperature: we assume that the final temperature is that of the body B. Next we can imagine that the air or steam in the cylinder is placed in contact with the body B, to which it gives up heat while its temperature remains unchanged: in order that this may happen the air must be compressed by the return of the piston. In this way a quantity of heat H_2 will be ejected by the engine. If now the cool body is removed, the compression of the air or steam will continue without any loss of heat, so that its temperature will rise. In the end we may thus return to the initial state of the engine. During the cycle of operations H_1 units of heat will have been absorbed, H_2 units will have been ejected, and W units of work will have been done. Under conditions of maximum efficiency where no heat passes 'of itself', the cycle of operations which we have described will be reversible. By the first law of thermodynamics we shall obviously have $W = H_1 - H_2$.

§ 180. *Carnot's principle.*

Carnot enunciated the principle that the efficiency of a reversible engine is the greatest which it is possible to obtain with a given range of temperature. Furthermore, it depends only on the temperatures between which it works: in other words, it is independent of the nature of the bodies A and B, and of the substance (air, steam or whatever it be) which the engine uses.

We can establish the truth of Carnot's principle as follows:

Suppose that we had two engines R and S, each working with the same two bodies A and B. Let R take H_1 units from A, give H_2 units to B and do work W_r. Similarly let S take H_1 units from A, give h units to B and do work W_s. We thus have $H_1 - H_2 = W_r$, $H_1 - h = W_s$; and therefore $W_r - W_s = h - H_2$. If it were possible that the engine R performed more useful work than the reversible engine S, we should have

$W_r > W_s$ and therefore $h > H_2$. We could then reverse the engine S and form a compound engine of S reversed and R. In a complete cycle of this compound engine, work $W_r - W_s$ would be done: A would receive back the heat taken from it, and from B would be taken $h - H_2$ units of heat. We could in this way obtain useful work without drawing any heat from the source, and this is an operation which is contrary to all our experience. We cannot convert the heat of a cold body into work for then, without consumption of fuel, we should get unlimited supplies of motive power. Hence we may conclude that the efficiency of a perfect reversible engine is the maximum possible, and further that it depends solely on the temperatures between which the engine works. It is always possible to get work out of the heat of a body which is hotter than surrounding bodies. But, just as you cannot get blood out of a stone, so you cannot get work out of a body which is colder than surrounding bodies. On this simple fact the second law of thermodynamics is based.

Carnot's efficiency function.

Let W be the work obtainable by taking H units of heat from the source and using them in a perfect reversible engine. Then, by definition, the *efficiency* of the engine is W/H. If now T and T_0 are the temperatures between which the engine works, then Carnot's principle asserts that

$$W/H = f_1(T, T_0),$$

where $f_1(T, T_0)$ means some function of T and T_0.

We can write this result in a more useful form by imagining that our engine works through an infinitesimal cycle in which the range of temperature is dT. Let dW be the work obtained in such an infinitesimal cycle. Then we shall have

$$\frac{dW}{H} = f(T)\,dT,$$

and Carnot's principle asserts that the *efficiency function* $f(T)$ is the same for all substances at the same temperature.

§181. *The absolute (Kelvin) scale of temperature.*

Because the efficiency function is the same for all substances at the same temperature, Lord Kelvin suggested in the year 1848 that it might well be used to measure temperature.

He assumed that T is the temperature of the source, T_0 that of the condenser, and that W is the work done by a reversible engine when H units of heat are taken from the source. Then, by Carnot's principle,

$$W/H = f_1(T, T_0),$$

where f_1 denotes some function of T and T_0.

Kelvin then went on to suppose that the temperature of the source was kept fixed and equal to T, but that the temperature T_0 of the condenser varied. As the scale of temperature can be graduated at our pleasure, Kelvin proposed to make its intervals such that W, as T_0 varied, was proportional to $T - T_0$. With such a graduation we have

$$W/H = f(T)(T - T_0),$$

where $f(T)$ denotes some function of T only. Moreover, this graduation will apply universally, as Carnot's principle is independent of the substance used in his reversible engine.

Now plainly the colder the condenser, the more work can we do by taking a given quantity of heat from the source. Let us then choose zero temperature to be that temperature of the condenser at which *all* the heat taken from the source can be turned into work. Thus we have $T_0 = 0$, when $W = H$. Hence $T_0 = 0$, when $T - T_0 = 1/f(T)$. We therefore have $f(T) = 1/T$. When, therefore, the scale and zero of temperature are suitably chosen,

$$W/H = (T - T_0)/T,$$

where W is the work done by a reversible engine in taking H units of heat from the source at temperature T, the condenser being at temperature T_0.

It is found experimentally that temperature, as thus measured, agrees very closely with temperature as measured from $-273°$ C. on an air thermometer. As we have said previously, temperature as thus measured is called *absolute temperature*: it is always used in abstract discussions concerning the theory of heat.

§ 182. *The efficiency of a reversible engine when temperatures are measured on the absolute scale.*

Carnot's principle for an infinitesimal cycle of range dT of his reversible engine may now be written

$$\frac{dW}{dT} = \frac{H}{T},$$

provided that temperature be measured on the absolute (Kelvin) scale.

Now by the first law of thermodynamics the work done by a perfect engine, working between temperatures at which H_1 and H_2 units of heat are respectively taken from the source and put into the condenser, is $W = H_1 - H_2$. Hence, when our engine works between temperatures at which these quantities of heat are respectively $H + dH$ and H, the work done, dW, will equal dH. In such circumstances we shall have

$$\frac{dH}{H} = \frac{dT}{T},$$

so that H will be proportional to T.

If then a quantity of heat H_1 is taken from the source at temperature T_1, and if in the same cycle of a perfect reversible engine a quantity of heat H_2 is returned to the condenser at temperature T_2, and if work W is done in the cycle, we must have

$$\frac{W}{T_1 - T_2} = \frac{H_1}{T_1} = \frac{H_2}{T_2},$$

when temperatures are measured on the absolute (Kelvin) scale.

It follows that the efficiency of our engine, as measured by the ratio of the work done to the supply of heat, is $1 - T_2/T_1$.

§183. *The indicator-diagram for Carnot's cycle. Isothermals and adiabatics.*

Let us, following Carnot, make a diagram to represent the changes in state of the air or steam which is used as the substance of a perfect reversible engine.

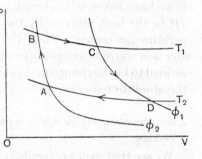

We measure the volume of our gas horizontally and its pressure vertically. The curve BC represents a change of state during which H_1 units of heat are absorbed by the engine, the temperature T_1 remaining constant. The curve CD represents the change of state during which the temperature falls to T_2, no heat being either absorbed or given out by the engine. The curve DA represents a change of state during which a quantity of heat H_2 is returned to the condenser, the temperature T_2 remaining constant. Finally, the curve AB represents a change of state during which no heat is absorbed or given out by the engine though the temperature rises from T_2 to T_1. The curves BC and AD for which the temperatures are constant are called *isothermals*. The curves CD and BA are called *adiabatics*.

§184. *Entropy.*

We have seen that in a reversible cycle the value of H_1/T_1 corresponding to the change of state BC is equal to the value of H_2/T_2 which corresponds to the change of state AD.

If now the two adiabatics AB and CD are close together and any isothermal of temperature T be drawn to intersect them, and if, further, δH be the energy absorbed or ejected in the part of a reversible cycle corresponding to the portion of isothermal intercepted between the two adiabatics, then the quantity $\delta H/T$ will be the same for all isothermals. Following Clausius (1822–1888) we can put this equal to $\delta\phi$, so that $\delta\phi$ is $\delta H/T$.

In our original diagram we can imagine that between the adiabatics AB and CD a large number of intervening adiabatics are drawn. If, then, we take $\int dH/T$ from any point on one adiabatic to any point on the other, its value will be constant. Thus we can call AB the adiabatic $\phi = \phi_2$, and CD the adiabatic $\phi = \phi_1$. Furthermore, $\int dH/T$ taken by any path between the two adiabatics will be equal to $\phi_1 - \phi_2$.

We have thus proved that dH/T is an exact differential if taken along any part of the cycle of a reversible engine.

Although we have illustrated Carnot's principle by a simple gas engine, the foregoing results, like the principle itself, are generally true. If we have any system changing its state by a reversible process and if dH be the heat taken in by the system at the moment when its temperature lies between T and $T + dT$, then the value of $\int dH/T$ between any two states is independent of the path between those states and is defined to be the change in the *entropy* of the system, T being, of course, the absolute temperature.

Every spontaneous change in a physical system leads to an increase in its entropy.

We see that every reversible change in an isolated system will leave its entropy unaltered, for, since the system is isolated and the change reversible, the gain of entropy in one part of the system will be exactly balanced by its loss in the other part. On the other hand, every irreversible change in an isolated system will increase its entropy. Such irreversible changes take place when heat passes 'of itself' from one part of the system to another part at a lower temperature. For simplicity, suppose that our isolated system consists merely of two bodies; and let an infinitesimal amount H of heat pass of itself from one body at absolute temperature T_1 to the other body at absolute temperature

T_2. Then the entropy of the first body will be diminished by H/T_1 and the entropy of the second body will be increased by H/T_2. Hence the total entropy of the system will be increased by

$$H\{1/T_2 - 1/T_1\}.$$

But heat always passes from the hotter to the colder body, so that $1/T_2 - 1/T_1$ must be positive.

Hence the entropy of the system is increased by the irreversible change in its state. We thus reach the general conclusion that only those changes are spontaneously possible in any physical or chemical change of state of a system which leads to an increase of its entropy. Moreover, such a system will be in stable thermal equilibrium when its entropy is a maximum, that is to say, when the entropy cannot be continuously increased without changing the conditions of the system.

§ 185. *The two fundamental principles of thermodynamics.*

Thus in connection with the physico-chemical conditions of any material system there are two important quantities. The first is the internal energy E of the system. This is a constant if the system be isolated: it can only be changed by adding or subtracting energy in one of its many forms. The second quantity is the entropy ϕ of the system. This quantity, like E, is independent of the past history of the system: in other words, $d\phi$ and dE are exact differentials. Thermodynamics develops the consequence of two principles $E = \text{constant}$ and $d\phi > 0$. Expressed in words, these two laws state that the energy of every isolated system is constant and that its entropy cannot diminish.

An analogy, which Maxwell drew out between mechanics and thermodynamics, throws some light on the nature of entropy.

If a fluid at a pressure p increases in volume from v to v_1, it does work W against external resistance, where $W = p(v_1 - v)$. Similarly, if a body at absolute temperature T increases in entropy from ϕ to ϕ_1, its internal heat-energy will increase by H, where $H = T(\phi_1 - \phi)$. If both processes take place at the same time, and the internal energy is thereby changed from E to E_1, we shall have

$$E_1 - E = H - W = T(\phi_1 - \phi) - p(v_1 - v).$$

Volume is a quantity without a change of which no work can be done by a fluid. But the amount of work done is measured, not by a change of volume alone, but by that change multiplied by the pressure.

Entropy is a quantity without a change in which no heat can enter or leave a body. But the change of heat is measured, not by a change of entropy alone, but by that change multiplied by the absolute temperature.

§ 186. *The nature of entropy.*

The conception of entropy is difficult, because it does not represent anything which we can immediately apprehend by the senses. Change in entropy is quite distinct from change in temperature: equally it is distinct from the change which results in loss or gain of heat. Entropy, however, is an idea which was bound to arise in thermodynamics, however the subject was developed. In fact, in the developments of Rankine (1820–1872) and Lord Kelvin, who sought to estimate the available energy of a natural system, and in the work of Helmholtz, who attempted to gauge its free energy, the integral which represents entropy necessarily found a place.

We may naturally enquire why that part of the energy of a material system which is available for work should always tend to diminish. The answer would appear to be that available energy is orderly energy and that disorder is a characteristic property of crowds. Heat is the expression of the motion of large assemblages of molecules. It is thus a property of the crowd or of the swarm, and, therefore, constantly tends to become less and less available for mechanical work as the disorderliness of the crowd increases.

§ 187. *Entropy and the direction of time.*

It is well known that the fundamental laws of dynamics effect no discrimination between past and future. They thus leave the direction of time undetermined. We do not in fact reach a stage in the investigation of natural phenomena when the direction of time is important until we get to laws resulting from the properties of large aggregates. Entropy provides the only physical test of the direction of time: if t be time, then to accord with our experience it must be so measured that $d\phi/dt$ is a positive quantity. It is, perhaps, somewhat disconcerting that the best way in which the scientist can measure the direction of the time-process in the Universe is by estimating the increase in its disorder! Whether this fact is compatible with the belief that our own is 'the best of all possible worlds' I will not discuss. I will merely remark that the disorder with which we are dealing is physical and not moral.

Entropy and the end of the Universe.

In popular language we can express the second law of thermodynamics by the statement that the heat of the world is running down. The general tendency of any isolated system is towards a uniform temperature in which heat is not available for work. Our statements have been formulated with reference to physico-chemical systems: we have said nothing as to the possible application of the second law of thermodynamics to biological phenomena. Lord Kelvin felt the necessity of such exclusion when he said that "it is impossible, by means of *inanimate* material agency, to derive mechanical effect from any portion of matter by cooling it below the temperature of the coldest of the surrounding objects". I believe, however, that so far no result in biochemistry gives us reason to doubt the universal truth of the second law of thermodynamics. Some living agents seem to be highly efficient when viewed as machines; but none is able to increase the organisation of the heat-energy upon which it thrives.

If the cosmos be infinite, we cannot extend to it as a whole the results which have been obtained for finite isolated systems. If, however, the cosmos, as is highly probable, is finite, there is nothing to prevent such extension, and we can assert that the available energy of the cosmos as a whole is steadily diminishing. It would seem that the ultimate result of such a process must inevitably be a uniform distribution of heat. In the material realm nothing could then happen. Out of such a Nirvana escape would only be possible through some such agency as that of Maxwell's* 'sorting demons'. Such might reorganise the energy which had become unavailable for work and so allow the cosmos once again to start on a new career.

Alternatively, there may be portions of our finite cosmos where the second law of thermodynamics is reversed: or it is possible that cycles of time occur during which such a reversal takes place. The idea that there are alternate cycles during which the world, as it were, is alternately wound up and runs down was familiar in ancient thought: it was a part of the regular Stoic creed. Of it we can only say that it is unwarranted by any experiments which we can make or by any processes of Nature which we can observe.

* Maxwell, discussing the limitation of the second law of thermodynamics (*Theory of Heat*. Longmans, 1891, p. 338), merely wrote of "a being who can see the individual molecules". Such beings were called 'demons' by Thomson (Lord Kelvin) according to the authors (P. G. Tait and Balfour Stewart) of *The Unseen Universe*. Macmillan, 1875, p. 89.

To call into existence 'sorting demons' to rescue the cosmos from ultimate stagnation is but a picturesque way of avoiding an appeal to Divine action. Our speculations point to the fact that in the end, after inconceivable aeons have passed, the cosmos will be stagnant unless some external Creative Power intervenes. Similarly, as we shall see, speculation points to a beginning of that process of the aggregation of matter out of which the cosmos as we know it has resulted. We thus seem driven to the belief that God lies behind phenomena, even though we take no account of the values of the world but merely survey the changing states of its material organisation. We will, however, reflect again upon this belief when, in Lecture XVIII, we consider the cosmological argument for God's existence.

§ 188. *Light.*

Our knowledge of the external world is derived through our senses. Touch, taste and smell merely give us knowledge of what is happening in our immediate neighbourhood. Sound extends such knowledge, though not, under normal circumstances, for more than a few hundred yards. Only sight (and heat phenomena, allied in their nature to light) enables us to explore greater distances and, in particular, the sidereal universe. It is then of especial importance that we should understand the nature of light, so far as it is known, and have some knowledge of the discoveries by which its properties enable us to frame pictures of the life-history of the stars.

Light as an electro-magnetic phenomenon.

At the outset it must be confessed, as has been already stated in §148, that we do not know the ultimate nature of light. The classical investigations of Maxwell led finally to the theory that light, like all other forms of radiation, is an electro-magnetic phenomenon. In the year 1888, Hertz (1857–1894) confirmed experimentally Maxwell's theory. *In vacuo*, light and analogous forms of radiation travel approximately in straight lines, the so-called rays of light. Further, at right angles to the straight line in which light is travelling there will always be an electric force E. This changes its magnitude harmonically. At any instant, E is the same at points, situated along the line of the light, of distance λ apart, where λ is called the wave-length of the ray of light. If Ox be the direction of the ray of light, the value of E, at any given instant and at a distance x from the origin O, will be proportional to

$$\sin 2\pi (x - a)/\lambda,$$

where a is a constant. At any given point, E changes with enormous rapidity. We can picture this change by supposing the sine-curve to move with the velocity of light in the direction of its propagation. We may thus take

$$E = k \sin \frac{2\pi}{\lambda}(x - a - ct),$$

where k is some constant, t is the time and c is the velocity of light. As has already been said, *in vacuo* $c = 300,000$ kilometres per second. The frequency of light is the number of oscillations made by the electric force E in unit time. It is usually denoted by ν, where $\nu = c/\lambda$. For green light in the middle of the visible spectrum ν is 600 million million or 6×10^{14} vibrations per second.

It is an experimental fact that the frequency of radiation is not changed when we pass from one transparent medium to another. The velocity of propagation p and the wave-length are alike altered; in fact, if μ be the index of refraction of the medium, $p\mu = c$.

At right angles alike to the direction of propagation and to the direction of E there is an oscillating magnetic field H. With suitably chosen units, H and E are, at any point and at any instant, numerically equal.

We cannot really say more of light than that it is a phenomenon, with the physiological properties of which we are familiar by constant experience, and that in connection with it there are manifested the oscillating electro-magnetic phenomena which we have described. Most nineteenth-century physicists felt it necessary to assume that light travels through a luminiferous ether. We have previously said, in § 150, that such an ether has never been experimentally detected: we may add that, if it exists, its properties are unlike those of any material substance with which we are familiar. Maxwell's equations lead to a mathematical abstraction which we may describe as a field of vectors which are arranged and change according to definite laws. Whether these vectors can ever be adequately pictured by images which satisfy our senses is doubtful. Those senses have been so fashioned that they are unlikely to be able to convey in concrete form concepts which will increasingly result from the mental evolution of humanity. Perhaps most modern physicists would be content to describe radiation as "the transfer through empty space of energy unassociated with the motion of electrons or material particles".

To the astronomer it is, of course, a fact of enormous importance that light *in vacuo* travels in geodesics which, in our approximately

Euclidean space, can be regarded as straight lines. It is to him equally important that in media of varying density the rays of light are curved: they are thus bent as they pass through the earth's atmosphere.

§ 189. *The polarisation of light.*

We have not yet described the full complexity of, shall we say, ordinary sunlight.

In the first place, it consists of a mixture of light-waves of different lengths. Radiation for which λ is constant is called *monochromatic* radiation: if it is visible it will be of a single definite colour. The spectroscope resolves visible radiation into monochromatic components.

A more complex fact in relation to light is that, in general, the direction of the electric force E, although always perpendicular to the direction of propagation, does not remain uniformly in the same plane. In the special case when E is always in one and the same plane P, which also contains the direction of propagation, then the light is said to be *polarised* in a plane perpendicular to P. In fact, the plane of the associated magnetic intensity H is then called the plane of polarisation. But natural radiation, even when it is monochromatic, is unpolarised. Such radiation, as we have seen, comes from within the atom; but any particular atom only ejects it for a very short time. The total amount of monochromatic radiation which we get from any normal source is a contribution from innumerable atoms all emitting light of the same wave-length. Even though the light emitted by each should be polarised (and this appears to be probably true), the contribution made by the aggregate of atoms will be such that the direction of E is undetermined, save in so far as it is at right angles to the direction of propagation.

Light can be polarised by reflection at a plane mirror under certain circumstances and also by being passed through certain cyrstals.

§ 190. *The intensity of radiation.*

We have said that radiation is the transfer *in vacuo* of energy unassociated with matter. We have also seen that, according to the special theory of relativity, energy has mass. If then we have a beam of radiation of energy E per unit volume, this will be equivalent to the transfer through space of matter of mass E/c^2 per unit volume. This mass will be travelling with velocity c, and hence its momentum per unit volume will be E/c. If now this radiation impinges directly on a material screen which absorbs it all, there will be a rate of destruction of momentum equal to $c \times E/c$, that is, E per unit area of the screen. But pressure is the measure of rate of destruction of momentum. Hence the pressure on a screen, which absorbs radiation of energy-density E directly impinging upon it, is a force of E units per unit area.

The amount of energy in a beam of radiation which passes per unit time through unit area perpendicular to the beam is usually called the intensity of the beam. If I be the intensity, we evidently have $I = Ec$, where c is the velocity of the radiation.

When light or other radiation is diverging from a uniformly luminous sphere, the same amount of radiant energy will pass in unit time through the surface of any imaginary concentric sphere. Now the area of a sphere is proportional to the square of its radius. Hence the intensity of radiation from a uniformly luminous sphere varies inversely as the square of the distance from its centre. If, then, we measure the intensity of the radiation received from the sun at the earth's surface, we can compute its intensity at the surface of the sun itself.

Radiation pressure.

We have said that all forms of radiation exert pressure on material screens which absorb them. Equally pressure will be exerted by radiation on a screen which partially reflects it. In other words, sunlight exerts pressure when it falls on an absorbing (or reflecting) surface. We know that a jet of water will knock a man over. Similarly, and for exactly the same reason, a beam of sunlight, if sufficiently strong, ought to be able to knock him over. But, as Eddington has dryly remarked, it would probably shrivel him up first. Naturally, the pressure of sunlight is very minute, though instruments have been devised for detecting it. The pressure was predicted by Clerk Maxwell as a necessary consequence of the electro-magnetic theory of light. It was first observed experimentally in 1900 by Lebedew, who shortly anticipated the independent and more careful observations of Nichols and Hull.

Comets and their tails.

The most familiar natural phenomenon which is caused by the pressure of sunlight is the comet's tail. We are all of us familiar with the popular superstition that, if a comet's tail were to strike the earth, its doom would be sealed. The fact, however, is that a comet's tail is as like to an airy nothing as anything we can conceive. Its length must be measured in tens of millions of miles, but its density, according to Schwarzschild, can be so low that there is less material in two thousand cubic miles of the tail than in a cubic inch of ordinary air. It appears that a comet consists of an aggregate of meteorites, together with fine dust and associated gases. In the depths of space it is invisible and possesses no tail. As it begins to approach the sun and is warmed by the sun's radiation, gases and fine dust ooze out of the central nucleus and, as they diffuse around it, form the envelope of the comet's head. The gases absorb solar energy and begin to shine: the dust reflects the sunlight: so the comet's head begins to shine brightly. At the same time the pressure of sunlight drives away the finer particles from the head and these streaming away form the brightly shining tail which grows longer and brighter the more nearly the comet approaches the sun. Because of its mode of formation the tail streams directly from the sun. As the comet moves away from the sun reverse processes take place: it rapidly diminishes in brightness. Furthermore, it loses its tail, the minute particles of which fly off into space with great velocities. So far from a comet's tail being a sort of club which could strike the earth with disastrous effect, it is formed by one of the most minute pressures which the physicist can measure.

§ 191. *The Doppler effect.*

We have said that the angle through which a ray of sunlight is turned by refraction depends upon the wave-length. The spectroscope is the instrument which thus separates composite light into its monochromatic elements. It creates the spectrum, a series of lines corresponding to light-waves of varying frequency. Within the range of wave-length for which radiation can be perceived by man as visible light, a definite colour corresponds to each wave-length. In this way the colours of the rainbow arise. A rainbow is, as it were, a spectrum formed by a natural spectroscope whose refracting prism is a drop of water. If a luminous gas at a given pressure emits various kinds of monochromatic radiation, the wave-lengths of these kinds of radiation will be the same wherever in the Universe the gas may be. As the pressure of a luminous gas changes, slight differences in the wave-lengths of its emitted radiation can be observed: what the physicist calls a 'pressure shift' arises because the various atoms of gas can, owing to their proximity, influence one another.

A much more important influence in slightly changing the apparent wave-length of a definite type of radiation is known as the Doppler effect. To it attention was first called by C. J. Doppler (1803–1853) in the year 1842. It was, however, Fizeau, and not Doppler, who first applied the principle correctly to stellar motions: for this reason Continental writers often refer to it as the Doppler-Fizeau effect. The effect can be elegantly explained by the special theory of relativity and is of singular value, because it enables us to perform the apparently impossible feat of determining the velocity of a star, in the line of sight relatively to ourselves, merely by examining its light through a spectroscope. In fact, if the distance between the source of radiation and an observer is changing with a velocity whose component in the line of sight is w, we shall have

$$\lambda' = \lambda(1 + w/c), \qquad \text{or} \qquad (\lambda' - \lambda)/\lambda = w/c,$$

where λ is the original wave-length, λ' the observed wave-length and w is reckoned positive for a motion of regress. What this means is that, if a star is receding from the earth, the lines of its spectrum will be shifted towards the red end of the spectrum, where the wave-lengths are longer than at the violet end. If the star is coming towards us, the lines of its spectrum will be shifted towards the violet. The amount of the shift can be measured with amazing accuracy with modern instruments and hence velocities of approach or regress can be determined most satisfactorily. Of course, such radial velocity must be corrected for the earth's motion round the sun before it can be expressed as a motion relative to the sun.

Let us suppose that between the source of radiation and the observer there is a uniform medium in which light travels with velocity q. Suppose further that the frequency of the light is ν. Further, let the source of the light be travelling with velocity v in the direction $O'x'$ of the figure, O being the observer and O' the source of the light. Let the ray of light which passes from the source to the observer make an angle θ with Ox and let k be the perpendicular from O' on Ox.

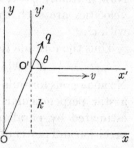

The ray of light under consideration will be a wave motion which can be analytically expressed as regards all but its amplitude by

$$\exp\left\{2\pi i \nu \left[\frac{x'\cos\theta + y'\sin\theta}{q} - t'\right]\right\},$$

where t' is the time.

Now the two sets of axes are moving with respect to one another with velocity v. Hence in the (x, y) system there will be a different measure of time t; and the old coordinates and time (x, y, t) will be connected with the new (x', y', t') by the Lorentz transformation of the special theory of relativity.

This transformation is expressed by the relations of §92,

$$x' = h(x - vt); \qquad y' = y - k; \qquad t' = h(t - vx/c^2);$$

where $h = 1/\sqrt{1 - v^2/c^2}$. If we employ this transformation, the preceding equation of wave motion may be written

$$\exp\left\{2\pi\iota\nu h\left(1 + \frac{v\cos\theta}{q}\right)\left[\frac{\left(\dfrac{\cos\theta}{q} + \dfrac{v}{c^2}\right)x + \dfrac{\sin\theta}{hq}(y - k)}{1 + v\cos\theta/q} - t\right]\right\}.$$

Thus wave motion of frequency ν at O' becomes wave motion of changed frequency ν' at O, where ν' is given by

$$\nu' = h\nu\{1 + v\cos\theta/q\}.$$

It is to be noticed that in this formula the direction of the light and the direction of v are the same when $\theta = 0$. If we change the sign of q, and if w denote $v\cos\theta$, so that it is the velocity of the star in the line of sight, we shall have $\qquad \nu' = h\nu\{1 - w/q\},$

where w is positive for a motion of regress.

Since $\nu = c/\lambda$, we see that the respective wave-lengths will be connected by the relation

$$\lambda/\lambda' = \{1 - w/q\}/\sqrt{1 - v^2/c^2}.$$

Now normally $q = c$, the velocity of light *in vacuo*. Further, stellar velocities are such that their squares are negligible in comparison with c^2.

Thus the formula for the Doppler effect may be written

$$\lambda' = \lambda\{1 + w/c\} \qquad \text{or} \qquad w/c = (\lambda' - \lambda)/\lambda.$$

No analogous formula exists by which we can determine the velocity of a star perpendicular to the line of sight. Such velocities must be estimated by parallax observations which, unfortunately, lack the precision and power of spectroscopic applications of Doppler's formula.

§192. *Isotropic radiation.*

Suppose that we have a heated hollow body maintained at a uniform temperature. Radiation will pass from it into the interior in all directions. Obviously, when heat equilibrium is established, there is no reason why waves in one direction should be of greater intensity than waves in any other. In such a case the radiation is called isotropic.

The pressure of isotropic radiation can be readily obtained. Suppose that we have a column of parallel radiation impinging obliquely on a plane area S of a material screen, which, if we like, we may imagine to be a part of the interior surface. Let θ be the angle between the direction of radiation and the normal to the screen. The pressure of the radiation will be proportional to the area of the cross-section perpendicular to itself which corresponds to S, that is to $S \cos \theta$. If then E be the energy-density (by which we mean the energy per unit volume) of the radiation, the pressure upon the screen will be of magnitude $ES \cos \theta$ and will act at an angle θ to the normal to the screen. We may resolve this into a pressure $ES \cos^2 \theta$ normal to the screen and $ES \cos \theta \sin \theta$ tangential to it.

If now we wish to determine the pressure of isotropic radiation on the screen, we must sum for all values of θ the pressure made by radiation which impinges at an angle θ; and we must do this for all possible orientations of the incident radiation. We must thus take for the normal pressure the average value of $\cos^2 \theta$ over the surface of a sphere (we must take a sphere and not a hemisphere in order to include the intensity of reflected radiation). Hence the normal pressure will be

$$ES \int_0^\pi \cos^2 \theta \sin \theta \, d\theta \Big/ \int_0^\pi \sin \theta \, d\theta = \tfrac{1}{3} ES.$$

The tangential pressure will be obviously zero.

We thus have the important result that the pressure of isotropic radiation on any surface is normal to that surface and in magnitude per unit area is equal to one-third of its energy-density.

§193. *Equilibrium of radiation.*

To determine the quality and quantity of the radiation emitted by a star is naturally a problem of great importance. We can best approach it by considering what happens inside a hot hollow body at a uniform temperature which is emitting radiation. Some radiation will be continuously emitted from the walls into the interior: conversely, radiation from the interior will be absorbed by the walls. If the temperature be constant, these must balance and equilibrium be established. Now not only will such equilibrium determine the energy-density of the radiation within the enclosure, but *it will also determine its quality*, that is to say, it will determine the distribution of this density between various wave-lengths. The proof of this fact can be readily obtained from the second law of thermodynamics. Let us suppose that we have two hollow spheres (or hollow bodies of other shapes) which we will call X and Y; and further let us suppose that, although these two bodies are at the same temperature T, the density of radiation of wave-length between λ and $\lambda + d\lambda$ is greater in X than in Y. Then we can, at all events in theory, make a small hole connecting the two bodies and put in it a screen which is transparent only to this particular range of wave-length. Through this screen more radiation of this quality will pass from X to Y than passes from Y to X. Thus Y will have more such radiation than can be in equilibrium when its walls are at the temperature T. Its walls therefore will rise in temperature and similarly the walls of X will fall in temperature. We can use this difference of temperature so that Y is the source and X the condenser of an engine. By periodically repeating the process we can drive the engine indefinitely. Thus we should convert heat of uniform temperature T continuously into mechanical work. We know, however, that any such process is impossible by the second law of thermodynamics. Hence the quality (or distribution between various wave-lengths) of the radiation within a hollow body maintained at a temperature T depends only upon T.

It follows from this investigation that equilibrium-radiation at temperature T is definite alike in quality and quantity. When T is known, it must be possible to find the energy-density of such radiation and also the way in which this energy is distributed between the various wave-lengths. It should be observed that our result implies that a mixture of radiation of different wave-lengths in arbitrary proportions is not, in general, in equilibrium with any temperature. We often get from the stars such mixtures and then we define the *effective temperature* of the star to be T_e, when the star emits in all as much radiation as a perfect radiator of equal area raised to the temperature T_e, a perfect radiator being defined as a body emitting equilibrium-radiation. Effective temperature is thus a measure of quantity (but not of quality) of radiation.

The absorption and emission of radiation balance in thermal equilibrium.

An apparent objection to the theory which has just been outlined is that different bodies at the same temperature emit, when they are not in thermal equilibrium, different qualities of radiation, that is to say, they emit radiation of corresponding wave-lengths in different amounts. If, for instance, glass and iron be taken from the same part of a hot fire, the iron will appear to be strong red in colour, while the glass is but faint red although its temperature is the same as that of the iron. In fact the two bodies, though at the same temperature, are emitting red radiation in different amounts. In the history of physical discovery in the nineteenth century Balfour Stewart (1828–1887) deserves to be remembered, inasmuch as he insisted that equilibrium-radiation inside an impervious hollow body of uniform temperature must nevertheless be of the same quality and quantity, whatever the material of which the body might consist. From this fact it follows that at any given temperature the power of a body to absorb radiation must be exactly balanced by its power to emit radiation of the same wave-length. Thus a good reflector like a polished copper ball must both absorb and emit radiation feebly. When such a ball is in thermodynamical equilibrium and radiation falls upon it, it absorbs a small fraction of this radiation and reflects the rest: the radiation which it emits will be precisely equal to that which it absorbs, and this together with the amount which it reflects will make up the full radiation stream.

§ 194. *Black-body radiation.*

The body which is in perfect equilibrium with the radiation emitted from itself is called an ideal 'black-body' or perfect radiator. It absorbs all the radiation which falls upon it and for the same reason it emits the complete amount and exact kind of equilibrium-radiation which one would get inside an impervious enclosure whose walls were maintained at the same temperature. In other words, it has no selective absorption and therefore no selective emission. For this reason equilibrium-radiation is often called 'black-body' radiation. We may get a very good approximation to it by measuring the radiation at an assigned temperature of a body coated with lampblack. This is found to be very nearly the same in quantity and quality as the radiation which comes from a small hole in the side of a closed vessel maintained at the same temperature.

§ 195. *Radiation from the sun and stars.*

Neither the sun nor presumably any of the stars radiates heat like a perfect 'black-body'. The sun is, in fact, not a mass of matter at a uniform temperature. Heat is continuously flowing from its interior to its surface, from regions of high temperature to regions of lower. The quality of the radiation is changed in this process; and that which finally emerges from the star into space is not 'black-body' radiation. The sun is probably gaseous; at all events it is liquid only at its core. Emergent radiation of certain wave-lengths has on the whole come from lower depths where the sun is hotter than at the surface, while that of other wave-lengths has come from higher up where the sun is comparatively cool.

Radiation from the planets.

No planetary surface is perfectly black. It is a commonplace that the planets, like the moon, shine by light reflected from the sun. But owing to their own temperatures they also emit radiation, though it is of such long wave-lengths that it is invisible. Their surfaces absorb less of the sun's radiation and consequently emit less radiation than would be absorbed and emitted by perfect 'black-bodies' at the same temperature.

Radiation within a star.

We may consider in somewhat more detail what happens to radiation inside a solid hot body such as a star. As we do so, we must anticipate some of the results which will be set out in the next lecture. Radiation is, in the first place, emitted by atoms; and Bohr's model assumes that in emission an orbital electron of the atom passes from one orbit to another of lower energy. Denote the two states of the atom by the suffices 1 and 2 and let E_1 and E_2 be the energy in the two states. By the fundamental formula of the quantum theory the frequency ν of the radiation emitted will be given by the relation (§ 204)

$$E_1 - E_2 = h\nu,$$

where h is Planck's constant. The same atom will absorb energy of this wave-length when the reverse process takes place inside the atom. Now, if a solid hot body were throughout at a uniform temperature, the atoms within it would so distribute their internal states as to make the entropy of the body as large as possible. Therefore, corresponding to any atom changing from state 1 to state 2, there would be another atom changing from state 2 to state 1. Thus, on balance, absorption and emission of radiation by the atoms of a body at uniform temperature must be exactly equivalent. From this result we may deduce Kirchhoff's law. Let the ratio of the amount of heat emitted by a body to the amount emitted by the same body were it a perfect radiator at the same temperature be called its emissive power. Similarly, let its absorptive power be defined as the ratio of the amount of heat absorbed by the body to the amount absorbed by the perfect radiator at the same temperature. Then Kirchhoff's law states that for a given wave-length and at a given temperature the absorptive power is for all bodies equal to the emissive power.

In a star, however, where the temperature falls as we pass from the interior to the surface, the preceding adjustment for a uniform temperature fails. At a layer within the star of high temperature, radiation is emitted of a quantity and quality suited to that temperature. An external layer at a lower temperature receiving such radiation will absorb that of which the frequencies are suited to its various atoms. But these atoms on account of their lower temperatures will not emit equal radiation of the same frequencies. Thus there will be deficiencies, which we actually see in the spectra of the stars which are crossed by dark lines known as absorption lines.

§ 196. *Absorption lines.*

For many years after their discovery by Fraunhofer (1787–1826) in the year 1814 the nature of absorption lines was a puzzle. G. R. Kirchhoff (1824–1887) gave substantially the following explanation in the year 1860. He pointed out that whenever a body, other than a perfect 'black-body', is emitting radiation at a particular temperature, the quantity of such radiation of a particular wave-length λ can never be greater than a certain fraction f of the quantity R of equilibrium or 'black-body' radiation of this wave-length emitted at the same temperature. The fraction f must be always less than unity because it measures, as it were, the defect in the power of the body to emit radiation of wave-length λ. Equally, by Kirchhoff's law just quoted, the same fraction will measure the power of the body to absorb radiation: it will absorb a fraction f of an amount of incident radiation R' of wave-length λ.

We will now restrict our consideration to radiation of the particular wave-length λ. Suppose that a lower layer of hot gas within a star was emitting radiation of amount R', and that it was at the same temperature as an exactly similar upper layer absorbing radiation of amount R, then we should have $R = R'$. If, however, the lower layer is emitting radiation of amount R' and is at a higher temperature than the absorbing layer, then an amount of radiation fR' will be absorbed by the upper layer and an amount of radiation $R'(1-f)$ will be transmitted. In addition, the absorbing layer will emit an amount of radiation fR. Thus the total quantity of radiation sent forward by the absorbing layer will be

$$R' - f(R' - R).$$

Now R' is greater than R, for, when the temperature of a substance is raised, not only are new kinds of radiation produced, but the intensity of every particular kind of radiation is increased. Hence the quantity of radiation sent forward by the absorbing layer will be less than that which it receives from below: we shall get a black line. Thus the characteristic yellow lines of sodium are black as seen in the sun's spectrum. They appear bright when we see them in the spectrum of a candle flame because the mantle of the flame in which combustion is complete is hotter than the inner flame which gives rise to the continuous background of the spectrum.

It cannot be said that a finally complete theory of Fraunhofer's lines has even yet been reached, though there is no doubt as to their general character. Absorption of radiation, such as produces the dark Fraunhofer lines, is the result of a number of processes which form a complicated interaction in an incandescent gas. In such a gas there will be three kinds of energy. There will be (1) energy of radiation, (2) the internal energy of atoms or molecules, and (3) kinetic or translatory energy of molecules and of such free electrons as may be present. Of such translatory energy temperature is the measure.

Radiation impinging on atoms may produce states of excitation and ionisation which represent increases of internal energy. When molecules collide, as they are supposed to collide in the kinetic theory of gases, the collisions are perfectly elastic. But in the collision of excited molecules, internal energy may be released, as it were, and shew itself as increased energy of translation. Collisions are then said to be *super-elastic*. The reverse process may take place and in a collision some of the energy of translation may be absorbed into one or both of the colliding molecules: the collision is then said to be *inelastic*. Furthermore, energy of radiation may interact with solitary electrons. Then not only the kinetic energy of the electron but also both the wave-length and the direction of the radiation are altered. Because of the alteration in direction the radiation is said to be scattered: the phenomenon is known as *the Compton effect*.

Suppose that, when an electron within an atom passes in the Bohr model from one orbit to another, it emits radiation of wave-length λ. Then when radiation of this wave-length impinges on such an atom it may be absorbed. It may subsequently be emitted again as radiation of the same wave-length when we have *resonance*: or the electron may jump from its excited orbit to some orbit, other than that with which we started, in which case radiation of a different wave-length will be emitted and we have *fluorescence*.

If radiation of a particular wave-length, moving in a definite direction, falls upon a large number of atoms of the same kind in an incandescent gas, it may be absorbed as we have just stated and emitted in resonance. But the emitted radiation will have all possible directions and hence the strength of the original beam will be much reduced. Probably the Fraunhofer lines are produced in this way. The radiation from higher regions of temperature within the sun persists, for the most part, as radiation of its original wave-length, but is scattered by the appropriate atoms of the external region of lower temperature through which it passes. But there will, in addition, be the subsidiary changes due to super-elastic and inelastic collisions and to fluorescence phenomena. All will require to be taken into account when any attempt is made to estimate the relative blackness of the Fraunhofer lines.

§ 197. *Stefan's law.*

In the year 1879, Stefan suggested that the energy-density of equilibrium or 'black-body' radiation was proportional to the fourth power of the absolute temperature. His result was obtained by an examination of the figures reached in certain experiments where there were many sources of error. None the less it was correct, as subsequent enquiries have established. We can prove Stefan's result by using Carnot's principle. Suppose that E is the energy-density of equilibrium-radiation within an enclosure of volume v and absolute temperature T. Let dH be the heat added when v and T respectively are increased by dv and dT. Then by the principle of conservation of energy we shall have, if p be the pressure within the enclosure,

$$dH = d(Ev) + p\,dv.$$

But we have seen in § 192 that the energy-density of isotropic radiation is three times the pressure, hence

$$dH = 4p\,dv + 3v\,dp.$$

Now the increase in entropy $d\phi = dH/T$; and this may be written

$$4\frac{p^{\frac{1}{4}}}{T}d\left(vp^{\frac{3}{4}}\right).$$

But, by Carnot's principle, the entropy is an exact differential; and, moreover, the pressure, being one-third of the energy-density, is a function of the absolute temperature only. We must therefore have

$$p^{\frac{1}{4}}/T = \text{constant}.$$

Hence $E = aT^4$, where a is a constant.

Suppose now that radiation is passing in thermodynamical equilibrium in all directions within the interior of a body maintained at a steady temperature. Let E be the energy-density of the radiation; and consider in the interior a plane area S through which the radiation passes. Since the radiation is isotropic, we must calculate on the basis of an energy-density $\frac{1}{2}E$ when we fix attention on radiation passing through S from one particular side to the other. The waves comprising the energy-density will be incident at all angles; and, if all the waves were incident at an angle θ with the normal to S, they would cause an amount $\frac{1}{2}EcS\cos\theta$ to pass through S in unit time, c being, as usual, the velocity of light.

Hence the quantity of radiation passing per unit time from one side to the other of S will be

$$\int_0^{\pi/2} \frac{E}{2} cS \cos\theta\, 2\pi \sin\theta\, d\theta \Big/ \int_0^{\pi/2} 2\pi \sin\theta\, d\theta,$$

since this represents the average of $\frac{1}{2}EcS\cos\theta$ over a hemisphere.

The quantity passing is thus $\frac{1}{4}EcS$ per unit time.

As an immediate consequence of this result it follows that, if in the surface of a 'black-body' we cut a small hole of area dS, the amount of radiation passing through it will be $\frac{1}{4}Ec\,dS$ per unit time.

Thus the amount of radiation emitted by any perfectly radiating surface of absolute temperature T is σT^4 units of energy per unit area per unit time, where $\sigma = ac/4$. The quantity σ is usually called Stefan's constant: its value has been determined by numerous physical experiments to be $5 \cdot 72 \times 10^{-5}$ ergs per sq. cm. per sec.

§198. *Planck's law.*

Stefan's law gives us the energy of the radiation per unit area emitted per unit time by a perfectly radiating surface. Its quality is given by a law enunciated by Planck in the year 1900. This law was the development of a formula which Wien discovered in the year 1893. It may be conveniently stated as follows. Let $E_\lambda d\lambda$ be the energy of the radiation per unit area emitted per unit time by a perfectly radiating body, the radiation being of wave-length between λ and $\lambda + d\lambda$. Then

$$E_\lambda = c_1 \lambda^{-5}/(e^{c_2/\lambda T} - 1),$$

where c_1 and c_2 are definite constants and T is the absolute temperature of the body. Planck's formula is in excellent agreement with the results of observation. It is reached by a somewhat elaborate investigation based upon the quantum law: in fact, the study of 'black-body' radiation opened the way to the quantum theory*.

From Planck's law we can derive Stefan's law. For the total energy emitted per unit area per unit time will be

$$\int_0^\infty E_\lambda d\lambda = \int_0^\infty \frac{c_1 \lambda^{-5}\, d\lambda}{e^{c_2/\lambda T} - 1}.$$

* A proof of Planck's formula will be found in A. S. Eddington, *The Internal Constitution of the Stars*. Cambridge University Press, 1926, chapters II and III.

If in this result we put $c_2/\lambda T = x$, it becomes

$$\frac{c_1 T^4}{c_2{}^4} \int_0^\infty \frac{x^3\,dx}{e^x - 1} = \sigma T^4, \text{ where } \sigma = \frac{\pi^4 c_1}{15 c_2{}^4}.$$

This value of σ agrees with that given in § 197, for in the usual units

$$c_1 = 3 \cdot 71 \times 10^{-5} \text{ and } c_2 = 1 \cdot 435.$$

Equally we can prove by Planck's formula a result originally enunciated by Weber in the year 1888, but usually termed Wien's law, that the wave-length which corresponds to maximum intensity of radiation at any temperature T is proportional to $1/T$.

For, if
$$E_\lambda = c_1 \lambda^{-5}/(e^{c_2/\lambda T} - 1),$$

we have
$$\frac{dE_\lambda}{d\lambda} = 0, \quad \text{when} \quad 5c_1 \lambda^{-6} (e^{c_2/\lambda T} - 1) = \frac{c_1 c_2}{T} \lambda^{-7} e^{c_2/\lambda T}.$$

Thus, if we put $c_2/\lambda T = x$, we shall have a maximum value of E_λ at the point given by

$$5(e^x - 1) = xe^x, \qquad \text{or} \qquad e^x = 5/(5 - x).$$

This equation has a single root $x = 4 \cdot 965$; and therefore the maximum value of E_λ occurs when λ varies as $1/T$.

Since the constants c_1 and c_2 in Planck's law have been satisfactorily determined, we can make a diagram in which wave-lengths are measured horizontally and the corresponding energy of radiation emitted per unit area per unit time is measured vertically. Corresponding to any particular temperature we can, by the use of Planck's formula, draw the curve shewing the distribution of the energy of radiation among the various wave-lengths.

Obviously, Planck's formula is of enormous value and importance. We can, by the use of an instrument called the bolometer, measure the energy of radiation corresponding to various wave-lengths when such radiation is received from the sun or even from some of the brighter of the stars: we can thus discover how far they radiate like 'black-bodies' and what their surface temperatures approximately are. In this way, during the present century, great progress has been made in the study of the fixed stars. In fact, the spectroscope and the bolometer together have been fundamental in developing the new science of astrophysics.

§199. *Visual magnitudes and Fechner's law.*

Whoever casually surveys the heavens on a clear night will notice that the stars differ in apparent brightness. It is naturally important to classify this difference.

The principle of classification rests upon what is known as Fechner's law of sensation. This physiological law can be best understood by taking its most simple illustration. Suppose that we have any just perceptible difference in the intensity of some sensation; then, according to the law, this difference is not absolute but is proportional to the actual intensity of the sensation. More generally, differences in intensity which correspond to the same fractional part of the whole are equally perceptible by the senses, whatever be the magnitude of the intensity.

Let I be the intensity of the cause of a sensation, and let dI be the change in intensity which corresponds to a change dS in the corresponding sensation. Then, according to Fechner's law, dS is proportional to dI/I. Hence, if k be a constant,

$$dI/I = k\,dS, \qquad \text{or} \qquad \log I = kS + c,$$

where k and c are both constants. Thus, by choosing our zero of sensation correctly, we can say that sensation, that is to say, the effect which any cause produces on our senses, is proportional to the logarithm of the intensity of the cause.

Stated in its simplest fashion as regards light, Fechner's law asserts that we measure percentage differences of brightness. A well-trained eye is said to be able just to perceive a one per cent. difference of brightness.

§ 200. *Measures of magnitude.*

It follows from the previous investigation that, when we seek to estimate the visual magnitudes of stars, we must make our measures depend on the logarithm of the amount of light received.

Let R be the amount of light received from a star and m its visual magnitude. Then we take logarithms to the base 10, and put

$$\log R = km + c.$$

Now magnitudes are so measured that the brighter star has the smaller magnitude. Further, there is a convention now universally adopted by which, when we say that one star is five magnitudes brighter than another, we mean that from the one we receive 100 times as much light as from the other. Hence

$$\log(100R) - \log R = -k(m+5) + km;$$

thus $\qquad\qquad 5k = -\log 100, \qquad \text{or} \qquad k = -2/5.$

Hence if R_1, m_1 and R_2, m_2 are the amounts of light received and the magnitudes respectively of two stars, we have

$$m_1 - m_2 = -\tfrac{5}{2}(\log R_1 - \log R_2).$$

This formula enables us to state, when we know the differences of magnitudes of two stars, the ratio of the amounts of light which we receive from them. For example, a star of the first magnitude is 251·2 times as bright as a star of the seventh magnitude. There is, of course, no reason why we should not give negative magnitudes to very bright stars. Thus the visual magnitude of the full moon is about −12·5, while that of the sun is − 26·72.

Absolute magnitude.

The absolute magnitude of a star is the measure of the actual amount of light which it emits. In order to measure the ratio of the absolute magnitudes of stars we must imagine them placed at the same distance. This distance is usually taken to be 10 parsecs. Now we have seen that the amount of light received from a star varies inversely as the square of the distance of the star. Hence if R_p be the amount of light received from a star at a distance of p parsecs, and if R be the amount of light received at a distance of 10 parsecs, then

$$R_p/R = (10/p)^2.$$

If M be the absolute magnitude of the star and m its visual magnitude, we know that

$$M - m = \tfrac{5}{2}\log{(R_p/R)} = 5\log{(10/p)}.$$

Thus $$M = m + 5 - 5\log_{10}p.$$

This formula enables us to write down the absolute magnitude of a star provided we know its visual magnitude and its distance.

The Purkinje effect.

The disadvantage of using the eye to measure star magnitudes is that different observers differ in their estimates: what is called the *personal equation* always enters in. Moreover, for some unexplained reason, a physiological fact known as *the Purkinje effect* vitiates human estimates. If two differently coloured sources of light appear equally bright and we diminish their intensity in the same ratio, the bluer source will then appear the brighter. In illustration of this there is the common experience that in a dark room blue objects can be seen more distinctly than red. Artists, moreover, usually paint their shadows blue. There is, therefore, much to be said for using contrivances which are independent of human judgments. The most common of such contrivances is the photographic plate. The relative photographic brightnesses of stars can be estimated from the diameters of their images when these are well focussed: they can also be determined from the densities of the images when these are purposely taken somewhat out of focus. Of course, for such comparisons the photographic plates must be exactly similar in nature and exposures must be of the same duration.

Estimates of magnitude made by photographs differ, however, from those made by humanity, because the light to which the photographic plate is most sensitive is of shorter wave-length (bluer) than that to which the eye is most sensitive. This, of course, we all know, inasmuch as a photographic plate can be developed without being fogged in a room lit by red light. The difference between the visual magnitude and the photographic magnitude of a star is called its *colour-index*.

Other methods of measuring intensities of light received have been devised. Of recent years devices for measuring radiation of all wave-lengths have come into general use. Such I need not describe beyond saying that their working usually depends on the thermo-electrical or photo-electrical properties of metals. What is important for our purpose is that the heat radiation of distant stars may now be easily and fairly accurately measured.

§ 201. *Radiation and human sight.*

Both Fechner's law and the Purkinje effect illustrate physiological peculiarities of humanity, but neither is as remarkable as the existence of the human eye and the practical limitation of its sensitiveness to what we naturally call visible light. It has been seen that the total extent of the wave-lengths which occur in radiation is enormous. The longest waves, such as those used in wireless telegraphy, can be several kilometres in length. The waves of visible light are measured in 100,000ths of a centimetre; and these are 10,000 times as long as some of the X-rays, which themselves are many times as long as the γ-rays. There are, at present, gaps in this scale of radiation; but it is practically certain that these gaps will be closed as we learn to manufacture rays of intervening wave-lengths. All forms of radiation travel with the speed of light, have similar electro-magnetic properties and are modifications of a single process which consists in the transference through space of energy unassociated with matter. Now, save for heat radiation, of which the waves are shorter than those of visible light, light itself was the only form of radiation known to us until recently. Though we can perceive heat radiation in a dull sort of way by means of its physiological effects, the only form of radiation to which we are acutely sensitive is that within a narrow range constituted by visible light. This is a range of wave-lengths ranging from four to eight hundred-thousandths of a centimetre: it is an absurdly insignificant part of the whole range of existing radiation. So small are both the wave-lengths and the range of visible light that in working with them it is customary to employ as unit *the Ångstrom, which is one hundred-millionth of a centimetre*. Thus light waves vary from 4000 to 8000 Å. in length.

Two conclusions force themselves upon us as we reflect upon these facts. First, we are impressed by the extraordinarily narrow perception of the Universe given to us by our senses. It is as if the Universe were a piano of at least some sixty octaves and our hearing were limited to one of them. We can only use wireless radiation by employing elaborate apparatus: yet there is nothing in the ultimate nature of things which should prevent conscious beings from using wireless rays as directly as we now use rays of light.

But the reason why we are thus limited to a particular narrow range of wave-lengths, within the vast range of all kinds of radiation, is that we are products of terrestrial evolution, creatures of sunlight. *We are descendants of a vast sequence of animal forms in which eyes with their sensitiveness to solar radiation gradually developed*. By the spectrobolometer the quality of sunlight received upon the earth can be measured. It is thus found that the greater part of the solar radiation which we receive is within wave-lengths which vary between 3000 and 10,000 Å. Practically, the sun radiates like a 'black-body' in accordance with Planck's law, its deviation from this law being somewhat further affected by the absorbing properties of the earth's atmosphere. When the primitive eye came into existence it was naturally adapted to use that quality of radiation which was especially present in sunlight: thus arose our sensitiveness to radiation from 4000 to 8000 Å.

It follows from this fact that a physicist, knowing Planck's law and the temperature of a star, together with the extent to which the star deviated from thermal equilibrium, could prophesy the wave-length of the radiation to which creatures on any planet of the star were sensitive, if the atmosphere of the planet did not materially upset the quality of the light received from the star. *The appropriate faculties of animals are thus determined by the field of radiation in which they have been evolved*. Had we been evolved in a different field of radiation we should have doubtless developed some faculty for using that field.

Such considerations bear upon the question as to how far colours in themselves have an objective existence. The colour red is the way in which we perceive radiation of a particular wave-length. Can it be said to exist in itself when it is created by our response to this particular type of radiation. For us wireless waves have no colour, for we have no vision tuned to them. We are, in fact, blind to all but an infinitesimal stretch of the total range of radiation. Colour, it is plain, only comes into existence when subject and object combine, and the percipient has such faculties that he can change certain combinations of radiation of appropriate frequencies into colour schemes. This leads us to the thought that, had our evolution been other than it has been, the pleasures of colour and doubtless those of sound might have been vastly extended. In particular, had we any organ of sense capable of using X-rays, the aid which we now get from the most powerful microscopes would be as nothing compared with our natural power of perceiving small objects.

Lecture ix

THE QUANTUM THEORY AND RÖNTGEN RAYS

§ 202. *The first form of the quantum theory.*

The essential feature of Bohr's work on the structure of the atom was that he applied the quantum theory to the origin of spectral lines. This famous theory, which continues to be a source of perplexity to physicists, is, as Sommerfeld remarks, a product of the twentieth century. It was first propounded by Planck at the end of the year 1900, in order to evade difficulties connected with the theory of so-called 'black-body' radiation (§194), the radiation of heat within a space enclosed by a body maintained at a steady temperature.

The law of equipartition of energy rests upon apparently unassailable dynamical principles. According to the law, if two interacting systems of particles be in equilibrium with one another, they must have reached a state in which the mean kinetic energy of all the particles in each system must be equal for each degree of freedom of the particles. Lord Rayleigh pointed out that, as a necessary consequence of this law, radiation from a perfect radiator ought to appear in the form of indefinitely short waves. But, as stated in §198, Wien had already enunciated a law (which corresponds to experimental fact) that the maximum intensity of radiation of a perfect radiator is associated with a wave-length proportional to $1/T$, where T is its absolute temperature. Thus a highly important general law of statistical mechanics led, if Rayleigh's arguments were valid, to a definitely wrong conclusion.

To avoid the opposition between fact and theory, Planck assumed that, if radiation of frequency ν is emitted or absorbed by a material body, only whole multiples of an elementary quantum of energy ϵ will be involved; and we shall have

$$\epsilon = h\nu.$$

The constant h is Planck's quantum of action; and its value in C.G.S. units is $6 \cdot 545 \times 10^{-27}$ erg-seconds. Its dimensions are those of energy multiplied by time. By some writers the quantity h itself is described as the quantum: we shall adopt the more usual mode of speech and say that energies emitted in quanta, multiples of a quantum $h\nu$, where h is Planck's constant and ν is a number defining the type of radiation which is emitted. It is convenient to use the term *unit of action* for Planck's constant h.

It is well to express the quantum law slightly differently in order that its extraordinary character may be clear. We therefore enunciate it in the form that *whenever energy associated with matter is transformed into radiation, the transformation does not take place continuously but in small packets or quanta of finite amount; and the amount of energy which constitutes a quantum is hv, where v is a number which, if the wave theory be true, is the frequency of the radiation, and h is Planck's constant.*

Planck's assumption can be enunciated in the different form that, in statistical investigations of thermodynamics, particles cannot be distinguished unless the products of their linear momenta and corresponding coordinates, resolved along each of the three axes, differ by a quantity greater than h. Thus, if the coordinates of a particle be x_s and its corresponding linear momenta be p_s, where $s = 1, 2, 3$, and if the coordinates and momenta of another particle be denoted by accented letters, then for the two particles to be distinguishable for statistical purposes we must have

$$x_s p_s - x_s' p_s' > h. \qquad \qquad \dots\dots(1)$$

As initially put forward the quantum law was merely empirical. During the present century it has repeatedly justified itself by the way in which it explains observed phenomena. There seems to be no doubt whatsoever that Nature is such that the law holds good. Thus Nature herself cannot discriminate between particles unless the inequalities (1) are satisfied. We shall shew shortly that we ourselves cannot carry out observations unless the product of coordinate and momentum errors is greater than h. But it seems certain that in Planck's law human limitations are not in question. The law expresses a characteristic of the interaction of matter and energy, of a most surprising kind, which apparently belongs to the inner nature of things.

§ 203. *The photo-electric effect.*

Einstein in the year 1905 made one of the two great scientific advances associated with his name when he applied the quantum theory to atomic phenomena and thus extended the use made of it by Planck in the statistical theory of radiation. Einstein was led to his advance by an endeavour to explain what is known as *the photo-electric effect.*

When radiation of short wave-length impinges on a metal plate there are emitted from the plate cathode-rays, which are streams of electrons moving with great velocities. Now the intensity of the incident radiation is proportional to the number of electrons emitted, but it has no effect on their velocities. Moreover, the maximum limit of these velocities of the emitted electrons depends upon the wave-length of the incident radiation. These surprising results are found to be true for ultra-violet light, but are even more marked when the shorter X-rays are employed as incident radiation.

Suppose that monochromatic radiation (§ 189) of frequency ν impinges on the metal plate. Electrons will consequently emerge from the plate with different velocities, but we find that these velocities have a maximum which is never surpassed. A natural explanation is that a certain variable amount of work, P say, must be done to free an electron from within the plate: P will only vanish if the electron is initially free and not bound within a molecule.

Let the electron thus freed by means of the work P emerge with velocity v and have mass m. Then, combining Planck's quantum law with the principle of energy, Einstein gave the equation

$$\tfrac{1}{2}mv^2 + P = h\nu.$$

Suppose now that V is the potential which would produce a stream of electrons of velocity v in a cathode-ray tube. We shall have, if e be the charge on an electron,

$$eV = \tfrac{1}{2}mv^2.$$

Hence
$$eV = \tfrac{1}{2}mv^2 = h\nu - P.$$

The corresponding equation for X-rays takes a more simple form inasmuch as, if the work P is of the order of $h\nu$, when ν is the frequency of ultra-violet light, it will be negligible in comparison with $h\nu$ when we deal with X-rays whose frequency is ten thousand times as great.

Thus for X-rays Einstein's photo-electric equation is

$$eV = \tfrac{1}{2}mv^2 = h\nu.$$

The equation represents the law of generation of cathode-rays when X-rays of wave-length c/ν are incident on a metal plate. But equally it represents another phenomenon. When streams of electrons are generated with potential V in a cathode-ray tube, they will have velocity v; and, if they are then directed on to the anti-cathode, they will produce among other radiation X-rays whose frequency is ν.

§ 204.   *The connection between energy emitted by an atom and the frequency of the radiation produced. Quantisation of action.*

From Planck's law that radiant energy of frequency ν is emitted in quanta $h\nu$, we are led to postulate that, if we have an atom which can by emitting radiation pass from a state in which its internal energy is

E_1 to a state in which its internal energy is E_2, the wave-length of the radiation emitted will be ν, where

$$E_1 - E_2 = h\nu,$$

and h is Planck's constant.

Quantisation of action.

If a particle oscillates in a straight line under a force directed to its mean position and proportional to its displacement, it is said to form a linear oscillator. When Planck investigated the state of thermo-dynamical equilibrium between matter and radiation he pointed out that this state could not depend upon the mechanism of the exchange of energy. Consequently he assumed that the state was produced by electrons vibrating as linear oscillators. This led to the equation

$$\int p \, dx = nh,$$

where n is an integer, p is the linear momentum of the particle corresponding to the linear coordinate x, and the integral is calculated for a complete period of oscillation. The expression $\int p \, dx$ is known as the integral of action of Maupertuis (1698–1759); and, when $\int p \, dx = nh$, we say that the integral of action is quantised.

§ 205. Bohr's quantised orbits. General quantum conditions for a particle in a constant field of force.

When Bohr put forward his initial theory of the hydrogen spectrum in the year 1913, he assumed that the electron-satellite could only rotate round the nucleus in a series of circular orbits. Such orbits must also, he postulated, be quantised. Thus Bohr postulated that only those orbits were possible for which

$$\int p \, dq = nh,$$

where n is an integer, q is an angular coordinate, p is the corresponding angular momentum, and the integral is calculated for a complete period.

If a be the radius of the orbit, m the mass and ω the angular velocity of the electron, we must have

$$ma^2\omega \int_0^{2\pi} d\theta = nh, \qquad \text{or} \qquad 2\pi ma^2\omega = nh.$$

It was soon recognised that the electron-orbits within an atom should be not only circular but also elliptic. Rules were needed whereby they might be similarly quantised. By the year 1916 the Wilson-Sommerfeld conditions had been enunciated; and a more general form of the quantum conditions was given by Einstein in the year 1917.

The two quantum conditions for a particle describing an elliptic orbit admit of simple expression. They are:

(1) The product of the average angular momentum of the particle by the angle swept out during a complete revolution is equal to $\tau_1 h$, where τ_1 is an integer and h is Planck's constant.

(2) The product of the average radial momentum of the particle by the amount by which the radius changes during the revolution is equal to $\tau_2 h$, where τ_2 is an integer. The radial momentum is momentum in the direction of the radius vector drawn from the nucleus; and, in computing the amount by which the radius changes, increase and decrease must be added together.

We will now give the Wilson-Sommerfeld quantum conditions for the motion of a particle in a constant field of force, that is to say, in a field which does not vary with the time. The basic ideas belong to that development of analytical dynamics which is associated especially with the names of Lagrange (1736–1813) and Hamilton (1805–1865). We assume that the motion of the particle is either periodic or 'conditionally periodic'; and by the latter term we mean that its motion can be compounded of periodic motions of possibly different periods. Assume further that the general coordinates are 'separated', that is to say, that they can be so chosen that p_r only involves q_r. Then the quantum conditions for the motion of the particle are

$$\int p_r \, dq_r = \tau_r h, \qquad r = 1, 2, 3,$$

where τ_r is an integer, h is Planck's constant, and the integral is taken over a complete period. The three integers τ_1, τ_2, τ_3, needed, in general, to define the quantised motion of the particle, are usually called the *quantum-numbers*.

It should be remarked that when a coordinate q is an oscillating variable, like the radius vector of an elliptic orbit, the integral $\int p \, dq$ would be zero if p were a one-valued function of q. It is, however, a two-valued function; and, when the integral is represented by a contour on the appropriate Riemann surface, we get for it a non-zero value.

The Einstein quantum conditions.

Hamilton's principle of Least Action, which is the fundamental theorem of analytical dynamics, takes an especially simple form when we are concerned with the motion of a particle in a constant field of force. In this case the integral of action

$$\int \sum_{r=1}^{3} p_r \, dq_r$$

(in which the coordinates need not be separated) is invariant for any change of space-coordinates, inasmuch as it is equal to $\int \dfrac{mv\,ds}{\sqrt{1 - v^2/c^2}}$, where v is the velocity of the particle of mass m and the integral is taken along the trajectory s.

Suppose now that we are dealing with the conditionally periodic motion of a particle but that the three generalised coordinates are no longer separated. Then the quantum conditions are comprised in the statement that the integral of action taken round any closed curve in the domain of the motion is an integral multiple of Planck's constant.

Such is the form which Einstein gave to the general quantum conditions. We easily see that, when the variables are separated, it yields the Wilson-Sommerfeld conditions.

Action is atomic.

Expressed in physical terms, the generalised quantum law asserts that in periodic or in conditionally periodic processes *action* is atomic. Action is a quantity of outstanding importance in modern mathematical physics. It is hardly necessary to state that the term, as we now use it, has no connection with the term as used in Newton's third law of motion, which affirms the equality of the action and reaction of forces. Action, as the term is used in analytical dynamics, is of the dimensions of energy multiplied by time. It belongs naturally to Minkowski's world and is a dynamical absolute, independent of the way in which space-time is divided up by any particular observer.

Entropy is also an absolute quantity, independent of the way in which space-time is stratified. Moreover, action and entropy, widely different as they are, resemble one another in being difficult to grasp imaginatively. Most of the quantities which seemed of importance in pre-relativity dynamics and physics could be abstracted from experience; but, *per contra*, they varied as the sections of Minkowski's world were changed. Yet, just as we saw in § 186 that entropy was bound to emerge in any investigation of the nature of heat, so action emerged naturally in nineteenth-century analytical dynamics.

Suppose that, in any volume V of space, we know the 'proper' or statical invariant-mass density ρ_0 of the mass at each point. Then the total mass within the volume will be $\int \rho_0 \, dV_0$, where dV_0 is an element of 'proper' volume. This mass is, by Einstein's formula $E = c^2 m$, the same as the energy contained in the volume. Suppose, however, that instead of taking a three-dimensional volume of space we take a four-dimensional volume of space-time and similarly compute the mass inside the volume. The result will be a quantity which represents the result of energy operating for a certain 'proper' time t_0. This quantity is *action*. From Planck's investigations it appears that action is not infinitely divisible. Processes such as radiation, the absorption of radiant energy and the scattering of light, may involve very small quantities of action; in them nothing happens until the action amounts to as much as Planck's unit of action. We cannot say that action grows during the very small time when we await its appearance: "it was not and it is", seems to be all that we can say.

It appears, further, that a unit of action has no quality. Energy has quality, so that we can speak of yellow light or blue light; yet action has no such characteristics. Consider, for example, the emission of yellow sodium radiation. A quantum $h\nu$ consists of $3 \cdot 44 \times 10^{-12}$ ergs of energy. Its distinctive colour (there are two lines close together) is due to the fact that the frequency $\nu = 5 \cdot 26 \times 10^{14}$ vibrations per second approximately. Hence $h = 6 \cdot 545 \times 10^{-27}$ erg-seconds. If we observed the light under different conditions our measures, alike of the energy and of the frequency, would be different. In fact, we know, by the Doppler effect, that for a rapid velocity of recession the colour of light, that is to say, its apparent frequency, is altered: light so moving is shifted towards the red and such shift corresponds to a diminution of ν. But h remains unchanged, however the measure of frequency may be altered.

§ 206. *Bohr's theory of the hydrogen spectrum.*

We will now give the elementary application of quantum principles by which Bohr in the year 1913 brilliantly explained the Balmer-Ritz series of lines which, as we stated in § 167, constitute the spectrum of hydrogen.

He assumed that, as in the Rutherford model, the atom of hydrogen consists of a nucleus of charge e, round which an electron of mass m and charge $- e$ is rotating with velocity v in a circle of radius a. If the angular velocity be ω, we have $v = a\omega$. The mass of the nucleus is very large compared with m, so that we may assume that the nucleus is fixed.

The electron moves in its circle under a force of electric attraction e^2/a^2. Thus
$$ma\omega^2 = e^2/a^2. \qquad \qquad \ldots\ldots(1)$$

According to Newtonian mechanics the electron might move in a circle of any radius. But according to Bohr's quantum conditions only certain radii are possible. These are given by the formula

$$2\pi m a^2 \omega = \tau h, \qquad \qquad \ldots \ldots (2)$$

for the average angular momentum of the planetary electron is $ma^2\omega$ and the radial momentum is zero. Hence we have

$$a = \frac{\tau^2 h^2}{4\pi^2 e^2 m} \quad \text{and} \quad \omega = \frac{8\pi^3 m e^4}{\tau^3 h^3}.$$

Thus only a discrete series of orbits within the atom is possible, their radii being given by assigning to τ integral values from unity upwards. Now the kinetic energy of the electron is

$$\tfrac{1}{2}mv^2 = \tfrac{1}{2}ma^2\omega^2 = \tfrac{1}{2}e^2/a.$$

Moreover, its potential energy will be $-e^2/a$, if we measure from zero potential energy at an infinite distance. Hence the sum of the kinetic and potential energies of the electron will be

$$E_\tau = -\tfrac{1}{2}e^2/a = -\frac{2\pi^2 m e^4}{h^2 \tau^2}.$$

Suppose now that the electron jumps from an orbit for which $\tau = k$ to an orbit for which $\tau = n$, where $k > n$. In so doing it will emit energy

$$E_k - E_n.$$

Moreover, such energy will appear as radiation of frequency ν and must therefore obey the quantum law

$$E_k - E_n = h\nu.$$

We shall therefore have

$$h\nu = \frac{2\pi^2 m e^4}{h^2}\left\{\frac{1}{n^2} - \frac{1}{k^2}\right\},$$

or

$$\nu/c = R\left\{\frac{1}{n^2} - \frac{1}{k^2}\right\}, \qquad \ldots \ldots (3)$$

where

$$R = 2\pi^2 m e^4/ch^3. \qquad \ldots \ldots (4)$$

Now, if c be the velocity of light, $c = \lambda\nu$, so that ν/c is the reciprocal of the wave-length, and thus it is what we have called the wave-number.

We thus get the Balmer-Ritz series of spectral lines; and, moreover, Rydberg's constant R, as calculated from the formula (4), is exactly in agreement with its experimental determination. We have, in c.g.s. units, $R = 109,675 = 1\cdot1 \times 10^5$ approximately.

The radius of the hydrogen atom and the velocity of the electron within it.

The investigation which has just been given shews that, when the electron of the hydrogen atom is in the circular orbit for which its energy is a minimum, its distance from the nucleus will be

$$a = h^2/4\pi^2 e^2 m.$$

Now, in electrostatic c.g.s. units,

$$e = 4{\cdot}77 \times 10^{-10}; \qquad h = 6{\cdot}545 \times 10^{-27}; \qquad e/m = 5{\cdot}31 \times 10^{17}.$$

Hence $$a = {\cdot}528 \times 10^{-8}.$$

This value of a we naturally choose as the measure of the radius of the hydrogen atom. It is of order 10^{-8} cm., as had previously (*vide* § 24) been surmised from the theory of gases.

We know that the velocity of light $c = 3 \times 10^{10}$ in c.g.s. units. If v be the linear velocity of the planetary electron of the hydrogen atom in the orbit of radius a, we readily get

$$v = 2\pi e^2/h = 2{\cdot}187 \times 10^8,$$

or $$v/c = 7{\cdot}29 \times 10^{-3}.$$

Thus the linear velocity of the planetary electron in its minimum circular orbit is about $(1/137)$th of the velocity of light, or some 1360 miles per second.

§ 207. *Elliptic orbits for the hydrogen atom.*

We now proceed to shew how the *two* quantum conditions of the Bohr-Sommerfeld theory arise in the case when the planetary electron of the hydrogen atom describes elliptic orbits round the nucleus.

We take the nucleus as the fixed origin of polar coordinates r, ϕ. Then, if the mass of the electron be m and the magnitude of its charge e, its kinetic energy will be

$$\frac{m}{2}\{\dot{r}^2 + (r\dot{\phi})^2\},$$

and its potential energy will be $- e^2/r$.

The moment of momentum will be $mr^2\dot{\phi}$ and the radial momentum will be $m\dot{r}$. Hence the possible quantised orbits will be given by

$$\int_0^{2\pi} mr^2\dot{\phi}\,d\phi = \tau_1 h \qquad \text{and} \qquad \int m\dot{r}\,dr = \tau_2 h,$$

the second integral being taken for values of r corresponding to a complete revolution.

Now the rate at which area is swept out by the planetary electron is a constant, as we know by Kepler's second law*. Hence we may put

$$mr^2\dot{\phi} = k;$$

and the first quantum condition becomes

$$2\pi k = \tau_1 h. \qquad \qquad \dots\dots(1)$$

The orbit, being an ellipse, may be written

$$l/r = 1 + \epsilon \cos \phi,$$

where ϵ is the eccentricity and l the semi-latus-rectum. Thus

$$- l\, dr/r^2 = - \epsilon \sin \phi \, d\phi.$$

Hence

$$m\dot{r}\, dr = m\frac{dr}{d\phi}\dot{\phi}\, dr = k\epsilon^2 \frac{\sin^2 \phi}{(1 + \epsilon \cos \phi)^2}\, d\phi.$$

Thus the second quantum condition becomes

$$k\epsilon^2 \int_0^{2\pi} \frac{\sin^2 \phi\, d\phi}{(1 + \epsilon \cos \phi)^2} = \tau_2 h, \quad \text{or} \quad 2\pi k \left\{ \frac{1}{\sqrt{1 - \epsilon^2}} - 1 \right\} = \tau_2 h. \quad \dots(2)$$

From (1) and (2) we get

$$1 - \epsilon^2 = \frac{\tau_1^{\,2}}{(\tau_1 + \tau_2)^2}.$$

The energy of the electron at any point of its orbit will be

$$E = \frac{m}{2}\{\dot{r}^2 + (r\dot{\phi})^2\} - e^2/r$$

$$= \frac{k^2}{ml^2}\left\{ \frac{1 + \epsilon^2}{2} + \epsilon \cos \phi \right\} - \{1 + \epsilon \cos \phi\}\frac{e^2}{l}.$$

Since the energy is constant this expression must be independent of ϕ. Thus

$$E = \frac{k^2}{ml^2}\left\{ \frac{1 + \epsilon^2}{2} \right\} - \frac{e^2}{l} \quad \text{and} \quad \frac{k^2}{ml^2} = \frac{e^2}{l}.$$

Therefore

$$E = - \frac{2\pi^2 me^4}{h^2}\frac{1}{(\tau_1 + \tau_2)^2}.$$

We see then that the expression for the energy of the elliptic orbits of the electron in the hydrogen atom is the same as that of the circular orbits, save that instead of one quantum-number τ we have the sum $\tau_1 + \tau_2$ of two quantum-numbers τ_1 and τ_2. Thus, though the circular orbits of Bohr are a thoroughly satisfactory explanation of the Balmer-Ritz series of spectral lines, yet equally the elliptic orbits of Sommerfeld account beautifully for the facts. This is a warning that no theory can be deemed final, however accurately it suits observed facts, until it has

* Kepler's laws are formally enunciated in § 229 of Lecture X.

been proved that no other theory is equally adequate. We are always in danger of forgetting this truism: and, when we do so, we build on unsatisfactory foundations.

The previous investigation seems to shew that the occurrence of two quantum-numbers τ_1 and τ_2 in connection with the elliptic orbit is unnecessary. We have, however, an instance of what is known as *degeneration*: the elliptic orbit, if elliptic coordinates were used, could be described by a single variable. In general, whenever an orbit, instead of filling a three-dimensional region, fills only a two-dimensional or a one-dimensional region, we need only two or one quantum-numbers respectively.

The fine structure of the hydrogen lines.

When the lines of the Balmer-Ritz series forming the spectrum of hydrogen are carefully examined, it is found that each consists of a group of lines close together. What we have hitherto regarded as a single line is thus a set of many fine but almost coincident lines. Sommerfeld has shewn that this structure can be explained if (*a*) the orbits of the planetary electrons are elliptic and if (*b*) the relativity variation of mass with velocity is true.

We have seen that elliptic planetary orbits are possible. Further, we have seen that velocities corresponding to circular orbits within the atom approach to within $7\cdot29 \times 10^{-3}$ times the velocity of light. Now in elliptic orbits linear velocities vary in accordance with the law $mr^2\dot{\phi} = k$: hence there is sufficient variation of electron-velocities within the atom to make the relativity variation of mass due to change of velocity significant. Because of it the elliptic orbits are not closed: the planetary electron makes rather more than one complete revolution between two successive times when it is nearest to the nucleus, and thus a two-dimensional region is filled. Somewhat complicated mathematical analysis gives a formula for the corresponding frequency of emitted radiation which accurately accounts for the fine structure of the spectral lines.

Were it not for such a result we might conjecture that Bohr's model of the atom was a brilliant but deceptive flight of fancy. Yet, although the quantum theory seems the repudiation of Newtonian mechanics, those parts of the Bohr-Sommerfeld theory that do not belong to the quantum theory not only use the principles of classical mechanics but even need the refinement by which Einstein has modified the Newtonian scheme.

In the investigation just given τ_1 is known as the azimuthal quantum-number and τ_2 as the radial quantum-number. We notice that, when the radial quantum-number τ_2 vanishes, we have a circular orbit. Furthermore, it is clear that, though τ_2 can vanish, the minimum value of τ_1 is unity. Moreover, if a and b are the semi-axes of the elliptic orbit, we shall have

$$\tau_2/\tau_1 = (a-b)/b.$$

Thus τ_2 is a number expressing the ellipticity of the orbit.

Suppose now that n be the total quantum-number of an elliptic Bohr orbit; and, to obtain agreement with a conventional notation, let l be the azimuthal quantum-number.

Thus $$\tau_1 = l, \qquad \tau_1 + \tau_2 = n.$$

Since $n > 0$ and $l > 0$, there will be n possible elliptic orbits corresponding to the total quantum-number n; and they will be given by $l = 1, 2, \ldots n$.

The Zeeman and Stark effects.

At the close of last century Zeeman, a Dutch physicist, put a Crookes' tube, through which a discharge was passing, between the poles of an electro-magnet. He discovered that the spectral lines of the emitted light were split up by the *magnetic* field so that each had three components slightly separated from one another. In the year 1912, Stark, a German physicist, shewed that the spectral lines of hydrogen are split by an *electric* field. Further investigations have shewn that the spectral lines emitted by atoms in electric and magnetic fields are very complex. But it appears to be true that they correspond to changes of energy between orbits which result from combining with the forces due to the field those which result from the inverse square law of attraction to the nucleus of the atom.

Such orbits in three dimensions need three quantum-numbers for their description. In fact, the azimuthal quantum-number l must be divided into equatorial and polar quantum-numbers. If m be the polar quantum-number, it can assume any integral value, including zero, from $-(l-1)$ to $(l-1)$. Experimental confirmation is hardly yet complete; but we may state as a highly probable conclusion that the number of general three-dimensional orbits corresponding to the total quantum-number n is the number of combinations (n, l, m), where

$$l = 1, 2, \ldots n; \qquad \text{and} \qquad m = -(l-1), \ldots 0, \ldots (l-1).$$

Thus, since m has $(2l-1)$ values for any particular value of l, the

number of possible orbits corresponding to the total quantum-number n will be
$$1 + 3 \ldots + (2n - 1) = n^2.$$

These results lead to *the general picture of the Bohr-Sommerfeld hydrogen atom*.

Corresponding to a total quantum-number $n = 1$, we have a single possible orbit $(1, 0, 0)$ for the electron-satellite in what is known as the innermost K-shell.

Corresponding to a total quantum-number $n = 2$, we have four possible orbits for the electron-satellite in what is known as the L-shell. They are $(2, 0, 0)$, $(2, 1, 1)$, $(2, 1, 0)$, $(2, 1, -1)$.

Similarly, corresponding to a total quantum-number $n = 3$, we have nine possible orbits in the M-shell. Theoretically the shells and the corresponding orbits continue indefinitely.

§ 208. *The periodic system of the elements.*

It might be thought *à priori* that such an elaborate investigation into the hydrogen atom, and the possible orbits of its electron-satellite, was of little significance as regards the elements of higher atomic number. The mathematician knows that 'the problem of three bodies' has not yet been solved. Hence, when two electrons simultaneously rotate round a common nucleus, their motions cannot be determined. Of course, a slight modification of the previous discussion of the hydrogen atom will give the theory of singly ionised helium He^+, or of doubly ionised lithium, Li^{++}. But the motions of the electrons in neutral helium, and in all atoms of more complex elements, cannot be determined by a mathematical formula. Sommerfeld, on the assumption that electron-orbits have an actual existence, has said that "the topography of the interior of the atom belongs to the future".

But it is a most remarkable, though possibly not wholly surprising, fact that *the possible orbits of the satellite electron of the hydrogen atom correspond, with one significant modification, to the arrangement of the electrons in unexcited atoms of higher atomic numbers*.

The modification is due to the discovery of 'the spinning electron'. It is obviously possible that an electron, considered as a bit of negative electricity, might rotate round its own axis. If so, it should be the centre of a small but strong magnetic field and, in addition, it ought to be subject to the quantum law. Two electrons, as we know, repel one another according to the law of the inverse square; those rotating in opposite directions ought to attract one another when close together.

The existence of the spinning electron has apparently been demonstrated by what is known as the Stern-Gerlach experiment*. In the year 1921 Stern and Gerlach sent a beam of uncharged silver atoms through a vacuum under the influence of a non-uniform magnetic field. They found that the beam of atoms was split up by the field into two beams which were equally and oppositely deflected. Subsequent experiments on other elements in which there is a single electron in the outermost shell have given similar results. They are explained on the assumption that this single electron can have opposite types of spin, respectively parallel and anti-parallel to the axis of the atom. Clearly, if this explanation holds good, there must be two different kinds of hydrogen atom. These two forms of hydrogen have, in fact, been discovered. Further researches have revealed that the angular momentum corresponding to the spin of the electron is one-half of a unit of action.

We now see that, corresponding to any orbit of a hydrogen atom, we have four numbers. These are the three quantum-numbers n, l, m previously defined and a symbol, conventionally represented by $\frac{1}{2}$ or $-\frac{1}{2}$, to indicate the spin-quantum of the electron describing the orbit.

We can, then, in the K-shell of the hydrogen atom have two different possible orbits $(1, 0, 0, \frac{1}{2})$ and $(1, 0, 0, -\frac{1}{2})$.

In the L-shell we can similarly have $2 \cdot 2^2$ orbits, represented by $(2, 0, 0, \frac{1}{2}), (2, 1, 1, \frac{1}{2}), (2, 1, 0, \frac{1}{2}), (2, 1, -1, \frac{1}{2}), (2, 0, 0, -\frac{1}{2}), (2, 1, 1, -\frac{1}{2}), (2, 1, 0, -\frac{1}{2})$ and $(2, 1, -1, -\frac{1}{2})$.

Generally, we can have in the nth shell $2n^2$ orbits.

In the year 1927 Pauli put forward his celebrated *exclusion principle*. If it be assumed that in the general unexcited atom no two satellite electrons can have the same four quantum-numbers, the orbits of the electrons will correspond to those possible for the satellite electron of the hydrogen atom.

Thus helium has two oppositely spinning electrons in the K-shell.

When elements of successively higher atomic numbers are formed by adding electrons, such electrons will be in the succeeding L-shell. When we reach an element for which this shell is completed the shell will contain 8 electrons: it is, in fact, known that such completion leads to the inert gas neon of atomic number 10.

In the succeeding M-shell there will be an addition of 8 electrons before we get to the inert gas argon of atomic number 18. When the shell is completed it will contain 18 electrons; and when, in addition to

---

* A good semi-popular account of the experiment will be found in C. G. Darwin, *The New Conceptions of Matter*. Bell, 1931, pp. 136 *et seq.*

these, there are 8 electrons in the succeeding N-shell, we get the inert gas krypton of atomic number 36. Further description is unnecessary. We may, however, add that radium of atomic number 88 is a symmetrical atom with, in successively larger shells, 2, 8, 18, 32, 18, 8, 2 atoms. The numbers are connected by the equality

$$88 = 2[1^2 + 2^2 + 3^2 + 4^2 + 3^2 + 2^2 + 1^2].$$

Of course, Pauli's exclusion principle is merely empirical. A reason has yet to be discovered why two electrons of the same spin cannot occupy the same orbit of an atom.

§ 209. *Wave mechanics and the Born-Dirac calculus.*

We have now said enough to make it clear that the quantum theory, as Bohr and Sommerfeld applied it to the atom, is a scandal to human thought. Its striking successes only serve to increase the scandal. We cannot doubt the fundamental postulate that radiation is emitted from atoms in quanta of energy measured by $h\nu$, where h is Planck's constant and ν is a number called the frequency of the radiation. But that an electron could circulate round a nucleus without emitting radiation is contrary to all our beliefs. Again, while the photo-electric effect seems definitely to bring us to a corpuscular theory of light, yet the phenomena of diffraction and interference, which we shall describe in §§ 216 *et seq.*, seem decisively to negative any such theory.

Vigorous attempts have naturally been made to reduce the discordant facts to a coherent whole. Two such may be briefly mentioned.

There is, in the first place, the theory known as *wave mechanics* which has been mainly created by the genius of de Broglie and Schrödinger. This theory seeks to describe matter in terms of waves and to use to this end the concept of 'group-velocity' invented by Rayleigh in connection with the propagation of waves in a dispersive medium.

Suppose that a small particle having inertia, such as an electron, to be of invariant mass m and to be moving with a constant velocity v. Then, as we have seen in § 107, if W be its energy and p its momentum,

$$W = mc^2 / \sqrt{1 - v^2/c^2}, \qquad p = mv / \sqrt{1 - v^2/c^2} = Wv/c^2.$$

In the theory of wave mechanics there is associated with this particle a transverse wave whose equation is of the form

$$\psi = a \cos 2\pi\nu (t - x/V), \qquad \qquad \ldots\ldots(1)$$

where ψ is the height of the wave, a its amplitude, ν its frequency and V its phase-velocity. We take $\nu = W/h$, and $V = c^2/v$, so that $p = h\nu/V$. These assumptions seem at first sight to be arbitrary and irrational.

Some justification of them is, however, immediately given by the consideration that quanta of light, or photons, as they are now commonly called, travel with velocity c.

If, in the assumption just made, we put $v = c$, we get

$$W = h\nu \qquad \text{and} \qquad p = h\nu/c.$$

The first equation gives the energy of a quantum of light, and the second gives the momentum which, as we have seen, we must attribute to such a quantum of light.

Suppose now that we denote by zero suffices 'proper' quantities (§§ 103, 105) and also corresponding axes 'fixed' with reference to the moving particle. They will, of course, be connected with quantities referred to axes with respect to which the particle is moving with velocity v by the Lorentz relations (§ 93):

$$x_0 = (x - vt)\,k, \qquad y_0 = y, \qquad z_0 = z, \qquad t_0 = (t - vx/c^2)\,k,$$

where
$$k = 1/\sqrt{1 - v^2/c^2}.$$

Obviously an associated wave must be stationary in the proper system, and hence its form must depend upon the time by a factor $\cos 2\pi\nu_0 t_0$, where ν_0 is the proper frequency and we make a suitable choice of the origin of time.

Such a form may be written

$$\cos 2\pi\nu_0 k\,(t - vx/c^2).$$

If now we take

$$v = \nu_0/\sqrt{1 - v^2/c^2} \qquad \text{and} \qquad V = c^2/v,$$

this form becomes $\qquad \cos 2\pi\nu\,(t - x/V).$

But the index of refraction of the medium in which ψ-waves of the form (1) travel is a quantity $\mu = c/V$.

We therefore have $\mu = v/c$; and, in consequence,

$$\mu = \sqrt{1 - \nu_0^2/\nu^2}. \qquad\qquad \text{......(2)}$$

This formula defines the variable refractive index or, in other words, the *dispersive character* of space for the waves associated with a particle whose nature is characterised by the number ν_0.

Suppose now that we have a large number of waves differing slightly in frequency and travelling in a dispersive medium whose refractive index is given by equation (2). Such waves are said to constitute a group. At certain places where all the members of the group agree in phase the amplitude of the resultant wave will be great. We can prove that these places will be crests of a wave travelling with a *group-velocity U*, which in general differs from the phase-velocity.

Suppose that ν is changed into $\nu + \delta\nu$, then μ will become $\mu + \dfrac{\partial\mu}{\partial\nu}\delta\nu$.
The wave (1) will become

$$\psi_{\nu+\delta\nu} = a_{\nu+\delta\nu}\cos 2\pi(\nu+\delta\nu)\left\{t - \frac{x}{c}\left(\mu + \frac{\partial\mu}{\partial\nu}\delta\nu\right)\right\}$$

$$= a_{\nu+\delta\nu}\cos 2\pi\nu\left\{t - \frac{\mu x}{c} + \frac{\delta\nu}{\nu}\left(t - \frac{\mu x}{c} - \frac{\nu x}{c}\frac{\partial\mu}{\partial\nu}\right)\right\} \text{ approximately.}$$

All these waves will be in phase to give a great amplitude as a result of their conjunction, if t and x are connected by the relation

$$ct = x\left\{\mu + \nu\frac{\partial\mu}{\partial\nu}\right\}.$$

Thus the group-velocity is U, where

$$\frac{1}{U} = \frac{1}{c}\frac{\partial}{\partial\nu}(\mu\nu).$$

Now $\mu\nu = \sqrt{\nu^2 - \nu_0^2}$. Hence $U = c\mu$, or $U = v$. Thus the velocity of a particle is the group-velocity of the associated waves.

It now becomes plausible to suggest that such a particle as an electron actually consists of a group, or segment of a group, of monochromatic waves. We may, if we desire concrete imagery, imagine that such waves move in some 'sub-ether'. But what we measure as the velocity of the electron will be the group-velocity of these waves. Since monochromatic waves are infinite in length while an electron is finite in its dimensions, it is natural to postulate that of each of the waves of our group we take but a segment containing a limited number of wave-crests. By a celebrated theorem due to Fourier any such segment can be built up of monochromatic waves of differing frequencies. Further, a segment of a ψ-wave containing only, say, fifty crests will behave to some extent as an infinite train. Moreover, we can shew that with high-speed electrons such a segment will have a length comparable to the dimensions of an atom.

Suppose, for example, that our electrons, each of mass m, are set in motion, as in G. P. Thomson's experiments, by an electric field of some 20,000 volts. Their velocity will be $v = 8\cdot5 \times 10^9$ cm. per sec. approximately.

Now, by the formulae just obtained, the wave-length of the constituent ψ-waves is

$$\lambda = V/\nu = h/p = h\sqrt{1 - v^2/c^2}/mv.$$

But $h = 6\cdot545 \times 10^{-27}; \qquad m = 9 \times 10^{-28}.$

Hence $\lambda = 7\cdot3 \times \sqrt{1 - v^2/c^2}/v = 8\cdot2 \times 10^{-10}$ cm.

Thus a length of a constituent ψ-wave containing fifty crests would be of size 4×10^{-8} cm. Such a length is, of course, far smaller than anything which we can directly measure. We could only perceive its wave character by using a diffraction grating of the kind provided by natural crystals.

Such considerations, coupled with the undoubted fact of the diffraction of electrons, together with the numerical agreement between experiment and theory, appear to justify Schrödinger's assumption that a particle or electron is constituted by a segment of a group of waves of neighbouring frequencies. It is, in the language usually used, a wave-packet. Classical dynamics, on this view, regards phenomena as though the associated wave-group obeyed the laws of geometrical optics.

Unfortunately, according to de Broglie*, the promising beginning of the theory is deceptive. The particle must be more than a wave-packet or it would be dispersed by diffraction. Yet it seems also impossible to sustain the view that the particle exists as a singularity in the wave. Equally we cannot rest satisfied with the view (§ 147) that with the particle there is associated a sort of pilot-wave. The fundamental differential equation reached by Schrödinger has shewn itself 'immensely fruitful'. But from it we get the *probability* that a particle will be found at a certain place at a certain time. When we are dealing with two particles we need a six-dimensional 'sub-etherial' space in which to imagine the motions of the two sets of waves. In short, the wave theory is a mathematical artifice and not a physical explanation of the nature of a particle.

An alternative calculus, developed since the year 1925 by Heisenberg, Born and Dirac, abandons any hope that we can picture the behaviour of electrons and similar particles. It takes account only of observed facts and primarily therefore of the frequencies of the spectral lines emitted by atoms. Two-dimensional manifolds are formed which contain all the differences of energy-levels which correspond to the spectral lines. The algebra of these matrices, as they are called, has led to a new calculus. It is powerful, beautiful and coherent and has a certain predictive capacity. Possibly it must be accepted in lieu of physical images, and we must allow that when we get to particles as small as the electron we reach a region of behaviour so unfamiliar that ideas derived from normal experience do not suffice to describe it.

* See the general introduction to L. de Broglie's *Wave Mechanics*, to which reference was made in § 147.

§ 210.   *The Heisenberg uncertainty-relations.*

Difficulties so fundamental and so intriguing as those associated with the quantum theory are a direct incentive to enquiry and to the development of speculative theory. Within the last few years they have led to a recognition of the limitations imposed by the very nature of things on fundamental measurements which we make. These limitations have been formulated in the uncertainty-relations or principle of indeterminacy which originated with Heisenberg in the year 1927.

Before Heisenberg's fundamental paper appeared physicists had always assumed that they could measure lengths as accurately as they pleased. Though it was recognised that minute errors might enter into any measure of length, it was assumed that they had their origin in the imperfection of our instruments or methods and could by improved technique be diminished at our pleasure. Measurements of time always reduce to measurements of length, and with regard to them the same assumption was made. Heisenberg has forced us to realise that such assumptions are untrue.

Consider an attempt to locate an electron. Obviously we cannot locate it unless we can see it. We cannot see it unless light scattered by it enters the eye. Now when light falls upon a particle and is scattered by it, the particle recoils with a momentum proportional to that of the incident light. But light interacts with matter and electrons in quanta, or photons, of energy $h\nu$, where h is Planck's constant and ν is what we call the frequency of the light. A photon with such energy will have momentum $h\nu/c$ or h/λ, where λ is what we call the wave-length of the light. Any electron which scatters light must then deflect at least a photon of the light. The electron must thereby gain momentum.

Suppose now that O be an electron, Oy the axis of a microscope which we use that we may see the electron, and Ox a line perpendicular to Oy, which is both in the focal plane of the microscope and also in the plane in which the electron moves after collision with the photon. Suppose, further, that light comes from $y = -\infty$, strikes the electron and is scattered through an angle α before it enters the microscope. Suppose also that the electron subtends an angle 2ϵ at the object glass of the microscope. Then obviously α lies between $\pm \epsilon$.

Now, in c.g.s. units, $h\nu$ is for ordinary light of order 10^{-12}; and, if m be the mass of the electron, mc^2 is of order 8×10^{-7}. Hence it may be readily proved, by putting down the classical equations of energy and momentum for the collision of a photon and electron, that the change in the frequency of the light due to scattering is negligible. Hence, by using the principle of conservation of momentum, we see that the change in the momentum of the electron along Ox is $(h\nu/c)\sin\alpha$. Moreover, if the electron initially had a velocity along Ox, small compared with that of light, this conclusion would be unaltered.

Since α can have any value between $\pm\,\epsilon$, the uncertainty in the subsequent momentum along Ox is

$$\delta p_x = \frac{2h\nu}{c}\sin\epsilon.$$

But we know by the theory of the microscope that the position of the electron along Ox can only be obtained with a possible inaccuracy

$$\delta x = \lambda/2\sin\epsilon.$$

Thus, under average conditions,

$$\delta x\,\delta p_x = h.$$

This result is typical of all that are obtained. Suppose that for any particle, such as an electron or proton, we take the conjugate coordinates p and q of analytical dynamics. Thus p and q can be respectively length and momentum, or time and energy, or angle and angular momentum. In each case the product of p and q is of the dimensions of action. *The uncertainty-relations state that the measurement of any one coordinate produces in the conjugate coordinate an uncertainty such that the inaccuracy in the coordinate measured multiplied by the uncertainty in the conjugate coordinate is on the average equal to Planck's constant h.*

Thus, if p be measured with an error δp, it will produce an uncertainty δq in q such that on the average

$$\delta p\,\delta q = h.$$

Thus the error δp implies the average error $h/\delta p$ in q. It is hardly necessary to say that the consequent error may occasionally be much greater or much less than the average. But we can never find position with absolute accuracy: the greater our accuracy, the greater will be the inaccuracy in the corresponding momentum. So also we can never find with absolute accuracy the time at which a particle is in a certain position: the greater the accuracy, the greater will be the inaccuracy in the measure of the energy of the particle.

We must, moreover, understand that our inability is not due to the imperfections of our instruments or to any other human limitations. It is inherent in the very nature of things. In this connection we recall that the constant h was introduced by Planck because in his thermodynamical investigations he found that nature did not discriminate between two particles unless they differed in the product xp_x by more than h, x being a coordinate and p_x the corresponding momentum.

Einstein's principle of relativity effected a revolution in physics by using the hitherto unobserved fact that we cannot discover absolute time. It seems likely that Heisenberg's uncertainty-relations will be even more revolutionary, inasmuch as they shew that we can never discover at one and the same time the position and momentum of a particle. Hitherto our dynamics has been based upon the belief that, say, if E be the energy after a time t of a particle falling under gravity, then

$$E = \tfrac{1}{2}mg^2t^2;$$

and we have assumed that this equation would hold good however small E and t might be. Obviously this assumption flatly contradicts the Heisenberg formula

$$\delta E\,\delta t = h.$$

Similarly the hitherto accepted differential equations of dynamics, when applied to small variations of p and q coordinates, fail.

Needless to say, just as the relativity corrections are not noticeable for bodies moving with normal velocities, so the Heisenberg relations are obscured when we deal with normal dynamical problems. It is only when errors are considered, which are so small that their product in c.g.s. units is of the order $h = 6{\cdot}5 \times 10^{-27}$, that we notice the deviation from classical assumptions.

§ 211. *The present state of the quantum theory. Lindemann's speculations. The concepts of space and time.*

Since Einstein in the year 1905 used the quantum theory to explain the photo-electric effect, the question as to whether light consists of particles or waves has been insistent. The discovery of the diffraction of electrons has but increased the need for answering the question, for it inevitably led to the enquiry as to whether the electron is a particle or a wave-packet. We have seen that the wave mechanics of de Broglie and Schrödinger does not, as was at first hoped, put an end to perplexities. We can say definitely that the endeavour to represent material particles as special forms of waves has broken down. Wave mechanics is a mathematical device of great elegance and power but not a physical explanation of experiments which seem to lead to contradictory notions. Until recently it seemed as though all that we could do was to hold fast to two ends of a chain of which the intervening links were hidden from us. Such a mode of proceeding Poincaré*, a little unkindly, described as being characteristic of 'the embarrassed theologian'. He defended

* H. Poincaré, *La Science et l'Hypothèse*. Flammarion, n.d., p. 192.

it by the plea that both ends of the chain may express true physical relationships and that the contradiction may lie in the images with which we have clothed reality.

Of late some light has begun to shine in the darkness; and the Heisenberg uncertainty-relations seem to shew that our difficulties arise from a belief, which we have wrongly derived from experiments with gross matter, that space and time are absolutes measurable as exactly as we please. In fact, the accurate determination in space and time of point-instants for ultimate particles like electrons is impossible. It now appears that time and energy, momentum and position are statistical concepts.

Lindemann, in an essay* which is both acute and singularly suggestive, has emphasised these conclusions and has indicated how recognition of them may lead to the unravelling of present perplexities. He reminds us that the mean energy of a molecule in a gas (that is, the energy averaged over a large number of molecules) can be fixed very accurately: it is proportional to the absolute temperature of the gas, which has a definite value. Now, if we have a number of indistinguishable particles forming a dynamical system in equilibrium with its surroundings, we may assume that all will pass through all phases and that the time-average of any measurable quantity characteristic of any particle will be the mean at any instant of this particular quantity averaged over the whole number of particles. Hence the average temperature of a molecule of the gas taken over a period of time is the same as the temperature of the gas. Temperature has thus a statistical character; and it is possible to determine at any given moment for a single molecule its mean deviation from the average temperature. Of course, the temperature of a single molecule is an absurd term: we speak of the energy of a molecule. Lindemann concludes† that "energy is just as much a statistical concept as temperature. It has no meaning unless averaged over a finite time, any more than temperature has a meaning unless averaged over a considerable number [of molecules]".

The concept of space is built upon the notion of distance; and distance is not 'the amount of emptiness' between two points but is ultimately the result of operations with a measuring rod. Now no measuring rod of the actual world resembles our ideal solid body. Such

* F. A. Lindemann, *The Physical Significance of the Quantum Theory.* Clarendon Press, 1932.

† *Ibid.* p. 109.

a rod, it seems, consists of a number of linked particles vibrating, even at the absolute zero of temperature, round their mean positions. Thus even at a constant temperature a rod will only have an average length. It will never continue to be of precisely the same length for any appreciable period of time. Of course, the uncertainty of position of the particles at the end of a rod is negligible for ordinary processes of measurement, because Planck's unit of action h is exceedingly small in comparison with such transfers of action as those with which we normally concern ourselves. If, however, we were trying to measure lengths of the order of the dimensions of a Bohr atom, say 10^{-8} cm., our difficulties would be overwhelming.

From Lindemann's standpoint the wave-aspect of photons and electrons is a makeshift, a partially successful attempt to evade the difficulties caused by our assumption that we can measure lengths in space-time as accurately as we please without introducing momentum and energy. It is most interesting to notice in this connection that a wave-packet can be short and then the particle which it represents will have its position along the wave fairly well determined; but in this case the monochromatic waves which built up the packet will differ markedly in wave-length and we shall be correspondingly uncertain as to the momentum in the direction of the wave. Alternatively, we can fix the momentum accurately by fixing the wave-length; but then the wave corresponding to the particle is monochromatic and of infinite length, so that any statement as to the position of the particle is impossible.

When the wave theory is applied to the Bohr orbits of the hydrogen atom, it is found that the first orbit must be represented by a continuous blurred ring of which the orbit is, as it were, the central thread. The electron can be at any point of the blur and apparently at all points at the same time: we can merely describe the probability that it will be in any particular point of the blur. This almost nonsensical statement is an inevitable result of the inadequacy of a space-time description of a process which is indeterminate in space and time.

Lindemann points out that Heisenberg's uncertainty-relations clearly reveal such inadequacy. If we have an electron rotating round a nucleus and as near to it as possible, the product of the error in the angle described and the angular momentum introduced as we determine the angle must on the average be h. Now the angle, since the electron has spin, can be determined with a maximum error 2π. Hence the corresponding angular momentum must be on the average $h/2\pi$. If now we assume that this angular momentum is due to electrostatic attraction according to the law of the inverse square, we get the first Bohr orbit. But to speak of the orbit is nonsense. The electron is in an uncertainty domain, and any attempt to locate it in space or time would break up the existing dynamical system of nucleus and electron. At most we can say that the 'orbit' represents the mean position of the electron averaged over a long time.

Naturally we enquire how we can take the first step to an 'orbit' which admits of a space-time description. Obviously we must first consider the case when we can say that the electron lies on one half or the other of its 'orbit'. We can then locate it with a maximum error π, and this fact implies an angular momentum h/π. Evidently we thus get the second Bohr 'orbit'. The 'orbits' corresponding to successively high quantum-numbers can now be built up in an obvious fashion. In the end, for large quantum-numbers we get orbits with regard to which we can make a correspondingly large number of observations: we have, in fact, the classical theory. Bohr's *correspondence principle*, that "the classical laws are the limit to which the quantum laws tend when states of very high quantum-number are reached", thus emerges as the natural result of the fact that a space-time description is possible when we can take as many observations as we please with, in each case, a relatively negligible error.

Lindemann shews satisfactorily how the diffraction of light, regarded as a stream of photons, can be deduced from the uncertainty-relations. But his investigation of interference rests on an empirical basis that needs, I think, more explanation than is yet forthcoming.

We shall henceforth, in discussing the various forms of radiation, continue to use the language and ideas of wave motion. But it is to be understood throughout that we do not assert that waves of radiation have a physical existence. All radiation may consist of corpuscles of energy, each of magnitude $h\nu$, where ν is a number of dimensions -1 in time which defines the particular type of energy under consideration; and the success of wave-pictures may be due to the fact that they serve to express space-time indeterminacy in regions which are so small that Planck's constant becomes important.

§ 212. *Röntgen or X-rays.*

As we stated in Lecture VII (§ 154), it was in the year 1895 that Röntgen discovered the X-rays which have proved so important in physical theory. They were produced when the electrons of cathode-rays struck the glass wall of a highly exhausted cathode-ray tube: and Röntgen found that they travelled in straight lines. We stated, further, that ten years later Barkla proved that the rays were similar to rays of visible light save that, if we may continue to use conventional language, the wave-lengths of the latter are about ten thousand times as large as those of the former. Now-a-days, X-rays are produced by allowing the electron-stream of the cathode-ray tube to impinge, not on the glass wall, but on a piece of metal with a high melting point which is termed the *anti-cathode*.

The measured wave-lengths of hard X-rays lie between $1 \cdot 5 \times 10^{-7}$ cm. and a length less than 10^{-8} cm. The frequency of the shortest rays is more than 3×10^{18}, this being the number of oscillations in a second.

The two types of Röntgen radiation.

The X-rays produced when the rapidly moving electrons of the cathode-stream strike the anti-cathode are of two types, called respectively *impulse* and *characteristic* X-rays.

Whenever a moving electron is stopped, we believe that an electromagnetic disturbance arises which travels through space with the velocity of light. For this reason when the electrons hit the anti-cathode they cause *impulse* radiation. An impulse is, as it were, a single solitary wave. But a possible mathematical expression for any such solitary wave is an aggregate of Fourier series, and thus the impulse can be regarded as the aggregate of a determinate and continuous series of monochromatic waves. Hence impulse radiation will give rise to a continuous spectrum if it be analysed as visible light is analysed by the spectroscope. It is found that the hardness (that is to say, the penetrative power which is measured by the frequency) of impulse radiation increases with the voltage of the cathode-ray tube in which it is produced. We have, in short, a reversal of the photo-electric effect.

In addition to such impulse radiation it is found that the anti-cathode sends out radiation of a definite series of discontinuous wave-lengths. The wave-lengths which thus form a line spectrum depend on the substance of which the anti-cathode is made and are different for different substances. Because they are characteristic of the substance which emits them they are called *characteristic* X-rays. Obviously they must manifest some property of the atoms of the element of which the anti-cathode is composed. It is found that the hardness of characteristic radiation increases approximately as the square of the atomic number of the element from which it is derived.

Impulse radiation is of little theoretical importance. But characteristic Röntgen radiation has led to notable advances in physical theory and, in particular, to increased knowledge both with regard to the internal structure of complex atoms and also with regard to the arrangement of atoms in crystals.

In what follows, when we speak of X-rays without qualification, it is to be understood that characteristic X-rays are alone under consideration.

§ 213. *The origin of characteristic X-rays.*

How are characteristic X-rays produced? The answer, confirmed by a whole series of investigations, is that the impinging electrons of the cathode-stream penetrate *into the atoms* of the metal of the anti-cathode and drive out planetary electrons belonging to the inner rings of the atoms. Electrons belonging to such inner rings are firmly held, because they rotate near and under the attraction of a nucleus whose positive charge is measured by the atomic number of the atom. Hence, unless the impinging electrons are moving with high speeds, no inner electrons of the atom will be detached. Further, we need higher speeds to detach electrons from atoms of a high atomic number than from atoms for which the atomic number is relatively small.

When a planetary electron is hit with sufficient velocity to drive it from its orbit (we may, if necessary, allow that the term 'orbit' includes an associated region of indeterminacy) it does not in general jump to a larger orbit, because the electrons in the outer rings drive it away. It passes outside the atom altogether, and becomes one of the electrons emitted by the anti-cathode. But it has left a vacant orbit, and an electron from an outer ring can move to take its place. In this movement energy of radiation is given out as an X-ray.

Just as a visible spectrum is produced by the outer electrons of an atom jumping from one possible orbit to another, so an X-ray spectrum is produced by electrons jumping from outer to inner shells or rings. We cannot, of course, see an X-ray spectrum directly with the human eye: but, as we shall shew shortly, we can make use of the fact that a photographic plate is sensitive to X-rays.

It is a striking fact that the spectroscopic behaviour of Röntgen rays is more simple than that of rays of visible light. The reason is that X-rays arise when electrons jump from outer orbits to orbits near the nucleus of the atom where, to a first approximation, laws are relatively simple. But visible light arises when electrons on the outer boundary of the atom change their orbits; and not only is the number of such possible changes of orbit almost unlimited but also "the nuclear charge loses its regulative power"*.

X-rays are produced, as we have said, by outer planetary electrons jumping to vacant positions in inner shells or rings of the atom. Such jumps as can take place are relatively few in number and each will give an X-ray of definite wave-length. If ν be the frequency of the ray and E the energy given out by the planetary electron in its jump, we shall have (§ 203) ν determined by the quantum law

$$E = h\nu,$$

where h is Planck's constant.

§ 214. *The connection between the atomic number and characteristic X-rays of an element.*

We have said in § 212 that, as we pass from element to element in the modern form of Mendeléev's Periodic Table, the frequencies of corresponding lines of the X-ray spectra vary roughly as the square of the atomic number. We can prove this fact, and also that to a first approximation the innermost electron of an atom moves in a circle whose radius is inversely proportional to the atomic number, by an easy extension of our previous analysis. We assume, throughout the investigation, the adequacy of the Bohr model of the atom, but the mathematical formulae agree equally with Lindemann's use of the uncertainty-relations.

We assume that the motion of an inner electron of an atom is dominated by the charge on the central nucleus and that, in comparison with it, we can ignore the effect of all the other planetary electrons.

Let E be the nuclear charge of an atom of atomic number n, e being the charge on an electron and m its mass. We shall have $E = ne$.

Consider the circular motion of an inner electron of the atom: let a be its radius and ω its angular velocity.

Because a central force eE/a^2 causes the electron to move in a circular orbit of radius a with velocity ω, we have

$$eE/a^2 = ma\omega^2.$$

Further, by Bohr's quantum condition, we have

$$ma^2\omega \times 2\pi = \tau h.$$

---

* The words are those of A. Sommerfeld, *Atomic Structure and Spectral Lines.* Translated by H. L. Brose. Methuen, 1928, p. 141. Sommerfeld's book was an authoritative exposition of the state of the theory when the book was written.

Thus
$$a = \frac{\tau^2 h^2}{4\pi^2 e^2 m} \cdot \frac{1}{n}.$$

Hence our approximate analysis indicates that the innermost electron of an atom moves in a circle whose radius is inversely proportional to the atomic number.

Moreover, the potential energy of the electron is approximately $-Ee/a$, if zero energy corresponds to $a = \infty$; and its kinetic energy is

$$\tfrac{1}{2} m a^2 \omega^2 = \tfrac{1}{2}\frac{Ee}{a}.$$

Thus the total energy is

$$-\tfrac{1}{2}\frac{Ee}{a} = -\frac{2\pi^2 m e^4}{\tau^2 h^2} \cdot n^2.$$

Since the frequency of the emitted radiation varies as the change in the energy of a jumping electron, we see that for different elements corresponding frequencies will be approximately proportional to n^2.

§ 215. *The K-, L- and M-series of spectral lines.*

To Barkla we owe the discovery of the fact that, in the characteristic X-rays emitted by any element, there are two types represented by two series of spectral lines conventionally denoted by the letters K and L. Subsequently Siegbahn discovered traces of the existence, in the atoms of high atomic number, of a third M-series.

The K-type of radiation is the most penetrating: it has been observed from sodium (atomic number 11), for which even the K-radiation is somewhat soft, up to tungsten (atomic number 74), for which the rays are extremely hard. To produce the still harder K-radiation of elements with higher atomic numbers we should need to bombard the anti-cathode with electrons of velocities difficult to obtain experimentally. The L-type of radiation is, for the same element, softer than the K-type. It has been observed from copper (29) up to uranium (92). For the lighter elements the L-type of radiation would be too soft to be easily observed. Finally, the M-type of radiation, which is softer than the L-type, has been observed with difficulty only for some of the heaviest elements. Each of the three types of radiation consists of a number of spectral lines. Each type becomes harder as the atomic number increases.

Moseley, in the year 1913, obtained the K-group of X-ray spectral lines by crystal analysis and made advances on which the modern theory has been largely based. That theory in its present form assumes the Bohr model of the atom: a positive central nucleus surrounded by planetary electrons arranged in concentric shells. Successive shells counting from the centre are, as has been stated previously in § 208, called the K-, L-, M-, N-, ... shells.

When K-radiation is excited, an electron must first be knocked out of the K-shell by a cathode-ray electron which has penetrated into the atom. In order that this may happen the energy of the intruding electron must be at least sufficient to drive the electron from the K-shell. Thus for elements of high atomic number the necessary velocity of the intruding electron must be very great. When the electron is knocked out of the K-shell, the gap will be filled up by another electron which will probably fall from the L-shell but which may fall from the M-shell or even from the N-shell. In this process energy will be emitted as radiation, which will have different wave-lengths according as there is a fall from the L-, M- or N-shells. We thus get the spectral lines *constituting the K-series.* Since the energy emitted is proportional to the frequency of the emitted radiation, the wave-length due to the fall L to K will be greater than that due to the fall M to K, and this in turn greater than that due to the fall N to K. On the other hand, the probability of the first fall is greater than the probability of the second, which is greater than the probability of the third. Hence the intensity of the first line is greater than that of the second, and this in turn is greater than that of the third. In exactly the same way the L-series of lines will be obtained if first of all an electron is knocked out of the L-shell and if then an electron falls to take its place from an M- or an N-shell.

There are small differences in the energy emitted as an electron falls, say, to the K-shell from different orbits in, say, an L-shell. Such differences shew themselves in simple cases when orbital energy is calculated according to relativity-mechanics: they give a fine structure to the spectral lines of the K-series. Such a fine structure equally exists in the L- and M-series. Recent work has revealed the existence of other X-ray spectral lines, besides adding largely to the series previously known. A vast amount of investigation has thus confirmed the value of the model of the atom given in § 208. But we would end our brief discussion by emphasising the importance of Moseley's fundamental discovery that atomic number, and not atomic weight, determines the sequence of X-ray spectra. From this discovery there came, as we stated in § 26, the modern form of Mendeléev's Periodic Table.

§216. *The interference of light.*

Before we can explain how X-ray spectra are produced by crystals we must briefly describe the phenomena familiar to all students of physical optics, the *interference and diffraction* of light. To these phenomena reference has been repeatedly made in connection with the dispute as to whether light is to be regarded as corpuscular or as a wave phenomenon. Here we will merely recall that the experimental results on which the quantum theory is based seem to make it certain that the energy of radiation of frequency ν is distributed in little packets of size $h\nu$, where h is Planck's constant. The phenomena of interference and diffraction, on the contrary, appear to afford conclusive evidence that light (and all other forms of radiation) is propagated by a continuous wave motion.

Interference rests upon the fact that waves of water (and therefore of light, if light be a wave phenomenon) may be superposed one on another: it was first clearly enunciated by Thomas Young (1773–1829) in the year 1801. It is most readily explained by an analogy. Suppose that we drop two precisely similar stones into a still pond. From each as centre similar water-waves will spread out. Where these meet a sort of lattice-pattern will be formed. If two crests come together we shall get a wave of double the maximum height of the original waves. When two troughs come together we get a wave of double the maximum depth. When a crest and a trough coincide the surface of the water is undisturbed.

Now exactly the same phenomenon of interference is observed when rays of light of equal wave-length cross one another: we get a lattice-pattern of light and darkness, light where the waves do not neutralise one another, darkness where crests and troughs cancel out.

Fresnel (1788–1827) devised a simple experiment to illustrate this phenomenon. He reflected light from a source S at two mirrors AB, BC inclined at a very small angle to one another. If S_1 and S_2 be the images of S in the two mirrors, the reflected light will consist of rays of precisely similar quality, apparently coming from two adjacent points 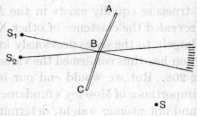 S_1 and S_2. Where the rays overlap in the angle S_1BS_2 produced, interference takes place, and dark and light fringes are observed on a distant screen.

If it be admitted that light travels in continuous waves, interference admits of a simple mathematical expression and explanation.

A wave of light, of amplitude (maximum height) a and wave-length λ, may be written

$$y = a \sin \left\{ \frac{2\pi}{\lambda} (x - ct) + \epsilon \right\}.$$

Here y is the height of the wave at a distance x measured along its length from the origin, c is the velocity with which it travels and t is the time at which y is measured. The quantity ϵ is called the *phase* of the wave: it serves to measure the initial state of the wave at the origin.

If two waves of similar amplitude and wave-length but of different phases overlap, the resultant effect at any point may be written

$$y = a \sin \left\{ \frac{2\pi}{\lambda} (x - ct) + \epsilon_1 \right\} + a \sin \left\{ \frac{2\pi}{\lambda} (x - ct) + \epsilon_2 \right\}$$

$$= 2a \sin \left\{ \frac{2\pi}{\lambda} (x - ct) + \frac{\epsilon_1 + \epsilon_2}{2} \right\} \cos \frac{\epsilon_1 - \epsilon_2}{2}.$$

Thus we shall have

$$y = 2a \sin \left\{ \frac{2\pi}{\lambda} (x - ct) + \epsilon_1 \right\}, \qquad \text{when} \qquad \epsilon_1 - \epsilon_2 = 2n\pi;$$

and $\qquad\qquad y = 0, \qquad \text{when} \qquad \epsilon_1 - \epsilon_2 = (2n + 1)\pi,$

where n is any integer, positive, negative or zero.

When, therefore, the phases differ by an even multiple of π we get strong illumination; and when they differ by an odd multiple of π we get darkness. Independent sources of light obviously cannot have nicely adjusted phase-differences and therefore they cannot be made to produce interference effects.

§ 217. *The diffraction of light.*

The experimental basis of what is called the diffraction of light is the fact that the sharp edge of a thin plate of metal on which light impinges does not throw a sharp shadow. The light bends slightly into the region of the shadow and, moreover, there is more bending for the long red waves of light than for the short violet waves. If light travelled accurately in straight lines and were not a wave motion, there could be no such bending at a sharp edge: the shadow would itself be sharp.

Fresnel was the first to explain such diffraction satisfactorily, on the assumption that light is a wave phenomenon. The explanation depends upon Huyghens' Principle. This Principle was enunciated in a treatise on light published by Huyghens (1629–1695) in the year 1690 and may be stated as follows. From a source of light as a centre waves travel outward in all directions, and those waves which started simultaneously are at any moment on what is called the same *wave-front*. Huyghens postulated that every point on the wave-front, being a centre of vibration, could be regarded as the source of a new disturbance or, if we prefer so to say, of secondary waves. These pass out from the point in all directions. Because these secondary waves have their origin not in independent but in related disturbances, it is possible (and is actually the case) that those which emerge behind the wave-front neutralise one another. Similarly, those which emerge before the wave-front only have a combined effect at points on successive portions of the wave-front as it travels forwards. Huyghens' Principle is supported by what appears to be conclusive experimental evidence. Fresnel deduced from it that, as regards the shadow cast by the straight edge of a metal plate, the secondary waves diverging from those parts of the wave-front not shut off by the plate would produce the observed effects of the bending of light into the shadow.

Diffraction gratings.

Suppose that on the silvered side of a plane sheet of silvered glass a large number of thin straight lines be ruled parallel to one another at equal but very small distances d apart. Then light incident on the silvered glass will be reflected save when it meets these lines. The lines themselves will disperse the light, so that we actually have the reflected light proceeding, as from the image of the source, through a series of fine clear slits. By Huyghens' Principle each slit will be the source of waves diverging in all directions. Such a ruled surface forms what is called a *diffraction grating*.

We can make such a grating for use with transmitted light by ruling lines on unsilvered glass. When used with transmitted light, that is, with light which has passed (with refraction) between the fine ruled lines, it is called a *transmission grating*.

As we shall see, interference between the secondary rays diffracted from the slits between various lines of either type of grating can be employed to produce a spectrum or series of spectra when the distance d between the lines is of the same order of magnitude as, but a little greater than, the wave-length of the incident light.

Diffraction gratings can equally be made by drawing large numbers of fine parallel lines on planes or surfaces of polished metal. If the metal mirror on which lines are thus ruled be spherically concave, it will focus the diffracted rays due to reflection: and it can therefore be used to obtain spectra without the aid of a glass eye-piece. This form of grating is especially valuable in experiments with ultra-violet light to which glass is opaque.

In all diffraction gratings the distances between the fine ruled lines must be of the order of the wave-lengths of visible light. Now such wave-lengths range from $3 \cdot 75 \times 10^{-5}$ cm. to $7 \cdot 5 \times 10^{-5}$ cm. Thus, in a diffraction grating for use with visible light, we must have the fine lines ruled so closely together that there are some thousands of lines to the inch. Optical research has been greatly facilitated by the fact that the American Rowland (1848–1901) invented a machine for accurately drawing such lines on a plane or concave surface.

If we wished to make a diffraction grating for X-rays we should have to rule our lines 10,000 times as close together as they are ruled in diffraction gratings for visible light. This is obviously impossible: yet, as will be seen later, crystals can be used as natural diffraction gratings because their constituent atoms are regularly arranged at such small distances apart that the crystals are almost ideally suited to the diffraction of X-rays.

§ 218.   *The direct passage of plane waves through a slit.*

In order to exemplify the assumptions underlying diffraction and interference we will apply them to investigate what happens when light from a distant source falls directly on a slit in a metal plate and, after passing through the slit, is received on a distant screen. We assume that the slit is long and its edges parallel, so that the experiment can be regarded as taking place in two dimensions.

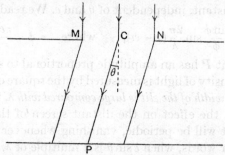

The figure indicates the parallel waves of light which come from a distant source and pass normally through the slit MN. We assume that the width of the slit is e and that λ is the wave-length of the light. We seek to find the effect of the light at various points of a screen which is normal to the original direction of the waves and at a distance from the slit large compared with e.

Let C be the middle point of MN and let P be a point on the screen at which the effect of the waves is to be found, the angle between CP and the original direction of the waves being θ.

Consider now that secondary wave parallel to CP which passes through the slit MN at a distance y from C. 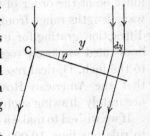 The corresponding original wave, after changing to the direction CP, will have its phase altered in comparison with the central wave by an amount due to the additional distance $y \sin \theta$ through which it must pass in order to get "level with" the wave moving along CP.

We may take the central wave in the direction CP to have for its equation

$$z = a \sin \frac{2\pi}{\lambda} (x - ct),$$

where c is the velocity of the wave, a its amplitude, and z its height.

Then the corresponding wave at a distance y from C will be given by

$$z = a \sin \frac{2\pi}{\lambda} (x - ct - y \sin \theta).$$

Now, if the distance of the screen be great compared with e, we may imagine that all the parallel waves unite at P. Their aggregate effect will be

$$z = \frac{k}{e} \int_{-e/2}^{e/2} \sin \frac{2\pi}{\lambda} \{x - ct - y \sin \theta\} dy,$$

where k is a constant, independent of θ and e. We readily get

$$z = k \frac{\sin \phi}{\phi} \sin \frac{2\pi}{\lambda} (x - ct), \qquad \text{where} \qquad \phi = \frac{\pi e \sin \theta}{\lambda}.$$

Thus the light at P has an amplitude proportional to $\sin \phi / \phi$.

Now the intensity of light is measured by the square of its amplitude. Hence *when the width of the slit is large compared with* λ, the small wave-length of light, the effect on the distant screen of the light passing through the slit will be periodic, vanishing whenever ϕ is a multiple of π or, in other words, when $e \sin \theta$ is a multiple of λ. Moreover, it is readily seen that, when $\phi > \pi$, the intensity diminishes rapidly, so that the whole light on the screen is practically confined to a region for which θ is very small.

On the other hand, when *the width of the slit is reduced* until it is equal to the wave-length of the incident light we get $\phi = \pi \sin \theta$. With this value of ϕ the amplitude $k \sin \phi/\phi$ steadily decreases as θ increases from 0 to $\pi/2$. Thus the light spreads out in all directions from the slit with an intensity which steadily diminishes as the inclination to the normal increases.

We conclude that waves which directly impinge on a slit will pass through it with practically no spreading if the width of the slit is large compared with the length of the waves. But, when width and wavelength are of the same order of magnitude, such waves spread out after passing through the slit.

This conclusion reveals the cause of an apparent discrepancy between the behaviour of sound-waves and light-waves which for long made men hesitate to accept the undulatory theory of light. The length of sound-waves* is measured in feet, and thus sound-waves will expand in all directions when they pass through an opening a few feet wide. But light-waves passed through such an opening would practically not spread at all, as their length is measured in hundred-thousandths of an inch. Light-waves would, however, be spread by passing through an opening of size comparable with their own wave-length; but X-rays would pass through this opening without spreading, as their wavelengths are of the order of magnitude of one ten-thousandth of the wave-length of visible light. Nevertheless, as we shall see shortly, X-rays can be made to spread by passing through openings between the regularly spaced molecules of crystals, for the distance apart of such molecules is comparable with the wave-length of an X-ray.

§ 219. *Theory of a plane transmission grating.*

Let $B_1 B_2 \ldots B_n$ be a section of a transmission grating, the lines of

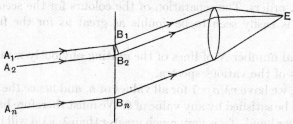

which are drawn perpendicular to the plane of the paper and at a distance a apart, so that $B_1 B_2 = a$.

---

* It must, of course, be remembered that sound-waves are compression waves in air while light-waves are transverse vibrations in the 'ether'. The mathematical formulae, however, shew that similar effects might be expected.

Suppose that an incident group of parallel rays (of the same wave-length and phase) and a corresponding diffracted group of parallel emergent rays make angles θ_0 and θ respectively with the section of the grating made by the plane of the paper. We suppose, further, that the set of parallel rays which thus emerge are gathered by a convex lens to a focus E. Such rays will in general be out of phase and will therefore largely neutralise one another; but if θ is suitably determined, they will be in phase and so will produce brightness at E.

Now the first two rays will be in phase on emergence when the projection of B_1B_2 on the first incident ray differs from its projection on the second diffracted ray by a multiple of a wave-length.

We must therefore have

$$a\,(\cos\theta - \cos\theta_0) = n\lambda, \qquad \ldots\ldots(1)$$

where n is a whole number and λ is the wave-length of the incident light.

The relation (1) is the fundamental equation for a diffraction grating. Substantially, the same equation holds good for a reflection grating, that is to say, for light reflected at corresponding points between a series of fine grooves: we have only to imagine that the diffracted rays are folded through two right angles about the axis $B_1B_2 \ldots B_n$.

If the diffracted rays fall on a distant screen we do not need the convex lens to gather them together. We shall necessarily get bright lines on the screen corresponding to the various values of θ given by equation (1).

Further, as λ changes, so do the values of θ given by (1). Hence composite light is analysed by the grating, which thus gives a spectrum.

Corresponding to the values $n = 1, 2, \ldots$ we have spectra of the first, second, ... orders. The separation of the colours for the second-order spectrum is easily seen to be double as great as for the first-order spectrum.

The total number N of lines of the grating obviously measures the brightness of the various spectra.

If $a < \lambda$, we have $n\lambda/a > 1$ for all values of n, and hence the equation (1) cannot be satisfied by any value of θ. We must therefore have $a > \lambda$. On the other hand, if a is very much greater than λ, $n\lambda/a$ will be a small quantity for a comparatively large number of values of n from 1 upwards. Under such circumstances spectra of all the earlier orders will be crowded together on the screen which receives them. What is called the dispersion of the grating will therefore be insufficient to enable us to use it to get satisfactory spectra.

Thus in a plane grating the constant a, which measures the distance between every successive pair of fine parallel lines, must be *greater than* the wave-length of the radiation to be measured *but not too much greater.*

§220. *Diffraction by a crossed grating or lattice.*

Most people have looked through very fine gauze at a distant source of light and are familiar with the beautiful diffraction spectra which are thus to be seen. If, for instance, we look through a fine cambric hand-kerchief at the glowing filaments of an electric lamp, each filament will appear to be surrounded by a series of coloured diffraction fringes. If the wave structure of light be granted, the theory of such spectra is simple.

We will, in the first place, imagine that a sheet of silvered glass is ruled with two sets of fine parallel lines perpendicular to one another, successive lines perpendicular to Ox_1 being a length a_1 apart, and the corresponding distance for lines perpendicular to Ox_2 being a_2.

Suppose now that a typical ray of light is incident on this crossed transmission grating. Let the cosines of the angles which it makes with Ox_1 and Ox_2 be α_0 and β_0. Similarly, let the cosines of the angles of the corresponding diffracted ray be α and β.

Then corresponding to an incident bundle of parallel rays we shall get a bright point on a distant screen when α and β for the diffracted rays are given by

$$\left.\begin{aligned} a_1(\alpha - \alpha_0) &= n_1\lambda, \\ a_2(\beta - \beta_0) &= n_2\lambda, \end{aligned}\right\} \qquad \dots\dots(2)$$

where n_1 and n_2 are integers.

Equations (2) give us the theory of the twofold range of spectra which correspond to varying values of n_1 and n_2.

It is clear that the crossed grating which we have just discussed is equivalent to a grating formed by a plane regular arrangement of 'diffraction centres' or 'scattering points', these points corresponding to the minute reflecting rectangles which are left on the silvered glass when the opaque diffraction lines are ruled upon it. Apertures in the gauze take the place of scattering points but the controlling equations (2) remain unaltered.

§ 221. *Diffraction by a space-lattice.*

Suppose now that there are placed one behind another, at equal distances a_3 apart, exactly similar rectangular arrangements of scattering points such as we have just described.

Let Ox_3 be an axis perpendicular to the axes Ox_1 and Ox_2. We have in imagination constructed a space-lattice whose scattering points are arranged parallel to the three axes Ox_1, Ox_2, Ox_3 in such a way that the distance between any successive pair of points which are parallel to the axis Ox_r is a_r.

Suppose now that a bundle of parallel rays whose direction-cosines are α_0, β_0, γ_0 is incident on this lattice. Then a bundle of corresponding parallel diffracted rays will produce brightness on a distant screen if their direction-cosines α, β, γ satisfy the three equations

$$\left. \begin{aligned} a_1(\alpha - \alpha_0) &= n_1\lambda, \\ a_2(\beta - \beta_0) &= n_2\lambda, \\ a_3(\gamma - \gamma_0) &= n_3\lambda. \end{aligned} \right\} \qquad \ldots\ldots(3)$$

These equations therefore determine the spectra due to diffraction through our space-lattice.

Owing to the facts that space has only three dimensions and that our lattice is extended in all these three, the complete parallelism that we might expect between a space- and a crossed-lattice breaks down. Light is only diffracted by a space-lattice when there is a relation between the wave-length of the light and its angle of incidence. Thus, if composite light be incident on a space-lattice, the diffracted light will no longer correspond to all wave-lengths in the incident light: in what we might be tempted to call the spectrum of an order determined by n_1, n_2 and n_3, light will be monochromatic.

For we have $\qquad\qquad \alpha^2 + \beta^2 + \gamma^2 = 1,$

$$\alpha_0^2 + \beta_0^2 + \gamma_0^2 = 1.$$

Hence, by (3),

$$\lambda = -2\frac{\alpha_0 n_1/a_1 + \beta_0 n_2/a_2 + \gamma_0 n_3/a_3}{n_1^2/a_1^2 + n_2^2/a_2^2 + n_3^2/a_3^2}.$$

This equation gives the wave-length of the monochromatic light which is diffracted and which corresponds to the numbers n_1, n_2 and n_3.

Diffraction by a space-lattice is equivalent to a series of reflections.

We will now shew that diffraction by a space-lattice is equivalent to the aggregate of a series of reflections at certain planes which are parallel to one another and which each pass through a network of scattering points.

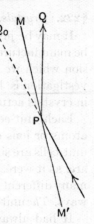

Let an incident ray $(\alpha_0, \beta_0, \gamma_0)$ impinge on a scattering point P in the direction PQ_0, and let the corresponding diffracted ray (α, β, γ) be in the direction PQ. Further, let MM' be a section of the median plane which bisects the angle between PQ_0 and PQ and is at right angles to the plane QPQ_0.

Let θ be the angle which both PQ_0 and PQ make with this median plane: we shall then have

$$\cos 2\theta = \alpha\alpha_0 + \beta\beta_0 + \gamma\gamma_0.$$

Thus, if we square and add the equations (3) when written in the form

$$\alpha - \alpha_0 = n_1\lambda/a_1,$$
$$\beta - \beta_0 = n_2\lambda/a_2,$$
$$\gamma - \gamma_0 = n_3\lambda/a_3,$$

we shall get
$$\sin\theta = \frac{\lambda}{2}\sqrt{n_1^2/a_1^2 + n_2^2/a_2^2 + n_3^2/a_3^2}.$$

The equation of the median plane can be readily obtained. Choose Q and Q_0 on their respective rays so that $PQ = PQ_0$. Then any point on the median plane will be equidistant from Q and Q_0.

Hence, if P be the point (ξ, η, ζ), the median plane is
$$n_1(x - \xi)/a_1 + n_2(y - \eta)/a_2 + n_3(z - \zeta)/a_3 = 0.$$
Because the n's are whole numbers this is a plane which will pass through a network of the scattering points of our space-lattice.

Obviously we may think of the rays $(\alpha_0, \beta_0, \gamma_0)$ and (α, β, γ) as reflected at the median plane. Hence diffraction by the lattice is equivalent to a series of reflections at successive planes parallel to the particular median plane which corresponds to the wave-length of the light which is diffracted.

When composite light is incident on a space-lattice of finite dimensions the incident beam will, on the whole, pass in a straight line without diffraction through the lattice. But certain particular rays of the composite light suffer reflection. The wave-lengths of these rays are, as we have seen, determined by the structure of the lattice.

In our previous work we have only dealt with lattices where the sets of scattering points could be arranged on mutually perpendicular axes. Obviously this limitation is unnecessary and can be overcome by the use of mathematical formulae applying to oblique axes.

§ 222. *Crystals*.

It may be justly observed that such a thing as a space-lattice cannot be manufactured, and it might therefore be contended that the discussion which we have just undertaken is practically valueless. The investigation is, however, of the highest importance, because the atoms in crystals actually form such regularly arranged space-lattices.

Each unit-cell of a crystal contains a regular arrangement of the atoms or ions of the elements of which the crystal is composed. All unit-cells are similar and similarly placed in the crystals in which they are, as it were, molecules. Naturally a unit-cell can be constructed in many different ways by joining up atoms of the space-lattice in different ways. *The* unit-cell is that which to our imagination seems most simple.

It had always been assumed in crystallography that the regular structure of crystals was due to regular arrangements of similar atoms in similar unit-cells: but only since the advent of X-ray analysis has this speculative inference been proved. Accurate knowledge is now being rapidly obtained both of the size of unit-cells and of the distribution of atoms within them. In this way a largely extended knowledge of the structure of substances in common use is being gained. Even when substances in bulk are not crystals they contain crystalline ingredients which, as in the case of the razor, have important properties when suitably ordered.

The nature of the bonds which unite the atoms within a crystal cell are only imperfectly surmised. They are obviously electrical in the case, say, of common salt, for which positive ions of sodium and negative ions of chlorine unite together. But it is difficult to understand the nature of the forces which, say, unite the various atoms of carbon in the elementary cell of the diamond.

X-ray spectrum analysis as applied to crystals may be regarded as a voyage to Lilliput. It enables us to get some ten thousand times nearer to the ultimate structure of things than we can get by the microscope or by any device which employs visible light. Such analysis ought, in the long run, to tell us how every substance is built out of its atoms. But even then we shall wish to know of the forces which bind the atoms together; and intra-atomic physics will remain to be further developed. Even X-ray analysis does not take us to fundamentals. There are probably countries beyond Lilliput where the Lilliputians themselves are giants.

§223. *The diamond.*

As a simple example of the way in which the atoms of a substance are arranged when it assumes a crystalline form we may take the element carbon. Carbon, of course, is of peculiar interest to humanity as it enters into the constitution of 'foods and fuels, dyes and explosives', not to mention our own bodies. It appears, in fact, to be an essential element in living matter.

Everyone knows that carbon can crystallise as the diamond, but it is not so generally known that it can also crystallise as graphite, the blacklead of Victorian hearthstones. In the diamond five atoms of carbon are arranged, one at each of the corners and one at the centre of a regular tetrahedron: such an arrangement constitutes a unit-cell. A regular tetrahedron is by definition a four-sided solid each face of which is an equilateral triangle. If we imagine the unit-cells of the diamond arranged on a plane as they are arranged in the gem, their bases will assume the form of figure 1. The heavy points are the carbon atoms at the corners of the bases of the tetrahedra: the light points are vertically beneath the centres and vertices of the tetrahedra. All the vertices of the tetrahedra will be in a plane parallel to the plane of the paper. With the carbon atoms at these vertices we can build up above them new unit-cells and so gradually construct a crystal of finite size: in fact, a diamond. The strongest bonds will join neighbouring atoms and can be pictured as uniting the centre to the corners of the unit-cell. It may be observed that every carbon atom is at the centre of gravity of four others.

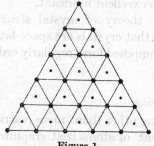

Figure 1.

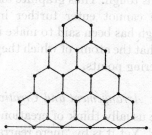

Figure 2.

It is found that the planes in the diamond which are parallel to the one drawn in the figure are planes of natural cleavage. Diamond-cutters are naturally familiar with the existence of such planes, which they use in their work. There are, of course, cleavage planes parallel to every tetrahedron face of the unit-cell.

The dimensions of the unit-cell of the diamond have been found by X-ray analysis and are such that the distance between the centres of two neighbouring carbon atoms is 1.54×10^{-8} cm. Why the diamond should be so brilliant when light shines upon it has not, I think, been explained. Its hardness is due to the fact that the structure of unit-cell is alike simple and firm. The density, which is about 3.5 times that of water, is fairly high. The density of graphite, the other crystalline form of carbon, is only about 2.3. Evidently, therefore, there must be in the unit-cell of graphite a different spacing of the carbon atoms which causes them, on the average, to be farther apart than they are in the unit-cell of the diamond.

It appears that the graphite cell can theoretically be derived from the diamond by causing the carbon atom at the centre of the elementary tetrahedron to fall to the centre of the triangular base. We thus get a crystalline substance formed of layers of atoms, the arrangement of the atoms in each layer being indicated in the second figure of the diagram. This figure has been derived from the first by turning the light points into heavy points and then joining them up in a different fashion. Evidently the new mode of junction gives hexagons arranged as in the honeycomb. The arrangement of the atoms in alternate layers of the graphite is obtained by rotating the second figure in its own plane through two right angles round any one of its corners. The bonds joining atoms in different layers in the graphite arrangement of atoms are longer than the horizontal bonds and, in consequence, lack strength. Hence layers of graphite slide over one another easily, though each layer is tough. Thus graphite makes an excellent lubricant.

We cannot enter further into the theory of crystal structure. Enough has been said to make it clear that crystals are space-lattices and that the atoms of which they are composed form regularly ordered scattering points.

§ 224. *Arrangement and Creative Activity.*

We usually think of creation as being other than 'mere rearrangement'. Yet it is by 'mere rearrangement' of atoms that graphite and diamond differ from amorphous carbon, just as by 'mere arrangement' of electrons and protons the various elements of matter have been made. Apart from the possibility that all types of energy and therefore of matter may result from the warping of space-time and so be fitly described as geometrical form (or structure) without substance, the analysis alike of matter and of crystals indicates that, in the process of orderly arrangement, there is what we may justly term Creative Activity. What is new seems to emerge from orderly arrangement: in fact, various kinds of formal groupings of protons and electrons make in the aggregate the rich diversity of the inorganic universe. A cathedral differs from a heap of stones in that mind has been active in the shaping and arrangement of the stones. Are we justified in contending that similarly the activity of mind may be found in the arrangement of protons and electrons which constitutes the carbon atom and in the subsequent grouping of such atoms which makes the diamond? Those who answer the question in the negative do so because they believe that, in the future, humanity will discover invariable sequences which will enable us to 'make' carbon atoms and diamonds. But shall we then 'make', or shall we merely discover how God makes? In short, can we speak of causation apart from uniformities which express the Will of God? Some consideration will be given to this question in Lecture XVII.

§ 225. *Crystal measurements of, and by, X-rays.*

The theory of crystal measurements of, and by, X-rays may now be briefly described.

Laue in the year 1912 first noticed the peculiar interaction of crystals and X-rays when he photographed X-rays diffracted by crystals. He realised that a space-lattice exists within a crystal and that it is as nicely adjusted to the wave-lengths of Röntgen radiation as is a Rowland grating to the wave-lengths of ordinary light. Sir W. H. Bragg and his son developed alike the theory and the experimental technique so that, on the one hand, Röntgen rays from a given cathode-ray tube and from an anti-cathode of given material can be measured in terms of the constants of a specified crystal, while, on the other hand, the structure of a given crystal may be measured by means of a Röntgen ray of definite wave-length.

The lattice constants of natural crystals are of the order of magnitude 10^{-8} cm. Röntgen rays have wave-lengths which lie between 10^{-8} and 10^{-9} cm. Thus the lattice constants are greater than the wave-lengths of the rays but not too much greater. Hence crystals form natural gratings for the diffraction of X-rays.

Suppose now that a bundle of such rays, parallel to one another, is incident on a crystal. The diffraction of rays of certain selected wave-lengths will, as we have seen, be equivalent to reflection at a suitably chosen net-plane, that is to say a plane containing a whole network of scattering points.

In the figure the parallel lines MN, M_1N_1, ... represent parallel net-planes. When a bundle of rays is incident in the direction AB, some few will be reflected by the first net-plane MN while the rest pass on. Some of these latter are reflected at the second net-plane and the remainder pass on, and so throughout the crystal. It is to be remembered that even a small crystal will contain a very large number of parallel net-planes.

Now the reflected rays will normally interfere and largely neutralise one another. But they will combine together and give a sudden 'flash', which will make its mark on a photographic plate provided the angle of incidence is so adjusted that the reflected rays are in phase.

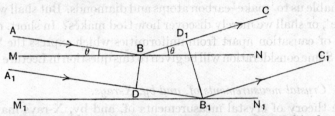

Let AB make an angle θ with MN, and suppose that BC is the corresponding reflected ray. Let A_1B_1 be a parallel ray incident on M_1N_1 at B_1, B_1C_1 being the reflected ray. Further, let ϕ be the angle which BB_1 makes with M_1N_1. Draw BD and B_1D_1 perpendicular to A_1B_1 and BC respectively. Obviously the reflected rays will be in phase if

$$B_1D - BD_1 = n\lambda,$$

where λ is the wave-length of the incident rays and n is an integer. Thus we must have

$$n\lambda = BB_1 \cos(\phi - \theta) - BB_1 \cos(\phi + \theta)$$
$$= 2BB_1 \sin\phi \sin\theta$$

or

$$2d \sin\theta = n\lambda, \qquad \qquad \dots\dots(1)$$

where d is the distance between the two reflecting planes.

The fundamental relation (1) is the basis of the theory of the diffraction of X-ray crystals. In deducing it we have only mentioned two net-planes, but in actual practice thousands of such planes are involved in the production of a bright 'flash'. We need not repeat that this 'flash' cannot be seen by the human eye: we must use indirect methods such as photography to register its occurrence.

§226. *The achievement of X-ray analysis.*

It is unnecessary to describe in detail the ingenious experimental methods by which the Braggs and others have applied the previous theory to determine the arrangement of atoms and ions in crystals. They are able to describe the form of, and distribution of atoms within, cells whose linear dimensions are about one hundred-millionth of an inch.

Only a few years ago such an achievement would have seemed impossible. Then the microscope seemed to be the only instrument by which we could see small objects. Now, indirectly, it is possible, in no metaphorical sense, to 'see' by X-rays.

When we see an object, we observe the changes which the object makes in light which falls upon it before reaching the eye. In the course of his evolution man has acquired the capacity to interpret such changes with remarkable skill: and the now innate faculty is developed in each of us by life's experiences. The microscope magnifies such changes and so increases our power of sight. But there is a limit to what the microscope can do and this limit depends upon the wave-length of ordinary light. When waves strike upon an object smaller than their own length there is a small confusion near the object but ultimately the waves pass on unchanged. No microscope, therefore, could enable us to see objects whose dimensions were less than the wave-length of ordinary light. It is because X-rays are some ten thousand times smaller in wave-length than rays of ordinary light that we are enabled to 'see' individual atoms and molecules.

There will, I think, be general agreement that the voyage to Lilliput which X-ray spectrum analysis enables us to make leaves us with a sense of wonder and mystery. We have reached a region where lengths are a hundred million times as small as those with which we normally deal. But we have not reached ultimate simplicity: on the contrary, we begin to approach regions in which for ultimate particles space-time concepts fail. Atoms apparently are all built to pattern: yet assuredly those of any particular element can exist in a vast number of different states; and, as we have seen, atoms of the radio-active substances seem to possess individuality, for apparently only its own nature determines when or why any particular atom will break up. Beyond the atom, as one of its constituents, there is the electron. The electron, in its turn, seems to be not simple but complex past present understanding. Of the forces which maintain it as an entity we are ignorant. Equally we do not know the nature of the forces by which protons and electrons are held together in atomic nuclei. In fact, our voyage to Lilliput ends by leaving us overwhelmed by the almost infinite complexity of the Universe. That it could have come into existence without the fiat of an ordering Mind I cannot believe. And, in my view, as men of science are probing into the ultimate (or penultimate) nature of things, they are discovering God's plan and thereby proving that there is some kinship between the mind of man and that of God. In fact, our quest for knowledge is not hopeless, simply because God has given us power to understand His works and ways.

Yet we must emphasise that man has only just begun the search typified by physical investigation, though he has been a million years upon this earth. It is to be expected that our first puny efforts to know how God has built the Universe should leave us excited and astonished. But ought not the rapid progress, already made in little more than a century, to leave us certain that as the millennia pass, the mind of humanity will expand to an ever fuller apprehension of the Divine Mind? To know ever less incompletely God's plan and to feel called ever more definitely to conduct which the religious man describes as His service—such would seem to be the reason of the continued existence of humanity upon this earth.

§ 227. *General conclusions.*

It may be convenient to end with a summary of the main conclusions to which the modern study of matter leads.

All matter is built up of hydrogen-nuclei (or protons) and electrons. Each proton has a single positive charge, equal and opposite to the negative charge on the electron. The atoms of the various chemical elements only differ in their structure. Their nuclei apparently consist of compact groups of electrons and protons, with helium-nuclei and possibly neutrons as subordinate constituents of such groups.

The net positive charge on the nucleus of an atom of an element is measured by its atomic number. This number is also the number of the electrons which, when the atom is electrically neutral, are satellites to the nucleus. There are probably in the material of the surface of the earth, apart from isotopes, ninety-two different chemical elements, some of which undergo spontaneous transformation into others. Quite possibly elements of higher atomic number may exist under the conditions which prevail within the distant suns which we call 'fixed stars'. We must not assume that there are the same limits of atomic stability when pressures are enormously greater or less than those with which we are familiar upon earth or when temperatures run up to tens of millions of degrees on the Centigrade scale.

Atoms are chemically alike when, in an electrically neutral state, they have the same number of satellite electrons. But atoms which are chemically the same may differ in the constitution of their nuclei. In such cases we have isotopes with the same chemical properties but with different atomic weights. Equally there exist isobars, which are elements of different atomic numbers but the same atomic weight. In their nuclei are the same number of protons, but different numbers of electrons.

The nucleus is the heart of the atom, well guarded by its shield of electrons. Of late successful experiments have been devised by which the nucleus of lithium has been artificially broken up. This initial success may possibly be so extended that the nuclei of many elements are similarly disintegrated. No progress has as yet been made with the artificial synthesis of nuclei.

The fundamental elements, the ultimate 'things' of matter, are two, the proton with its positive charge and the electron. If the two could come together and annihilate each other we should have actual destruction of matter. Astronomical physicists believe, as we shall see in due course in Lecture XI, that such destruction takes place in the suns scattered through space and that it is the main source of the energy which these suns send out as radiation.

It is in any case certain that in the atoms of all the elements vast quantities of energy are stored. Some of this energy is liberated in astonishing quantities when the radio-active elements disintegrate. If all the stuff of which matter consists could be transformed into energy, the amount would be determined by Einstein's law $E = mc^2$, where E is the energy due to the destruction of a mass m of matter, and c is the velocity of light.

Atomic physics has quite definitely reduced matter to protons and electrons. Are these 'elements' real and substantial in the sense that nothing else is real and substantial? The answer is certainly in the negative. Among the things of the Universe that have relative permanence the mind picks out those whose existence is of especial importance in practical life. The man who ignored the relative permanence of matter would soon perish. Moreover, matter not seldom presents itself as something hard and unyielding, such as a brick wall or a bullet. So there is an ineradicable tendency in the human mind to think that the Universe is built up of small hard objects. When we are told that the ultimates of the physical Universe are protons and electrons we picture them as little billiard-balls. And, therefore, it is well to recall again the words, already quoted in Lecture I, by which Poincaré, with his urbane wisdom, ridiculed those who seek to explain physics by the mutual collisions of atoms. "Are we to understand that God, in contemplating His work, experiences the same sensations as we ourselves when present at a billiard match?"

All inertia is probably electrical, like the inertia of an electron. Hence it is possible that the proton is, like the electron, a manifestation of electricity—whatever that may be. It seem unnecessary to postulate two unknowns, matter (or protons) and electrons, when one will suffice. But the theory of relativity has somewhat weakened arguments pointing in this direction, because it has apparently shewn that the fundamental laws of attraction and repulsion, which were formerly assumed to be peculiar properties of material particles and of electrical charges, are general consequences of the relativity of our observational knowledge. We must, as we have seen, learn to distinguish true 'laws of Nature' from disguised identities, and also to discover how far such laws are statistical averages, before we can safely base upon them speculative conclusions with regard to the ultimate stuff or stuffs out of which the physical world is constructed.

In abandoning the billiard-ball notion of protons and electrons, we must remember that physics does not tell us of things in themselves but only how they behave. *It is the science of mutual relations.* The theory of relativity has emphasised this fact. "It is structure, not material, that counts", as Eddington has concisely said. The ether of nineteenth-century physicists has become a ghost of its former self. But the ghost is space-time with its varying structure. What we call matter is a symptom of space-curvature: and, in analysing matter till we reach protons and electrons, we are but tracing the curvature of space till we reach discontinuities of which we can give no adequate explanation. Are these discontinuities the origin of the adjacent curvature, and due to foreign bodies embedded in space? It is perhaps, as we have already indicated, more reasonable to say that we perceive the statistical average of collections of warpings of space and that we speak of this average as an electron or as matter. But even as we make such a statement we hesitate: what certain knowledge have we of the ultimate bases of our concept of space?

Whatever conclusions may ultimately be reached, it is certain that we cannot ascribe to matter greater reality than we give to light. Light has no material basis: it is simply energy propagated through space as particles or waves. Yet it has inertia and the energy of which it consists is as permanent as matter, if indeed it is not the same thing. Thus the exclusive substantiality of matter is an illusion: it is no more substantial than moonshine. The illusion is strong because of our daily needs and because of the fact that we are made of this self-same matter. But let a man live under abnormal conditions and other standpoints become reasonable. The professional radiographer has no doubt as to the actuality, the substantiality, of the γ-rays with which he works. Were he to ignore it, he would rapidly perish of malignant dermatitis. Yet γ-rays differ from light only in the size of the waves of which they are composed.

Of late the extent of our ignorance, and the ease with which unjustifiable assumptions are accepted, has been emphasised by the discovery of the Heisenberg uncertainty-relations. These relations shew that, if absolute measurements of position or time could be made, they would give rise to infinite momenta or energy respectively. In consequence, space and time seem to be, like temperature, statistical concepts derived from observation of the behaviour of varying lengths over relatively long periods of time. Furthermore, there exist very small regions of space-time where definite measurements are impossible, not merely on account of human limitations, but by the very nature of things. To speak of the position of a proton, electron or photon in such a region is meaningless. Further investigation may modify present conclusions, but it seems as though such success as the wave theory of radiation has had has been due to the fact that mathematically a wave may be made to express the fundamental uncertainties.

The uncertainty-relations and determinism.

From the Heisenberg relations it follows that in small space-time regions we cannot make an observation without altering the future of the system which we observe. Ideally, we can thus observe the past but we cannot predict the future. This statement, however, must be coupled with recognition of the fact that, though it is true for a single ultimate particle, yet our physical laws relate to immense numbers of particles for which statistical averages are invariable. Thus the question as to whether the uncertainty-relations afford an escape from determinism is answered by different physicists in opposite ways. Some insist strongly that such vast aggregates are involved that escape from rigid uniformity is impossible. Others, however, point out that determinism is bound up with notion of causality or, at any rate, of invariable sequence. Such sequence does not exist when we cannot define identical circumstances. To put the matter in another way, the old dynamics seemed to determine the future completely, because its creators assumed that they could find simultaneously the exact initia position and velocity of a particle. Now that such an assumption is seen to be untrue, if Heisenberg's view be admitted, we have no longer rigorous laws but only laws of probability. Further, as Lindemann has rightly insisted, if our laws are statistical laws, they cannot be expected to apply to processes involving comparatively few units of action. Physiologists may in due course discover that some of our primary mental processes are so fine that they are associated with small multiples of Planck's constant. If such discovery be made, volition will be free; and the feeling that we are free to act, which belongs to our normal experience, will no longer be irreconcilable with the postulates of physics.

The physical and the psychical.

We would end with a warning. A confused apprehension of the fact that matter is not, as regards its inertial property, essentially different from energy and radiation is now fairly common. As a consequence we are often assured that 'materialism' is obsolete and that 'all is spiritual'. Yet the truth is that energy and, as a particular example, sunlight belong completely to the material world and exactly resemble matter in being distinct from that which we term spiritual. Spiritual activity involves thought, will and purpose: it cannot exist apart from mind. The human mind reaches spiritual understanding as it arrives at the knowledge that goodness, beauty and truth express the ultimate character of the Universe. There is no doubt that in our own experience mind needs matter that it may express itself; and the relation of mind to body we shall discuss later towards the end of Lecture XVII. But, of course, we may not say that there is no distinction between mind and matter. Similarly, mind and radiant energy must not be confused: and the suggestion that radiant energy is spiritual implies a complete failure to understand the implications of the analysis of matter which has been made by modern physicists.

In brief, the distinction between the physical and the psychical has not been removed. We shall see in §§ 444, 445 that the problem of consciousness forces us to assume some common ground whereby mind and matter are able to interact. But the fact that matter may be merely a manifestation of energy does not in the least help us to understand in what such common ground consists. Matter, energy and radiation are physical entities. Mind and spirit belong to the psychical realm.

Lecture x

THE SOLAR SYSTEM

§ 228. *Ancient speculation.*

When man first began to speculate as to his habitat he naturally thought of the earth as a more or less flat thing, the solid substratum of his activities. Inevitably he regarded it as fixed. This naïve view appears in the Old Testament; and from Jewish popular thought it was taken over into the Christian creeds.

A truer conception of the earth as a spherical body arose first, so far as we know, among the Ionian Greeks. It became general among their educated men and was, for instance, accepted by Aristotle. The radius of the earth was actually determined by Eratosthenes about 200 B.C.

Most Greek thinkers, however, assumed that the spherical earth was fixed, the centre of the Universe. It is true that the contrary view that it rotated round the sun was suggested by Aristarchus of Samos about 250 B.C. But his opinion failed to maintain itself: the adverse criticism of Archimedes survives as an explanation of its failure.

The generally accepted belief that came from the Greeks into medieval European thought was that the planets revolved in crystal spheres round the earth and that the whole scheme of things was enclosed in a final sphere in which the fixed stars were set. There is evidence to shew that this scheme of crystal spheres, the vehicles of the heavenly bodies, related in some mysterious way to the divine harmonies of the Universe, was a Pythagorean doctrine. It accorded well enough for popular thought with the system of astronomy which was bequeathed by Alexandria to medieval Europe. This system, largely owing to the authority of Hipparchus (*c.* 130 B.C.), was geocentric. From Hipparchus, Ptolemy some 250 years later derived not only the fundamental assumption that the earth was the fixed centre of the Universe but also much of the material for his great work the *Almagest* which, published about A.D. 140, was for some fourteen centuries held to be authoritative. Ptolemy accounted for the motions of sun, moon and planets, so far as they were then observed, by supposing each to move in a small circle (the epicycle) whose centre moved round the earth on another large circle. With increasingly accurate observations the Arab astronomers found it necessary to add further epicycles until the whole system became vastly complicated.

§ 229. *The rise and triumph of the heliocentric theory.*

Sceptical enquiry led to a different order of ideas with the rise of the scientific spirit subsequent to the Renaissance. Copernicus (1473–1543) on his death-bed saw a printed copy of his book, *On the Revolutions of the Celestial Bodies*, in which he put forward the view that the earth moved round the sun. He retained, however, the idea that the planets moved in circles; and, moreover, he assumed that the fixed stars were equidistant from the centre of the Universe, which consequently remained spherical and finite. Thus for Copernicus the sun was central in the Universe: it was not one of many 'fixed' stars.

In comparison with this naïve view Giordano Bruno (*c.* 1550–1600) half a century later made a picture which both enriched and enlarged human imagination when he suggested that there exists an infinity of worlds in space. For him the Universe, far from being enclosed in some crystal dome, extended to infinity; and in it there were literally innumerable suns similar to our own.

From a mass of observations, extending over many years, made by the astronomer Tycho Brahé (1546–1601), his former assistant Kepler (1571–1630), at the beginning of the seventeenth century, derived three laws of planetary motion and made almost inevitable the hypothesis that the sun was the centre of a planetary system to which the earth belonged.

Galileo made good use of the telescope, even if he did not invent it; and, by his discovery of Jupiter's moons, contributed to the establishment of the heliocentric hypothesis. But his advocacy of it brought upon him persecution by the Roman Catholic Church. It is almost incredible that, as recently as the second and fourth decades of the seventeenth century, a European man of science of international fame should have been forced by ecclesiastics to deny that the earth moves round the sun! Arguments in favour of the earth's motion gradually won the allegiance of experts. They became conclusive when Newton announced the principle of gravitation and from it derived Kepler's laws. With the publication of the *Principia* in the year 1687 the nature of the solar system was finally settled and the sun took its place as one of the innumerable 'fixed' stars with which the heavens are strewn.

This achievement naturally ranks as one of the great triumphs of the human mind.

Kepler's laws.

The first two of these laws which Kepler derived from Tycho Brahé's observations were published in the year 1609. They state that

(1) The orbit of each planet is an ellipse with the sun in one of its foci.

(2) The radius vector from the sun to each planet sweeps out equal areas in equal times.

The third law, published ten years later, states that

(3) The squares of the periods of the planets are proportional to the cubes of their mean distances from the sun.

Kepler died after an unhappy life in the year 1630: his genius in extracting such simple laws from the observations laboriously compiled by his predecessor has made him famous in the history of astronomy.

§230. *Newton's fundamental assumption.*

Newton took for his guiding principle the assumption that every particle of matter attracts every other with a force which is directly proportional to the product of the masses of the particles and inversely proportional to the square of the distance between them. This law was for him an empirical result: the reason why it held good he did not pretend to explain. We have seen that Einstein, in refining the law, has made it a consequence of the way in which we measure space-time so that, unless undetected assumptions have crept into his analysis, it is a disguised identity. Even with the assumption of the (very nearly) correct law of universal gravitation Newton would not have solved the problem of planetary motions had he not, in effect, invented the differential and integral calculus to provide the necessary analysis. This calculus makes it possible to shew that, with Newton's law of gravitation, a sphere or spherical shell of matter of uniform density attracts as though all its mass were concentrated at its centre.

If we had a system consisting of the sun and a single planet and if all the matter in each was arranged in spherical shells of uniform density so that sun and planet were both spherical, and if there were not other planetary bodies to interfere, sun and planet would each describe ellipses round their common centre of gravity.

In the solar system both the sun and the planets are nearly spherical in shape and the density of all is distributed roughly in concentric shells. Moreover, the sun is so much more massive than all the planets combined that the centre of gravity of the solar system is near the sun's centre. Thus apart from disturbances caused by the attraction of one planet for another, the planets describe what are approximately ellipses round the sun. Their perturbations can be determined by calculations which become exceedingly laborious as increasing accuracy is sought. But the agreement of computation with observation in lunar and planetary theory is marvellous. The only discrepancy that is not so minute as to be attributable to errors of observation is the motion of the perihelion of Mercury. This discrepancy, as we have seen, has been accounted for by Einstein's refinement of Newtonian mechanics.

§ 231. *The members of the solar system.*

As is well known, in the solar system the sun itself is surrounded by nine great planets, Mercury, Venus, the Earth, Mars, Jupiter, Saturn, Uranus, Neptune and the recently discovered Pluto. In addition there are some 900 minor planets or asteroids. All revolve in the same direction round the sun: their orbits are all nearly in the same plane and are almost circular ellipses. The planets, moreover, rotate round their axes in the same direction: and such moons as they have move, for the most part, in approximately the same plane and in nearly circular ellipses round the planet to which they are attached. There are a few significant and puzzling exceptions to the rule that all satellites move in the same direction round their respective primaries. Jupiter, for instance, has nine moons and the two outermost move in a retrograde direction. Saturn has a sixth outer retrograde satellite, faint and distant. Neptune's one moon has similarly a retrograde motion.

§ 232. *The earth: its shape, size, density and mass.*

By measurements on the surface of the earth it is possible to calculate both its size and shape. In shape it is a sphere slightly flattened at the poles. The form and dimensions of the earth are alike best determined by the measurement of meridian arcs (portions of lines of longitude) in different latitudes. Its equatorial diameter is 12,750 km. or 7925 miles: that joining the poles is 43 km. or 28 miles less. A number of experiments have been devised to determine the mass of the earth, the most delicate involving the use of a torsion balance. They agree in giving the mass as approximately 6×10^{27} grammes. Knowing the size and mass of the earth we can determine its density, which is nearly $5\frac{1}{2}$ times that of water.

§ 233. *The distance and size of the sun.*

The mean distance of the sun is obtained by *parallax measurements.*

Most educated people read astronomy happily and easily until the notion of parallax enters in: then they begin to feel at a loss. Yet the idea of parallax is simple. The parallax of a distant point P is nothing but the difference between the directions of P as seen by two observers.

In order to avoid the trouble which would be caused in astronomical calculations by specifying the position of the observers on the earth, it is usual to work with *equatorial horizontal parallax* for which the two observers are supposed to be so situated that one is at the centre of the earth and the other at a position on the earth giving the greatest possible parallax. Thus the equatorial horizontal parallax of a point P, which we speak of concisely as its parallax, is simply the angular equatorial semi-diameter of the earth as seen from P.

Direct measurements will not give us accurately the parallax of the centre of the sun: it is large and over-poweringly bright, and, of course, the equatorial horizontal parallax of its centre as determined from the earth is a small angle. But we can find the parallax of, say, one of the larger asteroids which rotate round the sun as do the planets. Then, from the known dimensions of the earth, the distance of the asteroid can be determined. This distance will give us the dimensions of the solar system and hence the mean distance of the sun. Other methods can, of course, be used. The various results obtained confirm one another remarkably.

The mean parallax of the sun is 8″803; and the error in this measurement is probably not more than ·001″.

The mean distance of the sun is very nearly 150 million km. or 92,870,000 miles. This distance is sometimes termed *the astronomical unit*.

Knowing the distance of the sun, we can rapidly find its size. Its diameter is 1,390,000 km. or 864,000 miles.

§ 234. *The mass of the sun.*

A first approximation to the determination of the ratio of the masses of the sun and earth is easy.

Let S be the mass of the sun, E the mass of the earth and let r be the mean distance between them. Further let γ be the constant of gravitation. Then, by Newton's law of attraction, the force between S and E at the mean distance r will be

$$\gamma \frac{SE}{r^2}.$$

If a be the radius of the earth and g the value of gravity at its surface, we must have

$$g = \gamma \frac{E}{a^2}.$$

Knowing g, E and a we can thus determine γ. Its value in C.G.S. units is $6\cdot7 \times 10^{-8}$. Between bodies of ordinary dimensions the attraction due to 'gravitational' force is thus very small: it only becomes important when we are dealing with huge masses like the sun and earth.

The force of attraction of the sun maintains the earth in its approximately circular orbit. Thus, if ω be its angular velocity,

$$\gamma \frac{S}{r^2} = \omega^2 r.$$

Thus

$$\frac{S}{E} = \frac{r^3 \omega^2}{ga^2}.$$

Knowing r, ω, g and a we can by this formula determine S/E.

More accurate results are got by elaborate and complicated calculation from the perturbations of the planets which are near the sun.

The mass of the sun is thus determined to be $1\cdot985 \times 10^{33}$ grammes.

The sun's density.

The mean density of the sun, as calculated from its size and mass, is $1\cdot41$ times that of water. Thus the earth is about four times as dense as the sun.

It is surprising and significant that the sun's density should be so small. From spectroscopic analysis of its light we know that it contains many heavy elements. Moreover, the earth almost certainly had its origin in matter ejected from the sun: and such matter would naturally come from near the sun's surface, where its density is small, rather than from its interior where the density must be large. From this and other considerations the conclusion has been reached that the sun is largely gaseous with possibly a liquid centre. If the sun is wholly gaseous the pressure near the centre must be enormous. The pressure at the centre of a sphere, of the size of the sun and of uniform density equal to the sun's density, is easily calculated to exceed 1000 million times the atmospheric pressure at the earth's surface. The sun's actual central pressure must be greater than this amount. If the ordinary gas law $pv/T = $ cons. (§175) is even approximately obeyed within the sun, its central temperature must rise up to millions of degrees on the Centigrade scale.

§ 235. *The planets in general.*

Naturally the masses and densities of the moon and of all the planets have been determined. The dimensions also of the solar system are accurately known. One or two facts may be mentioned. Jupiter, the largest of the planets, has some 317 times the mass of the earth: it has, therefore, nearly one-thousandth of the mass of the sun. Its equatorial diameter is nearly 90,000 miles. In mass and bulk Jupiter is more than equal to all the other planets of the solar system added together. The planet's density is 1·34 times that of water and is therefore practically the same as that of the sun. Its mean distance from the sun is nearly 500 million miles.

Until the discovery of Pluto, Neptune was deemed the outermost planet, and its orbit was regarded as an indication of the size of the solar system. Neptune's mean distance from the sun is about 2800 million miles and its period is 164·8 years. Its mass is a little more than 17 times that of the earth; and its density is about 1·6 times that of water, rather more than the density of the sun. From Neptune the sun would have an apparent diameter of about the size of that of Venus as seen from the earth when she is nearest to us. The sun must give on Neptune some 500 times as much light as we get from full moon, so that daylight on the planet would be adequate for our eyes. But the heat which the planet receives from the sun is wretchedly small. If there be no 'greenhouse effect' (*vide* § 243 *infra*) and if no heat escapes from the planet's interior, its surface temperature must be − 220° Centigrade. At this temperature the nitrogen of our atmosphere would be a solid and its oxygen a liquid near solidifying point.

The newly discovered planet Pluto was found early in the year 1930, in accordance with a prediction made by P. Lowell (1855–1916) in the year 1915. While the mean distance of Neptune from the earth is 30 astronomical units, that of Pluto is 40 such units. (It will be remembered than an astronomical unit is the mean distance of the sun from the earth, 92·87 million miles.) But the orbit of Neptune is nearly circular, while that of Pluto has an eccentricity ·248: hence the orbits of the two planets, so far as distance from the sun is concerned, actually intersect one another. The period of Pluto seems to be about 247 years; and its mass is thought to be less (possibly much less) than two-thirds that of the earth. Its size has not yet been accurately determined, but its diameter is probably about one-half that of the earth.

Some *comets*, of course, are members of the solar system moving in vastly elongated orbits. But, though picturesque objects when they return to the neighbourhood of the sun, they are so small in mass as to be barely worth reckoning in any calculation of the size of the solar system.

§ 236. *Laplace's theory of the origin of the solar system.*

It is well known that the great French mathematician and astronomer, Laplace (1749–1827), at the end of the eighteenth century, put forward a theory of the origin of the solar system. It first appeared when the *Exposition du système du monde* was published in the year 1796 and was a refinement of certain speculations published forty years earlier by Kant who, being a philosopher and not a mathematician, did not escape a pitfall which Laplace avoided.

Laplace imagined that a primeval hot nebulous mass of gas was in rotation. As it cooled it contracted but, in order to conserve its angular momentum, it rotated the faster as it shrank in size. At a certain stage in the process the speed of rotation became so large that it gave rise to a centrifugal force at the equator greater than the force of gravity there. The result was that gradually more and more of the matter at the equator was flung off into space in a series of rings. These rings, as the matter forming them cooled, became the planets and the central nebulous mass which remained behind became the sun.

This theory has not successfully emerged from the criticism to which it has been subjected. Such a rotating mass of gas as Laplace imagined, when it broke up through rotation, would normally separate into two approximately equal masses and would, in fact, form a system of two stars, a binary star, such as is common in the Universe. Moreover, if, owing to the tidal influence of remote stars, the matter which left the cooling nebular mass took the shape of a pair of filaments, these would not be massive enough to form planets: they would scatter into space.

§ 237. *The modern theory.*

We need, then, another explanation of the origin of the solar system. This is furnished by the hypothesis that at some distant period in our sun's history a wandering star by chance came so near as to disintegrate it. The hypothesis was originally propounded by Chamberlin and Moulton. It was modified by Jeans, who in his most recent work has accepted certain arguments of Jeffreys.

All agree that 'an accident', the chance close approach of another sun to our own, gave birth to the solar system. The rogue star, as it has been wittily described, produced enormous tides in the sun and tore out of it a great filament which broke up into separate nuclei almost at once. Such a tidally ejected filament would be thicker in the centre than at its ends: so we expect to find the planets formed from the central nuclei, Jupiter and Saturn, of greater mass than the rest.

As the various nuclei revolved round the sun they would at peri-helion be in danger of breaking up owing to the great tides raised by the sun. The larger planets were, when first formed, probably gaseous and their satellites were probably produced in this way. The smaller planets and satellites will have cooled more rapidly than the larger. Gravitation within them will have been smaller than on the more massive planets and it is therefore to be expected that they lost much of the lighter material which belonged to them at disruption. In this way we can account for the fact that the great planets have much smaller densities than the small ones.

§238. *The origin of the earth-moon system.*

The theory which assigns the formation of the solar system to disruption caused by a wandering star accounts satisfactorily for most of the facts. We have seen that the sun and planets are on the whole in one and the same plane: this will have been the plane in which the wandering star moved. We understand equally why the planets all move in the same direction round the sun in this plane: this will have been the direction of the wandering star's motion. The rotation of the sun itself will have been produced by the angular momentum of the tidal material which ultimately fell back into it. Thus, though we must admit that no reason can be assigned for the retrograde motion possessed, as we have seen, by a few moons of the more distant planets, the theory adequately accounts for the main features of our solar system.

It is, however, disconcerting that the existence of our own moon is difficult to explain. The moon is exceptionally dense and unexpectedly massive. In fact its mass is about 1/80th of that of the earth and its density is $3\frac{1}{3}$ times that of water. Only two moons of Jupiter and one of Saturn, out of all the moons of the solar system, are more massive; and our own moon's density is more than twice that of any of these three moons. Our moon was certainly formed from the earth: but, if formed from a gaseous earth by tidal disruption due to the sun, we should expect it to be much less massive than it is.

In default of a more convincing explanation there exists a theory which supposes that the moon was broken from the earth, when the latter was mainly liquid, owing to the chance that the tides raised by the sun had the same period as the natural period of pulsation of the then ellipsoidal earth-moon mass. Because of the equality of these two periods, what is known in physics as 'resonance' would be set up. Forces making for instability, which normally would be dissipated by the conjunction of different frequencies, produce effects which are added together when the frequencies coincide. In the end the addition sums to an amount too large for safety. The simplest example of the process occurs with a child's swing. Even slight pushes when the swing is exactly at the end of its rise are very effective. In a similar way the tides due to the sun, happening to coincide in period with the natural vibrations of the earth-moon ellipsoid, were so effective as to disintegrate the ellipsoidal mass and to cause the massive moon to break away.

In the next lecture we will give the investigation which determines the probability of such a near approach of a wandering star to an assigned sun that a planetary system is formed from the sun. That a planetary system can only arise from such an 'accident' seems *à priori* improbable. That the existence of our moon should also be due to a chance combination of circumstances increases our doubt* as to whether the theory which at present holds the field will ultimately survive criticism.

§ 239. *The moon.*

It is almost certain that the moon has no atmosphere. When a star passes behind the moon, we observe a quite sudden disappearance. There is then, in what is technically known as the occultation of the star, no change in brightness such as we should expect if for a brief time the star were seen through the moon's atmosphere. Similarly at an eclipse of the sun there is no distortion of the light received from the points where the edge of the sun is cut by the moon: such light does not present the appearance of having passed through an atmosphere on the moon. Moreover, shadows of the moon's mountains which we can

---

* Since the statement in the text was written H. Jeffreys has further examined the resonance theory of the moon's origin. In a paper of the year 1917 (*Monthly Notices of the Royal Astronomical Society*, vol. LXXVIII, pp. 116–31) he shewed that the requisite coincidence of periods implied that the earth could not be homogeneous. But tidal currents in an outer shell flowing over a central core would produce friction. Such friction, according to a paper of the year 1930 (*ibid.* vol. XCI, pp. 169–73) would be sufficient to upset the resonance theory. Jeffreys therefore suggests that "the moon has been separate from the earth ever since the early catastrophe that formed the planets" and that "the original disruptive encounter of the sun and star was not merely a close approach but an actual collision".

see when they are made by sunlight are completely black: there appears to be no haze connected with them.

As the moon has no atmosphere, anything resembling terrestrial life cannot exist upon it. We naturally enquire why there should be a difference with such profound consequences in two bodies, like the earth and the moon, which had a common origin. The reason is probably to be found in the fact that the 'velocity of escape' for the earth is nearly five times as great as that for the moon.

§240. *Velocity of escape.*

The theory of velocity of escape is simple.

Suppose that we have two bodies of masses M and m respectively rotating round one another and free from all extraneous influence. Let v be the velocity of m with respect to M. Then the velocities of m and M with respect to the common centre of gravity of the two bodies will be

$$v_1 = \frac{Mv}{M+m} \quad \text{and} \quad v_2 = \frac{mv}{M+m} \text{ respectively.}$$

Thus the kinetic energy of the bodies, measured with the common centre of gravity as a fixed origin, will be

$$\tfrac{1}{2}\frac{Mm}{M+m}v^2.$$

The potential energy of the bodies when at a distance r apart will be

$$\text{cons.} - \gamma\frac{Mm}{r},$$

where γ is the Newtonian constant of gravitation (§234).

Since the sum of the kinetic and potential energies of the system is constant, we have

$$\tfrac{1}{2}\frac{Mm}{M+m}v^2 - \gamma\frac{Mm}{r} = \text{cons.}$$

We therefore have

$$v^2 = \gamma(M+m)\left\{\frac{2}{r} - \frac{1}{a}\right\},$$

where a is a constant. Thus m will, if a be positive, move round M in an ellipse of semi-major axis a. When $1/a$ vanishes, this orbit becomes a parabola. This happens when

$$v^2 = 2\gamma(M+m)/r.$$

If then m be projected at a distance r from M in any direction with this or with any greater velocity, it will never return. This velocity is therefore called the *velocity of escape*.

Naturally, in using this formula we may neglect the small number m. The velocity of escape at the surface of the earth is given by taking, in c.g.s. units, $M = 6 \times 10^{27}$ and $r = 6.4 \times 10^8$. Further, we have seen that the value of the constant of gravitation γ is given by $\gamma = 6.7 \times 10^{-8}$. We thus get $v = 11.2$ km. per sec. Similarly, the velocity of escape for the surface of the moon is 2.4 km. per sec.

§ 241. *Conditions of escape of a gas from a planet's atmosphere.*

When we apply the idea of velocity of escape to explain the loss by the moon of its atmosphere it is necessary to use certain results of the kinetic theory of gases. According to this theory, as it was briefly outlined in § 24, the pressure of a gas is caused by the fact that its molecules are moving rapidly in all directions. They continually collide with one another and with the sides of the vessel in which the gas is contained and in such collisions they behave as if they were perfectly elastic spheres. The theory, of course, deals with averages: it does not enable us to say how any particular molecule behaves, but only how molecules behave in the aggregate. Hence it is not surprising that an important number in the theory is the 'mean-square velocity', which is the velocity whose square is equal to the mean of the squares of the velocities of individual molecules. It can be proved that the mean-square velocity varies as $T^{\frac{1}{2}}$, where T is the absolute temperature of the gas. It also varies inversely as the square root of the molecular weight of the gas. At 0° C. and in kilometres per second the following numbers give mean-square velocities for various important gases:

Hydrogen	...	...	...	1·84
Helium	...	...	...	1·31
Water-vapour	...	...	·62
Nitrogen	...	...	...	·49
Oxygen	...	...	...	·46
Carbon-dioxide	...	...	·39

Now, obviously, on a planetary body the velocity of escape for any particular gas will be far lower than the mean-square velocity of the gas, inasmuch as molecules moving more quickly than the mean will rapidly escape and thus in due course the whole gas will vanish into space.

Jeans, whose researches are authoritative, calculates that at any particular temperature the critical state of affairs arises when the mean-square velocity for that temperature is between 1/3rd and 1/5th of the velocity of escape. When the mean-square velocity is 1/3rd, the gas escapes; when it is 1/5th, it is retained.

Atmospheres of moon, sun and earth.

If this calculation be correct, the moon must have lost even its heavy gases when it was really hot: at 0° C. hydrogen, helium and (much more slowly) water-vapour would disappear. The sun is so massive that it could retain even its lightest gases: we know it to possess hydrogen and helium in abundance. The earth might be expected to have lost its hydrogen; but one is left with the uncomfortable feeling that it might also have lost most of the water-vapour and carbon-dioxide which, as we shall see in Lecture XII, probably formed its initial atmosphere, inasmuch as at its birth it was presumably at least as hot as the present surface temperature of the sun (6000° C.). However, it most certainly did not have such a loss, or we should not be here to-day. Our mental discomfort probably points to the fact that we do not yet fully understand the circumstances attending the birth of earth, moon and planets.

Since the moon has no atmosphere, there can be no water on its surface, for, if there were, such water would evaporate and then escape.

With no atmosphere, the surface of the moon must become very hot by day and cold by night, the more so since its days and nights are each a fortnight long. Our satellite is, in fact, singularly ill-adapted to support life such as exists upon the earth.

§ 242. *Other worlds than ours.*

Probably no speculative enquiry, to which science can supply even fragmentary materials for an answer, is of greater interest to humanity than the possibility of the existence of other inhabited worlds. We have already said that, within half a century of the publication of the Copernican system of astronomy, Giordano Bruno was led by it to propound the doctrine of the infinity of worlds in space. He was exhilarated by the feeling that the Universe was unenclosed by any crystal dome. Copernican astronomy, as he speculatively developed it, made the Universe for him wider, grander, freer, so that he could exult, like a true child of the Renaissance, in escaping the confines of the world-picture accepted by contemporary theology. His speculations* were naturally not welcome to the Roman Church, in which the rigid and oppressive dogmatism of the Counter-reformation had followed a time

---

* With reference to Bruno's condemnation P. Tannery (*Histoire de l'Astronomie ancienne.* Gauthier-Villars, 1893, p. 102) remarks that the plurality of worlds is useless if they are not inhabited; if they are, "la conception primitive du christianisme subsiste difficilement".

when the scientific freedom of Nicholas of Cusa (1401–1464) was not incompatible with the position of a cardinal of the Church. In the year 1600 Bruno went to the stake for his 'heresy'.

History has proved that to burn men for their opinions is not, on the whole, a good way of suppressing those opinions. Though to-day we no longer unquestioningly accept Bruno's idea that space is infinite—it is, on the contrary, probably finite—yet increasingly we are confirmed in the belief that there must exist many inhabited worlds other than our own. As I try to set out reasons for this statement it is well to remember that we are moving in a region of probability rather than certainty; and I will admit that at each stage of my argument an *advocatus diaboli* in the person, say, of a Jesuit astronomer could produce reasons plausible, if not convincing, for a view contrary to that which I personally accept. In the present lecture I must be content to indicate the possibility that life exists on other planets of our own solar system. Later we will consider the probability that other and similar planetary systems exist alike in our galactic Universe and in the great nebulae which are scattered like islands in the depths of space.

§ 243. *Is Venus habitable?*

As we enquire whether possibly there are other habitable planets in our solar system, we naturally consider especially the two planets adjacent to ourselves. These are Venus and Mars. Venus is nearer to the sun than we are: Mars is farther away. The surface of Venus is very little less than that of the earth, and the density of the planet is about 88 per cent. of the density of the earth. In other words, a man who weighed 12 stone upon the earth would weigh a little over 10 stone on Venus. Unfortunately, we do not know how rapidly Venus rotates and it is just possible that it always keeps the same face towards the sun. If this is so, the dark side, of course, is almost certainly uninhabitable. On the other hand, recent investigators have found that considerable heat is radiated from the dark side of Venus and they estimate that the temperature there is about − 25° C. From the bright side of Venus our instruments receive more heat, but the greater part of the difference seems undoubtedly due to the reflection of radiation from the sun. It might be thought that a temperature of − 25° C. was so low as *ipso facto* to exclude the possibility of life on Venus. But Venus is covered by dense clouds and it is probably the temperature above the higher opaque clouds which is thus measured. The general opinion of astronomers seems to be that the atmosphere of Venus above the surface visible to ourselves is less extensive and less dense than our own; but, if the visible surface consists of dense clouds, the atmosphere near the planet will be inaccessible to our investigation. In the accessible atmosphere observations shew that there is little oxygen or water-vapour: the presence of these gases would be indicated in the spectrum of the light reflected from the planet.

The 'greenhouse effect'.

Now the effect of the atmosphere of a planet is most important, for it acts like the glass in a greenhouse. It is well known that glass is transparent to the visible rays of light but it is opaque to heat-rays of longer wave-lengths. When the sun's radiation passes into a greenhouse the shorter waves are absorbed by the surfaces on which they fall and longer heat-waves are emitted. Thus only a fraction of the sun's radiation which enters a greenhouse is transmitted out through the glass: the rest is transformed into radiation of longer wave-lengths and remains to raise the temperature of the glass-covered building.

A planet's atmosphere is similarly to a certain extent transparent to light but opaque to heat. It thus follows that a sufficiently dense atmosphere may raise the temperature of the surface of a planet well above that which it would have if it were radiating like a 'black-body' according to Stefan's law. For instance, it is calculated that 37 per cent. of the radiation received from the sun by the earth is reflected back into space, mainly by the clouds, and so does nothing towards warming the earth. The remaining heat available to warm the earth would, if the earth radiated according to Stefan's law, keep it at an average temperature of − 26° C. It is, however, at an average temperature of about 14° C. Practically the whole of this difference is due to the 'greenhouse effect' of the earth's atmosphere.

It appears then that, if the apparent surface of Venus is its real surface, the planet is probably uninhabitable. If, however, we only see the outermost layers of dense clouds, there may be beneath them congenial warmth and an atmosphere containing oxygen and water-vapour in which there can flourish life similar to that which exists upon our earth. We have previously referred to the fact that the free oxygen in the earth's atmosphere may possibly be the result of vegetable activity in past ages of the earth's development. There is, as we shall explain in Lecture XII, some evidence to support the view that originally the earth was surrounded by dense masses of carbon-dioxide and that the carbon extracted by vegetable life now exists in the carboniferous rocks. It may, of course, be that vegetable life has never developed on Venus and that consequently no such free oxygen has there been liberated as we find upon the earth. Yet Venus appears to be singularly like the earth in its size and density; and presumably the planet resembles the earth in its origin. We should, therefore, expect it to be better suited than any other satellite of the sun to be the abode of life similar to that of which we are the product.

Are there intelligent beings on Mars?

The possibility that there is intelligent life on Mars has been a subject of widespread popular interest ever since Schiaparelli announced the discovery of the so-called Martian canals. In the year 1877, Schiaparelli (1835–1910) first stated that Mars was crossed by a large number of fine, dark, straight lines. Four years later he announced that many of these lines became double at times. All these lines, which must be many miles wide and cannot therefore be accurately described as canals, were observed in the reddish, presumably dry, region of the planet: some observers believe that they have found markings within the darker areas of the planet similar to the ' canals' in the reddish regions.

While there is no reason to doubt that there are markings on Mars, it is probable that the majority of astronomers would be unwilling to affirm that they resemble artificial constructions made by intelligent beings. Such fine detail as the so-called canals can only be observed by an expert in the use of the telescope who takes advantage of moments of ' good-seeing'. It should be remembered that photographs give averages of ' good-seeing' and ' bad-seeing', and consequently they are inferior for such work to the human eye. Now in all delicate observational work much depends upon the personal equation of the observer. Men of unquestionable integrity tend to see what they desire. Without, then, in any way impugning the good faith of Schiaparelli and those who have confirmed his observations, we shall probably be wise to doubt their accuracy. An expert like Barnard (1857–1923) shewed genius with the telescope and had exceptional experience with some of the finest of modern instruments. He was unable to confirm the existence of the canals and his drawings merely shew features which might result from the interplay of natural phenomena.

It is certain that in the Martian winter a white cap appears at its pole: such a cap is familiar in photographs of the planet. Numerous other seasonal changes can be observed. There is no doubt, moreover, that Mars is covered with a haze which is largely opaque to violet light. Recent observations suggest that the water-vapour above the surface of Mars is some 5 per cent. and the oxygen some 15 per cent. of that normally found in the earth's atmosphere: too much reliance, however, must not be placed on these figures. The rapidity with which the polar caps melt suggests that they have nothing like the thickness of the ice-caps of the earth: in fact, all the evidence goes to shew that Mars is, as compared with the earth, deficient in water and that a large portion of the planet's surface must be desert. All these facts lead to the conclusion that we cannot confidently affirm that life exists on Mars.

When, however, we reflect how amazingly adaptable* life is under the very varying conditions which exist upon the earth, we are led to regard it as highly probable that at any rate lower forms of life will be found on Mars. If the existence of the so-called canals could be demonstrated, we could conclude that they were almost certainly the work of intelligent beings. We cannot say whether such intelligence would be associated with mammalian evolution as in the case of humanity. It is quite possible that there might have taken place on Mars a growth of that mental activity which is so marked on earth in ants, bees and wasps, so that brain development on the planet in its finest forms would be associated with a physical structure wholly different from our own.

§ 244. *The tides.*

To most of us who are not concerned with ships or their navigation the tides are known as a curious phenomenon of Nature which tends to interfere with the regularity of sea-bathing. We are probably aware that the average interval between successive high tides is about $12\frac{1}{2}$ hours. It may be also that we have been told that the interval between high tides on two successive days is exactly the interval between two successive passages of the moon across the meridian, a fact which makes it certain that moon and tides are closely connected. But the fact that the tides are important in the long history of the partnership of earth and moon is not common knowledge; yet 'tidal friction' operating for millions of years has changed and is changing the length of the day and has lengthened and is still lengthening the distance of the moon from the earth.

* Compare, for instance, the use, mentioned later in § 313, of copper and vanadium as alternatives for iron in the blood.

The cause of the tides: the equilibrium theory.

Tides are caused primarily by the attraction of the moon for the water in the oceans on the surface of the earth. The attraction of the sun has smaller but similar effects. We will first set out what is called the equilibrium theory of the tides, in which we proceed on the assumption that both earth and moon are at rest.

Let M and E be centres of moon and earth. Suppose that ME cuts the earth's surface in the points A and B, the former being nearer to M. Let m be the mass of the moon, that of the earth being taken as unity, so that $m = 1/81$. Let R be the moon's distance ME, the earth's radius EA being the unit: thus $R = 60$. Let, as usual, g denote the acceleration due to the earth at its own surface.

The moon attracts as though all its mass were concentrated at its centre. Hence the acceleration due to the moon's attraction at E will be gm/R^2. The like acceleration at A will be $gm/(R-1)^2$. The difference between these two accelerations will be F_A, the tide-raising force per unit mass at A. Hence

$$F_A = \frac{gm(2R-1)}{R^2(R-1)^2}.$$

Since R is large, this is approximately $2gm/R^3$. Thus the tide-raising force due to a body at a considerable distance is proportional to the mass of the body and varies inversely as the cube of its distance.

Further, we notice that there is equally a tide-raising force at B given by

$$F_B = gm/R^2 - gm/(R+1)^2$$
$$= \frac{gm(2R+1)}{R^2(R+1)^2}$$
$$= 2gm/R^3, \text{ approximately.}$$

Thus the tide-raising forces at opposite sides of the earth are approximately equal. Many who can understand that the moon raises a tide at A cannot make out how it can possibly raise a tide at B: they fancy that at B, on the equilibrium theory, there should be low and not high tide. But, of course, the moon at A pulls the water from the earth while at B it similarly pulls the earth from the water.

If we put $m = 1/81$ and $R = 60$, we get

$$F/g = \frac{1}{8,800,000}.$$

Thus the tide-raising force due to the moon is very small. Naturally, the sun can equally cause tides. For such tides $m = 330,000$, $R = 23,500$ and $F/g = \dfrac{1}{19,000,000}$. Thus the sun's tide-raising force is a little less than half that of the moon.

§ 245. *The tides in theory and observation.*

In our 'equilibrium theory' investigation of the cause of the tides we have ignored alike the rotation of the earth and the unequal distribution of land and water on its surface. Ocean currents cannot immediately bring the sea into equilibrium under tide-raising forces, because the earth is moving with relatively rapid rotation owing to the fact that it revolves on its axis once in 24 hours. The depth of the sea affects the free motion of waves on its surface: in shallow areas there is much friction. Land masses interfere with ocean currents; and ocean basins are most irregular in depth and shape. For such reasons there are places where high tide occurs at practically the time when low tide would be expected on the equilibrium theory.

Michelson in the year 1913, however, devised a beautiful experiment for demonstrating the truth that the tides are due to gravitational forces derived from the moon and the sun. He half-filled with water a perfectly straight iron tube some 500 feet long which had a window at each end and was sealed air-tight. This tube was placed horizontally in the earth in one direction and a similar tube was placed horizontally in a perpendicular direction. With one exception all the expected tidal consequences of the attractions of the sun and moon were observed, when delicate measurements were made of changes in the heights of the water at the ends of the tubes. The exceptional result was that the heights observed were only some 70 per cent. of those predicted by theory. It thus appears that the solid earth rises and falls under tidal forces, though only to some 30 per cent. of what would be its rise and fall were the earth liquid. This rise and fall at its greatest is about 9 inches and there is no 'lag'. The earth thus appears to be perfectly elastic and to have the rigidity of steel.

§ 246. *Tidal friction: the lengthening of the day.*

The moon, as we have seen, causes tides to sweep round the earth in just under 25 hours. In the deep oceans little friction is caused by such motion; but in shallow seas tidal action causes much fluid friction, which leads to the dissipation of energy as heat. This energy comes mainly from the earth's energy of rotation, so that tidal friction lessens the rate of rotation of the earth and therefore lengthens the day. (We shall also see shortly that it lengthens the month.) Of course, the effect is very small. The earth has a vast stock of rotational energy; and, even though it has been calculated that tidal friction leads to a rate of dissipation of energy equal to some two thousand million horse-power, the day is only thereby lengthened by 1/1200th of a second per century. Our day accordingly will only increase by one second in 120,000 years. So small an amount seems ludicrous; but, inasmuch as the age of the earth is of the order of a thousand million years, the aggregate change in the length of the day owing to tidal friction is both significant and important.

The conclusion just enumerated is reached by obtaining, from a study of ancient observations, what is called the sidereal secular acceleration of the moon and by then separating the parts of this acceleration due respectively to planetary and tidal influences.

Suppose that there were no tidal friction. Then the moon would, if not disturbed by the sun or other planets, describe an ellipse of small eccentricity round the earth. Owing to the disturbing action of the sun the moon's actual motion is, however, highly complicated: such motion is computed in what is called lunar theory. When this computation is finished, there remains the disturbing effect resulting from the influence of the planets of the solar system. This produces what are technically called *secular perturbations*, or perturbations which run on from age to age. Among them is a change in the length of the month. At the present time the sidereal month (that is to say, the period of a complete revolution of the mean moon of lunar theory measured with reference to the fixed stars) is, owing to planetary disturbance, slowly becoming shorter. In consequence the moon is going ahead of the position which it would have were the influence of the planets negligible. Planetary perturbations are, in fact, producing an acceleration, measured in seconds of arc, of $12''02$ per century per century. Thus at the end of t centuries the moon, owing to planetary perturbations, will be $\frac{1}{2} \times 12 \cdot 02 \times t^2 = 6 \cdot 01 t^2$ seconds (of arc) ahead of its position as indicated by the more simple computation which ignores the planets. We may add that the sidereal month will thus continue to become shorter, owing to planetary perturbations, for some 24,000 years: after that time a reversal will take place and the month will slowly lengthen.

Ancient observations.

Now records of ancient eclipses should indicate (as Halley pointed out more than two centuries ago) the secular acceleration of the moon with reference to the sun; and it has long been known that the value of such acceleration is about 22″ per century per century. In a series of papers* J. K. Fotheringham has examined afresh the ancient records, considering in turn ancient occultations and conjunctions, equinox observations, lunar and solar eclipses. He concludes from his investigation that the sidereal secular acceleration of the moon has been, for the last few thousand years, 21″6 per century per century and that the similar acceleration of the sun has been 3″ per century per century. Too much reliance must not be placed on these figures for, as Fotheringham says, his investigations of solar eclipses "only confirm what is clear from the discordances in the times of occultations, etc., and in the times of lunar eclipses, that the ancients had great difficulty in determining the time". But it appears that, when due allowance has been made for planetary perturbations, there is left a sidereal secular acceleration of the moon of 9″6 per century per century. This residual secular acceleration of 9″6, and also the sidereal secular acceleration of the sun of 3″, must be due to a gradual slowing down of the earth's rotation and a consequent lengthening of the day. The former is well explained by tidal friction of the magnitude previously indicated. But Fotheringham's estimate of the sidereal secular acceleration of the sun is almost twice as large as would be expected. As Jeffreys† says, either an unknown cause is producing a secular acceleration of the sun, or part of the observed value is in error.

Tidal friction and its effect on the moon's motion.

The way in which tidal friction increases the length of the day is easily intelligible; but its secondary effects in lengthening the month and causing the moon to recede from the earth are more difficult of comprehension. Briefly, we may say that, inasmuch as the tidal friction retards the earth's rotation, it diminishes the earth's angular momentum. But, if the earth and moon be regarded as a system free from external interference, the angular momentum of the system is constant by the fundamental principle of the conservation of angular momentum.

Hence the angular momentum lost by the earth must be gained by the moon and will therefore alter the moon's orbital motion. The change both causes the moon's distance from the earth to increase and also lengthens the month.

* *Monthly Notices of the Royal Astronomical Society*, vols. LXXV, LXXVIII, LXXX, LXXXI, published in the years 1915, 1918, 1920.

† H. Jeffreys, *The Earth*. Cambridge University Press, 1924, p. 216.

The nature of a simple mathematical investigation may be shortly indicated.

Let M and m be the masses of the earth and moon and v their relative velocity when at a distance r apart. Their centres describe relatively to one another an ellipse of semi-axes a and b, say, and of latus rectum $2l$.

Let G be the common centre of gravity of the earth and the moon and let the angular momenta round G of the two bodies, when their masses are all supposed concentrated at their centres, be A_M and A_m respectively. Then, if γ be the constant of gravitation, we can readily shew that

$$A_M + A_m = \frac{mM}{\sqrt{M+m}} \sqrt{\gamma l}.$$

Suppose now that R_M and R_m are the angular momenta of the earth and the moon due to rotation round their centres.

Let accented letters denote the new values of all these quantities owing to tidal friction which increases the length of the day from d to d'. Then because R_M is proportional to the rotational velocity of the earth, $$R_M'/R_M = d/d'.$$

Because there is no tidal friction on the moon we may put $R_m = R_m'$. Hence since the total angular momentum of the system is constant, we must have

$$\frac{mM}{\sqrt{M+m}} \sqrt{\gamma} \{\sqrt{l'} - \sqrt{l}\} = R_M \left\{1 - \frac{d}{d'}\right\}.$$

This result shews that the latus rectum of the orbit of the moon increases with the length of the day; and, inasmuch as we know the ratio of R_M to $\sqrt{\gamma l}\, \dfrac{mM}{\sqrt{M+m}}$, the change under present conditions can be calculated.

Though a more complete investigation would be necessary for a rigid proof, we may fairly assume that l and a will increase together.

Further, the rate at which a radius vector from the earth to the moon sweeps out area is readily proved to be $\frac{1}{2} \sqrt{l} \sqrt{\gamma (M+m)}$.

If, then, T be the length of the month,

$$\frac{\pi a b}{T} = \frac{1}{2} \sqrt{l} \sqrt{\gamma (M+m)}$$

or $$T = 2\pi a^{\frac{3}{2}}/\sqrt{\gamma (M+m)}.$$

Thus the length of the month will increase as the mean distance of the moon from the earth increases.

It may be added that, as the sun has more than 300,000 times the mass of the earth, tidal friction does practically nothing to alter the length of the year. "It is improbable", wrote Sir George Darwin* (1845–1912), "that the year is, from this cause at any rate, longer by more than a few seconds than it was at the very birth of the solar system."

§ 247. *The past of the earth-moon system.*

The foregoing investigation only indicates roughly the nature of the calculation by which the past and future of the earth-moon system can be investigated. To Sir George Darwin we owe the initiation of a series of researches of absorbing interest.

They indicate that 'in the beginning' the day and the month were nearly equal, the former being the shorter and not quite 5 hours long; and at that time the centre of the moon was distant somewhat more than 9000 miles from the centre of the earth. Such must have been the state of affairs when first the moon was torn from the earth. Had the month then been a little shorter than the day the rotation of the earth would have been accelerated by tidal friction and the moon would have been drawn towards the earth into which it would ultimately have fallen. Evidently, therefore, the first month was slightly longer than the co-temporaneous day. As a consequence tidal friction began at once to retard the earth's rotation. Immediately after the birth of the moon there can have been no such atmosphere or sea as appeared later: but under dense clouds of vapour the still liquid earth must have bubbled and surged. The tidal forces due to the moon must have been comparatively great: for if we put $R = 2 \cdot 3$ in our previous calculation we get $F/g = 1/200$. Following the moon, a great wave of molten rock raised by this force must have swung round the earth. It is probable that the crust of the earth rapidly solidified: when water appeared upon it the tides must have been gigantic. In the end conditions with which we are familiar slowly came into existence. Calculations as to the time that has elapsed since the birth of the moon necessarily lack precision: Jeffreys has suggested that some such figure as 4000 million years is probable.

As is well known, the moon continually keeps the same face to the earth at the present time. The existence of its great craters is evidence

* G. H. Darwin, *The Tides*. Murray, 3rd ed. 1911, p. 293. These lectures form a brilliant 'popular' exposition of the work of Darwin himself and of other authorities.

that its internal heat formerly shewed itself in violent volcanic action. This suggests that there must have been a time when our satellite was liquid and when the earth raised enormous waves of lava upon its surface. If it ever rotated rapidly upon its axis the frictional resistance of such tides must have diminished its rate of rotation. Moreover, such friction must ultimately have been so effective that the moon ceased to move relatively to a line joining the centres of the earth and moon. But, according to Darwin, there is still in the moon a solidified earth-tide, revealed in the fact that the moon's equator is not quite circular, the longer axis being directed towards the earth. It should be added that tidal friction on the moon, in diminishing its rate of rotation, must have called into action forces tending to push the earth away from the moon. Owing, however, to the fact that the mass of the moon is only 1/81st part of the mass of the earth, the effect of such forces must have been small.

The future of the earth-moon system.

The future of tidal evolution is at least as interesting as its past. It appears that for vast ages to come the day will continue to grow longer and the moon's distance will increase until ultimately the day and month become equal and such that each contains 47 of our present days. (The number 55, originally given by Darwin, seems to be less accurate than the now accepted figure.) The earth and its satellite will each keep the same face to the other and thus they will rotate round one another as though attached to a rigid bar.

§ 248. *The end of the earth-moon system.*

It thus appears that tidal friction has already done for the moon what it will ultimately do for the earth. But earth and moon are not likely to revolve as though rigidly attached until after a period many times as long as that which has passed since the birth of the moon. Even when they do so, further changes due to the friction of solar tides will operate, unless the earth's oceans vanish or freeze. On the assumption that the oceans will remain, Darwin says that the day will become longer than the month. Lunar tides will now be again generated though, as the motion of the earth will be very slow relatively to the moon, tidal friction will be small. That friction, however, will act in opposition to the solar tides: the moon will slowly approach the earth and ultimately will fall into it. Jeffreys speculates that an alternative fate awaits our satellite: it may be torn to pieces by the ultimate tidal forces and its fragments may then form a ring round the earth like the rings of Saturn. But the whole sequence of changes originating in the solar tides will be exceedingly slow. Whether life upon this earth will survive to provide witnesses for any of them will depend, in part, upon how long the sun will continue to shine. That question can only be investigated by gathering, from a study of the bright stars, material from which to construct the past history and probable future of a luminary such as our own*.

* Alike in the present and in the next lecture I have availed myself of the stores of information contained in Russell-Dugan-Stewart, *Astronomy*, 2 vols. Ginn, 1927. This important text-book gives an admirable conspectus of the state of astronomical science in the year 1926.

Lecture xi

THE GALACTIC UNIVERSE AND
THE GREAT NEBULAE

THE GALACTIC UNIVERSE

§ 249. *The 'fixed' stars.*

By the ancients the visible stars were supposed to be 'fixed' in the spherical dome in which they were thought to be carried daily round the earth: by contrast the planets were 'wanderers'. We still keep the term 'fixed' stars, though in the year 1718 the great astronomer Halley (1656–1742) discovered that Arcturus and Sirius had both changed their places since the time of Ptolemy. The stars, in fact, only appear to be fixed because of the enormous distances which separate them from us. Such measurements as we can make shew that all are in relative motion with velocities that range up to more than 100 km. per sec. The sun's motion is (*vide* § 267) 19 km. per sec. relative to the naked-eye stars as a whole. (Later it will be seen that, when we pass outside our own universe to the island universes which are visible as the great nebulae, relative velocities which run up to thousands of kilometres per second are deduced by Doppler's principle from observations recently made.) The distances of the stars, alike from the sun and from one another, are inconceivably great. We have seen that the mean distance of Pluto from the sun, which may be taken to measure the size of the solar system, is 3700 million miles. But the distance between the sun and the faint star, Proxima Centauri, which is believed to be the nearest of the fixed stars, is about 25 million million miles, or little less than 7000 times the mean distance of Pluto.

Newton was the first astronomer to form a true idea of the distances of the stars: but it is only during the present century that astronomers have begun to fit accurate knowledge into a coherent scheme.

§ 250. *Instruments.*

Our increased and increasing knowledge of the stellar universe is mainly due to three instruments.

The *telescope* dates from the time of Galileo. He introduced the form still in use as an opera-glass and by observations with it contributed powerfully to the downfall of the Ptolemaic system of astronomy. In recent years some magnificent telescopes have been built, especially in America. They contain no new optical principles; but, in combination with improved photographic plates, their greater delicacy and precision as regards observation have been of much value. Such triumphs of the engineer's and glass-maker's skill are, needless to say, enormously expensive. For this reason, such gifts as have been made by rich men in America have placed that country in the van of astronomical research.

The *spectroscope* was developed shortly after the middle of the nineteenth century, when through a telescope observations were made on light which had been split up into its component wave-lengths by being passed through a prism. Equally, light can be split up by a *diffraction grating*. Such a grating was described in Lecture IX and we may recall that, in its simplest form, it is a piece of reflecting metal accurately planed and ruled with equidistant grooves, 10,000 or 20,000 to an inch.

Photographs with the spectroscope have been of increasing importance in recent investigation. Elaborate spectra can thus be obtained of distant stars. From such spectra we learn what are the elements in the surface of the star which are absorbing and emitting radiation, and also the state (temperature, ionisation, etc.) of those elements. Further, by the Doppler effect we can determine the velocity of the star in the line of sight.

§ 251. *The interferometer.*

Recently a new instrument has revealed its power. The *interferometer* of the American physicist, A. A. Michelson (1852–1931), is a modification of the telescope, in which a defect of the normal instrument is used as the basis of exceedingly delicate observations.

When rays from a distant point-source of light pass through a telescope they form, in the focal plane of the instrument, not a point but a 'diffraction disc' whose angular diameter varies inversely as the diameter of the object glass of the telescope. This defect is a result of the fact that, as we have seen, light does not travel in the straight lines of geometrical optics: it has a wave motion in the direction of propagation. In the interferometer the defect is made the basis of the instrument's utility. The object glass of the telescope is covered so as to prevent the passage of light save through two small areas, distant d apart, symmetrically placed on one and the same diameter. Corresponding to each area the light from a distant star makes, in the focal plane of the instrument, a small disc. Owing to interference these two overlapping discs are crossed by alternate dark and light bands. We proceed to prove that the distance between the centres of successive interference bands (that is, between the centre of a light and of an adjacent dark band) is x, where

$$x/f = \lambda/2d,$$

f being the focal length of the object glass and λ the wave-length of the light.

In the figure let A and B be the two small areas of the object glass whose centre is C. Let FF_1 be the focal plane, F being the principal focus and F_1 the centre of the bright band nearest to F.

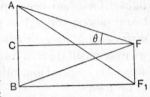

Evidently $AF = f$, $AB = d$ and $FF_1 = 2x$.

Let θ be the angle AFC. By hypothesis the light from a distant star which is incident at A and B is in phase. Because $AF = FB$, it will also be in phase at F. Since F_1 is the centre of the adjacent bright band of the diffraction disc, the light must be in phase at F_1. We must, therefore, have $AF_1 - F_1B = \lambda$, where λ is the wave-length of the light.

Remember now that FF_1 is a very small quantity. Then, to a sufficient degree of approximation,

$$AF_1 - AF = 2x \sin \theta,$$
$$BF - BF_1 = 2x \sin \theta,$$

and hence

$$\lambda = 4x \sin \theta.$$

But

$$\sin \theta = d/2f;$$

and thus

$$x = \lambda f/2d.$$

Clearly, if F_n be the centre of the nth bright band below F, we shall have $AF_n - BF_n = n\lambda$ and therefore $FF_n = nFF_1$. Our result is therefore established.

Suppose now that two stars which are close together are observed. Then, if α is their angular separation and y the distance between the centres of their diffraction discs, we have

$$y = \alpha f,$$

because the line joining a star to the centre of its diffraction disc passes through the centre of the object glass.

Let now d be altered so that, when the interferometer is pointed at the two stars, bright bands on one disc overlap dark bands on the other. Then, if the stars be equally bright, the interference bands will vanish. For the corresponding value of d we shall have $x = y$, and therefore $2d\alpha = \lambda$.

We can thus measure α if it be of a size comparable with the wavelength of light, which is among the most minute of accurately known lengths.

The interferometer can equally be used to measure the angular diameter α of a distant star if the star be thought of as two half-stars joined together, the light of each being concentrated at distances a little less than $\alpha/4$ from the centre of the whole star.

The amazing delicacy of the interferometer will best be understood by reference to a triumph of its use which attracted public notice a few years ago. The instrument was applied at the end of the year 1920 to measure the angular diameter of Betelgeux*, and the result was found to be ·047″. In other words the apparent size of the star is that of a bright halfpenny 70 miles away! The star's probable parallax is ·017″. Hence its diameter must be about 250 million miles or 300 times the diameter of the sun. Figures such as these shew how minute are the observations which modern astronomers must be able to make before they can obtain some of the vast numerical estimates of their science.

It is probable that future progress in astronomical observation will come through the invention of new instruments like the interferometer, rather than by further improvements in the telescope.

§ 252. *Astronomical measures of distance.*

The distances of the 'fixed' stars are so great that for them we need specially large units of measurement.

The popular unit is the 'light-year', that is, the distance which light travels in a year. Light travels 3×10^{10} cm. in a second: it will therefore travel approximately $9\cdot5 \times 10^{17}$ cm. in a year, for in one year there are $3\cdot15 \times 10^7$ seconds. Thus a light-year is roughly equal to $9\frac{1}{2}$ million million kilometres or about 5·9 million million miles. For rough work it is satisfactory to remember that a light-year is 6 million million miles.

The astronomer, in computing distances of the 'fixed' stars, works with 'annual parallax', which is the difference of a star's direction as seen from the earth and from the sun (it being assumed that the earth

---

* The apparent angular diameter of the star varies from ·034″ to ·047″. Its light also varies; and possibly the star pulsates with a period of some six years.

is at its mean distance from the sun). Thus parallax, as the term is used in connection with the stars, is half of the angle which a star appears to move through as the earth moves from one extremity of its orbit to the other. The corresponding unit of distance of the astronomer is the 'parsec', which is the distance of a star whose parallax is one second of arc. The parsec is thus equal to 206,265 times the earth's mean distance from the sun.

Thus   1 parsec = 19·2 million million miles

$$= 3·08 \times 10^{18} \, \text{cm.}$$

$$= 3·26 \, \text{light-years.}$$

The advantage of working with parsecs is that, if d be the distance of a star in parsecs and if p be its annual parallax in seconds of arc, $d = 1/p$. For rough work we usually assume that 3 parsecs = 10 light-years, and 1 parsec = 20 million million miles.

§ 253. *The shape and size of the galactic universe.*

The outcome of recent research is to shew that the stars which we can see with the naked eye are but a small fraction of the number revealed by a telescope: and they in turn are few compared with the number recorded on a photographic plate when placed in the eye-piece of a great telescope. But practically all belong to a vast universe of stars which has the Milky Way for a sort of rim: for this reason it is called the *galactic universe*. In shape this universe is almost certainly lenticular, that is to say it resembles a double-convex lens. In more homely language, it is bun-shaped. Its plane of symmetry is termed the *galactic plane*. As we shall explain shortly, the number of stars within our universe is estimated, by a most risky process of extrapolation, to be more than 30,000 million: our sun appears to be one of such stars and in no way exceptional save that in the possession of a planetary system it has an apparently rare dignity.

There is now a general tendency among astronomers to differentiate between the galactic universe as a whole and a smaller aggregation of stars to which our sun belongs. The latter is commonly called the *local star-cloud*. The whole galactic universe is probably coiled like a spiral nebula; and, in it, far from the centre, is the much smaller flattened group or local system of stars to which our sun belongs. This group will not be sharply separated from the whole, and, in so far as it has a shape, will probably resemble a thick bun. There is much uncertainty both as to the dimensions of the local star-cloud and as to those of the whole galaxy. According to a careful estimate made by Seares* at the end of the year 1927, the local system, which must contain many million stars, has probably a diameter of 6000 parsecs. Our sun is in the galactic plane and, assuming that the local system is spheroidal, the centre of this system is some 40–50 parsecs south of the galactic plane. Possibly (but see § 283) the local system corresponds to the sort of knot or condensation which we observe in the arms of the immensely distant spiral nebulae, the whole galaxy itself corresponding to such a spiral. The sun is less than 100 parsecs from the centre of the local system. The galaxy is, according to Seares, a vast organisation some 60,000–90,000 parsecs in diameter. Its centre is about 20,000 parsecs distant from our sun in the direction of the constellation Sagittarius.

But the fact that the centre of the galactic universe is in this particular direction is almost the sole certainty that emerges from recent research. We shall see in § 275 that the study of differential galactic rotation initiated by Oort leads to the conclusion that the galactic universe rotates round a point in the direction of Sagittarius which is distant some 6500 parsecs: this distance is but one-third of that which Seares believes to be probable. If the observations which appear to confirm Oort's work are accurate, the inner stars of the galaxy rotate on the average faster than the outer groups, and the velocity of the local star-cloud round the centre may be from 250–300 kilometres per second. Probably in the next generation further photometric observations will put an end to present perplexities.

§ 254. *The unity of the galactic universe.*

At the outset of any enquiry into the vast universe of stars to which we belong we naturally ask whether they are formed of the same kinds of matter as compose the solar system. The answer is a clear affirmative. The spectra of the stars are dark-line spectra like the spectrum of the sun; and practically all the lines in such spectra can be identified as those of known elements. Some few unidentified lines which come from exceptional stars are almost certainly due to the existence in such stars of unusual temperature and pressure conditions. We may say with confidence that, throughout the galactic universe, matter is everywhere composed of the same kinds of atoms and that their behaviour is everywhere governed by the same laws. In emphasising this impressive fact we do not claim that spectroscopic observations of the stars reveals all the elements which may exist in them. The radiation

* F. H. Seares, *Astrophysical Journal*, vol. LXVII, pp. 123 *et seq.*

which we see merely discloses the atomic structure of the exterior material in the stars: it gives us no information as to the structure of atoms of presumably heavy elements deep within them. But we can reasonably conclude that, if such heavy elements exist in distant stars, they also exist unrevealed in our own sun. And, further, if there are other planetary systems in our universe, such will be built of materials similar to those out of which our own has been constructed.

At one time it was thought that stars differed largely in chemical composition. Pioneers in spectroscopic work, such as Huggins (1824–1910) and Lockyer (1836–1920), found that, in the sun, iron and calcium lines take a prominent place, while, in Sirius, hydrogen lines stand out dominant. They believed that in due course Sirius would develop into a star like our sun and concluded that in the process complex elements would be formed from the more simple. The true interpretation of the facts, however, is that the sun is at a temperature of some 6000°, favourable to the production of iron and calcium lines, while Sirius is at a temperature of 11,000°, at which hydrogen is especially active in emitting (and absorbing) radiation.

Just as a furnace sends out light of different colours at different temperatures (we talk of 'red-hot' and 'white-hot') so the colour of the light received from a star tells us roughly its temperature. This temperature is, of course, that of the atoms in its exterior which are sending out the light which we perceive and is not the temperature within the star. The spectroscope, analysing a star's light, gives us more accurate knowledge than the crude test of colour: it informs us, in fact, of what is called the star's *spectral type*. Such types correspond to external temperatures, which range from some 3000° for dim red stars up to more than 25,000° for bright white stars. The types are also in part determined by the conditions of pressure and density under which the radiation which we perceive is emitted.

It may be added that stellar spectra give us no evidence that, in the evolution of the stars, complex atoms are being built out of simple atoms. Complex atoms seem to exist as abundantly in what are thought to be young stars as in those which are apparently old. In our present state of knowledge we are bound to say that, while on the earth some complex atoms are transforming themselves into more simple atoms, there is no clear evidence that any reverse process is taking place anywhere in the Universe.

§ 255. *The distances of the stars.*

The distance of a star is obtained by measuring its annual parallax. Now the parallax of the nearest star known to us, Proxima Centauri, is ·765″. The difficulty of measuring so small an angle is obvious. Not until the year 1838, in fact, were the parallaxes of any of the fixed stars accurately obtained. Since then there has been continuous progress, and now the distances of some 2000 stars are known as the result of parallax measurements. The errors are believed to be on the whole less than ·01″, which is the angle subtended by a halfpenny at 320 miles.

It is hardly likely that we have yet discovered all the faint stars which lie near the sun. Some near stars may, of course, be dark and therefore invisible; and such must be excluded from any statement which can be made. With such exclusion it can be said that, omitting the sun itself, there are known to be seventeen stars within 4 parsecs of the sun. Thus the star density in the neighbourhood of the sun appears to be greater than one star to 16 cubic parsecs: it is likely to be at least one star to 10 cubic parsecs. Moreover, there is some reason to believe that our stellar neighbours are fairly uniformly distributed in space. If this be so, the average distance between the stars will be a little more than 2 parsecs or about 40 million million miles.

It is practically impossible to measure an angle less than ·01″. Thus the distances of stars which are more than 100 parsecs away cannot be found directly by parallax measurements. But several ingenious arguments help us to estimate greater distances with more or less accuracy.

§ 256. *The open and globular clusters.*

Photographs of the heavens reveal that there exist clusters or relatively close aggregations of stars. These fall naturally into two classes: *open clusters* and *globular clusters*.

Each *open cluster* consists of relatively few stars (a few thousands at most), and these appear distinct from one another in a good telescope. All the clusters which are conspicuous to the naked eye are of this type. There are altogether some 200 open clusters known to us. They belong to the galactic universe and most (though not all) lie in the Milky Way. Some are fairly compact; but others form a loose aggregation and, when these latter are relatively near the solar system, they appear to be unconnected stars until investigation reveals that they have a common motion through space.

It is quite possible that loose open clusters are very numerous in space. It is believed, as will be seen later, that such clusters are the remains of close aggregates of stars which were born simultaneously and have gradually disintegrated under the gravitational effects of other stars of the universe. The open cluster which is nearest to the solar system appears to be some 40 parsecs distant: the most remote known is possibly a hundred times as far away.

The globular clusters are much more interesting and, in fact, very perplexing phenomena. Some seventy of them are known. In a good telescope a typical globular cluster looks like a 'dense swarm' of stars. It has great central condensation, is globular in form, and all the stars which compose it are very faint. The stars in the brighter globular clusters must amount to tens of thousands: it is, in fact, highly probable that in some globular clusters there are hundreds of thousands of stars. These clusters are almost entirely confined to one half of the celestial sphere: nearly all are within 90° of a point in the constellation Sagittarius and more than half are within 30° of this point.

The distances of those globular clusters which contain cepheid variables can be found, as we shall shortly explain. In these clusters the absolute (photographic) magnitude of the brightest stars can be discovered and, moreover, it is found to be constant: this magnitude is, in fact, about 1·5. Assuming that this constant magnitude holds for all the globular clusters, Shapley ingeniously determined the distance of all by measuring the apparent magnitude of the brightest stars in each. The result of this calculation of the positions of the globular clusters in space is to shew that they lie roughly on an ellipsoid of which the equatorial place coincides with the Milky Way. The maximum diameter of this ellipsoid is 75,000 parsecs and its centre 20,000 parsecs distant from the sun in the direction of Sagittarius (galactic longitude 325°). Can it be a mere chance that the globular clusters are thus symmetrically placed with regard to the Milky Way? If not, they must have some connection with our galactic universe. Shapley believes that the clusters are, as it were, 'boundary-stones' marking off our universe from surrounding space. He thus makes our universe far larger than it was supposed to be a generation ago. His view seems increasingly to commend itself to experts, and was one of the bases of the estimate of Seares given in §253.

The nearest globular cluster is about 6500 parsecs distant: the most remote known to us is some 70,000 parsecs away. Naturally, in order that the clusters may be visible at such distances, they must be of large size. The central dense portion of an average cluster is some 15 light-years across and the whole of a cluster has possibly a diameter of 100 light-years. The star density at the centre of a cluster is high: possibly 2000 times the density of stars in the neighbourhood of our sun. None the less, there is little chance of a collision between stars, as each star near the centre of the cluster would be something like one-half of a light-year or some 3 million million miles from its neighbour.

§ 257. *The cepheid variables.*

The *cepheid variables* are stars of which the brightness varies in a perfectly regular and characteristic way, a rapid rise to maximum followed by a slower fall: the visual range of variation may be as much as $1\frac{1}{2}$ magnitudes. Some short-period variables of the same character have periods of less than a day; but typical cepheids (so-called from the pattern star δ Cephei) have periods of about a week. The periods of similar variables in the Magellanic Clouds range up to more than one hundred days. The cause of the variation in brightness is unknown; but it is thought that cepheids are stars of low density which pulsate freely and that in such pulsations they change in luminosity. Some 170 cepheids have been discovered in the galactic universe (excluding those in the globular clusters which, as we have seen, just possibly do not belong to the galactic universe). The distances of a few of the nearer cepheids have been determined by parallax measurements. Their peculiarity is that their luminosity (or intrinsic brightness) and period are connected by a fixed law: when the one is known the other can be found. They are thus, as it were, 'standard candles' scattered through space. We need, therefore, only measure the period and apparent brightness of a cepheid and at once we know its distance. Thus Shapley could say in the year 1931 that the cepheid variable star "now has the distinction of being the astronomer's most important tool in measuring the universe".

The law connecting luminosity and period is an empirical discovery*; no reason for it can be given. There is, in fact, a possibility that the law is not invariably true: if so, important estimates of distance based upon it may have to be revised. Cepheids exist both in the globular clusters and also in the great spiral nebulae; hence, if the law holds good, we can measure the distances of these objects even though they are of the order of tens (or hundreds) of thousands of parsecs. The typical long-period cepheids surpass in absolute brightness most other stars whose brightness is known. A Magellanic Cloud cepheid of period one hundred days would be 20,000 times as bright as the sun, its absolute visual magnitude, according to the definition of § 200, being approximately − 6. (The absolute magnitude of the sun is 4·85.)

* Due to Miss H. S. Leavitt of Harvard Observatory.

§258. *Giant and dwarf stars.*

We can always measure the apparent brightness of a star. If then its distance can be determined in any way we can obtain its absolute brightness. The result of such investigations as it has been possible to make reveals an astonishing difference in the intrinsic brightness of the stars. Hertzsprung, in the year 1905, coined the terms giant and dwarf to indicate this difference. His names were only intended to describe relative brightness: as it happens, they often (though not invariably) give a correct indication of relative size.

In the year 1913 H. N. Russell took some 300 stars whose distances were then known and made a diagram in which their intrinsic brightness was plotted against their spectral type. The range of spectral types roughly corresponds to a colour (and hence to a temperature)

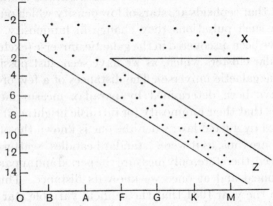

sequence. Russell's first result led to expectations indicated by the above figure in which the ordinates represent absolute magnitudes and the letters B, A, F, G, K, M represent spectral types which in the main correspond to temperatures ranging from 25,000° to 3000°.

As the distance, and therefore the intrinsic brightness, of more stars has become known, it has become possible to place more stars in the Russell diagram. The form which it takes is now roughly given by the figure opposite. The original line YZ of Russell's diagram still remains: to it Eddington has given the name of 'the main sequence'. There is still, moreover, a marked divergence between giants and dwarfs in class M. No intermediate stars in this class appear to exist.

Naturally, such a striking classification of the stars seemed to indicate some fundamental property of the stellar universe. For a time it seemed as though the broken line XYZ in the original diagram represented the course of stellar evolution. On this theory a giant began at X as a cool star of enormous size, shrank and became hotter until it reached the point Y; and then, as its state changed from gaseous to liquid, it ceased to shrink but radiated its heat away as it passed along the main sequence YZ. Unfortunately this simple picture of stellar evolution has failed to meet criticism. It has, of late, become clear that the contraction of a star will not supply the enormous quantities of energy given out in radiation. Further, it was pointed out by Edding-

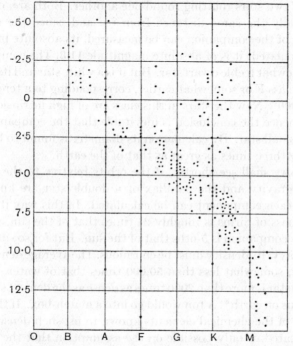

ton, in the year 1924, that, with the temperature that must exist inside a star, the elements of its interior must be almost completely ionised and that therefore a bright star, while remaining gaseous, can be almost indefinitely compressible. This idea, moreover, explained the existence of 'white dwarfs' which cannot be fitted into the Hertzsprung-Russell scheme of evolution.

No man can at the present time say what is the true picture of stellar evolution. A number of ingenious theories have been propounded. In each there are too many speculative hypotheses to permit of certain conclusions.

§259. *White dwarfs.*

The discovery of the white dwarf stars is one of the most unexpected results of recent astronomical research. To indicate their nature we may consider the star known as the Companion of Sirius. Sirius is the brightest star in the sky, and its apparent brightness (it is of absolute magnitude 1·3) is due to the fact that it is comparatively close to the solar system. Its parallax in consequence has been accurately determined: it is ·371″, corresponding to a distance of 51 million million miles. Now Sirius is a binary star, that is to say, the star which we see consists of two stars rotating round one another. Both are, of course, at practically the same distance from us: and, since the apparent brightness of the companion can be measured, its absolute brightness can be calculated: it is of absolute magnitude 11·3. The companion is thus a somewhat feeble dwarf star. But it is a white star and its spectral type is of class F or somewhat earlier, corresponding to a temperature of some 8000°. Now the stars in this class are of high intrinsic luminosity, and hence the conclusion is inevitable that the companion must be a very small star. By calculation its diameter is found to be 24,000 miles, only three times as great as that of the earth.

But, as we shall see shortly, if the orbits relative to the common centre of gravity and the parallax of a double star are known, the masses of each component can be calculated. In this way it is found that the mass of Sirius is roughly $2\frac{1}{2}$ times that of the sun, while the mass of its companion is 5/6ths that of the sun. But for so small a star to be so heavy, its density must be enormous. The average density must be, in fact, somewhat less than 50,000 times that of water. In other words, the star is more than 2000 times as dense as the densest substance known to us on earth*. A ton would go into a match-box. If the star be composed of the chemical elements known to us, such density, as we have indicated, is only possible on the assumption that the atoms in the star are stripped of all their outer electrons. We can imagine that then the heavy nuclei can be 'jammed together' far more closely than is possible under normal terrestrial conditions.

The existence of matter in such a state is, however, too surprising to be accepted without confirmation. Fortunately, Einstein's relativity theory supplies a test. A vibrating atom is, as was shewn in §132, analogous to a clock: and in an intense gravitational field a clock should slow down perceptibly. Now there is no doubt that, if the companion

---

* The densest terrestrial substance known is osmium (atomic number 76), of density $22\frac{1}{2}$.

has the density just suggested, the atoms which by their vibration are sending out light from its surface are in a very strong gravitational field. The radius of the companion being 1/36th of that of the sun, and the masses of the companion and the sun being in the ratio of 5 : 6, gravitational potential at the surface of the companion should be thirty times that at the surface of the sun. Observation will interpret the corresponding shifting towards the red by the Doppler effect: and accurate calculation shews that it will manifest itself as an apparent velocity of recession of some 20 km. per sec. Adams at Mount Wilson, in the year 1925, made the necessary observations. They were by no means easy, as they involved photographing the spectrum of a star which was less than 12″ distant from another star ten thousand times as bright. None the less, he found that the 'Einstein effect' existed and was 19 km. per sec. The observation was noteworthy, for it gave a new verification of the theory of relativity and confirmed the existence of stars of almost incredible density.

Only four 'white dwarfs' are known with certainty; but half of these are within four parsecs of the sun. Inasmuch as such stars are of low apparent brightness, they are not likely to be detected unless they are near to us. They may therefore be common objects in space. In the Russell-Hertzsprung diagram the 'white dwarfs' lie well below and to the left of the main sequence. There is thus an obvious difficulty in fitting them into any evolutionary scheme which regards descent down the main sequence as the normal evolution of a star. We are tempted to think of them as stars which have finished their course, if only because much energy would have to be put into a white dwarf to make it swell in size so that its congested nuclei might put on their normal girdles of electrons: and we do not know where such energy is to come from. But white dwarfs are but a part of the unsolved problem of stellar evolution. Their possible connection with novae we shall discuss in § 276.

§ 260. *Spectroscopic parallaxes.*

In 1914 Adams and Kohlschütter investigated photographs of spectra of the stars and shewed how such photographs could be used to estimate distances. They found first of all that they could distinguish between what are called giant and dwarf stars because, roughly speaking, some spectral lines are strong in the former and weak in the latter, while for other lines the converse holds good. Then they also found that the strength of typical strong lines in different stars was connected by a definite law with the absolute magnitude of the star. This fact allows the real brightness of a star to be found. Its apparent brightness can, of course, be measured and hence its distance can be obtained. This method of *spectroscopic parallaxes* has well been described as "one of the most extraordinary developments of modern astronomy". It indicates that we have not yet extracted from stellar spectra by any means all the information which they contain.

§ 261. *The total number of the stars.*

It is probable that only some 2000 stars were known to the ancients: with the naked eye (but in the whole sky) it is said that some 6000 can now be seen. Even a small telescope enormously increases the number which are visible, while with long exposures on a photographic plate attached to a large telescope the number becomes almost uncountable. Yet most certainly the number is not infinite. The stars are not uniformly distributed throughout space: they 'thin out' as we sound its depths.

Star-counts naturally depend on cooperation between different observatories. As it is impossible to photograph the whole sky in the manner required for such counts, selected areas are chosen. Counts are made for each of these areas of the numbers of stars of successive (photographic) magnitudes. On the basis of these counts estimates are made of the numbers of stars of different magnitudes in various parts of the sky. The numbers of stars of magnitudes down to below the 18th can thus be determined by direct observation.

Now first of all, it is found that, as we should expect, there is a great concentration of stars towards the Milky Way. Moreover, the concentration increases greatly for the fainter stars. Secondly, it is found that the number of stars brighter than a given magnitude increases enormously as the stars grow fainter; but the rate of increase is far smaller than it should be if the stars were uniformly distributed throughout space. This last conclusion rests upon the assumption that, on the whole, space is perfectly transparent, so that the light of the distant stars is not weakened by their distance. There is evidence that the assumption holds good save for known 'obscuring regions', which appear to be filled with vast masses of fine dust or of more highly diffused matter.

We proceed to give the simple mathematical argument by which the above conclusions are reached.

Let d be the distance at which a star appears to be of magnitude m.

By the definition of magnitude, given in § 200, a star of magnitude m

sends out 100 times as much light as a star of magnitude $m + 5$; and thus such a star sends out $(2 \cdot 512)^n$ times as much light as one of magnitude $m + n$. If the star were at a distance $2 \cdot 512d$ it would send us $\frac{1}{(2 \cdot 512)^2}$ times as much light as we get when it is at distance d; and therefore it would appear to be of magnitude $m + 2$.

Suppose now that two lists were made: one of stars of magnitude greater than m and the other of stars of magnitude greater than $m + 2$. Any star which appeared in the first list would appear in the second if its distance were $2 \cdot 512$ times as great. Hence, if the stars were uniformly distributed in space, a rise of two magnitudes would correspond to the ratio of the number of stars within spheres of radii $2 \cdot 512d$ and d respectively. The volumes of these spheres are in the ratio

$$(2 \cdot 512)^3 : 1 \quad \text{or} \quad 15 \cdot 86 : 1.$$

Thus, if the distribution of stars was uniform throughout space, an increase of two magnitudes in our star-counts should increase the number of stars in the ratio $15 \cdot 86 : 1$. The ratio of increase for one magnitude should therefore be

$$\sqrt{15 \cdot 86} : 1 \text{ or practically } 4 : 1.$$

Now statistics of the ratio of increase, prepared from star-counts, shew nothing like an increase of $16 : 1$ for two magnitudes. The increase begins by being about $8 : 1$ for the brighter (5th to 7th magnitude) stars; and for the 17th–19th magnitudes it falls to $4 \cdot 3 : 1$ in directions within the Milky Way and to $2 \cdot 7 : 1$ in the direction of the pole of the Milky Way. Clearly then the stars in our universe 'thin out' fairly rapidly at right angles to the Milky Way and not so rapidly, but quite definitely, as we go to great distances in the galactic plane. The majority of them will thus form a bun-shaped aggregation.

The photographic plates do not permit of the counting of stars which are fainter than the $18 \cdot 5$th magnitude. At this magnitude the number is still increasing. We have therefore to guess how the curve connecting number and magnitude should be drawn at higher magnitudes. Thus the total number of the stars in our galactic universe is doubtful. An estimate of less than 2000 millions, made by Chapman and Melotte in the year 1914, has lately been increased to 30,000 millions by Seares and van Rhijn. Kapteyn (1851–1922) would have put it still higher.

§ 262. *Stellar radiation.*

We have seen in § 197 that a perfect radiator of temperature T emits σT^4 units of energy per unit area per unit time. Stars are not perfect radiators: but it is convenient (§ 193) to define *effective temperature* by the statement that, if the effective temperature of a star be T_e, it will emit σT_e^4 units of energy per unit area per unit time. Thus a star of effective temperature T_e emits as much radiant energy as a perfect radiator of equal size raised to a temperature T_e. It will be remembered that all radiant energy travels with the velocity of light c.

The measure of the total radiation emitted by a star is called its *bolometric magnitude*. To-day this is usually determined by an instrument introduced by Coblentz which may best be described as a thermocouple in a vacuum. In the thermocouple the radiation from the star falls on the junction of two wires made of different metals, such as bismuth and antimony. These wires form part of an electric circuit in which there is a sensitive galvanometer. The junction of the wires is heated by the incident radiation; and, in consequence, there flows through the galvanometer an electric current proportional to the intensity of this radiation. With the aid of such a telescope as the 100-inch reflector of Mount Wilson, extraordinarily delicate measurements can be made by Coblentz' thermocouple. It is said that it would be sensitive to a candle two thousand miles away!

If E be the total radiation emitted each second by a star and M be its absolute bolometric magnitude we shall have, as a definition,

$$\tfrac{2}{5}M = -\log_{10} E + \text{cons.}$$

The constant is so chosen as to make a star's bolometric magnitude equal to its visible magnitude when the difference between the two is a minimum. The bolometric magnitude is then never greater than the visible magnitude.

If by a bolometer we measure the radiation received from a star and if further we know α, the semi-angle subtended by the star at the earth, we can find T_e, the effective temperature of the star.

For let E be the radiation emitted each second per unit area of the star. Then

$$E = \sigma T_e^4,$$

where σ is Stefan's constant. The radiation emitted by the star will spread out uniformly through space; and therefore that received each second per unit area at the earth's surface will be

$$E\alpha^2 \quad \text{or} \quad \sigma\alpha^2 T_e^4.$$

If now we know α, and if also we can measure the quantity $\sigma\alpha^2 T_e^4$, we can find T_e.

Conversely, if we know the radiation received from a star and if we can deduce its effective temperature from its spectral type we can find α, the semi-angle subtended by the star at the earth. Then, if we can find the parallax of the star, its diameter can be computed. Diameters computed in this way are, in general, in good agreement with those found by the interferometer.

Suppose now that T is the effective temperature of the sun, that the angular diameter of a star is $1/m$ times that of the sun, and that the radiation received from the star is $1/n$ times that received from the sun.

Then, if T_e be the effective temperature of the star and 2α be the angle subtended by it at the earth, we shall have

$$\sigma T_e^4 \alpha^2 = \frac{1}{n} \sigma T^4 (m\alpha)^2,$$

and thus
$$T_e = m^{\frac{1}{2}} n^{-\frac{1}{4}} T.$$

§263. *The radiant energy emitted by the sun.*

There is, of course, a difference between the light radiated from the sun and the total energy emitted by it, inasmuch as some of the radiant energy is in the form of wave-lengths which are not visible.

By means of an instrument, called the *pyrheliometer*, all the radiant energy of the sun of all wave-lengths is transformed into heat and then measured in units of heat. Measurement is made by allowing a beam of sunlight of definite cross-section to be completely absorbed by, say, a black disc of silver. The capacity of the disc for heat is known and the amount of heat received is measured by the disc's rise in temperature. Some of the sun's rays are of course absorbed by the earth's atmosphere, and to allow for such absorption corrections must be made. With a view to such corrections pyrheliometers have in America been attached to small balloons and sent into the upper air. The total quantity of radiant energy from the sun that falls in unit time on unit area of a surface placed at right angles to the sun's rays just outside the earth's atmosphere is called the *solar constant*. The name is a misnomer, as the solar constant varies slightly. But Abbot of the Smithsonian Institution has found the average value of the solar constant, as determined by long-continued measurements, to be $1\cdot35 \times 10^6$ ergs per sec. per square cm. or $4\cdot7 \times 10^6$ horse-power per square mile.

Now the earth's mean distance from the sun is $214\cdot8$ times the sun's radius. Hence, since all the radiation emitted from the sun will spread out uniformly through space, each square centimetre of the sun will emit $(214\cdot8)^2$ times as much energy as falls on a square centimetre at the distance of the earth. Thus each square centimetre of the sun's surface emits 6.24×10^{10} ergs per sec., or enough energy to work an 8 horse-power engine. Thus the sun is pouring out energy at an almost inconceivable rate.

We can find the effective temperature of the sun by putting

$$6.24 \times 10^{10} = \sigma T_e^4.$$

We get $T_e = 5750°$, this temperature being, of course, measured on the absolute Kelvin scale. Other methods of getting the effective temperature give slightly different results: all agree as well as could be expected. The actual effective temperature is about $6000°$.

The total energy radiated by the sun is 3.8×10^{33} ergs per sec. The mass of the sun is 2×10^{33} grammes. We see therefore that the sun must generate 1.9 ergs of radiant energy per sec. for each gramme of its mass.

§264. *Radiation emitted by the stars.*

The previous formulae enable us in certain cases to find the radiation emitted by typical stars.

We take first the star Betelgeux. Its angular diameter measured by the interferometer is, as we have seen in §251, variable and between $.034''$ and $.047''$: its effective temperature, as deduced from measurements by the thermocouple, is $3000°$. It emits about six thousand times the radiant energy emitted by the sun. Betelgeux is a red giant.

Another star, which has acquired the name V Puppis, is of interest. It is a 'spectroscopic and eclipsing binary' with a period of a day and a half, whose masses can, as we shall see, be determined. They are roughly nineteen and eighteen times the mass of the sun. As judged by their common spectral type, the effective temperatures of the two components must be about $22,000°$. The two components will radiate 11,000 and 9000 times as much total energy as the sun. And whereas the sun emits 1.9 ergs per gramme per sec., the components of V Puppis must emit 1100 and 1000 ergs per gramme per sec.

A third star is an effective contrast to V Puppis. It is a 'visual binary', of a period of 45 years, known as Krüger 60. Its components have masses which are respectively about one-fourth and one-fifth of the mass of the sun. Their effective temperatures are about $3200°$. The radiation emitted is but 1/100th and 1/500th of that emitted by the sun. The components emit per gramme per sec. $.07$ and $.02$ erg.

From these results we see that, while the stars are of the same order of mass, they differ enormously in intrinsic brightness and in the amount of energy emitted per gramme. The larger stars are the brighter and they are also the most energetic stars in that they emit most energy per gramme. These conclusions appear to be generally true.

§265. *Where does the sun's energy come from?*

We shall see in the next lecture (§318) that the age of certain igneous rocks, intrusive into sedimentary conglomerates, is determined by the Holmes-Jeffreys uranium-lead measurements to be 1340 million years. We may then fairly confidently assume that the earth's crust must have been solid for at least 1500 million years. During this time the sun must, in all probability, have been generating heat at a rate comparable with, but on the whole greater than, that which at present exists. Thus the total energy which has been generated by the sun since the earth was born is at least 9×10^{16} ergs per gramme of the sun's mass. Now no chemical reaction, such as the combustion of carbon, can provide anything like this amount of energy. Further, if the sun were merely radiating stored heat its temperature when the earth was born must have been more than a thousand million degrees. Such a temperature is fantastic. The shrinkage of the sun under its own gravitation will provide much energy; and, in the days when the age of the earth was put at 20 or 30 million years, such a source of the energy which it must have emitted since the earth was born was thought to be satisfactory. But, if the sun had condensed from matter scattered to infinity, its gravitational energy would only provide some 2×10^{15} ergs per gramme, less than one forty-fifth of what has been emitted since the birth of the earth.

We are left with the conclusion that the radiant energy emitted by the sun must be sub-atomic in origin. Several possibilities suggest themselves. The sun might in the beginning have consisted of a mixture of uranium and radium. Such a mixture would suffice to give the required output of radiant energy for several times as long as the 1500 million years which we have postulated. But radium breaks up too quickly and uranium too slowly to give the fairly uniform output which must, by the earth's fossil record, have certainly existed for the past 500 million years. And, moreover, we shall see that there are reasons which lead us to believe that the total age of the sun must be measured by millions of millions of years. If the sun's age be but 1 per cent. of such an estimate, the possibility that it has derived its output of energy from the disintegration of radio-active elements must be set aside.

An alternative possibility is provided by the fact that if the atomic weight of oxygen be 16, that of hydrogen is 1·008 (or more accurately 1·00778, according to Aston). This suggests that, if the sun was originally composed of hydrogen from which afterwards heavier elements were built up, it would lose ·008 of its mass in the process. Thus the possible loss of mass of the sun would be $1·6 \times 10^{31}$ grammes. Now, by the Einstein law connecting mass and energy, such a loss of mass would give as energy available for emission

$$1·6 \times 10^{31} \times c^2 \text{ ergs} \qquad \text{or} \qquad 1·4 \times 10^{52} \text{ ergs}.$$

We should thus get energy sufficient to last at the present rate of emission for $1·16 \times 10^{11}$ years. Even this period is less than one-twentieth of the age which Jeans is led by dynamical considerations to assign to the galactic universe; and there is no spectroscopic evidence to indicate that such a transformation of hydrogen is a feature of stellar evolution. We conclude that, while the possibility cannot be dismissed, such a source of energy is not probable.

The remaining alternative, first suggested by Jeans, is that the radiation emitted by the sun and other stars is due to the absolute annihilation of matter.

We have seen that the total energy radiated by the sun is $3·8 \times 10^{33}$ ergs per sec. This corresponds to a diminution in mass of

$$3·8 \times 10^{33}/c^2 = 3·8 \times 10^{33}/(9 \times 10^{20}) = 4·2 \times 10^{12} \text{ grammes per sec.}$$

Thus the sun is radiating away some four million tons of matter per second. We may suppose that this process results from protons and electrons coming together and completely annihilating one another. If it is taking place it would provide radiation at the present rate for 15 million million years. An obvious objection is that we have no experience of such annihilation of matter. To this objection the reply may be made that our chemistry is that of matter at temperatures of at most a few hundred degrees: we know little of what happens at temperatures of millions of degrees such as almost certainly exist within the stars. We conclude, therefore, that the hypothesis that stellar radiation results from the absolute annihilation of matter is more probable than any alternative.

§ 266. *Consequences of the annihilation hypothesis.*

If the annihilation hypothesis is true, it must follow that a star becomes less massive the older it grows. If all the stars of the galactic universe have been born in the same way from unstable matter on the rim of a vast rotating lenticular mass of gas, we may expect (*a*) that the older stars will have been composed of lighter elements, for the heavy elements will sink to the centre of the lenticular mass, and (*b*) that these same older stars will have radiated away more of their mass. If, further, we may expect that all the stars were originally of the same average mass, it will follow that young stars will be uniformly more massive than old stars.

§ 267. *The motions of the stars.*

We have seen that the stars are not fixed. Each star has a *proper motion* of its own on the celestial sphere; and such proper motion is defined as the star's apparent angular rate of motion (usually in seconds of arc per year) as seen from the sun.

A tenth-magnitude star discovered by Barnard has the largest known proper motion: it amounts to 10″25 per year.

The proper motions of the stars can often be successfully obtained by the comparison of photographic plates taken at intervals measured by years or decades. A 'blink microscope' is a device for making such comparisons which will reveal quite small proper motions. The proper motions, of course, tell us nothing of motion in the line of sight: such, however, can be found by Doppler's principle. By parallax measurements we can get the distances of fairly near stars; and by combining these with proper motions we can find tangential velocities, or in other words velocities at right angles to the line of sight, for such stars.

About 50 stars are known to have proper motions exceeding 2″ per year: some 200 have proper motions which exceed 1″ per year. But statistics are incomplete, as no adequate investigation has been made of stars fainter than the tenth magnitude.

The radial velocities (relative to the sun) of some 3000 stars of our galactic universe have been determined. A variable star, R.Z. Lyrae, has the greatest radial velocity known, some 385 km. per sec. Velocities of over 100 km. per sec. are uncommon: normally, velocities range between 10 and 30 km. per sec.

By knowing tangential and radial velocities we can get stellar velocities in space, referred to the sun as a supposedly fixed origin. There is, of course, no reason to believe that the sun is fixed. We can, however, only define its motion with reference to some external standard; and this standard we take to be the general average of the stars whose motions we can measure. Such stars are of necessity fairly near the sun: they form a bit of 'the local star-cloud'. The point towards which the sun is thus determined to be moving is called the *solar apex*. It is a point of R.A. 18ʰ and Declination 28°, towards which the sun is moving with a velocity of 19 km., or 12 miles, per sec.

We shall later (§ 275) discuss the motion of the sun with reference to the galactic universe as a whole.

§ 268. *Binary stars.*

With our present defective instruments we cannot ascertain by observation whether any stars have planetary systems attached to them. But it is certain that the single star, such as our own sun, is not typical of all stars in space. In fact, probably more than a quarter of the stars of the galactic universe are binary; that is to say, they consist of two stars rotating round one another. Perhaps of these binary stars 5 per cent. belong to multiple systems: in such cases the pair of stars is revolving in the gravitational field of other stars not remote from it.

As an example of a multiple system we may mention the star Castor. It consists of a pair of stars A and B which revolve round one another in more than 300 years: with this pair is associated a star C, 73″ distant, which is probably revolving round AB in a period exceeding 10,000 years. A, B, C are each 'spectroscopic binaries'. Thus what the naked eye views as the single star Castor is really a hexuple system.

Knowledge of double stars began in the middle of the seventeenth century when it was observed that one of the stars of the Great Bear was a double star. Sir William Herschel (1738–1822) in a systematic search found some 700 double stars before the year 1784. It should, however, be said that he did not differentiate between true binaries, which are gravitationally associated pairs, and spurious binaries or optical pairs, which are unconnected though they happen to be in the same direction when viewed from the earth. To-day about 20,000 true binaries are known to exist.

§ 269. *Visual and spectroscopic binaries.*

Visual binaries are discovered by visual observation with a good telescope. Training and natural aptitude are necessary for this work, and especially for finding the relative orbit of the two stars. The American astronomer, S. W. Burnham* (1838–1921), had a genius for such observation.

Very few pairs of stars are so widely separated that they can be resolved without the use of a good telescope. Some visual binaries are so close to one another that the best telescopes only just separate them.

* Burnham was the author of the great *General Catalogue of Double Stars*, 1906.

Still closer pairs can only be detected by observations with the spectroscope which reveal the different line-of-sight velocities of the two components. If one component is too faint to be visible, the changes in the line-of-sight velocity of the other, when allowance is made for the earth's motion, will still shew the disturbing influence of its companion. All such very close pairs are called *spectroscopic binaries*.

A few stars can be observed as binaries both visually and with the spectroscope, but the velocity changes of a visual binary are usually too small to be measured spectroscopically.

The periods of revolution of the visual binaries are long, averaging probably over 100 years. But long periods are difficult to determine with accuracy by observations made within a relatively few years: it is doubtful whether reliable orbits have yet been computed for more than 100 long-period binaries.

Over 1000 spectroscopic binaries are catalogued and orbits have been computed for about a quarter of them. It is found that more than half these orbits have periods of less than 10 days while less than a fifth have periods of more than 100 days. Those with the very shortest periods must be revolving practically in contact with one another. It is sometimes very difficult to distinguish between a pulsating star and a spectroscopic binary of which one component is invisible. Such evidence as exists at present goes to shew that only a small proportion of binary stars are the very close pairs usually termed spectroscopic.

The masses of the binary stars.

There is no known method of determining the masses of the isolated stars of space. But when we know the parallax of a binary star and the relative orbit of its components we can determine the sum of their masses. From what has just been said it is clear that, taking binary stars as a class, the period of the relative orbit and the separation of the components increase together. This is a most important fact for, as we proceed to prove, it suggests that binary systems are, as regards mass, of the same order of magnitude.

The *apparent orbit* of one component (the companion) of a binary star about another (the primary) can be found by plotting position-angles and angular distances. We thus get an ellipse. This ellipse is, however, not usually the true orbit nor is the primary in its focus, inasmuch as we are observing the projection of the real orbit on the celestial sphere. But, from the apparent orbit, the true orbit can be calculated by relatively simple geometry.

Suppose that m_1 and m_2 are the masses of the two components of a binary star. Let M be the mass of the sun and m of the earth. Suppose, further, that p is the period of revolution of the components of the binary measured in years and a their true mean distance, the unit being the distance of the sun from the earth. We know that m_1 describes an ellipse relative to m_2 just as the earth describes an ellipse relative to the sun. Also, by the formula giving Kepler's third law, which we previously obtained in § 246, we have for the star

$$p = 2\pi a^{\frac{3}{2}} / \sqrt{\gamma (m_1 + m_2)},$$

and for the earth-sun system

$$1 = 2\pi / \sqrt{\gamma (M + m)}.$$

Hence, neglecting m in comparison with M, we get

$$p^2 = a^3 M / (m_1 + m_2).$$

Thus, if p and a increase together, we may expect that $m_1 + m_2$ will remain of the same order of magnitude.

Let now the annual parallax (§ 252) of the binary be $\bar{\omega}$ and suppose that α is the measurement of the mean separation a in seconds of arc.

Then $\bar{\omega} a = \alpha$, and hence

$$p^2 \bar{\omega}^3 = \alpha^3 M / (m_1 + m_2).$$

In this formula M is known: p can be observed: α can be calculated by deducing the true orbit from the apparent. *If, then, the parallax $\bar{\omega}$ of the double star be known*, the sum of the masses of its components can be found. Such a calculation can be made for relatively few stars but, in the table that can thus be formed, the ratio $(m_1 + m_2)/M$ for visual binaries lies between ·45 and 11.

As a rule we cannot get the ratio of m_1 to m_2 unless the motion of the primary (we reserve the term for the component which is the easier to observe) can be measured with respect to some external point of reference. In this case the motion of the primary with regard to the centre of gravity of the double star can be found. The masses of some twenty pairs of components of visual binaries have been thus determined. They appear to range from one-fifth of the sun's mass to five times its mass.

The masses of spectroscopic binaries.

We have said that spectroscopic binaries are closer together and have shorter periods of revolution than visual binaries. For such stars we can only observe line-of-sight velocities, sometimes of both components but more often of the primary alone. Calculation from these observations, unfortunately, does not give us the true orbit of the star. For let O be the centre of gravity of the binary and A the primary component, and, further, let E be the earth. Then OA is a radius vector of the orbit. Our observation tells of changes in AM, i.e. in $OA \sin i_1$.

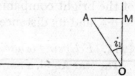

Thus OA may be large and i_1 small, or *vicê versâ*: we only know the product of $\sin i_1$ and the linear dimensions of the orbit. Take i to be the inclination of the plane of the orbit to the celestial sphere on which M is the projection of A. Then it is found that, when both spectra are visible, we can only compute $m_1 \sin^3 i$ and $m_2 \sin^3 i$, where m_1 and m_2 are the masses of the two components. The results seem to shew that the masses of components of spectroscopic binaries are of the same order as the sun. But some of the hottest stars have masses that may be, as is probably the case with each component of Plaskett's star (B.D. 6°, 1309), 100 times as great as the sun.

Thus while stars can be thousands of times as luminous as one another it would appear that their masses are fairly uniform. We may think of them as bullets of various sizes; and we must exclude cannon-balls and shot of the size of grains of sand from any comparison.

§ 270. *The mass-luminosity relation.*

If it is permissible to generalise from the relatively few results so far obtained we conclude that, while the stars vary enormously in size, density and absolute brightness, they vary but slightly in mass. It is, however, found that there is a connection between mass and absolute brightness which is approximately

$$L = m^3,$$

where m is the ratio of the mass of the star to that of the sun and L is the ratio of its radiation emitted to that of the sun, both being measured by a bolometer. This result is empirical and is but the simplest of a number of formulae which have been suggested. We must be content with it until more accurate values of L and m have been obtained for a larger range of stars. Meanwhile, we can assert that *the heavier a star is, the brighter it is.* What is the meaning of this fact? It naturally suggests that young stars are most luminous and that old stars, in radiating away their mass, lose in brightness. If the mass-luminosity relation is a true generalisation from rather scanty data, we ought, knowing the mass of a star, to be able to write down its absolute brightness. Knowing its apparent brightness we ought therefore to be able to calculate its distance. By such arguments the absolute magnitude of the bright companion in Plaskett's star has been computed to be − 6·4, and its distance more than 13,000 light-years.

§271. *Eclipsing binaries.*

The star Algol, a name derived from the Arabian astronomers, varies in the amount of light which it emits, the variations being repeated in just under three days. It is in this respect typical of some 200 stars. These stars are certainly not cepheids for, when we plot variations in brightness, the curves obtained for the Algol-like stars are of a quite different shape from the curves given by the cepheids. A mass of evidence points to the certain conclusion that the Algol-like stars are binaries of which one member regularly eclipses the other.

The stars are of short periods, measured by a few days, and are close to one another. Some components are definitely of ellipsoidal form, the natural explanation being that severe tidal action distorts them from spherical shape. The stars which shew such distortion are naturally exceptionally close together. A binary star in which the components are almost in contact as they revolve and in which the ellipsoidal form is therefore accentuated is the star β-Lyrae. This star gives its name to a whole class of importance in the general theory. Probably a β-Lyrae pair is a young binary which has resulted from the break-up of a single star, owing to the fact that by condensation its momentum had become too great for stability.

If the spectra of both stars of an eclipsing binary can be observed we can find the size of each of its components, because the light variation gives us the angle of inclination of the orbit to the celestial sphere. This was the first way in which the diameter of a star was ever measured. If we know the size and mass of a star we can determine its density. Some components of some eclipsing binaries are more dense than the sun; but some have densities which are incredibly small and not more than 1/500,000th of the sun's density.

§272. *The contrast between visual and spectroscopic binaries.*

In the β-Lyrae stars the periods of rotation and revolution appear to be identical. The components are either in contact or very near together. They are, as we have said, so distorted by mutual gravitation as to be ellipsoidal in shape. They thus shew every sign of having recently been born as a result of the fission of a single rotating star. Such a binary star is the heavy spectroscopic binary V Puppis previously mentioned: the sum of the radii of the components of the star is nearly nine-tenths of the radius of the relative orbit: its period is roughly a day and a half.

These stars appear to form one end of a continuous sequence of binaries the relative orbits of which, on the whole, gradually increase in period and eccentricity.

But while the spectroscopic binaries have, with few exceptions, periods which extend up to half a year and eccentricities which are less than ·25, the visual binaries on the whole have periods measured by tens of years and eccentricities equal to or greater than ·5.

The long periods and large orbits of visual binaries cannot, according to Jeans, have been produced by the action of tidal friction on close pairs. Such tidal friction will account for the development of spectroscopic binaries; but Jeans gives reasons for the belief that the periods of visual binaries are, on the whole, being reduced by encounters with other stars. Such encounters will turn orbits which are circular or nearly circular into eccentric ellipses of which the eccentricity will average ·66. Jeans concludes that visual binaries are pairs of stars which were born together as independent condensations in some parent nebula. They are, in fact, twins which originally described round their common centre of gravity orbits of very long periods. The periods of such orbits are gradually growing less. On the other hand, a spectroscopic binary is the result of the break-up of a star owing to the increase of its rate of rotation due to its decrease in size. The period of the relative orbit of its components is short but gradually lengthening. Though the eccentricity of this orbit may increase, it is not likely to increase to any great extent.

§ 273. *The ages of the stars.*

It seems probable that our sun was born, like the visual binaries, from a mass of unstable matter on the rim of a vast rotating nebula. Naturally we seek to know its age and the ages of neighbouring stars, which were presumably born about the same time.

Jeans has advanced an ingenious theory which puts the ages of the stars at from about 5 to 10 billion years (a billion = 10^{12}). He assumes that the visual binary stars were born with orbits which at first were circular. These orbits will have been 'knocked out of shape' by the influence of encounters (near approaches, but not actual collisions) with passing stars. In connection with the formation of planetary systems we shall subsequently reproduce the investigation of the probability of such encounters. Their average effect on binary orbits can be calculated and hence it is possible to say how long orbits of known eccentricity must have been in existence. The conclusion that the stars are of the order of 5 billion years old cannot be confidently put forward, but it is as probable as any which we can reach.

The result is apparently confirmed by another kind of investigation. It would appear that the stars must ultimately conform to Maxwell's law of the equipartition of energy among the molecules of a gas. Thus small stars will have large velocities and *vicê versâ* in order that the energies of the different stars may be uniform. Investigations by Seares seem to shew that stars near the sun have approximated to the final state: and the degree of approximation seems to be such as could be obtained after some billions of years.

All experts who have speculated as to the age of the galactic universe have recognised the ingenuity and intellectual power shewn in Jeans' investigations*. But it must be admitted that doubts as to the accuracy of his conclusions have increased during the last few years. We cannot say with confidence either when the stars of even the local star-cloud were born or what has been the course of their evolution.

§ 274. *Moving clusters.*

Investigation of the proper motions of the stars has revealed, as we have previously said, the existence of several moving clusters. These are groups of stars moving with approximately equal velocities in a common direction. Because of such motion the identity of a moving cluster persists.

The densest known moving cluster is called the Taurus cluster. In it there appears, according to Rasmuson, to be on the average one star in 8 cubic parsecs: it is thus more dense than the 'local star-cloud' to which our sun belongs. The members of this nearly spherical cluster form a 'flattened' system of some eighty stars, with flattening in the galactic plane; and the direction in which the cluster is moving is almost at right angles to the plane of flattening.

There are other important moving clusters, including one in Perseus and the huge Scorpio-Centaurus group, which shew the same sort of 'flattening'. The 'flattening' is, moreover, in these two clusters parallel to the galactic plane.

The number of stars in a moving cluster rarely exceeds a few hundreds. A small cluster in Ursa Major consists of about twenty stars

* Jeans' researches are gathered together in the volume *Astronomy and Cosmogony*. Cambridge University Press, 1928.

scattered over a wide area of the sky: it is 'flattened' at right angles to its direction of motion, but not in the galactic plane.

It is clear that when such moving clusters pass through the other stars in the galactic system they will gradually get 'knocked about'. In the end they will degenerate into individual stars moving at random. Shapley suggests that such moving clusters as exist may be all that is left of originally compact globular clusters which have been dragged by gravitation into the vast mass of the galactic system and have gradually suffered disintegration in passing through it.

But it is much more probable that they are remnants of clusters, much more numerous and highly unified than those which at present exist in our part of space, which were born of condensations at the rim of the vast rotating mass of gas, lenticular in shape, which was the probable source of the galactic universe. We shall see later that such masses of stars and gas can be observed in the depths of space as spiral nebulae. The condensations in the arms of these nebulae are far too large to be single stars and are almost certainly great clusters of stars. Such clusters, by their origin, would have a common direction and velocity. Similarly, in our own universe some clusters, by reason of their initial circumstances, may have managed to escape disintegration. Such may well be the globular clusters which now are the outside 'boundary stones' of the galactic universe. The moving clusters will be those which, though slowly undergoing disintegration by encounters as they pass through the main mass of the stars of our universe, are not yet entirely broken up. On the assumption that moving clusters have had such an origin, Jeans estimates that their present condition indicates an age of 10^{12} or 10^{13} years, the date of birth being the time when the stars first condensed out of the parent nebula.

§ 275. *Star-streaming and differential galactic rotation.*

Confirmation of such speculative conclusions appears to be given by the phenomenon of 'star-streaming' discovered by Kapteyn in the year 1904. Kapteyn examined the proper motions of all the stars for which information was available: such were necessarily local stars. He found that, beneath apparently random movement, there was a preference for two directions. Now it is known that the sun is moving with a velocity of some 12 miles per sec. towards the solar apex, this motion being with reference to the local stars as a whole. When this solar motion is eliminated from the apparent directions of motions of the stars, it is found they have a preference for motion backwards or forwards along a definite direction in the galactic plane. By altering the axes of reference we can say that there is a preferential motion in a single direction in the galactic plane. Of course the stars move to a considerable extent at random: beneath the random motions, however, is the linear motion discovered by Kapteyn. The natural conclusion to draw from this fact is that, in the beginning, the local stars had a uniform motion about the axis of the parent nebula. In spite of disintegration, traces of this motion must, it would appear, still persist in the linear motion in the galactic plane to which Kapteyn's star-streaming can be reduced. Such a conclusion must, however, be considered in connection with the recent discovery of differential galactic rotation which results from the investigations of Oort, Lindblad, Plaskett and others.

Differential galactic rotation.

It would appear that the whole galactic universe is in rotation about an axis, normal to the galactic plane, through a centre in galactic longitude 325° which is at a large distance R from our sun. We proceed to give the investigation which leads Oort to conclude that $R = 20,000$ light-years. As indicating the uncertainty of present knowledge, it may be said that Shapley's estimate of the value of R is rather more than twice as large; and we have seen in § 253 that Seares believes that R is equal to 65,000 light-years. The galactic centre is near the junction of Sagittarius, Ophiuchus and Scorpio, in the rift between the two branches of the galaxy. Probably the rift is caused by obscuring clouds which conceal the densest part of the galaxy. When we speak of differential rotation, we mean that, though our universe rotates, its rotation is not uniform, inasmuch as the velocity of rotation of any star group varies with the distance of the group from the centre.

The sun S being the origin, let the galactic longitude of the centre C be l_0 and let that of a typical star Q be l. Further, let the galactic latitude of the star be δ.

Let the projection of Q on the galactic plane be P, and let M be the projection of P on the line SC. Further, let $SQ = r$ and suppose, as will be the fact, that r is small compared with R.

Then $SP = r\cos\delta$, and the angle $PSM = l - l_0$. Hence

$$SM = r\cos\delta\cos(l - l_0).$$

Suppose now that the velocity V of the sun is in the galactic plane and perpendicular to CS.

Then, since r is small compared with R, the velocity of P is $V - SM\,\delta V/\delta R$, where δV is the change in V corresponding to a change δR in R.

Thus the velocity of P is

$$V - r\cos\delta\cos(l - l_0)\frac{\delta V}{\delta R}.$$

Now, if the galaxy rotated as a rigid system, V would be proportional to R and we should have $\delta V/\delta R = V/R$. Thus in a rigid system the velocity of P would be

$$V\{R - r\cos\delta\cos(l - l_0)\}/R;$$

and therefore the excess velocity of P due to differential rotation will be

$$\left(\frac{V}{R} - \frac{\delta V}{\delta R}\right)r\cos\delta\cos(l - l_0).$$

The component of this excess in the direction SQ will therefore be

$$\left(\frac{V}{R} - \frac{\delta V}{\delta R}\right)r\cos^2\delta\cos(l - l_0)\sin(l - l_0).$$

If then we put $A = \tfrac{1}{2}\left(\dfrac{V}{R} - \dfrac{\delta V}{\delta R}\right)$, the component of the excess velocity of Q in the direction SQ will be

$$Ar\cos^2\delta\sin 2(l - l_0).$$

Let now ρ be the radial velocity of recession of the star as seen from the sun. Further, let V_0 be the velocity of the sun towards the solar apex for the group of stars considered, λ being the angle between the apex and the direction of the star. Then we shall have Oort's formula

$$\rho = -V_0\cos\lambda + Ar\cos^2\delta\sin 2(l - l_0).$$

Obviously, in applying this formula, averages must be obtained which eliminate peculiar motions of the stars, just as the term $V_0\cos\lambda$ eliminates the peculiar motion of the sun. The stars for which averages are taken must, moreover, be so chosen as to form a natural group, localised in the same portion of space.

Observational results free from possible error are not easy to obtain. But there seems no doubt that differential galactic rotation does exist. There is general agreement that approximately $A = \cdot0155$ km. per sec. per parsec. The longitude of the centre of rotation is the same as that of the centre of the globular clusters. We may safely conclude that the two centres coincide and, further, that the clusters belong to our galactic universe. The mean velocity of these globular clusters with reference to stars in our neighbourhood has been found by Strömberg to be

272 km. per sec. in a direction within the galactic plane at right angles to SC. This velocity we may then assume to be the velocity V of our local star-cloud round the galactic axis. If it is correct, we can find R from our knowledge of A and V. The conclusion follows that we must be at a distance of some 21,000 light-years from the galactic centre. Further, the period of the rotation of the galactic universe must be about 150 million years. The necessary mass at the centre of the system needed to control the whole motion would be some 110,000 million suns.

The vertex of star-streaming is a little more than $20°$ from C. Hence it is hardly likely that star-streaming and differential galactic rotation are effects of the same phenomenon. But all conclusions, and especially the figures just given, must at present be regarded as tentative.

The phenomena of moving clusters and 'star-streaming' both point to the fact that in the galactic universe there are still traces of its original birth-formation. That universe is not a mass of stars which move at random and occasionally give birth to new stars by collisions. On the contrary our universe is apparently somewhat far advanced in a process of evolution whose beginnings we can faintly surmise. It probably represents a stage in the development of a single huge spiral nebula. Whether the stage is near finality we cannot say, for we cannot reach the central regions of the galaxy to discover what is happening there. But we can assert with high probability that traces of birth-structure have not been altogether eliminated; and, if Oort's conclusions as to the rotation of the galactic universe should be confirmed, its genesis will cease to be in doubt.

§ 276. *Novae or temporary stars.*

Everyone knows that occasionally a new star blazes out in the sky. Some of these stars have been brighter than any we normally see. Tycho's star in November of the year 1572 was for some days as bright as Venus: yet in sixteen months it had faded out of sight. A star as bright as Jupiter appeared in the year 1604; and every few years some similar (if not equally bright) star claims public attention. The examination of photographic plates naturally reveals novae which would otherwise escape notice, probably by reason of their great distance. From such examination it is estimated that in the galactic universe alone at least some twenty novae appear each year: novae also occur fairly frequently in the great nebulae.

In the days when it was thought that the whole of space was filled with stars moving at random, novae were thought to result from chance collisions between neighbouring stars. New stars were thus supposed to be born to replace those whose light had faded away: cold planets in this way became hot stars. The belief seems to appear in well-known lines of the typically eighteenth-century poet Gray:

> Till wrapped in flames, in ruin hurled,
> Sinks the fabric of the world.

But the idea that planets or stars which have lost their heat are thus again brought to incandescence and start a new lease of life finds no confirmation in modern investigation. Many novae have been visible as very faint stars before the time of their sudden brilliance. The rise to maximum brightness is very rapid, usually taking only a day or two. Almost immediately after the brightness has reached its maximum the nova rapidly fades. After a few weeks the rapid decrease slackens. Small fluctuations then take place and the star usually returns to its normal magnitude in ten or twenty years.

In the spectrum of a temporary star rapid and complicated changes naturally take place. When it is at its brightest the displacement of spectral lines usually indicates an enormous velocity of approach. In the case of the famous Nova Aquilae of the years 1918–19, the radiant energy came apparently through a shell of gas surrounding the star and moving outward from it with a velocity of some 1700 km. per sec.

The cause of the sudden liberation of energy, which we observe as the temporary brightness of a star, is unknown. Apparently the cause, whatever it may be, leads to a great development of energy beneath the star's visible surface. This in turn heats its atmosphere, or the nebulosity which surrounds it, and forces this gaseous covering to expand rapidly. There is, in fact, a tremendous explosion. The outbreak is brief. When all is over the star is, in apparent brightness, but little changed. Yet, in point of fact, there is a growing belief that changes of vast magnitude have actually occurred during the explosion. The new spectrum of the star is always of what is technically called an O or Wolf-Rayet type, which corresponds to a high temperature (it may be of 35,000°–40,000°) and great surface brightness. If then the apparent magnitude of the star is the same as when, before the explosion, its surface brightness was low, the brightness per square mile of surface must have enormously increased. Thus the total area of the star must have diminished to a very great extent. In fact, the new radius of the star would appear to be at times so diminished as to be less than one-tenth of its former value. In consequence, according to Milne, the increase in the density of the star may be between one-hundredfold and ten-thousandfold.

It would thus appear that a nova is produced when for some reason a star becomes unstable and, as it were, collapses upon itself. In the collapse a vast amount of gravitational energy is set free. This produces a sudden outburst of brightness accompanied by enormously increased radiation which expels the outer layers of gas of the star. As has been said, we can, after the sudden appearance of a nova, observe these outer layers moving from the star with velocities that may approach 2000 km. per sec. It is probable that, at times, the velocity of the outer layers slows down so that they gradually form a sort of spherical nebula round the star. Some so-called planetary nebulae, which we shall subsequently describe in § 279, consist of what are apparently such masses of gas lit up by a dense hot bright star at the centre. It is natural to assume that each originated as a nova.

Another type of dense star is the 'white dwarf' discussed in § 259. We can reasonably speculate that such stars have passed through the process of collapse which we term a nova. As has been said, white dwarfs are of small intrinsic magnitude. All those known are near the sun and it is therefore possible that in space they are very numerous.

If white dwarfs have all been novae, their possible abundance is congruous with the fact that the explosions which produce novae are, as we have stated, not rare. Hubble suggests that some thirty such explosions occur each year in the Andromeda nebula. Though experts differ, novae may be correspondingly numerous in our larger galactic universe, many being hidden by the clouds of the Milky Way. If such be the fact it may be true, as some assert, that every star in the cosmos is destined to pass in the course of its evolution through the climax which we term a nova. Obviously, as regards this belief, we can reach no opinion worth having until we know whether the life of a star is to be measured by tens of thousands of millions or by millions of millions of years.

If every star becomes a nova during its life-history, our sun ought in due course to collapse upon itself and end as a white dwarf. During the collapse the intense heat emitted by the sun would presumably destroy every living thing upon the earth. After the collapse, if the apparent magnitude of the sun was not greatly changed, evolutionary progress upon the earth might start again. But so long as the conclusions of the experts are as doubtful as at present, we need not be gravely anxious as to the possibility of a catastrophe more complete than that caused by the legendary Flood associated with the story of Noah's Ark.

§277. *The future of stars, sun and earth.*

If it be true that the ages of the stars must be reckoned in millions of millions of years and if their radiation results from the annihilation of their mass, we can speculatively estimate their future history.

The masses of what seem to be the youngest stars are, as far as we know, of the same order of magnitude as the mass of the sun. Thus in the last three or five billion (10^{12}) years the stars will at most have radiated away a mass comparable with that radiated by the sun. Such a mass is hardly likely to be more than a hundred times that of the sun if our deductions from our present limited knowledge can be trusted. But the radiation of stars is, we believe, according to some such mass-radiation law as $L = m^3$, and hence it is much more rapid for younger and more massive stars than for stars which are older and less massive. We thus reach the conclusion that our sun is likely to be many times its present age before it dies.

There is, of course, the possibility that only part of the matter in the bright stars is annihilated to form radiant energy. It may be, as Russell suggests, that part consists of 'giant-stuff' which radiates away rapidly and that a further part consists of 'dwarf-stuff' which radiates away slowly. We may further speculate that there is a residue of completely ionised 'ash' of which extinct white dwarfs will be made. But until the problem of stellar evolution is solved we cannot choose between the various possibilities. Whatever be the correct solution of that problem, it seems likely that our own sun has a future of thousands of millions of years before it ages perceptibly. So far as the sun's heat is concerned, the continued development of life upon this earth will be possible for very many times as long as the period during which terrestrial life has at present been in existence. It will be seen in Lecture XII that we may put the beginning of life upon the earth at about 1000–2000 million years ago. Thus the distance in time which separates man from the most primitive living organism may possibly be but an exceedingly small fraction of the distance which will separate the super-men'* of the far distant future from humanity of to-day. On the other hand, there is the possibility that the future of life upon the earth will not depend solely on the sun's heat. There is some evidence that the earth is drying up: certainly a belt of desert somewhat north of the equator is, geologically speaking, recent. We shall in the next lecture also indicate that there is reason to believe that the gases which over the face of the earth probably differ greatly from those upon it

* Such creatures need not be anthropoids, or even placental mammals.

when it first cooled. There is, however, no good reason to think that changes which affect living organisms on earth will be greater in the next 500 million years than in the equal period which separates us from the Cambrian era of the geologists. During this vast stretch of time life, and with it mind, can almost certainly flourish. Will progress continue, as seems probable: and, if so, what will be the mental stature of the creatures which will at the end dominate our globe?

§ 278. *The observing of the nebulae.*

Throughout the heavens we can observe, inadequately with the naked eye, more adequately by means of a good telescope, and still better by a good photograph taken with the aid of such a telescope, faint hazy clouds of light which are called nebulae. The number of such clouds is very great; and the more distant among them are of peculiar interest to the student of cosmogony.

It would appear that the nearer nebulae are extended luminous surfaces and that the central portions of the more distant nebulae have the same character: they are not dense clouds of bright stars. Now it is found that magnification by a telescope does not make such a surface appear brighter than it does to the naked eye. If then the light from it is so faint that it cannot be seen by the naked eye, it will be equally invisible in the telescope. On the other hand, a photographic plate records the cumulative effect of light, so that with a sufficiently long exposure we can see nebulae which the eye could never pick out, however good the telescope which it used. Practically, therefore, all observational work on nebulae is done by photography. The most suitable telescopes for the purpose are reflectors. In particular, the work done by Hubble with the 100-inch reflector at Mount Wilson has been of paramount importance in connection with the recent progress of our knowledge of nebulae.

§ 279. *Galactic nebulae.*

Many of the nebulae most easily visible belong to our own universe. They are usually to be found in the region of the Milky Way and are called galactic nebulae. Some of them consist of vast masses of obscuring clouds; and there seems to be little doubt that the action of these nebulae in obscuring the light of the stars which almost certainly lie behind is due to the fact that in them there is much fine dust: such dust has a great power of stopping light if it is a few millionths of an inch in diameter. In these dark nebulae there may, of course, be other material, some of it molecular in size and some of it as large as any of the planets.

Other galactic nebulae are bright objects. Of these the majority give spectra which consist of isolated bright sharp lines such as are produced when a rarefied gas glows brightly because of its high temperature. The rest give continuous spectra crossed by dark lines like the spectrum of the sun. Those nebulae which have gaseous spectra must almost certainly consist of vast masses of gas of very low density, the atoms of which are luminous because they are excited by the energy of radiation received from neighbouring hot stars.

The 'nebulium' lines.

In the spectra of many of these nebulae there are two characteristic green lines. For long these and certain other unidentified lines were a puzzle to physicists, as they have never been reproduced in any terrestrial laboratory. Some astrophysicists went so far as to suggest that they belonged to an unknown element to which the name 'nebulium' was given. But all elements of low atomic number have, as we know, been discovered. It was indeed possible that nebulium was an element whose atomic number was higher than 60; but this was most unlikely, because all the known elements which appear in the spectra of gaseous nebulae are of low atomic number. Towards the end of the year 1927, however, Bowen* shewed that the green nebulium lines are due to the familiar elements oxygen and nitrogen. When the density and pressure of a gas are very low, collisions between atoms are separated by relatively long periods of time (cf. §24). Atoms of the elements can then undergo internal changes such as cannot take place when collisions between atoms are frequent. In consequence, so-called 'forbidden' lines can appear in the very rarefied gases which compose the nebulae, though we do not get such lines on earth.

In more technical language, metastable states of an excited atom are states for which there is a long mean life before spontaneous radiation begins. Under what to us are normal conditions of density, an atom in such a state will fall to a lower state as the result of a superelastic collision (§196) long before it returns to the lower state spontaneously by emission of radiation. The 'nebulium' spectral lines are due to the spontaneous emission of radiation associated with electron jumps from metastable states in doubly ionised nitrogen and in doubly and trebly ionised oxygen.

* I. S. Bowen, *Astrophysical Journal*, vol. LXVII, pp. 1–15.

Planetary nebulae.

As we have previously stated in § 276, some of the galactic nebulae are known as planetary nebulae. They are so called because in a small telescope they resemble a planetary disc: they are round in shape and fairly sharply defined at their edges. Occasionally an exceptionally hot star can be seen at the centre of such a planetary nebula; and there seems little doubt but that the nuclei of these nebulae are always stars of the very hottest types and that these stars cause a surrounding mass of gas to glow.

THE GREAT NEBULAE

§ 280. *The great nebulae: their number.*

The galactic nebulae are not of any great interest save as illustrating the diversity of the forms assumed by matter in our own universe. The extra-galactic nebulae, which, as will be seen, can be fitly termed 'great nebulae', are far more important and exciting. Whereas the galactic nebulae are relatively few in number, the extra-galactic nebulae, which are revealed by photographs taken by means of the great American telescopes, are almost uncountable. In the year 1925, Seares estimated that about 300,000 nebulae could be reached with a 60-inch reflector and an hour's exposure. More recently, Hubble has estimated that two million extra-galactic nebulae are visible in the 100-inch reflector at Mount Wilson. He further estimates that the range of this telescope is about 14×10^7 light-years. Though, as we have seen in Lecture VI, it is probable that space is finite, its radius has not been determined. We shall see later (§ 290) that plausible estimates for the radius vary between $1 \cdot 7 \times 10^9$ and $2 \cdot 2 \times 10^{10}$ light-years. If we assume a mean value of 14×10^9 light-years the volume of the whole cosmos will be one million times the volume of that part of space visible in the Mount Wilson telescope. Further, according to Shapley, we have no indication that galactic systems are falling off in number per cubic million light-years as we go out from the sun. Thus we can with fair confidence assert that the number of extra-galactic nebulae in the cosmos must be of the order of a billion (10^{12}). Practically none of these can be seen with the naked eye. One of the brightest and most typical of such objects is the great nebula in Andromeda: its central portion is conspicuous without the use of a telescope, though its outer spiral arms are only adequately revealed by photography.

§ 281. *The shapes of the great nebulae.*

Practically all the extra-galactic nebulae are what is technically called 'regular', that is to say, they shew rotational symmetry about a central nucleus. This nucleus, as we have said, appears to consist of a mass of bright gas and not of densely aggregated stars. All these 'regular' nebulae (and the small 3 per cent. of exceptions we shall ignore) are arranged by Hubble in a continuous series ending in two divergent sequences of shapes. His series begins with nebulae which are circular in shape. They gradually become more and more elliptical, until after a certain point has been reached they diverge into two distinct series of forms. One of these consists of spiral nebulae in which arms emerge like equiangular spirals from the central nucleus. In the other series, the so-called 'barred spirals', what look like thick bars emerge directly from the central nucleus and only at the ends of such bars are there rudimentary spirals.

It must not be thought that in the photographs we always see these extra-galactic nebulae as they are represented in our rough description. The spiral nebulae are, in fact, usually lens-shaped when seen 'edge on': they only appear to have the shapes described when viewed from a point along the axis of the lens.

The various forms of Hubble's classification suggest that the spiral nebulae owe their characteristic configurations to rotation. Observations with the spectroscope have confirmed this suggestion. We have seen that it is possible to measure with a spectroscope velocities in the line of sight. When, therefore, we see a spiral nebula 'edge on', we can determine the velocities of its outer parts (though not of the arms, because they are too faint for observation) relative to the central nucleus. Observation is difficult; but experts conclude that the regular nebulae are certainly in motion and the extent of the rotation can be roughly determined. The velocity of motion in the plane of the lens appears to be nearly proportional to the distance from the centre, so that the inner portions of the nebula must approximately rotate like a solid body.

Jeans' explanation of the cause of the various shapes of the great nebulae.

Sir J. H. Jeans, who is our foremost authority on the configuration of rotating gravitational masses, suggests that the various shapes of the nebulae may be explained by mathematical theory. The spherical nebulae will consist of masses of gas with a dense central nucleus, the whole being in slow rotation. As the rotation increases, the external form of these nebulae will gradually change and they will become more ellipsoidal in shape. After a time, as the rotation further increases, instability will be set up. Such instability may take two forms. In one case, when the dense central nucleus is small, a rim will appear in the plane of rotation and matter will be ejected from the edge of this rim so that the spirals are formed. Such ejection will begin from two opposite points of the edge, where the tidal influence of surrounding, though distant, gravitational matter is especially felt. The barred spirals may arise from a different type of instability when, owing to the greater angular momentum, the rotating mass becomes a pseudo-ellipsoid with three unequal axes. Such a body would shed matter in two streams from the ends of its longest axis. The mathematical analysis of even relatively simple cases of equilibrium of rotating masses of fluid is difficult; and, when densities are not uniform, as is presumably the case with the spiral nebulae, accurate mathematical investigation is impossible. Speaking generally, however, it would seem as if pseudo-spheroids (corresponding to what are known as Maclaurin's spheroids in the more simple theory) give rise to the spiral nebulae, while pseudo-ellipsoids (corresponding to what are known as Jacobian ellipsoids) give rise to the barred spirals. On the other hand, it must be confessed that the Jacobian ellipsoids correspond to masses of uniform density and hence, as Jeans himself allows, the interpretation of the barred nebulae must be 'under suspicion'.

The spectra of the great nebulae.

Naturally, the spectra of the extra-galactic nebulae are of great interest. Such are continuous spectra crossed by many dark lines: in fact, they closely resemble the spectrum of our sun. The bluer portions of the spectra, however, are stronger than in the sun: for this reason the nebulae photograph well. The spectra, by their character, shew that the light which we receive from the nebulae must come from incandescent bodies surrounded by gases which absorb part of their light. They are thus the spectra of stars. This leads us to conclude that the nebulae are vast clouds of stars which are not visible as such because of their great distances. The great modern telescopes have succeeded in resolving the outer arms of the spiral nebulae into such clouds of stars. On the other hand, no such resolution of the inner nuclei has been made, and Jeans asserts that, should the central portions of the nebulae consist of clouds of stars, they could have no clearly defined structure. He* is thus led to believe that it is "extremely improbable that ellip-

* J. H. Jeans, *Astronomy and Cosmogony*. Cambridge University Press, 1928, pp. 336, 337.

tical nebulae and the central lenticular masses of other nebulae can be formed of stars or of any other type of particle averaging more than about an inch in diameter". It has already been stated that the appearance of the Milky Way, especially in the direction of Sagittarius, suggests that the central parts of our galactic universe consist of masses of dust and not of clouds of stars.

§ 282. *The distances of the great nebulae.*

There seems no reason to doubt that the extra-galactic nebulae are at distances from our galactic universe which are enormous compared with its dimensions. There is, in the first place, the important fact that they appear to be scattered uniformly throughout the heavens and not to have a concentration towards the plane of the Milky Way, as would be the case if they belonged to our own galactic universe. It is true that we cannot see them when we look in the direction of the Milky Way; but this fact is intelligible if they are very distant and are obscured by the clouds with which the Milky Way abounds. Another fact which causes us to regard them as very distant is that temporary stars (the novae of § 276) have been found in large numbers in certain of the spiral nebulae. Their average brightness at maximum has been observed photographically and can be compared with average maximum brightness of the temporary stars which flame out in our own universe. The comparison gives a distance which may be well over 500,000 light-years for the great nebula in Andromeda, which is one of the largest, brightest and presumably nearest of the spirals.

But the most certain estimate of the distance of this and other similarly bright spiral nebulae is afforded by the existence in them of cepheid variables. These variables undoubtedly belong to the nebulae and are not in the foreground, for none has been found in adjacent regions of the sky similarly far from the Milky Way. They are very faint; but their periods range from 18 to 50 days and they have the typical cepheid variation of light, a rapid rise to maximum and a slower fall. Such cepheids are, as we have previously said, the 'standard candles' of the heavens. From their period, as we believe, we can deduce their absolute brightness. Inasmuch as the brightest of them are fainter than the 18th magnitude at maximum, we again reach the conclusion that the Andromeda nebula is immensely distant. This distance has been calculated to be 270,000 parsecs; so that light from the nebula takes 870,000 years to reach us, though it travels at the rate of 186,000 miles per sec.

We naturally assume that the spiral nebulae scattered through space are roughly equal in intrinsic brightness, inasmuch as we may well believe that they contain similar distributions of equal amounts of matter. This belief is confirmed by such observations as we can make. On such an assumption the distances of the fainter extra-galactic nebulae can be calculated. Hubble is thus led to the conclusion that the most remote nebulae visible in the great Mount Wilson telescope are distant 140 million light-years.

§ 283. *The sizes of the great nebulae.*

If we accept the distance obtained for the Andromeda nebula, and all the evidence available confirms it, we can of course determine its size. It appears in the photographs to be some 3° in apparent diameter. This would correspond to an actual diameter of some 45,000 light-years. The total light from it which we receive is roughly equivalent to that of a 4th magnitude star. Its brightness must, therefore, be that of 1500 million suns. We may perhaps with fair accuracy assume that the centrifugal force caused by the rotation of the inner portion of the nebula balances the gravitational force. The period of rotation of the whole would then appear to be 17 million years and the mass of the central nucleus of 6′ in diameter would be equal to that of 270 million suns. The mass of the whole nebula is almost certainly many times greater than this: Hubble estimates that its weight is 3500 million times that of the sun.

It is thus evident that the spiral nebulae approximate in size to our own galactic universe. They are, in fact, island universes distributed throughout the depth of space. As Shapley, however, has said: "If we call them islands, the galaxy is a continent". Yet it is, of course, highly improbable that we inhabit an insignificant planet in a markedly exceptional universe: and it is almost certain that spiral nebulae of the same size and structure as the galactic universe will be discovered to exist in large numbers.

Quite recently Shapley has suggested that our galactic universe may be a 'super-galaxy'. By this he means to imply that it is neither a single spiral of exceptional size nor even a single united system of stars, but rather a flattened system of associated spirals or star-clouds. He has found in Centaurus such a super-system of galaxies, "glimmering on the brink of invisibility" about 150 million light-years away. It is surmised that there are in that system more—possibly far more—than 2000 separate galaxies: its greatest diameter appears to be some 7 million light-years. Similarly, a 'discoidal' super-galaxy, 10 million light-years distant in the Coma-Virgo region, has a linear diameter of several million light-years while its sub-systems have linear dimensions extending up to 20,000 light-years. The local star-cloud, to which our sun belongs, is probably analogous to these sub-systems and should be compared as regards size to galaxies like the Clouds of Magellan or the smaller isolated spiral nebulae.

§ 284. *The velocities of the great nebulae.*

Of late years much work has been done in an endeavour to discover what are, with reference to our own galactic universe, the radial velocities of the extra-galactic nebulae. Such velocities can only be obtained with reference to the earth on the assumption that the observed displacements of the lines of the spectrum can be satisfactorily explained by Doppler's principle (§ 191). The correction which eliminates the motion of the earth round the sun is relatively small and easily made. But the motion of the sun with reference to the galaxy has only recently been found and necessitates a much more important correction. We assume, as regards this latter velocity, that Strömberg's estimate of 272 km. per sec. (§ 275) is correct.

The first velocity of an extra-galactic nebula was found by Slipher. He estimated that the great nebula in Andromeda had a velocity of approach of 300 km. per sec. Some 220 km. per sec. of this velocity is, however, now known to be due to the motion of our sun with reference to the galaxy.

Observations to determine velocities of the great nebulae are very tedious, since most of the nebulae are so faint that an adequate spectrogram can only be obtained by an exposure continued for several nights. However, a fairly large number of observations, of which some fifty may be regarded as trustworthy, now make it certain that practically all the great nebulae are receding from our universe. Moreover, the more distant nebulae have the largest velocities. We have seen that it is not easy to determine the actual distances of the great nebulae, inasmuch as linear diameters and integrated magnitudes are difficult to assess. But the work of Hubble* in a great paper on extra-galactic nebulae, published in the year 1926, has been examined and extended by de Sitter† in a paper published four years later. The Dutch astro-

* E. Hubble, 'Extragalactic Nebulae', *Astrophysical Journal*, vol. LXIV, pp. 321–69.

† W. de Sitter, 'On the magnitudes...of the extragalactic nebulae, and their apparent radial velocities', *Bulletin of the Astronomical Institutes of the Netherlands*, vol. v, 1930.

nomer reached the conclusion that, if displacements in the lines of the spectra of the great nebulae are correctly interpreted by the Doppler effect, then on the average the velocities of recession of the nebulae from our galaxy are proportional to their distances from the galaxy.

Let v be the velocity of recession of a typical extra-galactic nebula, c being the velocity of light, and, further, let q be the distance of the nebula measured in millions of light-years. Then de Sitter finds the formula

$$v/c = q/2000. \qquad \qquad \ldots\ldots(1)$$

The great nebulae have of course peculiar motions which must be added to, or subtracted from, the average motion given by the formula (1). Such deviations correspond to a probable error of ± 140 km. per sec. in the value of v given by the formula. Thus the error becomes proportionally smaller the greater the distance of the nebula.

If we may assume that the observations which have led to de Sitter's formula are not at fault, it is obviously a result of the highest importance. No other formula relating to phenomena on anything like so large a scale has ever been discovered. How ought the result to be interpreted? It should be said, at the outset, that possibly the use of Doppler's principle to interpret displacements of spectral lines as velocities of recession may be erroneous. There is no doubt as to the reddening of the light which we receive: but Zwicky suggests that such reddening may be due to the gravitational pull of material bodies on light which passes near them, and for the suggestion there is some experimental evidence. If, however, the reddening is due to a motion of recession, the Universe as a whole—or the cosmos, as we have agreed to call it—must be such that the different island universes are travelling away from ourselves with enormous velocities which increase in proportion to the distances of such universes.

Now there is no reason to think that our galactic universe is the centre of the cosmos. If the whole of space is finite, our universe is related to the whole as is every other universe. The conclusion seems to be irresistible that the cosmos is itself expanding. In Lecture VI we investigated two forms of finite space which might to a first approximation represent the cosmos. One of them, de Sitter's cosmos (§§ 125 and 140), is ideally empty and for this reason is hardly a satisfactory approximation to fact. The other, Einstein's cosmos (§ 139), is such that the curvature is determined by the amount of matter within it: colloquially we may say that it is as full as it will hold. Einstein's cosmos has, however, not been proved to be stable. We proceed now to shew, incidentally, that it is unstable, as we investigate the nature of an 'expanding' cosmos which Lemaître* has devised to explain the apparent velocities of recession of the great nebulae. Lemaître's work was subsequent to, though independent of, similar investigations by A. Friedman.

As will be seen subsequently, it is as yet premature to assert definitely that the cosmos in which we find ourselves is such that its curvature varies with the time. We can, however, safely say that such a cosmos is free from difficulties which belong to any alternatives which have so far been suggested. It is strange that the possibility of such a cosmos was not investigated immediately after Einstein had published the general theory of relativity, inasmuch as Clifford†, with remarkably prophetic insight, had fully thirty years earlier contemplated that our space may have a constant curvature, "but its degree of curvature may change as a whole with the time. In this way our geometry based on the sameness of space would still hold good for all parts of space, but the change of curvature might produce in space a succession of apparent physical changes".

A little later in the same volume, Karl Pearson records as Clifford's opinion‡: "The hypotheses that space is not homaloidal, and, again, that its geometrical character may change with the time, may or may not be destined to play a great part in the physics of the future; yet we cannot refuse to consider them as possible explanations of physical phenomena, because they may be opposed to the popular dogmatic belief in the universality of certain geometrical axioms—belief which has arisen from centuries of indiscriminating worship of the genius of Euclid".

§ 285. *Lemaître's expanding (or contracting) cosmos.*

Let us assume that the cosmos is such that time-sections of space-time are homogeneous and isotropic, so that the Riemannian curvatures of space at every point and in every direction are the same positive quantity $1/r^2$. But let us further postulate that the radius r

* Friedman's paper appeared in the year 1922 in the *Zeitschrift für Physik*, vol. x, pp. 377–86. Lemaître's paper appeared in the year 1927 in the *Annales de la Société Scientifique de Bruxelles*, t. 47, série A, première partie, pp. 49–59. Important criticisms and developments will be found in de Sitter, *Bulletin of the Astronomical Institutes of the Netherlands*, vol. v, 1930, and in Eddington, *Monthly Notices of the Royal Astronomical Society*, vol. xc, 1930.

† W. K. Clifford, *Common Sense of the Exact Sciences*. Kegan Paul, 1885, p. 225.

‡ *Ibid.* p. 226. The term 'homaloidal' was defined in § 67.

and volume $2\pi^2 r^3$ of such finite Riemannian space alike vary with the time. We shall shew that with such variation the velocities of recession of the great nebulae may be the "succession of apparent physical changes" of Clifford's imagination.

As in § 139 we see that we may assume that the element of interval is given by

$$ds^2 = f^2 dx_0{}^2 - r^2 \{dx_1{}^2 + \sin^2 x_1 dx_2{}^2 + \sin^2 x_1 \sin^2 x_2 dx_3{}^2\},$$

where f is a constant, $x_0 = ct$, and r is a function of t only.

That the homogeneity of space may be preserved the pressure p must be everywhere uniform, though variable with the time. Similarly the density, though uniform throughout the cosmos, will be variable with the time. We put ρ equal to the *total* density at any point. If ρ_0 be the 'proper' density at the point we shall have (§ 122)

$$c^2 \rho_0 = c^2 \rho - 3p.$$

The pressure p is, in part, due to radiation and, in part, is due to the random motions of molecules of the gas of very small density which is supposed to be uniformly distributed throughout the cosmos. We know that radiation has no 'proper' mass or invariant mass, though it contributes to total density. Random motions of molecules, of course, cannot contribute to 'proper' mass.

With the assumptions that have been made, the energy-stress tensor has components given by

$$T_{ik} = (c^2 \rho + p) \lambda_i \lambda_k - p g_{ik}.$$

Further, by § 124, Einstein's gravitational equations for our medium are

$$G_{ik} - \tfrac{1}{2} G g_{ik} + \lambda g_{ik} = -\vartheta T_{ik}, \qquad \text{for } i, k = 0, 1, 2, 3,$$

where ϑ is the Einstein constant $8\pi\gamma/c^4$ (§ 126).

We now utilise the analytical results obtained, with a view to the present investigation, in § 115 (p. 142).

For $i = 0$, $k = 0$, we find

$$(3/r^2 - \lambda) f^2 + \frac{3}{c^2 r^2} \left(\frac{dr}{dt}\right)^2 = \vartheta \left[(c^2 \rho + p) \lambda_0{}^2 - p f^2\right].$$

For $i = 1$, $k = 1$, we have

$$(\lambda r^2 - 1) - \frac{1}{c^2 f^2} \left[\left(\frac{dr}{dt}\right)^2 + 2r \frac{d^2 r}{dt^2}\right] = \vartheta \left[(c^2 \rho + p) \lambda_1{}^2 + p r^2\right].$$

For $i = 2$, $k = 2$, we have

$$(\lambda r^2 - 1) \sin^2 x_1 - \frac{\sin^2 x_1}{c^2 f^2} \left[\left(\frac{dr}{dt}\right)^2 + 2r \frac{d^2 r}{dt^2}\right] = \vartheta \left[(c^2 \rho + p) \lambda_2{}^2 + p r^2 \sin^2 x_1\right].$$

For $i = 3$, $k = 3$, we have

$$(\lambda r^2 - 1)\sin^2 x_1 \sin^2 x_2 - \frac{\sin^2 x_1 \sin^2 x_2}{c^2 f^2}\left[\left(\frac{dr}{dt}\right)^2 + 2r\frac{d^2 r}{dt^2}\right]$$
$$= \vartheta\left[(c^2\rho + p)\lambda_3{}^2 + pr^2 \sin^2 x_1 \sin^2 x_2\right].$$

Assume now that random motions of molecules are so small that they may be ignored. We may then put

$$\lambda^0 = 1/f, \qquad \lambda^1 = 0, \qquad \lambda^2 = 0, \qquad \lambda^3 = 0.$$

Hence we shall have

$$\lambda_0 = f, \qquad \lambda_1 = 0, \qquad \lambda_2 = 0, \qquad \lambda_3 = 0.$$

The four equations just obtained now lead to

$$(3/r^2 - \lambda + p\vartheta)f^2 + \frac{3}{c^2 r^2}\left(\frac{dr}{dt}\right)^2 = \vartheta f^2(c^2\rho + p);$$

$$(\lambda - 1/r^2 - p\vartheta) = \frac{1}{r^2 c^2 f^2}\left\{\left(\frac{dr}{dt}\right)^2 + 2r\frac{d^2 r}{dt^2}\right\},$$

the latter equation being repeated three times over.

We therefore have the two equations

$$\frac{3}{r^2}\left(\frac{dr}{dt}\right)^2 + \frac{3f^2 c^2}{r^2} = \lambda f^2 c^2 + c^4 \rho \vartheta f^2;$$

$$\frac{2}{r}\frac{d^2 r}{dt^2} + \frac{1}{r^2}\left(\frac{dr}{dt}\right)^2 + \frac{c^2 f^2}{r^2} = c^2 f^2 \lambda - pc^2 f^2 \vartheta.$$

Let us now put $f = 1$. Then the element of interval in the space-time metric of our 'expanding' cosmos is given by

$$ds^2 = c^2 dt^2 - r^2\{dx_1{}^2 + \sin^2 x_1\, dx_2{}^2 + \sin^2 x_1 \sin^2 x_2\, dx_3{}^2\}.$$

For this cosmos the equations of the gravitational field have just been shewn to be

$$\frac{\dot{r}^2}{r^2} + \frac{c^2}{r^2} = \frac{\lambda c^2}{3} + \frac{k\rho c^2}{3},$$

$$2\frac{\ddot{r}}{r} + \frac{\dot{r}^2}{r^2} + \frac{c^2}{r^2} = \lambda c^2 - pk,$$

where dots denote differentiation with respect to t, λ is the cosmological constant, and $k = c^2\vartheta = 8\pi\gamma/c^2$. This form of the equations is due to Lemaître. It is to be remembered that, in obtaining these equations, we have assumed that random motions are negligible. Hence the pressure p is assumed to be solely due to radiation.

The equation of conservation of energy in Lemaître's cosmos.

From the first of Lemaître's equations we obtain, on differentiation,

$$\frac{2\dot{r}}{r^2}\left\{\ddot{r} - \frac{\dot{r}^2}{r} - \frac{c^2}{r}\right\} = k\frac{c^2}{3}\frac{d\rho}{dt}.$$

Hence, by the second equation,

$$c^2 \frac{d\rho}{dt} + \frac{3\dot{r}}{r}\{p + c^2\rho\} = 0.$$

This equation expresses conservation of energy in Lemaître's cosmos.

§ 286.   *The instability of the Einstein cosmos.*

We can now establish Eddington's result that the Einstein cosmos (§ 139) is unstable.

For that cosmos r is independent of t and $p = 0$. Hence, if r_e and ρ_e be its radius and density, we shall have, from the second of Lemaître's equations,

$$\lambda = 1/r_e^2;$$

and hence, from the first of his equations,

$$1/r_e^2 = k\rho_e/2.$$

These values of ρ_e and r_e we have already obtained in § 139.

Suppose now that the radius of Einstein's cosmos undergoes a change from r_e to r, where

$$r = r_e + \dot{r}_e \delta t + \tfrac{1}{2}\ddot{r}_e(\delta t)^2 + \dots.$$

Then, using both Lemaître's equations,

$$\frac{2\ddot{r}}{r} = \frac{2c^2\lambda}{3} - kp - \frac{k\rho c^2}{3} = -k\left(\dot{p} + \frac{c^2\dot{\rho}}{3}\right)_e \delta t + \dots$$

$$= k\delta t\left\{\frac{p\dot{r}}{r} - \dot{p} + \frac{c^2\rho\dot{r}}{r}\right\}_e + \dots.$$

Now in the Einstein cosmos $p = 0$. Let us assume, as seems legitimate, that, when its radius changes slightly, $\dot{p} = 0$. Then, when $\dot{r}$ is small and positive, $\ddot{r}$ is positive; and, when $\dot{r}$ is small and negative, $\ddot{r}$ is negative.

If then the Einstein cosmos begins either to expand or to contract, it will continue on the course begun. In other words, it is unstable.

§ 287.   *Geodesics in the Lemaître cosmos.*

Let us now consider the path of a material particle which moves freely in the field of the Lemaître cosmos. In the investigation we need not impose any restrictions on ρ or p.

The element of interval is, as we have seen, given by the equality

$$ds^2 = dx_0^2 - r^2 d\sigma^2,$$

when $dx_0 = c\,dt$, and

$$d\sigma^2 = dx_1^2 + \sin^2 x_1\, dx_2^2 + \sin^2 x_1 \sin^2 x_2\, dx_3^2.$$

The path of a material particle moving freely in the gravitational field of such a metric is the geodesic given by

$$\delta \int ds = 0.$$

Now
$$\delta \int ds = \int \delta \, ds = \int \frac{1}{2ds} \delta \left(dx_0{}^2 - r^2 d\sigma^2 \right)$$

$$= -\left[r^2 \frac{d\sigma}{ds} \delta \sigma \right] + \int d \left(r^2 \frac{d\sigma}{ds} \right) \delta \sigma.$$

Thus on a geodesic we must have $r^2 d\sigma/ds = w$, where w for the particular geodesic is independent of x_1, x_2, x_3 but is possibly dependent on t.

Let now $v = r \, d\sigma/dt$. Then v is the velocity of the material particle describing the geodesic.

We have
$$\frac{ds^2}{dx_0{}^2} = 1 - \frac{v^2}{c^2};$$

and hence
$$v^2/c^2 = w^2/(r^2 + w^2).$$

When the geodesic is described by radiation, we have $ds = 0$ and $v = c$, so that $w = \infty$. When the geodesic is described by a material particle, v is a random velocity. Now we have seen that the random velocities of the extra-galactic nebulae are at most 150 km. per sec. Hence for our own cosmos $v/c = 2^{-1} \times 10^{-3}$. Thus $w^2/(r^2 + w^2)$ is at most of order $4^{-1} \times 10^{-6}$, so that w/r is always a small quantity when w corresponds to the motion of an extra-galactic nebula. We can also say that, as r increases, v varies as $1/r$.

§288. Pressure, density and mass in the Lemaître cosmos.

We know (§192) that the pressure due to random motions of molecules of a gas is such that the pressure per unit area at any point is two-thirds of the kinetic energy per unit-volume due to random motions at the point. (In the investigation of §§190, 192 we must, of course, replace E/c^2 by ρ and c by v.)

Let us now assume that we may neglect radiation pressure. Then, on the assumption that Lemaître's cosmos is filled by a homogeneous gas in which the pressure is small and solely due to random motions, we may put $p = \frac{1}{3}\rho v^2$. Hence

$$3p/c^2\rho = w^2/(r^2 + w^2).$$

Now we have seen that $c^2\rho_0 = c^2\rho - 3p$. Hence

$$\rho = \rho_0 \{1 + w^2/r^2\}.$$

Further, we have seen that the element of interval in the Lemaître cosmos is given by

$$ds^2 = c^2 dt^2 - r^2 d\sigma^2, \quad \text{and that} \quad v = \frac{r \, d\sigma}{dt}.$$

If now dV be an element of volume measured with reference to fixed axes, and if dV_0 be the same element measured with reference to axes moving with the element, we shall have

$$dV = r^3 \sin^2 x_1 \sin x_2 \, dx_1 \, dx_2 \, dx_3;$$

and (by § 103) $dV = dV_0/h$, where

$$1/h = \sqrt{1 - v^2/c^2} = \frac{ds}{c \, dt}.$$

We easily see that $h = (1 + w^2/r^2)^{\frac{1}{2}}$.

The total volume of the Lemaître cosmos is

$$\int dV_0 = \int h \, dV = \int (1 + w^2/r^2)^{\frac{1}{2}} \, dV.$$

The total invariant mass is

$$\int \rho_0 \, dV_0 = \int \rho_0 c \frac{dt}{ds} \, dV = \int (1 + w^2/r^2)^{-\frac{1}{2}} \rho \, dV.$$

Also, if M be physical or relative mass and if m be invariant or proper-mass, we have $M = mh$.

Hence the total physical mass of the Lemaître cosmos is

$$\int h \rho_0 \, dV_0 = \int \rho_0 h^2 \, dV = \int \rho \, dV.$$

If now we assume that $(w/r)^2$ can be neglected in comparison with unity we shall have $p = 0$. Thus, when $p = 0$, the total invariant mass of the cosmos will be equal to the total physical mass and each by § 79 will be equal to

$$M = 2\pi^2 r^3 \rho.$$

The expansion of the Lemaître cosmos when the mass is constant and the pressure is zero.

Suppose now that $p = 0$ and that the expanding cosmos is of constant mass M. Then we have $k\rho = \alpha/r^3$, where α is a constant equal to $kM/2\pi^2$. Hence, from the first of the Lemaître equations of § 285, we have

$$\frac{\dot{r}^2}{c^2} = \frac{\lambda}{3} r^2 + \frac{\alpha}{3r} - 1.$$

Thus

$$ct = \int \frac{dr}{\sqrt{\dfrac{\lambda r^2}{3} + \dfrac{\alpha}{3r} - 1}}.$$

If the cosmos began as an Einstein cosmos of radius r_e and density ρ_e, we have

$$\lambda = \frac{1}{r_e^2} = \frac{k\rho_e}{2} = \frac{\alpha}{2r_e^3};$$

so that

$$r_e = \frac{1}{\sqrt{\lambda}} \quad \text{and} \quad \alpha = 2r_e.$$

We then have

$$ct/\sqrt{3}r_e = \int \frac{dr}{r - r_e}\{1 + 2r_e/r\}^{-\frac{1}{2}}.$$

This is the equation which connects the radius of Lemaître's cosmos with the time which has elapsed since it began, hypothetically, as an unstable Einstein cosmos.

Suppose now that the cosmos had such a beginning. Let r be its present radius and let t be the time which has elapsed since it ceased to be of some standard radius. Then, if we put $x = \{1 + 2r_e/r\}^{-\frac{1}{2}}$, we easily see that

$$ct/r_e = \log \frac{\sqrt{3}x - 1}{\sqrt{3}x + 1} + \sqrt{3} \log \frac{x + 1}{x - 1} + C, \qquad \ldots\ldots(1)$$

where C is a constant of integration.

It is clear that, when $r = r_e$, t is logarithmically infinite, so that the unstable Einstein cosmos takes, in theory, an infinite time to begin its expansion. Such theory would not, however, correspond to physical fact: an actual Einstein cosmos would almost certainly begin its expansion with little delay.

289. *The Doppler effect in the Lemaître cosmos.*

The element of interval in the Lemaître cosmos we have taken to be

$$ds^2 = c^2 dt^2 - r^2 d\sigma^2.$$

On a ray of light we have $ds = 0$, and therefore $d\sigma = c\,dt/r$. At any particular instant the radius of Lemaître's cosmos will be definite, and a point in the cosmos will be defined by the value of σ corresponding to it.

Suppose now that a ray of light is emitted at time t_1 from the point σ_1, and seen at the point σ_2 at time t_2. A consecutive ray will start at time $t_1 + \delta t_1$ and will reach the point σ_2 at time $t_2 + \delta t_2$. We shall then have

$$\sigma_2 - \sigma_1 = c \int_{t_1}^{t_2} \frac{dt}{r} = c \int_{t_1 + \delta t_1}^{t_2 + \delta t_2} \frac{dt}{r}.$$

Hence $\delta t_2/r_2 = \delta t_1/r_1$, where r_2 and r_1 are the values of r at the times t_2 and t_1 respectively.

If now δt_1 is the period of the emitted light, δt_2 will be the period of the observed light. Further, as we have previously seen in § 132, δt_1 would be the period of the same light emitted under the same physical conditions in the vicinity of the observer.

Suppose now that the change in the period is correctly interpreted, by Doppler's principle (§ 191), as a velocity of recession v of the source σ_1 from the observer σ_2. Then

$$v/c = \frac{\delta t_2}{\delta t_1} - 1 = \frac{r_2}{r_1} - 1.$$

Thus the apparent velocity of recession depends solely on the ratio of the radii of the cosmos at the times of emission and observation.

Suppose now that q is the distance of the source of light from the observer. Suppose further that this distance is so small that, if it be traversed in time δt, we can neglect the change in r during this interval. We can then put $q = c\delta t$, where our units are kilometres and seconds when $c = 3 \times 10^5$. And now we may write

$$v/c = \frac{r_2 - r_1}{r_1} = \frac{\delta r_1}{r_1} = \frac{\dot{r}_1}{r_1}\delta t,$$

so that $\qquad v/q = \dot{r}_1/r_1.$

Now, as we have seen in § 284, de Sitter's formula for the apparent velocities of recession of the great nebulae is

$$v/q = c/2000,$$

where q is measured in millions of light-years, v and c being measured in any units common to both. Thus these apparent velocities can be interpreted as evidence of the expansion of the cosmos; and r, the present radius of the cosmos, will be such that

$$\frac{1}{r}\frac{dr}{dt} = \frac{c}{2000} \times \frac{1}{10^{19}},$$

our units being kilometres and seconds. Thus, if the assumptions which we have made are legitimate, the rate of expansion of the cosmos is such that $\qquad r/\dot{r} = 6\cdot6 \times 10^{16}\,\text{secs.} = 2 \times 10^9\,\text{years.}$

If this rate has continued since the earth was born, the radius of the cosmos will have doubled in size in a time t given by $\log 2 = t/(2 \times 10^9)$ years. Thus it will have doubled in the past 1400 million years.

This rate is astonishingly rapid if it be true that the age of the galaxy ought to be measured in millions of millions of years. At such a rate the distances of the great nebulae will have doubled seven times over in the next 10^{10} years. Corresponding to this vast increase of distance the decrease in brightness of the nebulae will, by §200, be given by an increase in magnitude measured by $5 \times \log_{10} 2^7 = 10$. It follows that in 10,000 million years all spiral nebulae will be ten magnitudes fainter than they now are. We are thus singularly fortunate, if the cosmos is of an age to be measured by millions of millions of years, in being able to see any of the great nebulae! We may fairly conclude that *the time-scales of cosmic evolution are at present hopelessly contradictory.*

The explanation of the contradiction does not reside in the approximation by which the formula $v/q = \dot{r}/r$ was obtained. The accurate distance between two points σ_2 and σ_1 at a time when the radius of the cosmos is r_0 is $q = r_0(\sigma_2 - \sigma_1)$.

Now on a ray of light $\qquad \sigma = c \int dt/r.$

We thus have $\qquad \sigma/\sqrt{3}r_e = \displaystyle\int \frac{dr}{(r - r_e)\{r(r + 2r_e)\}^{\frac{1}{2}}}.$

Put now, as before, $\qquad x = \{1 + 2r_e/r\}^{-\frac{1}{2}};$

and we get $\qquad \sigma = \log \dfrac{\sqrt{3}x - 1}{\sqrt{3}x + 1} + D,$

where D is a constant of integration.

We shall shortly obtain the approximate value of r_e, and then we can shew, by the aid of this formula for σ, that the use of the accurate value of q does not appreciably affect our results.

§290. *The present size of our cosmos.*

In obtaining our previous results we have used as the sole numerical datum the formula giving the velocities of recession of the great nebulae. We now proceed to use what is believed to be the present density of matter in our cosmos to obtain the value of r_e, the radius of the Einstein cosmos, and of r, the radius of our cosmos at the present time.

Let ρ and r be the density and radius of our present cosmos, the Lemaître assumptions being assumed to be satisfactory, and let ρ_e be, as before, the density of the Einstein cosmos from which it hypothetically started. Then, since the mass of the cosmos has remained constant during its expansion, we must have

$$r^3 \rho = \alpha/k = r_e^3 \rho_e.$$

But $2/r_e^2 = k\rho_e$. Hence $r^3 \rho = 2r_e/k$.

Now we have seen that

$$\frac{dr}{dt} = \frac{c}{\sqrt{3}r_e}(r - r_e)(1 + 2r_e/r)^{\frac{1}{2}}.$$

Hence, if we put $y = r_e/r$, we shall have

$$\left(\frac{\dot{r}}{r}\right)^2 = \frac{c^2}{3r_e^2}(1 - 3y^2 + 2y^3).$$

Now

$$r_e^2/y^3 = r^3/r_e = 2/k\rho.$$

Hence

$$(1 - 3y^2 + 2y^3)/y^3 = \frac{6}{c^2 k\rho}\left(\frac{\dot{r}}{r}\right)^2. \qquad \qquad \text{......(1)}$$

We have seen that, in c.g.s. units, $\dot{r}/r = 1\cdot5 \times 10^{-17}$. Further, in such units, the value of ρ has been estimated by Hubble to be $1\cdot5 \times 10^{-31}$, which is probably too small, and by Oort to be 2×10^{-28}, which de Sitter considers to be considerably too large. We will try to find the size of the cosmos by accepting these two estimates as outside limits.

In the first place, we know, by § 126, that in c.g.s. units

$$k = 1\cdot87 \times 10^{-27} \qquad \text{and} \qquad c^2 k = 8\pi\gamma = 1\cdot68 \times 10^{-6}.$$

Hence

$$\frac{6}{c^2 k}\left(\frac{\dot{r}}{r}\right)^2 = 8 \times 10^{-28}.$$

Thus, according to Oort and Hubble respectively, the equation for y takes the form

$$(1 - 3y^2 + 2y^3)/y^3 = 4 \quad \text{or} \quad 5320.$$

By drawing the simple graph of the function of y under consideration, we see that only one positive value of y satisfies each of these equations. We have, in fact, $y = \cdot5$ or $\cdot057$.

Now $r_e^2 = 2y^3/k\rho$. We therefore have, in the respective cases, $r_e^2 = 6\cdot65 \times 10^{53}$ or $1\cdot36 \times 10^{54}$. Thus r_e lies between $8\cdot2 \times 10^{26}$ and $1\cdot17 \times 10^{27}$ cm., or between $8\cdot6 \times 10^8$ and $1\cdot23 \times 10^9$ light-years.

Since $r = r_e/y$, we see that the present radius of our cosmos must lie between $1\cdot64 \times 10^{27}$ and 2×10^{28} cm., or between 1720 and 21,600 million light-years. The larger of these two estimates is the more probable.

The mass of our cosmos.

The mass of Lemaître's cosmos can be readily calculated. We have seen that it is

$$M = 2\pi^2 \rho r^3.$$

Now, in c.g.s. units ρ lies between 2×10^{-28} and $1\cdot5 \times 10^{-31}$, while the corresponding values of r are $16\cdot4 \times 10^{26}$ and 2×10^{28}.

Thus M lies between $1\cdot74 \times 10^{52}$ and $2\cdot37 \times 10^{55}$ grammes. If the geometry of space is 'elliptic' (§ 44), the mass in the foregoing estimates will have been counted twice over.

Alternative expansion hypothesis.

There is, of course, the possibility that our cosmos did not begin as an Einstein cosmos. If this were the case, there would not be the connection $kM = 4\pi^2/\sqrt{\lambda}$, which we have assumed to exist between the mass of our cosmos M and the cosmological constant λ.

Let us assume that $kM_0 = 4\pi^2/\sqrt{\lambda}$, where $M_0 \neq M$. Then the equation of § 288,
$$3\dot{r}^2/c^2 = \lambda r^2 - 3 + \alpha/r,$$
becomes
$$3\dot{r}^2/c^2 = \frac{16\pi^4}{k^2}\frac{r^2}{M_0^2} - 3 + \frac{kM}{2\pi^2 r}.$$

Put now $x = 4\pi^2 r/kM_0$, $p = M/M_0$ and we get
$$\frac{3k^2 M_0^2}{16\pi^2 c^2}\dot{x}^2 = x^2 - 3 + 2\frac{p}{x}.$$

Now, if $y = x^2 - 3 + 2p/x$, we readily see that dy/dx will vanish when $x = p^{\frac{1}{3}}$, and that we shall then have $y = 3(p^{\frac{2}{3}} - 1)$.

Obviously in our problem x is positive, and we can limit our consideration to this case. A simple graph now shews that:

(a) If $p > 1$, y is always positive. Thus, if $M > M_0$, we see that, as r increases from a small positive quantity, $\dot{r}$, the rate of expansion of the cosmos, decreases until $x = p^{\frac{1}{3}}$ and then increases again.

(b) If $p < 1$, y is positive when x is small. As x increases, y diminishes to zero. Then, after being negative for a time, y vanishes again. Finally y becomes positive and increases to infinity. Thus as r increases from a small positive quantity, $\dot{r}$ vanishes for two values r_1 and r_2, let us say, of r.

If then $M > M_0$, the expansion of the cosmos must be assumed to begin in some inexplicable way. If the initial radius was sufficiently small the rate of expansion would slow down for a time and would then increase again indefinitely.

If, on the other hand, $M < M_0$, the cosmos could start with a finite rate of expansion and, when its radius became equal to r_1, the expansion would cease and it would begin to contract. Or it could start by contracting from a very large radius and, when its radius became equal to r_2, it would cease to contract and thereupon begin to expand again.

None of the preceding possibilities is very attractive. Perhaps, if we were forced to choose among them, we should assume that $M < M_0$ and that the cosmos has continuously expanded since a beginning at $r = r_2$.

When $M = M_0$ we have, of course, Lemaître's cosmos.

§ 291. *Some general reflections.*

If it be an impiety for the sons of men to attempt to scale Olympus, then surely an endeavour to measure the size of the cosmos is the crowning impiety of the mathematician turned astronomer. How far is it likely that the results obtained correspond to actual fact? This question is, in our present state of knowledge, singularly difficult to answer. Most certainly, as was pointed out in § 138, the Newtonian-Euclidean picture of the cosmos has broken down. If the cosmos is infinite in extent and if matter, whether aggregated into great nebulae or otherwise, is distributed throughout its extent, then the Newtonian scheme of potential collapses. Presumably Einstein's modification of the law of gravity would not prevent the collapse. If, on the other hand, matter occupies but a sort of island in infinite space, one would expect that under the influence of gravitation it would in the end aggregate into a single mass: such was Newton's opinion, as we shall see shortly (§ 292).

From difficulties of this kind the Friedman-Lemaître cosmos is free. Its space being finite and Riemannian, it will have no centre: every great nebula will bear the same relation to the whole as does any other. The cosmos, moreover, is in a steady state though the radius is changing; and the apparent velocities of recession of the great nebulae are explained naturally by the fact that the cosmos is expanding. Thus while the old scheme was not free from internal contradictions, the picture given by Lemaître has, so far as we know, no fatal flaw. Moreover, from it infinite space, that scandal to human thought, is banished.

Yet it must be admitted that the Lemaître cosmos arouses grave perplexities. Infinite time (and I, for one, feel compelled to assume that time is real) remains to trouble us. If indeed time be infinite, then we should have expected to find in the past some endless rhythmic alternation. But the beginning of the expanding cosmos takes us to some more or less definite point, and there leaves us. Instead of finding endless repetition in the past we seem forced to postulate creation in time. And though the second law of thermodynamics leads to the same necessity, the mental discomfort of the man of science, with his fundamental postulate of the uniformity of nature, is not thereby lessened. Doubtless the Lemaître cosmos is but a very imperfect picture, a first attempt at a rough approximation to the truth. But one cannot see that further refinements would lessen the mental uneasiness to which the present scheme leads. That uneasiness, as we have indicated, is for the moment increased by the fact that the Lemaître time-scale is hopelessly at variance with that demanded by Jeans' researches. It is possible, as we have suggested, that the reddening of light from the nebulae is not correctly interpreted as a velocity of recession. Some part of it might be due to other causes: in fact, more than the whole of it might be due to such causes and the nebulae might be approaching us in a 'contracting' cosmos. A cosmos which began with an infinite radius and will end as a single aggregate of matter would ease somewhat the general problem of time. But the present Jeans and Lemaître time-scales cannot both be final: what further changes will have to be made in the revision from which time-discrepancies vanish we cannot say.

An alternative metric for the cosmos.

Recently Einstein and de Sitter have indicated* that possibly expanding space with a Euclidean metric might represent known facts. They assume in their investigation that the element of interval is given by the identity

$$ds^2 = dx_0{}^2 - r^2 (dx_1{}^2 + dx_2{}^2 + dx_3{}^2),$$

where $dx_0 = c\,dt$, and r is a function of t only.

For such a metric the quantities G_{ik} can be readily calculated as in § 115, and the fundamental gravitational equations

$$G_{ik} - \tfrac{1}{2}Gg_{ik} + \lambda g_{ik} = -\,\vartheta\{(c^2\rho + p)\lambda_i\lambda_k - pg_{ik}\}$$

become

$$\lambda - 3\dot{r}^2/c^2r^2 = -\,\vartheta\{(c^2\rho + p)\lambda_0{}^2 - p\},$$

$$2r\ddot{r}/c^2 + \dot{r}^2/c^2 - \lambda r^2 = -\,\vartheta\{(c^2\rho + p)\lambda_k{}^2 + pr^2\}, \qquad k = 1, 2, 3.$$

In these equations $c^2\rho$ is the total energy-density and p is the pressure (supposed uniform) at any point of space.

Let us now assume that the velocities of all material particles in our space are negligible, so that p is due solely to radiation pressure. Then we may put $\lambda_0 = 1$, $\lambda_k = 0$. Assume further that the cosmological term λ vanishes. Then our gravitational equations become, if as before we put $k = c^2\vartheta$,

$$\dot{r}^2/c^2r^2 = \tfrac{1}{3}k\rho, \qquad \text{and} \qquad 2r\ddot{r} + \dot{r}^2 = -\,kpr^2,$$

the last equation being repeated three times over.

The second equation may be written

$$\frac{d}{dt}(r^{\frac{1}{2}}\dot{r}) = -\frac{kp}{2}\,r^{\frac{3}{2}}.$$

---

* A. Einstein and W. de Sitter, *Proceedings of the National Academy of Sciences*, vol. XVIII, 1932, pp. 213, 214.

Hence the first equation gives, on integration,

$$\log r = -\frac{p\sqrt{k}}{c\sqrt{3\rho}}t + \text{cons.}$$

We must therefore have

$$p = -c^2\rho \qquad \text{and} \qquad \dot{r}/cr = \sqrt{k\rho/3}.$$

Hence at any point of space there must be a uniform *pull* equal to the energy-density at the point. Further, if we use the value of $\dot{r}/r$ given in § 289, we see that we must have in c.g.s. units,

$$cr/\dot{r} = 2 \times 10^{27}.$$

Now $k = 1\cdot87 \times 10^{-27}$. Hence

$$\rho = 4 \times 10^{-28}.$$

But, as we have seen in § 290, such a value for the actual density of our cosmos is not impossible. We cannot therefore definitely reject the notion that our cosmos is of an expanding Euclidean type. When more accurate knowledge, alike of $\dot{r}/r$ and of ρ, has been obtained, we may be able to estimate with more confidence the character of the curvature of space.

Some writers view with repugnance all such space-time metrics as we have considered (with the exception of the original metric of de Sitter) because these metrics assume the existence of cosmic time. Into the original metric of de Sitter the three dimensions of space and the single dimension of imaginary time enter in an exactly similar manner: we preserved, in fact, Minkowski's abolition of the distinction between space and time. But none of the other metrics which has been suggested is in harmony with Minkowski's conception of the space-time continuum. This fact, however, will not distress those who are convinced that the future is uncertain while the past is definite and that each of us, in his life-history, does not merely meet events but causes them to happen.

Since the paper of Einstein and de Sitter has appeared, E. A. Milne has pointed out that the observed velocities of recession of the great nebulae can be satisfactorily explained even though space be Euclidean and the notion of its expansion be abandoned. Milne makes the assumption that the nebulae began with arbitrary movements in a volume within which they constituted a sort of central condensation in the cosmos. In his scheme space is, of course, infinite, but "there is no such thing as cosmic time". Some of us may think that infinite space is a heavy price to pay for the abolition of cosmic time. But only future research can determine whether in such matters the cosmos satisfies our desires.

Man and the cosmos.

The cosmological speculations which we have been considering are singularly interesting when set against the brevity of human life and the size of the human body. The radius of the cosmos, we have seen reason to believe, is, if we take a mean estimate, some 50,000 million million million miles. The time-scale of Lemaître's theory disappoints us because, in so short a time as 10,000 million years, the great nebulae will be ten magnitudes fainter than at present. There are many people who find such figures actually terrifying; and many others find in them a sort of repellent inhumanity. To all these persons the figures seem to dwarf man to utter insignificance; and such, indeed, is one way of regarding them. But we may also reflect that such stupendous figures measure the success of man's attempt to explore the cosmos. He can mount on the wings of his mind and pass untroubled through aeons of time before ever the earth was made and to distances which his most remote ancestors travelling as fast as light could not, had they lived till now, have reached. Is there not in such facts an indication that neither in time nor in space is man's mind limited as is his body? Are we not encouraged thereby to speculate that when the body decays the mind survives? That the cosmos of inference may become the cosmos of experience is, I think, not an impossible hope.

§ 292. *The probable origin of the cosmos.*

The existence of the great nebulae as fundamental units in the depths of space, coupled with the fact that they can all, with relatively few exceptions, be arranged in sequences which represent a steady development, naturally makes us regard them as singularly important in the evolution of the Universe. The majority of those who have speculated with authority as to the beginnings of our cosmos have assumed that initially matter within it was uniformly distributed throughout space. Of course, any such hypothetical distribution must have had an almost inconceivably slight density. The great philosopher Kant (1724–1804) assumed such a distribution of matter, as we said in § 236; but he also believed erroneously that, as it aggregated into distinct masses, these would acquire angular momentum with the mere passage of time. Laplace (1749–1827), in his cosmological speculations, avoided Kant's mistake and postulated an initial rotation which increased with condensation, the angular momentum remaining constant in accordance with the principles of Newtonian dynamics. Newton, however, though he preceded Kant and Laplace, suggested a picture of the evolution of cosmos which specially commends itself to modern astronomers. In the first of his *Four Letters to Bentley**, written towards the end of the year 1692, he said:

It seems to me, that if the matter of our sun and planets, and all the matter of the universe, were evenly scattered throughout all the heavens, and every particle had an innate gravity towards all the rest, and the whole space throughout which this matter was scattered, was but finite, the matter on the outside of this space would, by its gravity, tend towards all the matter on the inside, and, by consequence, fall down into the middle of the whole space, and there compose one great spherical mass. But if the matter was evenly disposed throughout an infinite space, it could never convene into one mass; but some of it would convene into one mass and some into another, so as to make an infinite number of great masses, scattered at great distances from one to another throughout all that infinite space. And thus might the sun and fixed stars be formed, supposing the matter were of a lucid nature.

There is little which needs alteration in this paragraph save that we must combine with it Einstein's suggestion that our space is Riemannian and therefore finite. We thus assume that in the beginning matter was uniformly distributed throughout the finite totality of space. According to Jeans' researches, it would then be gravitationally unstable. Currents would arise within it and it would begin to aggregate into distinct masses. Jeans gives reasons why a gravitational medium of very small density "and reasonable molecular velocity" should aggregate into masses of the size of spiral nebulae rather than of the size of stars. As we have previously seen, the mass of merely the central nucleus of the Andromeda nebula is probably that of some 270 million suns; and, though accuracy in such a matter is at present unobtainable, we may perhaps assume with Oort that the average mass of a nebula is that of some 100,000 million suns. The currents which arose in the original medium would, we must assume, furnish angular momentum to the nascent nebulae. As these gradually condensed we should get fairly rapid rotations and thus would arise the two observed sequences, beginning with nearly circular elliptic nebulae and ending with ordinary or barred spiral nebulae. If the original currents were "less than a kilometre per second" Jeans asserts that the angular momentum which they would generate would be sufficient to produce that known to exist in the two nebulae for which calculations have been made.

The origin of stars.

The arms of the Andromeda nebula, which are probably typical, consist of vast aggregates of stars arranged in what are roughly por-

* Bentley, *Works* (cited in § 133), vol. III, p. 200.

tions of equiangular spirals. The central masses, as we have seen, must, according to Jeans' calculations, be formed of particles averaging less than about an inch in diameter. It would appear then that, as the nebula shrinks and its rotation increases, such matter is ejected in the equatorial plane of the nebula. This matter condenses, as it were, into vast drops; and, under certain conditions, these drops would be of the size of stars and of the distances apart observed in the nearer spirals.

We thus have, as it were, a picture of the evolution of stars. Only experts can say how far this picture corresponds with facts. It is certainly attractive and persuasive. On the other hand, there are in it, of necessity, assumptions which may not be true. To many who have speculated in these regions the cause of the rotation which exists throughout the universe is a baffling problem; its origin in the random currents produced by initial instability they find unsatisfying.

§ 293. *A final enigma.*

A still more disconcerting enigma is furnished by the arms of the spiral nebulae. An examination of the photographs shews that all spiral nebulae possess in their arms just about two convolutions and no more. If these arms are orbits described by ejected matter which has congealed into stars we should expect them, in the first place, to be nearly circular and not open orbits such as equiangular spirals. Still further, they ought to increase in length with the passage of time: in fact, nebulae in an advanced stage of development ought to have thousands of convolutions. We are thus, as Jeans says, led to the conjecture that "the motions in the spiral nebulae must be governed by forces unknown to us". Jeans* concludes his discussion of the great nebulae with the following significant paragraph:

Not only so, but until the spiral arms have been satisfactorily explained, it is impossible to feel confidence in any conjectures or hypotheses in connection with other features of the nebulae which seem more amenable to treatment. Each failure to explain the spiral arms makes it more and more difficult to resist a suspicion that the spiral nebulae are the seat of types of forces entirely unknown to us, forces which may possibly express novel and unsuspected metric properties of space. The type of conjecture which presents itself, somewhat insistently, is that the centres of the nebulae are of the nature of "singular points", at which matter is poured into our universe from some other, and entirely extraneous, spatial dimension, so that, to a denizen of our universe, they appear as points at which matter is being continually created.

No man of science is really great unless he has that faculty of imagina-

* J. H. Jeans, *Astronomy and Cosmogony.* Cambridge University Press, 1928, p. 352.

tion which gives wings to his chariot of sober calculation. But, when an astronomer is led to postulate the appearance of matter from a fourth dimension, he has obviously reached those confines of knowledge to which we always come sooner or later. We naturally ask, even if we accept the picture of nebular evolution which has just been outlined, what caused the uniform mist initially to spread over the face of the void. Some activity outside and beyond the cosmos we seem forced to postulate. And when we consider the meaning of the galactic universe so far as it is revealed in the most advanced products of its evolution known to us, namely ourselves, we are forced to regard such activity as in some sense Divine. That is to say, there must be in it not only transcendent power but also purpose surpassing in its range all we can imagine; and within the purpose there must be regard for those moral and spiritual qualities which, emerging in ourselves, are of worth far transcending whatever values can be attached to the stupendous interplay of vast masses of matter during the great stretches of time which astronomy describes.

§ 294. *Are there other planetary systems?*

In Lecture X we reached the conclusion that in our own solar system life may possibly exist on two planets other than the earth. Moreover, we have reason to think that the sun belongs to a system of stars whose number is now variously estimated as lying between thirty and one hundred thousand millions. How many of these other suns possess planetary systems? We cannot unfortunately get any answer to this question by observation. Our instruments are woefully inadequate when we desire to discover whether planets are attached to the distant stars. It is only with the greatest difficulty that binary stars can be resolved in our telescopes. The fact that possibly one-third of the stars of our local star-cloud are either binary or belong to multiple systems makes it clear that we cannot argue that our own sun with its attendant planets is typical. It is natural that we who live on a planet should assume that the solar system is not an exceptional rarity in the galactic universe. Yet the conclusion that it is exceptional seems to be generally received by astronomers at the present day.

§ 295. *The frequency of stellar encounters.*

As we have said in § 237, no satisfactory origin of the solar system has so far been proposed save that which postulates the near approach of another star to our sun, this approach raising on the sun such violent tides that masses of matter which eventually formed the planets were ejected from it. If it be true that no other origin of a planetary system is possible, the existence of planetary systems must depend upon the number of such *encounters*, or *quasi-collisions* between stars, as have taken place during the past history of the galactic universe. In order to find this number we need to know the age of the galactic universe, the average velocity of stars within it, their average size and their density of distribution. Now we have previously indicated the reasons which have led Jeans to assign an age for the galactic universe of some millions of millions of years. We know, moreover, that the masses of the stars (or at least of such as can be weighed) are of the same order of magnitude as the mass of our own sun. Their sizes differ enormously; but it may be that our own sun is near the mean. We also know (§ 255) that the distribution of stars of all kinds is locally about one to every ten cubic parsecs. In reaching this figure, however, we assume that there are no absolutely black stars distributed throughout space: the assumption is probably correct, though some reasons have been given for the belief that there are as many dark stars as bright. By mathematical calculation of no great difficulty Jeans, using the numerical estimates to which the above assumptions lead, has reached the conclusion that the time-interval separating successive encounters of a given star of the galactic universe is substantially 5×10^{17} years. We proceed to obtain this result.

Let m and m' be the masses of two stars which after a certain time come to exercise an appreciable attraction on one another. Let v be the velocity of m' when it is at the point P at which the encounter may be considered to begin, S being the common centre of gravity of the two stars and v being measured relative to axes through S.

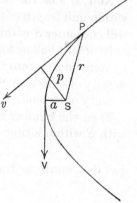

Let V be the velocity of m' at the moment of closest approach when the distance of m' from S is a. Let p be the perpendicular from S on the direction of v, and let $SP = r$.

If ρ be the distance between m and m' when m' is at P, we have

$$\rho m = (m + m')r.$$

Hence m' moves under an attractive force

$$\gamma \frac{mm'}{\rho^2} = \gamma \frac{m^3 m'}{(m + m')^2 r^2}$$

directed to S, where γ is the constant of gravitation.

Since the angular momentum of each of the two stars round S is constant, we must have
$$Va = pv.$$

Since the change of kinetic energy is equal to the work done by the attractive force
$$\tfrac{1}{2}m'(V^2 - v^2) = \gamma \frac{m^3 m'}{(m+m')^2}\left(\frac{1}{a} - \frac{1}{r}\right).$$

But by hypothesis $1/r$ is negligible. Thus
$$\frac{p^2}{a^2} - 1 = \frac{2\gamma m^3}{(m+m')^2 av^2}.$$

Now, for an actual collision between m' and m, the maximum value of a, the distance from the centre of m' to the centre of gravity at the moment of closest approach, must be less than the radius of either star, if we assume that they are equal in size.

We may then for average conditions put
$$m = m' = \text{the mass of the sun,}$$
$$a = \text{the radius of the sun,}$$
and
$$v = \text{a small stellar velocity} = 10 \text{ km. per sec. (say).}$$
(Since p increases as v decreases, the assumption of a small value for v will lead to a large value for p.)

We shall thus get a value of p which will determine a cylinder within which a star, moving parallel to the axis of the cylinder, must lie if it is to have an encounter at S with another star.

Now, if ν be the density in space of stars so moving, the number within unit length of the cylinder will be $\pi p^2 \nu$; and the number which will encounter S within a given time t will be $\pi p^2 \nu vt$.

In order to allow for stars coming from all directions we need, since ν enters linearly into this formula, only take ν to be the complete star-density of space, which we may assume to be that which we find in the vicinity of the sun, one star in somewhat less than 10 cubic parsecs.

Then the number of stars from every direction which will collide with S within a time t will be
$$\pi p^2 \nu vt.$$

In other words the time between consecutive encounters will be
$$T = \frac{1}{\pi p^2 \nu v}.$$

In c.g.s. units
$$a = 7 \times 10^{10}; \qquad \gamma = 6\cdot67 \times 10^{-8};$$
$$m = m' = 2 \times 10^{33}; \qquad \nu = 4 \times 10^{-57}; \qquad v = 10^6.$$

These values lead to $p = 2\cdot2 \times 10^{12}$, and $T = 1\cdot6 \times 10^{25}$.

But one year $= 3\cdot15 \times 10^7$ seconds.

Thus the time-interval between the successive encounters of a particular star with any chance star of the galactic universe will be 5×10^{17} years.

If we assign an average age of 5×10^{12} years to the stars, we must conclude that only one star in a hundred thousand can have formed a planetary system in the whole of its life. If, on the other hand, the average age of the stars is, as may well be, not more than 5×10^{10} years, only one star in ten million will possess a planetary system. On the assumption that there are about 1000 million stars in the dense regions of our galactic universe and that these stars are packed as closely as in the neighbourhood of the sun, we reach the conclusion that planetary systems must form within this group at the rate of one in 5×10^8 years.

§ 296. *The number of planetary systems in regions of local star-density.*

If such figures and the arguments on which they are based are even approximately true, we are led to conclusions which are surprising and probably to most of us disconcerting. In a part of the galactic universe in which 1000 million stars are packed as closely as in the neighbourhood of our sun there can be only some 10,000 (or, alternatively, some hundred) planetary systems. Further, these have been born at intervals of some 500 million years. Inasmuch as our own planetary system appears to be only 2000–4000 million years old, and at the outside some 5000 million years old, it must be one of the youngest of the planetary systems of the group of stars under consideration. We should naturally expect that, on some of the planets attached to each of these systems, life has appeared and evolved; and, further, there seems good reason to believe that the stars have continued to shine much as at present for the greater part of their lives. There is, therefore, some reason to think that, on planets belonging to the greater number of these planetary systems which have come into existence, life still maintains itself. If it has been continuously progressive, beings on planets of some of these systems must surpass ourselves in intelligence to an inconceivable extent. As Jeans says whimsically, "we may well be the most ignorant cosmogonists in the whole of space".

§ 297. *Life elsewhere in the galactic universe.*

If the estimate of 30,000 million as the number of stars in our galactic universe be correct, the number of planetary systems within it *might*, if the average star-density were that of the local star-cloud, be 300,000.

But, if planetary systems originate in actual collisions, there may be merely a few hundred of such systems in our universe. Even if the larger estimate be true, this number seems utterly disproportionate to the size of the galactic universe, *if we regard that universe as having been created with a view to the evolution of intelligent beings.*

It is certain that life and mind, as we know them in conjunction, cannot exist on any of the bright stars. The stars are vast furnaces with interior temperatures running up to many millions of degrees. We can, of course, speculate that mind is associated with the ionisation of atoms or with the disintegration of their nuclei at these high temperatures. As will be seen in subsequent lectures, we can assign no reason whatever why consciousness should be associated with animals, such as ourselves, who represent transformations of carbon compounds, in the presence of a mysterious phenomenon which we term life, at temperatures which lie between the freezing and boiling points of water. For all we know, mind might appear elsewhere in connection with complex physical changes in highly developed organisms of a nature totally different from ourselves, organisms which could only 'live' when the matter of which they were composed was in the state in which it exists in the bright stars.

But, if we keep within the limits of ascertained fact, we must allow that it is only upon bodies formed of inert matter, which has been ejected from the stars and has lost practically all its property of sending out radiation, that life can exist. Life thus appears to be a concomitant of what Jeans well calls "the dead ash of the universe"; and the suggestion forces itself upon us insistently that the cosmos was made for some end other than the evolution of life. Certainly, however, no such end is apparent to us.

My own feeling that the cosmos was created as a basis for the higher forms of consciousness leads me to speculate that our theory of the formation of the solar system is incorrect. The origin of the wide binary stars is, as we have seen, difficult to explain save on the assumption that they have come into existence as successive drops of condensation in the rim of the rotating nebula from which, as we assume, the galactic universe took its being. There is similarly a possibility that planetary systems arose in the initial turmoil attending the birth of the stars; but, if this possibility be a fact, then one or other of the computed ages of the sun and earth must be grotesquely inaccurate. We are thus led once again to the perplexity which arose in connection with the Lemaître time-scale.

§ 298. *Is the whole cosmos the home of intelligent beings?*

According to the opinion at present generally accepted by astronomers, the material in our galactic universe would make more—perhaps far more—than 30,000 million suns, while that in an average nebula would make more—perhaps far more—than some 2000 million suns. If then the stars in the spiral nebulae are billions of years old and if planetary systems in them have arisen from chance encounters or quasi-collisions between stars, we may, perhaps rashly, assume that in each spiral nebula there are at least some 1000 planetary systems. Thus scattered throughout space there would be in the great nebulae visible in our largest telescopes thousands of millions of planetary systems and, therefore, presumably thousands of millions of planets on which life can, and probably does, exist. Perhaps this conclusion may satisfy our instinct that the cosmos was created to be the home of intelligent beings.

Notwithstanding all the obscurity which surrounds our investigation, we can fairly conclude that there is reason to believe that life exists throughout the whole cosmos and that in many places its development has reached stages immeasurably in advance of that attained by man upon the earth. It is, of course, possible to argue that the life of our galactic universe has been much shorter than Jeans suggests and that the solar system is unique within the galactic universe. It is also possible to argue that the galactic universe is itself exceptional among the island universes with which space is strewn. I do not personally believe that the galactic universe will be ultimately found to be exceptional either in mass or in size or in any other way. We are inside it and so cannot yet get a true idea of its size and content. It may indeed be that ours is a universe where the central nucleus of matter has finally condensed into stars; but it is far more likely, as we have seen reason to think, that the centre of the galactic universe lies in the direction of the constellation Sagittarius within some of the dense diffused matter which forms one of the star-clouds of the Milky Way. There is such general uniformity among the great nebulae of space that it is highly probable that the galactic universe will be proved to be of the same general character as the large majority of them.

Even, however, if it should in time be demonstrated that the solar system is probably unique in the cosmos, I think that such uniqueness would be no satisfaction to the religious man who was told that the origin of the system lay in a chance encounter of two stars. To ascribe the source of this earth and, consequently, of life upon it to mere chance would undoubtedly offend religious sentiment. It is clear, however, that such offence would be lessened by the thought that other similar encounters had produced a vast distribution of life-bearing planets throughout space. The presence of such a vast distribution would indicate that accident was the handmaid of design; and the whole would take upon itself the appearance of having been planned—Divinely planned—for ends which must be worthy of the power and majestic unity displayed throughout.

§ 299. *The final state of the cosmos.*

If it be true that stellar radiation is due to annihilation of matter and that a star gradually burns away its mass, we may speculate that this process will continue until nothing is left of the star. In this case the end of all the matter in the star is radiation. Alternatively, we can imagine that, by some change of process due possibly to decreased temperature, radiation ceases before all the matter in the star is annihilated. It will then presumably end as an extinct star at a temperature not far removed from absolute zero. Imagination fails to picture the ultimate fate of a cosmos of such extinct stars. We have, however, seen that we can say (with much uncertainty) that our galactic universe will not reach this state until many millions of millions of years have elapsed.

We are naturally tempted to speculate as to what happens to the radiation emitted by the stars. Whatever be its source, the mass of the energy so sent forth by the bright stars of the galactic universe is, in the aggregate, enormous. Only a trivial fraction of this energy falls on other stars or their planets: practically the whole of it disappears into the void. If space is infinite we must conclude that such radiation is finally lost. If, however, space is finite, though unbounded, such radiation may either travel endlessly round the finite cosmos or there is the possibility that it will, under circumstances of which we have no experience, be transformed into matter.

§ 300. *Cosmic rays and the annihilation of matter.*

The existence in our atmosphere of a very penetrating form of radiation (that is to say, radiation of very short wave-length) has been known since at least the year 1906. This radiation was at first thought to originate in the earth. But a long series of experiments carried out by Millikan and his colleagues in America and by Kolhörster, Hoffmann and others in Germany seems finally to have shewn that the radiation comes from interstellar space. The intensity of the so-called 'cosmic rays' is apparently independent alike of the position of the sun and of the Milky Way. When they enter our atmosphere they are apparently unmixed with secondary β-rays (high-velocity electrons) such as would result from the interaction with matter of radiation of extremely short wave-length. By comparing the penetrative power of the cosmic rays with the hardest known monochromatic γ-rays, which result from the disintegration of thorium, Millikan is satisfied that the cosmic rays have, for the most part, a wave-length of some ·0005 Å. Mixed with them are ·2 per cent. of much harder rays, whose wave-length would appear to be but one-fortieth of that of the normal cosmic rays.

If the experimental facts are correct it would seem, as Millikan contends, that in general cosmic rays result from the formation of helium in interstellar space. Just as 'nebulium' lines (§ 279) can appear when density is very small so, if four hydrogen nuclei are free from collisions for a sufficiently long time, a helium nucleus might be formed from them. Presumably the radiation corresponding to this formation of helium would be emitted in quanta according to Planck's law

$$mc^2 = h\nu,$$

where m is the mass converted into radiation and ν the frequency of such radiation.

Now we know that when an atom of helium is formed from hydrogen, ·032 of the mass of a hydrogen atom is turned into radiation. Our equation is therefore

$$·032Hc^2 = h\nu,$$

where H is the mass of the hydrogen atom.

Now, in c.g.s. units, $H = 1·65 \times 10^{-24}$. Hence

$$\nu = 7·3 \times 10^{21} \quad \text{and} \quad \lambda = ·0004 \,\text{Å.} = 4 \times 10^{-12} \,\text{cm.}$$

It will be remembered that (§ 201) the Ångström is equal to 10^{-8} cm.

It would therefore appear that Millikan's contention is justified by the measured penetrative power of the cosmic rays.

The very small percentage of much harder cosmic rays will have a wave-length approximately given by

$$\lambda = ·00001 \,\text{Å.}$$

Now if it be assumed that protons and electrons can, under certain conditions, annihilate one another to form radiation, we may perhaps assume that the wave-length of the corresponding radiation is given by Planck's law. (The assumption is speculative, as we do not know that the reverse process takes place by which such radiation can be transformed into matter.) We should then have

$$Hc^2 = h\nu,$$

whence the wave-length of the radiation due to the annihilation of matter would be given by

$$\lambda = \cdot 000013 \text{ Å}.$$

Again the result appears to be confirmed by observation.

Thus, subject to further research, it would appear that in inter-stellar space there is a building-up of helium out of hydrogen and, on a much smaller scale, the annihilation of matter. It this be correct, we may anticipate that other elements of higher atomic number than helium are in process of formation, the energy resulting from such atom-building being small compared with that emitted in the formation of helium. Also we have good reason to speculate that, if matter can be dissolved into radiation in interstellar space, so also in the bright stars it is being annihilated. From the stars, however, the rays of wave-length ·000013 Å., which are the direct product of such annihilation, will not emerge into space. They will within the star rapidly be in-creased in length by Compton encounters (§ 196). In such encounters the electron which scatters the radiation will recoil with enormous energy; and this energy by further collisions will produce the heat of the star.

In connection with cosmic rays a possibility that is not wholly fanciful deserves mention. We have seen reason to believe that life exists throughout the cosmos and that, on many planets much older than the earth, such life will have reached a stage of evolution far beyond mankind. Beings of such advanced mental development would naturally try to send messages to, and receive them from, other planets. Such messages would be transmitted by radiation and naturally, if they could be artificially produced, very penetrative short-length rays would be used. It is not wholly improbable that, mixed with the cosmic rays which we receive, there are such messages. Attempts which have been made to discover them have, however, failed. But, after all, our present science is rudimentary. In another hundred thousand years humanity may have grown greatly in wisdom and understanding.

§ 301. *Extrapolation and its risks.*

When we know both the type of behaviour to be expected of some quantity dependent upon the time, and also the values of the quantity at a number of points of time, we can with a fair expectation of accuracy estimate its values at intermediate points. Such a process is termed *interpolation.* Suppose, however, that we know only the values of the function at certain points within a limited range of time together with its type of behaviour within that range, and that, on the basis of such knowledge, we try to estimate its values at far distant points outside the limited range. We then are committed to a process of *extrapolation* where error is highly probable.

All theories of the evolution of the cosmos are, in essence, attempts at extrapolation. Our direct knowledge of the cosmos extends at most throughout a period of three thousand years to the earliest astronomical observations of the Euphrates valley: for accurate observations we are practically limited to the last century. Happily we have such certainty as to the laws which govern the solar system that we could without serious error trace back the motions of the planets for thousands of years. In a sense it may be said that light from the most distant great nebulae which are visible at Mount Wilson tells us what happened in those nebulae as much as a hundred million years ago. But it has to be remembered that such a statement assumes that nothing has changed the light in the meantime. If, as Zwicky has suggested, the gravitational influence of stars and nebulae reddens light passing near them, such change does take place and profoundly alters our knowledge of the past.

The risks of extrapolation attach to all attempts to explain the origin of the cosmos. From the cosmogony which we have set forth in the present lecture serious inconsistencies and perplexities have not been absent. Even the origin of the solar system a few thousand million years ago is in doubt: and as regards the origin of the cosmos as a whole the difficulties are such that Lemaître has suggested that we should abandon even the belief that 'in the beginning' a vast uniformly diffused nebula filled all space. This belief, apart from the prestige which it gained from Laplace's support, is perhaps natural. A uniformly diffused gas is the obvious raw material out of which by some gradual process of evolution to construct great nebulae, star clusters, suns and planets. But the belief demands a colossal time-scale. We have seen that Jeans asks for some five billions of years for the evolution of a galaxy; and he must probably demand at least twenty times as long for the primary process whereby Laplace's uniformly diffused nebula aggregated into the masses of gas from which the great nebulae ultimately arose. Such a time-scale is almost certainly out of harmony with that to which any form of the theory of the expanding cosmos is likely to lead.

In consequence, Lemaître gives for the beginning of the cosmos a totally different type of extrapolation. We are to reject Laplace's vast and incredibly rarefied nebula uniformly filling an Einstein cosmos;

and in its place we are to imagine a single super-gigantic atom. With this atom, says Lemaître, space began; and the beginning of space marked the beginning of time. The radius of space started from zero. The mass of the original atom was practically equal to the present mass of the cosmos! This cosmos atom started on a process of radio-active evolution of which we see practically the last stages in the break-up of the few radio-active elements that still exist in the earth's crust. Its first fragmentation led to pieces from which the great nebulae ultimately resulted. Incidental to Lemaître's revolutionary theory is the hypothesis that the 'cosmic rays' of to-day are 10,000 million years old and tell us of the enormous radio-activity of the past.

I do not think that many cosmogonists have yet been persuaded by this theory of Lemaître. It is usually regarded as a brilliantly clever *jeu d'esprit* rather than a sober reconstruction of the beginning of the world. Yet we may well give due heed to certain facts which Lemaître emphasises. Ours is apparently a young universe. If man had first appeared upon this earth 100,000 million years hence, we should neither have known radio-active bodies nor would our telescopes have revealed the great nebulae. Though such materials for extrapolation remain, doubtless others, equally important, have vanished or are yet unknown to us. At present we are forced to speculate somewhat wildly as to the way in which the world began. As knowledge advances more satisfactory hypotheses may be constructed. But I doubt whether inference will ever allow man to know the physical circumstances of the beginning of the cosmos with the certainty with which, for example, he can infer the positions of the planets 5000 years ago.

§ 302.   *Need we postulate Divine intervention?*

Speculation as to the beginning of things attracts us all. The child asks how the world began: the philosopher turns away baffled by the same problem. Probably in us all there is the instinct that we are part of an incomprehensible machine, but that, if we could know the start, we could discover or infer the Starter. If we thus had evidence of the Starter, we might also gain knowledge of the Designer. In the end we might escape from the grip of the blind forces of Nature to the friendly care of Providence.

Now, mechanistic determinism is, when analysed, by no means a wholly satisfactory philosophy, as we shall endeavour to shew in Lecture XVII. But all to whom it is either a menace or a probable truth recognise that its limitations are likely to be most clearly perceived in connection with attempts to explain the beginning of those rigid sequences of which, according to the theory, we are the products.

To the philosopher the beginning of things suggests the problem of time. Is time real? In other words, do we merely observe what *is*; and do we by some limitation of perception import into our observations the notion of time? Or, on the contrary, do we take part in a 'becoming' by which the content of reality is enlarged and its richness increased? For me, personally, time is real, for I believe that our aspirations and struggles after goodness are real and of enduring value. But before the cosmos began there was, by hypothesis, no physical change within it. Can we say that real activity preceded physical change? Did time exist before the evolution of the world, inasmuch as thought never ceased with the Eternal Thinker? By such a question, and the issues which it raises, we are plunged at once into the most difficult problems of metaphysics.

The man of science has his own special perplexity. For him the time-process is measured by the continual increase of entropy. In the beginning the entropy of the cosmos was a minimum: in the end all energy will be chaotic, useless. The physical machine is visibly running down. As the physicist speculates, he asks why the serial character of human consciousness should give a direction for time in harmony with the second law of thermodynamics. Some would postulate a (none too good) entropy-clock in the human brain. But the relation to entropy of the time aspect of consciousness is but one element of the relation of matter to mind, that 'ultimate of ultimate problems' of which we shall say something in § 444. The law of entropy, unless indeed it be reversible elsewhere in the cosmos, points clearly alike to a beginning and to an end of those processes of material change which make life possible and seem to us inseparable from the physical world.

Must we then postulate Divine intervention? Are we to bring in God to create the first current in Laplace's nebula or to let off the cosmic fire-work of Lemaître's imagination? I confess to an unwillingness to bring God in this way upon the scene. The circumstances which thus seem to demand His presence are too remote and obscure to afford me any true satisfaction. Men have thought to find God at the special creation of their own species, or active when mind or life first appeared on the earth. They have made him God of the gaps in human knowledge. To me the God of the trigger is as little satisfying as the God of the gaps. It is because throughout the physical Universe I find thought and plan and power that behind it I see God as creator. Mere sequences are ultimately unintelligible: causation, apart from the Will of God, is, as Hume found it, obscure. The laws which the physicists discover may be mainly statistical; but to me they disclose the operation of Divine will. When we turn from the physical to the psychical and pass from matter to mind, creative activity, as I believe, reaches higher levels. At the highest goodness and truth shew, reflected in man, the image of God.

There are many to-day for whom old certainties have vanished, the old faith has crumbled. They pray with pathetic insistence, "O God, shew Thyself". I would have them look around. Everywhere, to those who have eyes to see, is the power and the presence of the Lord of Hosts*.

* The term 'Lord of Hosts' is the title of God of which the great Hebrew prophets made especial use. By it they emphasised God's sovereign majesty and power, including His control of the forces and processes of Nature.

Lecture xii

THE ORIGIN OF LIFE
AND THE GEOLOGICAL RECORD

THE ORIGIN OF LIFE

§ 303. *The coming of life to the earth.*

Scanty though our knowledge is of the past of our earth, we can be certain that at some stage of its history life appeared upon it. There is no reasonable doubt that, at the beginning of its course, the earth was at a temperature at least as high as the present surface temperature of the sun and therefore far too high to permit of the existence upon its surface of any kind of living organism known to ourselves. Water is a constituent part of all terrestrial organisms known to us. A temperature permanently higher than the boiling point of water would therefore be impossible for their continued existence. *À fortiori* temperatures, at which the rocks of the earth were molten, are quite incompatible with the presence of such living things. Since such things exist in vast abundance on the earth at the present time, there must have been an epoch when life first made its appearance upon the earth's surface.

From whence did life come and in what form or forms did it first appear? To neither of these questions can we give absolutely conclusive answers, but we will endeavour to indicate the conclusions which experts tentatively put forward.

§ 304. *Geology and the origin of life.*

For our knowledge of the types of organisms which have existed at successive periods of the earth's past we have to go to the science of geology. Experts in that science have worked out the order of the main groups of fossil-bearing rocks; and they can tell us what types of animals flourished in each, so far as such animals can be judged by skeletons which have survived as fossils. But in almost the earliest (Cambrian) rocks in which organic remains are well preserved there had already come into existence groups of animals, like trilobites, which are comparatively highly organised. We must conclude that, long before these rocks were deposited, there had been an elaborate development of life upon the earth: for we may certainly reject as absurd the alternative possibility that a vast number of complex organisms were transmitted through space to our globe. Thus it is not an exaggeration to say that, of the biological history of the earth, geology can only give us the closing pages. Those pages, sadly fragmentary, are of great interest. They reveal the gradual appearance and progressive development of more and more highly organised animals culminating in man. As we argue from the record which we know to the earlier period of which no record remains we conclude that, if we could trace back to the beginning the succession of living organisms upon the earth, we should finally reach a period when such as existed were of the most simple types, bits of living substance like the *amoeba* with which the medical student begins his course of zoology.

§ 305. *The living probably emerged from the non-living.*

Probably also, as we shall see, the earliest forms of life upon the earth were even more primitive and so small as to be ultra-microscopic. Where did they come from? Men whose judgment is entitled to respect differ in the answers which they give.

It may be held—and there are biologists of distinction who maintain this belief—that the living cannot have arisen from the non-living and that between the two there is a gap which cannot be bridged save by a special creative act. Those who take this view will say either that this creative act occurred: in other words, that God, when the earth was ready to support life, created primitive forms of life to exist upon it: or they will postulate that elementary organisms reached the earth in meteoric dust or some similar material from another part of our universe where life was already in being. Now the former alternative does not accord with what we know of Divine action in the cosmos. We do not meet with what we may call visible creative acts: *new things rather emerge within and through the natural order.* Although we cannot dismiss the meteoric hypothesis of the origin of life upon the earth as absolutely incredible, it is not likely that life would be transmitted in such a way from some region of the galactic universe where previously it had been able to exist. We, therefore, conclude that in all probability, at a particular stage of the earth's history, certain complex inorganic compounds were formed which made, as it were, a bridge from the non-living to the living. There was, in fact, a time when 'spontaneous generation' occurred. This implies, to those who accept the belief in the uniformity of Nature which is held by the modern man of science, that, if we could reproduce in the laboratory the conditions which existed upon the earth when life first appeared, we should cause it to appear once more.

§ 306. *Arguments in favour of 'spontaneous generation'.*

It must be admitted that no laboratory attempt to create life out of inorganic material has so far been satisfactory. But it must be remembered that conditions necessary for a successful experiment cannot easily be obtained, inasmuch as minute organisms are now present everywhere. To destroy all such organisms within a closed vessel, and then to create within the vessel conditions such that substances within it can by increasing chemical complexity become life-bearing, is well-nigh, if not quite, impossible. None the less, there is much evidence to suggest that there is no absolute gap between the living and the non-living.

In support of this statement we may point to the fact that so-called organic substances, which, as men thought, could only be produced by the agency of living animals, have been in increasing numbers made from inorganic compounds. The synthesis of urea by Wöhler at Giessen in the year 1828 was a highly significant step in this direction. Further, the mechanisms of the human body and its biochemical processes seem to be all capable of explanation in terms of the laws of physics and chemistry formulated for the inorganic world. In particular the same energy is put into and given out by a man, so far as can be determined by specially delicate calorimeter tests. Living matter, moreover, is associated with what are called colloidal solutions, which are, like the solutions of a fat in water, heterogeneous: they are not homogeneous like the solution of such a substance as common salt. Though colloids belong to a world of matter different from that of crystalline solutions, they occur among inorganic substances. Such facts as these appear to indicate that there is no natural boundary between the lifeless and the living, and to justify the assertion that "there is a smooth slide up to life".

We proceed now to give a necessarily speculative reconstruction of this passage from dead matter to living organisms.

§ 307. *'In the beginning.'*

We have seen that the earth began as a planet of the sun some two, or possibly four, thousand million years ago. Probably it cooled rapidly from its initial temperature which was, of course, that of the outer matter of the sun. Ultimately the cooling led to the formation on the earth of a solid crust above which were gases. What were these gases? They were probably water-vapour and carbon-dioxide. It is unlikely that there was any free oxygen. The oxygen which now forms part of our atmosphere almost certainly arose from the initial carbon-dioxide through the dissociation of its carbon and oxygen at times when the coal measures and other strata containing free carbon were laid down. Some other part of the initial carbon-dioxide is now a constituent of the sedimentary limestone rocks. Some of these rocks, in all probability, were produced by lime-forming organisms: they consist essentially of calcium carbonate.

It appears doubtful whether 'in the beginning' there was any nitrogen associated with the carbon-dioxide and water-vapour on the earth's surface. Possibly most of the nitrogen now in the earth's atmosphere originally existed in combination with metals of the earth's crust in the form of various nitrides.

§ 308. *The three fundamental elements of organic chemistry.*

The sun's rays a couple of thousand million years ago probably had much of their present quality and strength. But the rays which came to this planet did not have to pass in the upper atmosphere of the earth through the oxygen (or its allotropic modification ozone) which at present scatters the short-wave ultra-violet rays. Such rays fell upon, if they did not penetrate, the gases which originally covered the hot surface of the earth. Now carbon-dioxide and water contain the three elements carbon, oxygen and hydrogen from which the practically innumerable stable compounds of organic chemistry are made. In the language of chemists hydrogen is univalent: from its atom proceeds a single bond. Oxygen is bivalent and carbon quadrivalent. Hydrogen and carbon alone can by virtue of such valency form rings and chains of molecules constituting the elaborate series of hydrocarbons. When oxygen is introduced the complexity and number of possible compounds become enormous and their variety baffles description.

Thus on the earth at the beginning there were the fundamental elements from which the infinite variety of compounds of organic chemistry arises.

Now, by the synthetic action of chlorophyll (the green colouring-matter of plants), carbon-dioxide and water are turned into glucose and oxygen according to some formula such as

$$6CO_2 + 6H_2O = C_6H_{12}O_6 + 6O_2.$$

This process is only possible in sunlight, for energy (derived from the sun) is needed for such a formation of a carbohydrate. The details of the process by which water, carbon-dioxide and solar energy become sugar and oxygen are still, it would appear, somewhat mysterious. But it seems that, first of all, oxygen is separated alike from the carbon-dioxide and from the water-vapour: and that then the carbon atoms are linked up until six of them enter the resulting carbohydrate molecules.

§ 309. *The preparation for life.*

We can imagine that some such process took place under the influence of ultra-violet sun-rays in the heavy hot gases which covered the cooling earth more than a thousand million years ago. Further, we may conjecture that the metallic nitrides and the hydrogen from water-vapour would combine to set free ammonia.

But water, carbon-dioxide, sugars and ammonia can produce a whole series of molecules of increasing complexity; and such include the amino-acids which enter into the constitution of proteins. Now such a mixture, if formed to-day in our sea, would rapidly decay: it would, that is to say, be destroyed by micro-organisms. But when the earth was in its infancy there were presumably no micro-organisms to devour the food awaiting them.

§ 310. *The ascent to life.*

What happened? Probably there was a gradual ascent to life, during which colloidal carbon compounds became living things. In the first place we conjecture that catalysts and enzymes appeared, substances whose presence causes chemical reactions to take place though they themselves are apparently unchanged when such reactions have taken place. Then possibly there was developed some organised molecule, not yet an organism and yet more than an ordinary molecule, with a number of constituents each of which could reproduce itself only if the others were present. An analogy to such an organised molecule seems to be provided by filter-passing viruses, highly organised types of which cause hydrophobia and small-pox. They can multiply only in living tissue: they can pass through a porcelain filter which stops bacteria: and, further, they are ultra-microscopic so that their linear dimensions must be at most of the order of the wave-length of light. Investigation of such living or semi-living ultra-microscopic organisms is as yet in its infancy. Possibly the bacteriophage, an ultra-microscopic agent which destroys certain cultures of bacteria, represents a stage, earlier than the virus, in the increasing complexity by which the non-living passed into the living.

§ 311. *The first life.*

As soon as any organised molecule became an organism ready to multiply, it would have on the infant earth food in abundance. There would be no struggle for existence until some competitor appeared; and the competitor, if independent, would have had a poor chance of survival. More complex organisms, which were progressive descendants of the first to be formed, would however soon compete with other descendants and so begin the struggle for existence.

It might be objected that at the beginning there was, by the postulates which we have made, no free oxygen to provide energy for the earth's primitive organisms. Everyone knows that the energy of ourselves and of other mammals is derived from a process which may fairly be described as burning carbon in oxygen. If there were no oxygen in our atmosphere and none dissolved in the water of our seas all highly organised animal life would come to an end. To the objection that originally free oxygen was lacking it may be answered that primitive organisms did not need it: almost certainly they obtained their energy by fermentation. Confirmation of this possibility is thought to be given by the fact that embryonic birds and mammals still live by fermentation during the initial stages of the development of the fertilised cell from which they begin.

The above account of the origin of life is necessarily a speculative attempt to construct an unknown past. But it embodies only well-established facts and we may reasonably expect that the gaps within it will be bridged in due course. Such a scheme, modified possibly in detail, appears to find general favour with biochemists.

§ 312. *Primitive organisms: of one type or many?*

No one can speculate upon the first stages of life upon the earth without asking the question: Has all life upon the earth resulted from a single primitive organism or have different organisms arisen at different times to provide a whole series of organic departures? Probably the former alternative is to be accepted in view of the following considerations. Many molecules of organic chemistry are unsymmetrical. We can have right-handed and left-handed molecules, the corresponding crystals being, as it were, images of one another in a mirror. Light, for instance, on passing through certain sugar solutions can undergo either right-handed or left-handed rotation of its plane of polarisation. We should expect that in living organisms both kinds of asymmetry would appear equally often. The fact that only one kind actually occurs suggests that 'in the beginning' one form of living organism developed through a fortunate combination of circumstances and by successful multiplication prevented its mirror-opposite from emerging later. The argument is suggestive rather than conclusive. But the unique emergence of life—if indeed it was unique—corresponds to the apparently definite fact that in the course of evolution the same type of emergence* has seldom, or never, been duplicated at different epochs or places.

§ 313. *Was the earth's initial covering of gases essential or merely convenient?*

It may be asked whether life would have appeared upon the earth but for the combined presence on its surface of water, carbon-dioxide and sunlight. Are there in the elements hydrogen, oxygen and carbon special possibilities of combination which no other elements could offer? Do we need the three elements in abundance on the surface of a planet in order that life may appear upon it? Such questions are profoundly intriguing and most difficult to answer. It is true that from these elements there can be produced the hundreds of thousands of stable compounds whose investigation makes the science of organic chemistry. But one would *à priori* expect that with more complex elements of higher atomic number there would be even more possibilities of similar combination, though these are at present unexplored. And it is to be remembered that living organisms have a most unexpected habit of using other elements than the three which are plainly fundamental in their structure. Not merely does nitrogen enter into all protein but phosphorus seems to be essential in a variety of ways in living organisms. It occurs, of course, in the bones of vertebrates. But, moreover, in every cell or natural non-cellular piece of living protoplasm there is at least one nucleus. The nucleus always contains chromatin, a substance with a remarkable power of absorbing certain staining fluids like carmine. Of chromatin phosphorus is an invariable ingredient. Still more remarkable is the fact that chlorophyll, the green colouring matter of plants, contains magnesium; and it is indeed possible that the presence of this element is necessary in the process of 'reduction' which liberates oxygen. Once again sulphur occurs in the proteins; and chlorine, as hydrochloric acid, gives a needed acidity to the gastric juice of man. Even more remarkable is the fact that iodine is needed in the human thyroid gland. Marine organisms absorb iodine

---

* By 'emergence' we mean, not the appearance of a new mutation, but its success in modifying a species.

from sea-water: but it is difficult to understand why chickens should for good health need a minute supply of this none too common element.

Perhaps, however, the most surprising use of an unexpected element is in connection with the blood. The colouring matter in the red corpuscles of the blood is a solid substance called haemoglobin. This substance contains iron; and by virtue of that fact can unite with oxygen to form oxyhaemoglobin. Oxyhaemoglobin appears to be 'a loose molecular combination' from which oxygen diffuses when, as in the capillaries of the circulation system, the surrounding diffusion pressure of oxygen is low. When this pressure is high, as in the lungs, oxygen is taken up again. In this way oxyhaemoglobin, as the blood circulates, acts mechanically as a carrier of oxygen from the lungs to the tissues. Life in the higher vertebrates has thus seized upon iron and has made the element essential to its maintenance. But in the lower animals, for instance in the cephalopods (cuttle-fishes and allied forms) and some crabs, copper fulfils a similar function. Henze, in the year 1911, discovered that the blood of ascidians (sea-squirts) contains noteworthy quantities of vanadium; and later investigators have found that the polychromatic blood corpuscles of these creatures owe their colour to vanadium derivatives.

Such facts indicate an amazing adaptability on the part of living things. *Il faut vivre*; and, if iron is not available, copper will suit. Once a particular element has been given a fundamental *rôle* in a group of organisms, a supply of this element must be forthcoming or the group will perish. Yet the probability remains that, had the element not been initially available, living tissue would have made another kind of building material serve its end. One is left with the feeling that, even if carbon, hydrogen and oxygen had not been available, life might have found elements which would have been adequate for its needs. As regards terrestrial life, however, it may truly be said*: "From the materialistic and the energetic standpoint alike, carbon, hydrogen and oxygen, each by itself, and all taken together, possess unique and pre-eminent chemical fitness for the organic mechanism. They alone are best fitted to form it and to set it in motion; and their stable compounds, water and carbonic acid, which make up the changeless environment, protect and renew it, for ever drawing fresh energy from the sunshine".

* The quotation is from a singularly suggestive book by L. J. Henderson *The Fitness of the Environment*. Macmillan, 1927, p. 248.

§314. *Does life's supposed origin give any clue to its nature?*

Assuming now that life had some such origin as has been suggested, can it be held that we are any nearer to an understanding of its nature? I would unhesitatingly reply in the negative. The essential characteristic of living tissue is that it registers the past in such a way that what has been tends to determine the present. It is true that the present state of a mass of non-living material like a bar of iron is to some slight extent determined by its past history. But living tissue, in the fundamental phenomenon of cell-division, reveals an amazingly complete organisation and development according to plan; and to its activity there is no parallel whatever in the inorganic world. We have not the faintest understanding why a group of chemical substances, mainly built from carbon, hydrogen and oxygen, should have this sort of unconscious memory of past events, this ability to telescope history. We may, if we like, say that from the non-living the living has emerged. But equally we might postulate that some non-physical unknown called 'life' had manifested itself with increasing success, by the aid of a particular range of chemical molecules, as ever more complex organisms were built up.

Apparently in living organisms, as we have already said, the laws of physics and chemistry are never set aside. But, none the less, the categories of physics and chemistry are insufficient to explain the phenomena of life. If a speculative reconstruction of the origin of life is insufficient to explain its nature, much less does it afford any means of understanding the relation of matter to mind. Is life but the sign of the presence of mind? Is there mental awareness, to however slight a degree, in plants or in primitive animal organisms? We do not know. Is mind an emergent through living tissue from inert matter? If this question means that mind is but as it were froth on the stream of physico-chemical change, the answer is certainly in the negative.

I would claim that the emergence of life must be regarded as a sign of creative activity: and that such activity has brought a higher degree of reality into existence on earth. Nevertheless, the origin of life, like all origins, is in fact hidden from us. A still higher form of creative activity was manifested when, from mere response and from an almost mechanical trial and error, there began that awareness which was to culminate for us in the mind of man. In imagination we can see such creative activity proceeding for more than twelve hundred million years upon the earth; and the latter part of the process is actually telescoped for our personal observation as the infant becomes the thoughtful man. But we cannot explain what we observe. There is behind Nature, as it seems to me, a Power Who has created and guided and still sustains. His ways are wonderful and our understanding of them will ever be partial. The mystery of life is unsolved, probably insoluble. As I see the matter, life and mind are the supreme manifestations for us of God's creative might.

THE GEOLOGICAL RECORD

§315. *The rise of geological investigation.*

It is strange to think that two centuries ago men had no knowledge of the history of the earth save during the last three thousand years. The Bible preserved Jewish speculation and folk-lore: and elaborate calculations based upon its narratives caused Christians to believe that the creation of the world took place some four or five thousand years before the Christian era. The familiar date 4004 B.C. is, of course, due to Archbishop Ussher (1581–1656): but the opinions of Catholic theologians and the authorised teaching of the Roman Church were equally erroneous.

Our modern knowledge of the immense antiquity, alike of the earth and of life upon it, is due primarily to that accurate study of the different strata in the rocks of the earth's surface which constitutes the science of geology. The new science was first developed during the latter half of the eighteenth century and our own countrymen had no small share in the pioneer work: it 'can claim a peculiarly British ancestry'. Naturally the revolutionary conclusions of the geologists were resented in conservative theological circles; and the Bampton Lectures of the first third of the nineteenth century bear a petrified witness to the hostility of contemporary Oxford divines*. The publication in the year 1830 of Sir Charles Lyell's (1797–1875) *Principles of Geology*† marked an epoch. The work profoundly influenced Charles Darwin (1809–1882) and must rank with *The Origin of Species* as one of the two books which finally upset traditional beliefs as to the age of the earth and as to the origin and history of living creatures upon it. *The Origin of Species* was published in the year 1859.

* "Between 1800 and 1834 four of the Bampton Lecturers dealt with the conflict between science and religion, and three of them, Faber, Nares and Bidlake, adopted a tone of violent hostility to the new geological discoveries. V. F. Storr, *The Development of English Theology in the Nineteenth Century* 1800–1860. Longmans, 1913, p. 181.

† The twelfth edition was issued in the year 1875. As the article in the *Dictionary of National Biography* says: "the *Principles* practically gave the death-blow to the catastrophic school of geologists".

§316. *Gaps in the geological record.*

Since Darwin died, geological research has been actively pursued by men of many races. From many lands, and especially from North America, new knowledge has come, so that the main outlines of the geological history of the earth are now firmly established. Geological evidence has more and more tended to shew that species of animals and plants are not immutable. The record of the rocks exhibits a progressively higher organisation in animate nature as successive eras are examined; and not seldom this same record has revealed extinct forms of life which might well be ancestral to species now different from one another.

There are, nevertheless, many 'missing links': we cannot trace, as we would wish, the development of existing species from primitive organisms. In particular, there are but a few known fossils to bridge the gap between man and his ape-like ancestors—but a few links in the complete chain which we would like to exhibit. But, as Darwin himself cogently pointed out, we ought to expect the geological record to be imperfect. The soft parts of animals rapidly decay; their harder parts are seldom preserved as fossils. Of the rocks laid down in past ages only a small fraction are now on the surface of the earth and of these few indeed have been scientifically explored. They must be exposed in cliffs, quarries, railway cuttings and mines before the geologist has access to them. Moreover, great areas of the earth's surface have never been properly examined: and it must not be forgotten that many regions where important developments may have occurred are now beneath the sea.

Furthermore, fossils are only preserved in places where sediment is being continuously deposited by water or more rarely where successive layers of vegetation, preferably in marshy ground, lead to a slow accumulation of material. Wind-swept and normally dry uplands, and especially mountains, suffer slow but continuous denudation: and any animal remains upon them will probably dissolve into small fragments under the action of the elements, though in rare instances they may be swept away by the action of water and preserved more or less imperfectly in some low-lying sediment.

§317. *The ages of the different strata of the earth.*

These considerations not only make us expect that the geological record will be imperfect, but they also lead us to understand how difficult it is to get even a rough estimate of the relative ages of different strata in the earth's surface. We naturally assume that contemporary forms of life in adjacent areas will closely resemble one another: and the fact that much the same succession of animals and plants occurs over a great part of the world enables us to determine fairly satisfactorily which strata were laid down cotemporaneously in different places. But to determine the relative thickness of the rocks which separate two different epochs is extraordinarily difficult. Sediment at the mouth of a delta is deposited vastly more quickly than in a deep sea: on wind-swept rock there will be no deposit at all. Yet there was, until the present century, no better way of measuring the relative ages of different geological formations than by ascertaining the relative thickness of the rocks through which one would have to pass if all the formations were horizontally superimposed one upon another. Rough measurements of this type, which were supposed to correspond to an assumed common rate of deposition, were fairly often made. Naturally they did not pretend to be accurate.

Because such measurements were so inadequate as regards accuracy, and still more because the measure of the assumed common rate of deposition was so extremely difficult to estimate, scientific men until recently refused to attempt to indicate in years the ages of the different main strata of the earth. Estimates were given in 'popular' scientific works, but were repudiated by experts as worthless. There was no adequate basis of ascertained fact on which they could rest.

§ 318. *Measurements by radio-active decomposition.*

Of late, as we have seen in § 156, the rate of disintegration of uranium has offered a way of estimating the age of any rock in which uranium, free from admixture with lead, has disintegrated into helium and uranium-lead. Clearly we must be sure that, at the formation of the rock of which the age is to be measured, the uranium in it was free from admixture with the lead which is one of the products of its decomposition. Fortunately, as regards this necessity, uranium occurs in pitchblende in the form of a complicated oxide which crystallises separately from any lead compound which is found in the same ore. We must also be sure that radio-activity alone has altered the composition of the particular mass of rock which we take for examination. Heat and water are alike agents which might alter the ratio of uranium to lead, the former because it might produce re-crystallisation which would separate the derived lead from the uranium which produced it.

Holmes*, whose investigations followed earlier researches by Boltwood, believes that it has been possible to eliminate such sources of error as we have mentioned. He assumed, however, that the rate at which uranium breaks up is such that its average life is $7\cdot5 \times 10^9$ years, while the true time seems, as we have said in §156, to be $6\cdot6 \times 10^9$ years. Jeffreys†, therefore, modifies Holmes' figures, with the result that the beginning of the Tertiary era is put at sixty million years ago, the Carboniferous period at from 260–300 million years ago and the Devonian at from 310–340 million years ago. The same investigations give 560 million years as the age of the Archaeozoic rocks immediately preceding the Cambrian.

The age of the oldest known igneous rocks, as similarly determined, appears to be 1340 million years. But these rocks are "intrusive into conglomerates which must have been formed from still older rocks by sedimentation". Thus the age of the earth's ocean must be more than 1340 million years. We have seen that the present tendency of astronomers is to put the age of the earth at about two thousand million years: it is, however, generally agreed that four thousand million years is not impossible.

It may be added that Holmes' figures greatly exceed earlier estimates. These latter were obtained by attempted measurements of the aggregate thickness of the strata deposited since the Palaeozoic era began, coupled with an estimated rate of deposition of sediment. We have indicated that they cannot have been to any extent worthy of credit. But, perhaps because opinions once accepted are stubbornly held, some palaeontologists of repute still affirm that Holmes' estimates are ten or fifteen times too large. Nevertheless, in what follows all our time-estimates will be based on the belief that approximately 60,000,000 years separate the end of the Mesozoic era from our own time.

§319. *The main geological formations.*

For reference it is convenient to give a table of the main geological formations, the oldest being at the bottom. At the side we indicate the length of time which probably elapsed *during* the formation of each group of rocks. These numbers, as we have indicated, are still in dispute. It will be noticed that as we approach modern times the lengths of the

---

* A historical account of the subject will be found in A. Holmes, *The Age of the Earth.* Harper, 1913. Holmes' conclusions appear in a table to be found in *Discovery*, vol. I, 1920, pp. 118–23.

† H. Jeffreys, *The Earth.* Cambridge University Press, 1924, p. 68.

various eras tend to become shorter. This is to be expected as, naturally, we know more of recent geological epochs. It may be added that distinctions between recent successive strata are both more easily made and also more important than such as belong to the distant past.

		Million years
Tertiary or Cainozoic era	Pleistocene	60
	Pliocene	
Age of mammals	Miocene	
	Oligocene	
	Eocene	
Secondary or Meso-zoic era	Cretaceous	85
	Jurassic	
Age of reptiles	Triassic	
Newer Palaeozoic era	Permian	175
	Carboniferous	
	Devonian	
Older Palaeozoic era	Silurian	250
	Ordovician	
	Cambrian	
Archaeozoic era		300
Eozoic era		500

Knowledge of the kinds of life which flourished in the main geological eras and of the changes which took place in such eras is essential for an understanding of the literature of evolution. By means of such knowledge we can get a conspectus of the past history of the earth: and we can realise the force of some of the main arguments in favour of the mutability of species. Of the Eozoic period we know virtually nothing. During it the first life must have developed; but no records of that life remain in what are believed to have been the earliest sedimentary rocks. Such rocks, as an American writer says graphically, "have been soaked and honeycombed with molten rock coming from below, squeezed, mashed, folded, contorted, baked and partly melted". We are then not surprised that the only possible signs of organic life are certain beds of graphite, limestone and iron-ore which probably owe their origin to the activity of an immense number of somewhat primitive organisms.

§ 320. *The Archaeozoic era.*

In the following Archaeozoic period cellular plants and animals of primitive types must have reached a fairly high degree of organisation. Most of the animals were soft-bodied inhabitants of the sea and the mud: all were invertebrates. Scanty indications of life survive in worm trails and casts in Archaeozoic rocks of Montana which lie nearly 8000 feet below the Cambrian. Walcott, who discovered these traces, also found in limestone formations of the same geological era what are believed to be calcareous secretions of algae (sea-weeds).

§ 321. *The Palaeozoic era.*

But it was not until the Palaeozoic era had begun that we get, in a bed of greasy shale in British Columbia, delicate impressions of some of the soft-bodied animals which must have been so numerous. They are 'mere films of carbon against slate' but they shew with surprising detail of structure the presence of somewhat advanced invertebrate forms, among which are echinoderms, crustaceans and worms.

With the middle Cambrian formation we get an abundance of fossils, and, in particular, of trilobites. Marine plants also occur. The trilobites apparently had abnormally large eyes and may indeed have been blind. Possibly, therefore, they lived beneath dense clouds through which the sunlight could not penetrate or in the depths of the sea: more probably, they were adapted to life within the sea-mud of shallow sea-basins. The relatively sudden appearance of an abundance of fossils after practically complete dearth at the beginning of the Cambrian naturally arouses speculative enquiry. It may be that the organisms living at the earlier period had not acquired the ability to use lime-salts. It is more likely, however, that carbonate of lime was not available. There is an ingenious theory, possibly true, that the scavenging organisms of later times were not at first available. Decaying forms, therefore, gave off carbonate of ammonia which precipitated the lime in the water and so deprived of its use animals which otherwise would have had shells.

In the Ordovician rocks numerous marine animals developed shells. In this period, moreover, there occur what appear to be the remains of land plants: possibly, therefore, life began at this time to climb from the sea to the land. But it is not until the Silurian epoch that we get what are clearly fossil scorpions together with undoubted land plants. At the same time the extraordinarily interesting lung-fishes (*dipnoi*) make their appearance. Some of them still survive in a modified form and are worthy of attention because of their antiquity. But their chief significance lies in the fact that they can bury themselves in mud and thus survive during a dry summer because their swimming bladder acts as a lung. In these animals we have an indication of how gill-breathers became lung-breathers and thus, from the sea, were ready to colonise the land.

The Devonian formations.

In the Devonian period, whence come the Old Red Sandstone rocks, we can trace a significant development, especially of plants. Land plants become abundant. Amphibians are said to occur, though some experts doubt whether it has yet been established that the amphibians preceded the reptiles: all agree that it is highly likely that such was the natural order of succession among vertebrates. The primitive fishes of the Silurian, the ganoids, developed shining armour; and two pairs of paddles were in process of being replaced by flexible fins. Trilobites continued to swarm and, among crustacea, eurypterids attained a gigantic size.

The Carboniferous period.

Owing to the coal measures which occur within it, the Carboniferous period is more widely known among the public than any other geological era. The coal was laid down in swamps in which giant club-mosses and horsetails, ferns and seed-ferns grew rankly. The first true flying insects arose in the Carboniferous era and the reptiles then made their appearance. The insects were of ancient types apparently related to our dragon-flies and grasshoppers: they often attained to a relatively large size; yet it is said that they suffered from the curious disability of being unable to fold their wings. In the lower Carboniferous rocks, which were laid down in the sea, corals are numerous and varied.

The Permian period.

The Carboniferous period passed into the Permian, and with it the Palaeozoic era came to an end. During the Permian old forms began to die away under the pressure of a harsh and arid climate combined with glacial epochs of great severity. Evidences of other glacial epochs in early Palaeozoic and even in Archaeozoic times have been discovered; and, as all know, such epochs recurred during the recent Pleistocene era. Their cause is an absolute mystery unless we can assume, as A. Wegener (1880–1931) suggested, a shifting of the land surfaces of the earth whereby those now in tropical or temperate climates were at intervals exposed to Arctic cold. During the Permian epoch cycad-like forms were developed and put an end to the dominance of the Carboniferous flora. The reptiles began to make good their claim to be lords of creation in the Mesozoic era; and such mammal-like reptiles as theromorphs began to develop the temporal fossae characteristic of mammals.

§322. *The Mesozoic era.*

The new era ushered in by the Triassic period shewed that the rigours of the Permian had changed the face of animate nature. From higher mammal-like reptiles, known as cynodonts, mammals arose. The more progressive fishes began to develop a hard internal skeleton. But the reptiles swarmed everywhere. Some invaded the sea. Others, true reptiles called pterodactyls, invaded the air by means of a bat-like wing membrane. Some developed enormously in bulk until, in the Cretaceous era, they were huge masses of flesh, heavier than any other land animals in terrestrial history. Probably the dinosaurs were alike the dominant and the most progressive group of Mesozoic reptiles. They are remarkable for the fact that in the lower part of the spine a sort of second brain was developed. In some creatures the weight of this great nerve centre is estimated to have been more than ten times that of the brain: it seems in part to have controlled the limbs. There is, of course, no reason why a vertebrate should not have a second brain; and its brain need not necessarily be in its head. Small secondary nerve-centres exist at present in the mammals; but, when Nature made a large-scale experiment in the dinosaurs, it failed.

§323. *The origin of the birds.*

The most surprising development of the whole Mesozoic era was, without doubt, the change by which a reptile became a true bird. A quarry in Bavaria, of middle Jurassic rock useful in lithography, has given us not only pterodactyls but also two reptilian birds (one lacks its head) with teeth and feathers. T. H. Huxley (1825–1895), some half-century ago, spoke of birds as 'glorified reptiles', and the description is singularly true. Even to-day the first feathers of a chicken are formed from the upper layers of its skin, just as the scales of a lizard grow. The heart and aorta of a very young chicken resemble corresponding vessels in a crocodile; and, though one of the aortae becomes a mere rudiment in adult life, the surviving aorta of the adult bird passes obliquely across the body. Thus what seems at first sight an inexplicable bit of clumsiness on Nature's part finds a complete explanation in the reptilian origin of the birds.

A bird needs a fine correlation of faculties for effective mastery of the air: and we may with confidence postulate a considerable development of the front part of its brain during the Mesozoic era and simultaneously a change from cold to warm blood. The cold-blooded animal takes the temperature of the surrounding air; and the biochemical reactions of its body go slowly in cold weather, so that the animal tends then to be comatose. The warm-blooded animal has the more uniform alertness; but it is relatively spendthrift of heat; and it needs a covering of fur or feathers, if it is to be moderately economical. The change from reptile to bird was a marvellous transformation. That the fossil record should give conclusive evidence of its having occurred about one hundred million years ago must convince all, save those who will not listen to argument, that the realm of animate nature has come into existence by the process of evolution and not by special creation. The reptile-like birds of the Jurassic must gradually have changed into the forms which we know inasmuch as, in the Cretaceous period, we get birds which are of a modern type, save that they have not lost the teeth from their jaws.

§324. *The early mammals.*

We have said that during the early Mesozoic the mammal-like reptile gradually changed into the reptile-like mammal and thence into primitive mammalian forms. Of the latter in the Cretaceous and earlier rocks we find only monotremes and marsupials. As is well known, in all reptiles the young are hatched from eggs. The monotremes are egg-laying mammals: the marsupials bring forth their young alive but carry them at first in a pouch of the body. Now, when Australia was first discovered, all its mammals (with one exception) were either marsupials or monotremes. We naturally assume therefore that the land-bridges connecting Australia with the South-East of Asia were broken down at the end of the Mesozoic. Confirmation of this belief is afforded by the native Australian flora, which had either Mesozoic or quite early Tertiary affinities. It is, further, highly significant that evolution in Australia was slow and without any parallels to the vast mammalian developments which took place elsewhere on the earth. The fact confirms a generally accepted belief that all the great evolutionary developments of earth's history have been unique. We shall elsewhere give in some detail reasons for the conclusion that, save in relatively small adaptations to environment, Nature does not repeat herself.

§325. *The Tertiary era.*

The Tertiary era which followed the long development of the Cretaceous is *par excellence* the Age of Mammals. Invertebrates, fishes, reptiles and mammals have successively dominated the earth: we would give much to know what will be the next chapter in evolutionary history. The Age of Mammals has been relatively short, some sixty million years. But it must be remembered that even in the Devonian period the main structure of the higher mammals had been laid down. Differences of structural form which seem to us of vast importance are magnified by the fact that we too are mammals.

The divisions of the Tertiary era.

The Tertiary era began with the Eocene. During this long period, which was longer than all the rest of the Tertiary put together, the mammals were either monotremes and marsupials or else archaic types of placental mammals. The placental mammal is, of course, one in which an intimate union between mother and embryo is established by means of the elaborate placenta or 'after-birth', to use the midwives' term. None of these mammals had large brain capacity; and they were of such 'synthetic' types that it is hard to classify them among existing orders. As they evolved and advanced, there was a simultaneous modernisation of flowering plants.

Differentiations towards modern mammalian types became rapid during the Oligocene period. In this era the Primates, which had been represented by lemurs in the Eocene, were continued by long-tailed monkeys of extinct genera, and at the end by small primitive apes.

The Miocene era was genial. The forests developed enormously. Mammals flourished and in particular different types of anthropoid apes appeared.

In the subsequent Pliocene era there was a further modernisation of the mammals, species appearing which are obviously ancestral to types now living. But towards the end of the era the glacial epochs began. For example, in European rocks of the Upper Pliocene Arctic shells extend to the Mediterranean. The alternate progress and regression of the glaciers extended through the Pleistocene until within some 20,000 years of our own time: it may indeed be that we ourselves are living through an inter-glacial phase. Experts differ as to how many glacial and inter-glacial periods there have been. James Geikie* (1839–1915) described six such periods as distinguishable in Britain: the Germans find clear evidence of four in the Alps: the French measure by three glacial phases. If we take the French enumeration, the first phase will have taken place at the end of the Pliocene epoch. During the inter-glacial phase which followed it the Southern elephant roamed over Western Europe; and together with this beast we find the Etruscan rhinoceros, the great hippopotamus, a horse and other large mammals.

---

* *Vide* J. Geikie, *The Great Ice Age.* The first edition of this book was published in the year 1874 and the third twenty years later.

There followed another glacial phase somewhat after the beginning of the Pleistocene. This Lower Pleistocene glacial period was apparently the most severe in recent geological history. In it the ice-sheet was most far-reaching and the moraines of the great glaciers extended farthest from the mountain centres. It was followed by a great inter-glacial epoch in which the climate was mild: Merck's rhinoceros, the sabre-toothed tiger, the hippopotamus, certain monkeys and—perhaps the most important fact of all—Chellean man were characteristic fauna. After this pleasant era the climate gradually became colder and more moist: the woolly rhinoceros spread widely and Neanderthal man with his coarse Moustierian culture came to the fore. Man probably re-treated during the harshest rigour of this last (mid-Pleistocene) glacial phase, leaving the hairy mammoth to endure the ice and snow. As the phase ended we gradually pass into a modern world. At first the rein-deer flourish in cold dry steppe country and human culture is Aurig-nacian. Then, as the climate improves, we get the bison, the great ox and the prairie squirrel associated with what is called Magdalenian culture. Finally Neolithic man lives in the environment we know.

§326. *Tertiary geography.*

The fossil records of the Tertiary era enable us with fair certainty to reconstruct the great geographical changes of recent geological times. We have mentioned the severance of Australia from South-Eastern Asia. A number of facts connected with the fauna and flora of South America shew that it was separated from North America by a broad sea which covered most of Central America from the Eocene to the later part of the Miocene epoch. The continent of Africa was divided during the Tertiary era by seas into two separate areas. The fossil remains of curious dwarf elephants—one on Malta was only three feet high—occur in Sicily, Cyprus, Crete, etc. They indicate that, probably during the late Pleistocene, there were several land-bridges across the Mediterranean. As these sank, elephants, which during the Pleistocene flourished all over the world except in Australia, were isolated on the islands which remained. On these islands they degenerated and finally died out.

It is, of course, hardly necessary to say that the English Channel is a quite modern barrier between Great Britain and the Continent. Our fauna and flora are European and the breach probably did not take place until late Pleistocene times. Similarly, Ireland was joined to Great Britain, and comparatively recently the whole of the North Sea was a plain standing a little above sea-level. It is also certain that Alaska and Siberia have been often and for long periods connected by land. Other land-bridges have been postulated with regard to which scepticism is natural. Earthworms find sea-water a practically impregnable barrier. Yet groups of closely allied earthworms (*acanthodrilidae*) are found alike in New Zealand and South America. A land-bridge between these regions has therefore been postulated. But it is necessary to insist that, when we go behind the Tertiary era to the more distant past of the earth, the geography of the world is most difficult to ascertain. That there has been a connection between Europe and North America is widely believed. There are some who hold that the whole of America has swung away from Eur-Africa across what is now the Atlantic Ocean as the land-masses of the globe have moved over the viscous substratum. All such speculations need to be very critically examined.

§ 327. *The destruction of species.*

Throughout the whole geological record the complete disappearance of species constantly occurs. Our greater knowledge of mammalian history during the Tertiary era illustrates this phenomenon. The reflections which come from such fuller knowledge are disquieting, for we can trace the rise and development of fine mammalian types during long stretches of time and then, suddenly, they seem to be destroyed. Sometimes the destruction is complete. Sometimes it is partial, but complete in the particular region where the new species arose and established itself. American investigations have yielded the best known instances of such a disconcerting commonplace of geological history. Types belonging to the camel family, for instance, were apparently evolved during the Tertiary period in North America. Some of them migrated to South America and others to Asia by the then existing Alaska land-bridge. They still survive as camels in Central Asia and as llamas in South America. But in the Early Pleistocene they entirely vanished from their North American home-land.

§ 328. *The history of the horse.*

The history of the development of the horse is fairly complete and of great interest. The earliest fossils are found in Eocene deposits in Western North America. All these primitive horses were of small size, as is usual in archaic forms: some stood only a foot high at the shoulder. Also in the Eocene, though somewhat later, modifications of these horses were abundant in France and fairly common in England, which was then joined to the Continent. By the beginning of the Oligocene all the European horses had vanished. In America they multiplied, grew larger, lost some of their toes and developed teeth suitable for grazing on coarse grasses. Such horses during the Pliocene emigrated alike to South America and *via* Asia to Europe. By Pleistocene times horses had spread over the greater part of the world: the modern type of horse emerged, though there was an amazing variety of forms and a great divergence in size. Then the horse completely died out in North and South America. For some forty million years North America had been the centre of their development and of their migrations. Yet when the American continent was discovered by Europeans in the sixteenth century the horse had disappeared. Fortunately it had survived in the Old World through the Ice Ages of the Pleistocene, though sadly diminished in numbers and in varieties.

§ 329. *A mammalian slaughter.*

The disappearance of camels and horses from North America was part of a vast extinction of the higher mammals which occurred shortly after early man first appeared in Europe. It is said that over more than half the land surface of the earth a great variety of important mammals was rapidly exterminated. Many strange and powerful creatures, products of millions of years of evolution, passed utterly away: others survived in reduced numbers and in isolated regions. The cause of this vast slaughter is a mystery. But almost certainly it was due to disease; some micro-organism, suddenly acquiring great virulence, found itself able to destroy the greater number of the most advanced mammals then living. Apparently man and the primates to which he was most closely akin were, for the most part, able to resist the triumphant disease. Quite possibly the slaughter made man's struggle for existence less severe.

§ 330. *Man's end?*

One cannot contemplate such destruction without the feeling that in it there was unnecessary—even scandalous—waste. The fact that it can be paralleled by the extinction of highly specialised forms throughout earth's history increases rather than diminishes a sense of perplexity. Does it foreshadow man's own fate? Graham Kerr* suggests that possibly "mankind is fated to go on existing far into the remote future".

* J. Graham Kerr, *Evolution.* Macmillan, 1926, p. 234.

On the other hand: "It may be that his existence upon the earth is doomed to reach an abrupt end. Such has been the fate of the overwhelming majority of those forms of life that have flourished and had their day in earlier periods of the world's history. It may well be the fate of man also, and if this happens apart from the destruction of all life through cataclysmic changes in the physical conditions of the earth's surface, it will probably come about through conflict not with highly evolved forms of life comparable with himself, but rather with lowly organised microbes armed with deadly powers of multiplication, and immune to, or able to break successfully through, the protective arrangements of his body". The Professor, with professorial wisdom, gives us alternative visions of the future: but the more gloomy is the more probable.

Lecture xiii

THE EVOLUTION OF PLANTS AND SEX

THE EVOLUTION OF PLANTS

§ 331. Popular interest in evolution has been in the main limited to the evolutionary development of new species of animals, inasmuch as out of this process man himself has arisen. But the fossil record of past ages of the earth shews that evolution has been equally at work in the vegetable kingdom. Unfortunately, in the ancestral history of existing species of plants there are many gaps: we must trust that they will be diminished in number and size by further research combined with fortunate discoveries in palaeobotany.

The similarity of animals and plants.

It is to be expected that the evolution of animals and plants should have proceeded *pari passu* on the earth's surface in view of the fact that between the two phases of life there is a close similarity. Classic expression was given to this similarity in a still famous book by Claude Bernard (1813–1878) published in the year 1879: his *Lessons on Phenomena Common to the Life of Animals and Vegetables.* In this work Bernard shewed that between animals and plants there is a fundamental likeness as regards cell-division, growth, reproduction, respiration and even digestion. Moreover, in each the living tissue is irritable and responds to stimuli. And further, in each, heredity preserves likenesses from generation to generation though there is always the possibility of an incompleteness of inheritance; in fact, a potency of variation, a general inconstancy or instability, appears to be inherent in all living substance.

This similarity between animals and plants becomes the less surprising when it is remembered that between primitive representatives of the two types of life no clear line of division can be drawn. At one period of their development the slime-moulds (*myxomycetes*) closely resemble the bits of free-living protoplasm known as *amoebae*: opinions differ as to whether these slime-moulds should be rightly classed as animals or as plants.

§ 332. *The most primitive plants.*

It is certain that animals and plants alike began in the water. The plants, probably when they were still in the unicellular stage, acquired the power to make chlorophyll, the substance which gives its green colour to foliage. They were thus able to make direct use of the carbon-dioxide of the atmosphere and thereby to build up in their tissues carbohydrates and still more complex organic compounds. In this way they still convert a simple inorganic substance into living tissue: in fact, they have gained power by aid of the sunshine to use carbon-dioxide as food.

Probably unicellular chlorophyll-bearing *algae* must rank as among the most primitive of plants. The algae, or sea-weeds, form a vast range of differently organised aquatic plants. From them, probably, all other plants have sprung. Some algae reproduce by cell-division and others by cell-fusion. Cell-fusion is, of course, at the basis of the sexual reproduction which is as common in the vegetable as in the animal kingdom.

It is probable that the *fungi* developed from the algae and subsequently lost the power of making chlorophyll. They do not need chlorophyll as they are either parasitic on living organisms or saprophytic on their dead products or remains. Probably several groups of algae thus developed into fungi.

Bacteria are microscopic plants, devoid of chlorophyll, which reproduce by cell-division. They depend for their nutrition upon organic matter. They are rightly classed as minute fungi, though they may have arisen either from the viruses described in § 310 or by some parallel process. Most of our infectious diseases are caused by bacteria.

Many fossil sea-weeds are scattered through rocks of the Cambrian period; but, as we have said in the last lecture, the first land plants were probably established during the Silurian: it is certain that they became abundant during the Devonian era. By that time the fungi had apparently thoroughly well established themselves, for, as Scott* says, "the remains of the Early Devonian land-plants simply swarm with fungi". The fungi remain among the most troublesome of our parasites in field and garden: as parasitic pests they can boast a pedigree of more than 300 million years! The problem of evil, in fact, is much older than the Garden of Eden.

* D. H. Scott, *Extinct Plants and Problems of Evolution.* Macmillan, 1924, ɔ. 39.

§ 333. *Liverworts and mosses.*

Possibly we should set the fungi aside as of unknown origin; but we may assume that, when the chlorophyll-bearing algae passed to the land, they developed into liverworts and mosses. These plants have no true roots in the moist land on which they grow; and they have, as a result of fertilisation, a protecting case or capsule containing asexual spores. The liverworts are on the whole more simple than the mosses, for in many of them there is no differentiation between stem and leaf. Alike in liverworts and mosses there is an alternation of generations which occurs also, as we shall shortly describe, in club-mosses and ferns.

The club-mosses.

Next in the evolutionary scale to liverworts and mosses we must probably set the club-mosses or lycopods: they are a quite different class from the true mosses, with which they have no real affinity. They have true roots and can grow on drier land than the liverworts and mosses usually need. Like ferns and horsetails, they possess a well-developed vascular system (*vide* § 335) which does not exist in the mosses.

There are two kinds of club-mosses with significantly different life-histories. The life of one kind resembles that of the ferns. When its spores are sown, there results a prothallus, an organism not differentiated into stem and leaf. In the fern this prothallus is a little green plantlet: in the club-mosses under consideration it is more solid in build and often does not grow above the ground. But in each case on the prothallus the sexual organs are borne. From these by fertilisation there arises an embryo from which a new fern (or club-moss as the case may be) is developed. But there are other club-mosses which are technically termed heterosporous, for they have two kinds of spores, small and large. When the numerous small spores germinate each produces a male organ from which come the spermatozoids: the prothallus (or plantlet carrying this male organ) hardly exists. The large spores are few in number: each produces a substantial prothallus on which the female organs are borne. These when fertilised by the spermatozoids produce the club-mosses of the next generation. These particular club-mosses (and a similar kind of fern) are sexually the most highly differentiated of all the spore-plants. The small and large spores are respectively comparable with the pollen and embryo-sac of the seed-plants.

§ 334. *Spores and seeds.*

The distinction between spores and seeds is highly important. The spores are always minute and simple: they usually consist only of a single cell. Seeds, on the other hand, are complex bodies, of relatively large size, always composed of various tissues; and, moreover, the seed, as a result of the fertilisation of ovule by pollen, usually contains an embryo which is the rudiment of the young plant. The development of seeds is the event which, in the history of the evolution of plants, probably ranks next in importance to the making of chlorophyll: a single-celled spore is an inefficient means of reproduction compared with a seed.

§ 335. *The ferns.*

The ferns are highly important in evolutionary history and certain species are too well known to need description. Ferns, together with horsetails and club-mosses, are the highest of the spore-plants. Like the seed-plants they possess a vascular system, that is a system of fibrous strands specially adapted to conduct water and food-substances throughout the plant. As we have seen, in the true ferns, which are spore-bearing, an asexual generation normally alternates with the sexual generation represented by the prothallus.

The pteridosperms or seed-ferns.

In the Carboniferous period which followed the Devonian the swamps were overgrown with vast ferns, giant club-mosses and sturdy horsetails. Our coal measures largely consist of their fossil remains. The Carboniferous used to be called the Age of Ferns, because their fossil fronds appeared to indicate that some half of the then existing species were ferns. In fact, it was not until the present century that palaeobotanists discovered that most of the so-called ferns of the Carboniferous are really "seed-bearing plants, of fern-like habit". The origin of these seed-ferns, or pteridosperms, is a puzzle. For some time it was assumed that the seed-ferns arose from the true ferns and that, from the seed-ferns, most of the more recent seed-plants were derived. But true ferns and seed-ferns apparently shew no approach to one another in structural characters as the fossil record is traced backwards. It may be added that seeds of the Carboniferous period (which have probably for the most part been detached from species of seed-ferns) are among the most large and complex known to botanists. Modern plants have more simple and, it may be added, more efficient seeds.

§ 336. *The great botanical eras.*

A curious fact which one day may receive adequate explanation is that the times which divide the great geological eras are not invariably the times when the great botanical transformations occurred. The first of such transformations must have taken place when first the sea-weeds invaded the land. Of that epoch we know nothing. But a second great transformation took place in the middle of the Devonian period when the simple types of early Devonian times were succeeded by the relatively highly organised flora of the Carboniferous. Some of these more simple types, which are among the most ancient land plants known to fossil botanists, come from the Rhynie chert-bed of Aberdeenshire. The location of these most interesting relics of the early Devonian era was discovered by a Scottish geologist in the year 1913. The *rhyniaceae* are the simplest of known vascular plants. One species, about eight inches high, is leafless and rootless with spore-cases at the ends of its branches. It had 'breathing pores' and conducting tissue; and was thus adapted for life on land. A detailed examination of its characteristics shews that we cannot be wrong in thinking of it as a transformed sea-weed. My audience* will not be surprised that this at present unique instance of early progressive development came from Aberdeenshire.

As I have said, the first known botanical transformation of the late Middle Devonian gave us the ferns, seed-ferns, club-mosses and horse-tails whose development culminated in the Carboniferous. Doubtless preparation for the change had been in progress, though it is now concealed from us by the inadequacy of the fossil record. But relatively suddenly the world was covered by new forms of vegetation.

§ 337. *The age of cycads.*

A second remarkable transformation occurred at the close of the Palaeozoic era, during or just after the Permian epoch. At this time the Mesozoic flora largely replaced the vegetation of the great coal forests. The Permian epoch was arid and harsh. For long periods of time there was widespread glacial ice in places so far apart as Australia, India, South Africa and South America. Conditions were apparently such as invite or compel change and development, among plants and animals alike. After storm and stress the first mammals then appeared; and, apparently at the same time, the ancient forms of the Carboniferous were succeeded by the Mesozoic cycads, conifers and maidenhair

* The lectures were, of course, delivered in Aberdeen.

trees. Because these formed the dominant vegetation the period is sometimes called the Age of Gymnosperms or naked seeds.

The cycads.

In all the Mesozoic vegetation cycads and cycad-like plants were dominant, two out of every five plants belonging to this category. What was the origin of the cycad-like plants? The old doubts largely vanished when the 'seed-ferns' were discovered. The pteridosperms are primitive seed-plants, widespreading in their ramifications; and from some among them the Mesozoic cycads must be descended. But, just as the great reptiles of the Mesozoic are now extinct, so most of the cycads have passed away. Those that remain are always male or female: their fruit is, in general, in the form of a large cone, the female cone being somewhat larger than the male: and the numerous pollen grains from the male cone fall directly on the large ovules of the female without the intervention of stigma or style. Fossil cycads and cycad-like plants of the Mesozoic may differ widely from the living forms. For instance, these fossil plants were often bisexual. Some among them had flowers; and the flowers had normally both male and female organs. Thus the Mesozoic cycads constitute an extinct group clearly analogous to the higher flowering plants of modern times. Are the latter descended from some modification of a cycad-like group of plants? This is at least a tenable hypothesis: but such theories of descent still await confirmation by further discovery.

Descent or independent evolution.

In the year 1922 no less an authority than A. C. Seward expressed doubts as to whether the ferns of the Mesozoic had any connection by descent with their Palaeozoic predecessors. He suggested that in the latter part of the Triassic period we pass with remarkable suddenness to a new phase of plant evolution: one cycle is completed and another has begun. It may, therefore, be that in this era, as new lands emerged from the sea, new lines of evolution from marine plants began afresh. The possibility of such a series of developments as Seward suggests cannot be summarily set aside. But most experts consider it unlikely; and there is no hint of a parallel development in animal evolution. It remains true, as Seward says, that "persistence of type and from time to time the apparently sudden influx of new types, rather than a steady progressive development, are among the outstanding features of the history of plant-evolution".

When, however, we think of persistence of type we must not forget that variation throughout geological time has been continuous. No one, for instance, imagines that either a botanical revolution, or some evolution independent of previous development on land, took place in the interval separating the Upper and Lower Carboniferous rocks. Yet R. Kidston (1852–1924) stated authoritatively that there is not a single species common to the flora of these two eras. The fact is that at certain geological periods change became so rapid as in retrospect to seem violent. At each such period there was an apparently sudden influx of new types; and of them even the proximate cause or causes so far remain hidden from us, though we may speculate that changes in the environment gave the opportunity for numerous mutant characters rapidly to establish themselves. What is certain is that there have been periods when, as it seems to us, exceptional creative activity was manifested. Such in some cases have coincided with harsh conditions of existence: possibly new worlds, alike of animals and plants, are born in pain and suffering.

We shall discuss the machinery of evolution in Lecture XV, and the question will arise as to whether an unfavourable environment can stimulate the latent instability of the organism. It will then be seen that research, although a beginning has hardly yet been made, may ultimately enable us to discover the machinery by which the various forms of life change and new types are produced. But ultimate cause will probably always elude us. I believe that, at the end of all speculative enquiry, we are forced to the idea of a Power which willed the end before the earth was made.

§ 338. *The last botanical transformation.*

A further transformation of the face of the earth occurred during the middle of the Cretaceous period when conifers, maidenhair trees and cycad-like plants ceased to be dominant. The Age of Gymnosperms passed away and a modern flora began to be evolved. The modern flowering plants which characterise the new era are technically called angiosperms, for they have enclosed seeds like walnuts and acorns. We have seen that probably the angiosperms are descended from what are sometimes called pro-angiosperms, cycad-like plants which had features resembling those of modern flowering plants of primitive types. This evolution of angiosperms must have occurred on land in the early Mesozoic epoch: from the fact that such flowering plants appear to have spread southward in Europe, North America and Asia it has been conjectured that their place of origin was in the North Circum-polar area, when the climate there was mild and genial. Certain it is that the new flowering plants spread, during the later Cretaceous era, through the tropics as far south as Antarctica. As new types of these plants were evolved, the older floras of the early Mesozoic gradually died out, leaving but a few stragglers behind. With the dawn of the Tertiary era there appeared vegetation comprising familiar modern types, plants that are plainly ancestors of those now living. In fact, the Tertiary era is the age of mammals and flowering plants.

§ 339. *Mammals and angiosperms.*

It has been well said that the insects and the modern flowers go hand in glove with one another. As soon as the crocus blooms in England on an early spring day, the bees appear: the red clover when introduced into New Zealand failed until bumble-bees were brought to fertilise it. But there is an almost equally close association between the mammals and the angiosperms. For the latter comprise oaks, chestnuts and grasses together with cereals such as wheat, maize, etc. They yield the concentrated food-stuffs by which the vegetable feeders among the higher mammals are nourished. Our cows, sheep and pigs are, in a sense, parasites of the modern flowering plants; and we ourselves, partly vegetarian and partly carnivorous, are parasites alike of these domestic animals and of the cereals on which we and they feed.

§ 340. *The dicotyledons.*

The angiosperms are of two types. The more ancient and more numerous appear to be the dicotyledons, which have two seed-leaves and in which the leaves of the adult plant are veined like a net. To them belong such representatives of a primitive type as the magnolias and also the roses of our gardens and the buttercups and dandelions of our fields. Moreover, all our forest trees (so far as they are not conifers) are dicotyledons. The oldest of known fossil dicotyledons appear in Lower Cretaceous formations. They have been found in the Lower Greensand and approximately contemporary beds in our own country. A number of distinct genera have been discovered, and it is remarkable that in all of them the typical structure of the dicotyledons shews no primitive characters. Being thus highly differentiated they must have had a long history behind them even in Lower Cretaceous times. A few rare discoveries give indications that angiosperms existed before the Cretaceous. But, as Scott says, they seem then "to appear suddenly, in their full strength, like Athene sprung from the brain of Zeus".

The monocotyledons.

What are believed to be the latest evolutionary plant-forms are the monocotyledons, which have one seed-leaf and in which usually the veins of the adult leaf are roughly parallel. They are more important to man than the other group of angiosperms, for all cereals and grasses belong to the monocotyledons. They further include palms and rushes and such beautiful plants as lilies and orchids. Some experts assert that this particular group of plants is over-specialised and likely to be, as geological time is measured, short-lived exotics of earth's vegetation. But it must be admitted that the monocotyledons are found far back in the Cretaceous; and the palms of the Upper Cretaceous, for instance, are singularly modern in most of their features.

§341. Change in the Tertiary era.

The fossil record gives no indication of the initial connection of the two great groups of angiosperms. All we can say is that in later Cretaceous times the existing families of these flowering plants were already developed. They then appear to have formed a world-wide flora. During the Tertiary era there was a continuous efflorescence of new species, but their distribution became regional. Probably the rapid changes of climate in the various glacial epochs of recent geological eras stimulated the evolutionary activity of plants*. Soils were then mixed by the action of ice, snow and water. When glaciers and ice-sheets melted, virgin areas were ready for Nature to make new experiments. Most certainly herbaceous plants, which have no durable woody stem, throve vigorously and their types multiplied during the later Pliocene and Pleistocene eras.

§342. Conclusion.

Through the long history of earth's vegetation we can trace progress. Representatives of primitive forms still survive. The fossil record bears witness that many progressive forms lost their plasticity and became extinct. Yet continuously there has been progressive development such, for instance, as the change from the highly organised Carboniferous *cordaites* with its pith in a column or trunk to a modern oak with

* More accurately, as we shall see in Lecture XIV, marked changes of environment permitted the survival of mutant characters which, but for such changes, would have been eliminated. That new mutations, such as had not previously appeared, were produced by such changes of environment is most improbable.

its seasonal rings of secondary wood. And to-day man has discovered how to stimulate progress and is producing new varieties of flowers and fruit. How far his ingenuity and his desires will lead to permanent change in the vegetation of the earth we cannot yet say. Even if man himself is an episode, some of his activities may have an enduring influence on the future terrestrial history of animate nature.

SEX

§343. *The basal facts.*

We may say, without exaggeration, that the origin of sexual differentiation is 'lost in the mists of antiquity'. Among primitive non-cellular organisms, known as protozoa, the fusion of two cells which is central in the sexual process is but one form of reproduction. The higher metazoa are built up of many cells, each of which consists of a nucleus surrounded by cytoplasm and enclosed within a membrane. Such organisms cast off reproductive cells which by growth make new animals. These reproductive cells can be of two kinds. There are, on the one hand, those such as asexual spores which can develop without union with any similar cells: and such are probably the most primitive in character. There are, on the other hand, those reproductive cells which must unite in pairs before development can take place. These gametes, as they are called, are of two kinds: male and female. The female egg or ovum is relatively large and inert: the male spermatozoon is small and active. Reproduction through the union of gametes is normal among the metazoa.

Secondary differences.

Yet such a method of reproduction is very surprising and most certainly not what we should have imagined had we been constructing from fancy a world in which birth had to be the correlative to death. The more one reflects upon sexual differences, psychical no less than physical, the more surprising is it that each species should have within itself two groups so divergent as its male and female individuals. Such differences within a fundamental unity would be incredible were they not a commonplace of the world of animate nature. The physical differences of sex appear to affect profoundly the biochemical rhythm of the body: as we all know from observation of humanity they also invade the domains of thought and feeling.

From what may be called secondary aspects of sex much that is highest in the emotional life of man arises. None the less, I think it must be admitted that an exaggeration of the part played by instincts of sexual origin is not uncommon among certain of our modern psychologists. We cannot fail to recognise that in human life the influence of such instincts is far-reaching: they often combine with purely aesthetic or religious emotions. But it is worth while to insist that we could probably enjoy a sonnet or find a thrill in some phase of the worship of God even though, like the angels of our ecclesiastical lawyers*, we were non-sexual.

§344. *The reproductive cells.*

It is only during the present century that exact knowledge of the machinery of sexual reproduction has been gained. Much remains to be learned: in fact, we are only at the very beginning of researches which will probably be of immense practical value to the future progress of mankind.

Ovum and spermatozoon have alike a nucleus, though in the former the nucleus is surrounded by cytoplasm which is virtually non-existent in the latter. The government of the activities of a reproductive cell is centralised in the nucleus. A large part of the nucleus consists of a dense substance (which can be deeply stained by carmine) known as *chromatin*. Moreover, when a fertilised ovum is about to divide into two daughter-cells, the chromatin of the nucleus is seen to consist of separate pieces (resembling microscopic bits of knotted string) called *chromosomes*. The 'knots on the bits of string' are the *genes*: they appear to be the ultimate elements in the germinal material, elements which are held together by the chromosomes in 'linkage-groups'. By means of certain natural assumptions the theory of the gene is made, as we shall see in the next lecture, to explain Mendel's laws of inheritance. In every ordinary cell of each particular species of animal belonging to the metazoa there are the same number of chromosomes (the somewhat exceptional grouping of the sex chromosomes will be discussed shortly (§346)). Moreover, the non-sexual chromosomes are paired; and one chromosome of each pair has come from one parent and one from the other. It is a most remarkable fact of cytology that there is a double set of chromosomes to be seen alike in each cell of the body and in the germ-cells at certain stages of cell-division; and that the number of such chromosomes is, in general, constant for a particular species of animal or plant.

* I am informed that a strict Chancellor of an English diocese would refuse a faculty for the figure of an angel above, say, a font if the figure appeared to be either male or female!

§ 345. *Sexual fusion.*

The fusion of ovum and spermatozoon, by which the life of a new individual begins, is a complicated process which we shall describe briefly and allusively, without adding the many qualifications and amplifications necessary in a scientific treatise. In essence it consists, first of all, of a process of ripening of each cell during which one of each pair of chromosomes is cast away. The determination as to which of a pair of chromosomes shall be thus discarded seems to be a matter of pure chance. If, however, ovum and spermatozoon had each originally in its nucleus $2n$ paired chromosomes, there will be left in each after the ripening n single chromosomes. These will unite during cell-fusion and again form $2n$ paired chromosomes. Finally, as the process of fusion leads to cell-division, each of these chromosomes divides longitudinally and each half then passes to one of the two cells into which the fertilised egg divides. We thus get as the first stage of a new life two cells each of which has in its nucleus $2n$ paired chromosomes, of which one half (one from each pair) come from each parent.

We have said that, as a fertilised cell begins to develop into an adult organism, it divides into two daughter-cells. This process continues indefinitely. In successive division each chromosome of the nucleus of each dividing cell splits longitudinally into two and, of these two, one goes to each daughter-cell. Thus every cell in the body of the adult contains just as many chromosomes as there were in the first cell; and all these have arisen by successive longitudinal divisions of the original chromosomes. It is in this way that the groups of units of inheritance (or genes, as we have called them) are distributed throughout the whole adult organism. Cytologists always speak with wonder of the process of cell-division. If we could understand it we should be much nearer to an understanding of the meaning of life. Bateson said in the year 1913: "It is this power of spontaneous division which most sharply distinguishes the living from the non-living. The greatest advance I can conceive in biology would be the discovery of the instability which leads to this continual division of the cell". Others have felt with him that, as they looked at a dividing cell, they seemed to see beneath their gaze 'an original act of creation'.

Two technical terms are useful. When a cell has within it $2n$ paired chromosomes, it is said to have the normal *diploid* number. When the cell has but n single chromosomes it is said to have the *haploid* number. When parthenogenesis occurs, cells with a haploid number of chromosomes can develop into haploid organisms.

§ 346. *The distribution of the sex-chromosomes.*

We have hinted above that the sex-chromosomes cannot, without further explanation, be included in the previous description. Their nature and function can best be shewn by taking the concrete case of humanity.

In the female cell of the human species there are (if the singularly difficult counting of microscopic elements be correct) 48 chromosomes: in other words there are 24 pairs of chromosomes. In man, however, as opposed to woman there are just possibly but 47 chromosomes, or (much more probably) 47 plus a fragmentary 'bit' of a chromosome which acts as mate to a much larger chromosome which we may call X.

Let us give to the fragmentary piece, if it exists, the designation Y. Then in the male cell we have 23 pairs of chromosomes plus the pair (X, Y). In the female cell we have a pair of chromosomes corresponding to X: it thus contains 23 pairs of chromosomes plus the pair (X, X). The chromosomes X and Y are called sex-chromosomes. A pair (X, X) form a female; a pair (X, Y) form a male. Geneticists usually put the female cell first (*place aux dames*) and describe the sex-determining mechanism of man by the formula

$$(X, X)\text{---}(X, Y).$$

It must not be assumed that there is an identity between the two chromosomes which occur in the female cell and which we have denoted by (X, X). All that we wish to imply is that they are paired chromosomes. One comes from each parent.

We shall see later that there is a connection between the genes and the characters of an organism. Let us suppose, for simplicity of definition, that as sole determinants of any character* there are genes at corresponding points A and a of a pair of associated chromosomes. Then if the genes at A and a are identical, the organism is said to be *homozygous* in its genetic make-up as regards the character in question. If, however, the genes at A and a are different, the organism is said to be *heterozygous* as regards the particular character.

If, as regards a particular character, a strain is pure, it will be homozygous in the corresponding genes. Heterozygous organisms normally result from the mating either of two different strains or of

---

* The supposition is untrue to fact. Probably no character can be 'condensed and contained' in one particular gene. It is the interaction between contributory genes (which may be numerous), and between such genes and their environment, which makes any observable character.

strains that are not pure, difference and purity being, of course, terms only used with reference to the particular character.

The X-chromosomes of any species, in addition to determining sex, carry genes. The corresponding genes in the pair of X-chromosomes that determine a female may or may not be identical. Thus the X-chromosome carries genes which give rise to sex-linked characters; and such genes will differ in different strains. We must explicitly repudiate the idea that the sex-chromosomes have no other activity than the determination of sex. They often carry other factors and, when these are modified by 'mutation', sex-linked changes may appear in the offspring.

Mutation is the process by which a gene or set of genes is changed so that a new variety of organism is produced. We shall subsequently discuss it at length.

The two sexes must be roughly equal in numbers.

We can now see immediately how beautifully the simple sex-mechanism just described theoretically ensures an equal supply of boys and girls.

When fusion of ovum and spermatozoon takes place, one of each pair of chromosomes will be discarded. By rejecting one of the pair (X, X) in the female we necessarily get a single X. From the pair (X, Y) of the male we get either X or Y. After fertilisation we therefore have, with equal chances, either (X, X), a girl, or (X, Y), a boy.

It should be added that the theoretical equality in the number of male and female children is subject to ill-understood disturbing influences. Roughly, of children born alive, there are 105 boys to 100 girls. When account is taken of still-births and of abortions for which the sex can be determined, the ratio is said to become more nearly 150:100. Probably this great disparity, if it actually exists, is due to the existence in man of numerous sex-linked lethal factors.

§ 347. *An alternative sex-mechanism.*

It seems to be established that insects, amphibia, teleostean fishes and some of the higher mammals have the human mechanism $(X, X)—(X, Y)$ for determining sex. But birds and moths apparently have a mechanism given by the inverse formula $(W, Z)—(Z, Z)$. That is to say, in birds and moths there are in the male two similar sex-chromosomes (Z, Z) while in the female there is a Z-chromosome matched by a different W-chromosome.

We would insist, as before, that the symbol (Z, Z) denotes paired chromosomes, one of which comes from each parent, and that the two elements of a pair are not necessarily identical in their properties.

One cannot fail to be surprised that this inverse mechanism runs, apparently arbitrarily, through part of the animal world. None the less, experiments with the inheritance of sex-linked factors seem to demonstrate conclusively the existence of what is certainly an unexpected difference in such a fundamental matter as the determination of sex. The result leaves one with a feeling of disquiet, which, however, so great an authority as T. H. Morgan does not seem to share. He says* that "there are no grounds for supposing that the chromosomes involved in the (X, X)—(X, Y) and in the (W, Z)—(Z, Z) types are the same. On the contrary it is difficult to imagine how one type could change over directly into the other. There is no theoretical difficulty, however, in supposing that the change in balance that gives the two sexes may have arisen independently in the two types, even although the actual genes involved are the same or nearly the same in both".

§348. *Inter-sexes.*

The distinction between male and female in animate nature is by no means absolute. Many flowering plants develop stamens containing pollen or male-reproduction cells and also pistils containing ovules or egg-cells: these may occur in independent flowers on the same plant and sometimes even in the same flower. Such are technically called *monoecious*. The same plant has the reproductive apparatus of the two sexes. It is an hermaphrodite or inter-sex.

In the animal world inter-sexes exist, and among some organisms they are common. Most barnacles, for instance, are hermaphroditic: and the same appears to be true of many amphibia. In early stages of the development of the vertebrates the elements of both the male and female reproductive organs are present in both sexes. Sometimes abnormal developments take place, so that true inter-sexes result in adult life. Such are known alike in the higher vertebrates and in man. It is said, for instance, that among the pigs of the New Hebrides such inter-sexes are common. In spite of a morbid interest in such abnormalities in humanity, as, for instance, in the art and legends of Graeco-Roman civilisation, little is known as to their cause. Probably there are no sex-chromosomes in plants and animals where inter-sexes are

* T. H. Morgan, *The Theory of the Gene.* Yale University Press, 1926, p. 212. The researches of Morgan and his pupils can, without exaggeration, be described as epoch-making.

normal. Sex in such, if a predominant male or female development occurs, will be determined by conditions in the environment. When, however, an organism has definite sex-chromosomes and none the less an inter-sex occurs, we must postulate that the influence of such chromosomes is over-ridden by environmental conditions.

Such speculative inferences are borne out by the fact that age and circumstance will occasionally change the sex of certain animals. For example, the sex-chromosomes of the frog are of the type (X, X) in the female and (X, Y) in the male. Normally, an individual with (X, X) chromosomes develops female reproductive organs; but under exceptional conditions it may develop male organs and function as a male. Curiously, the reverse change by which an individual with (X, Y) chromosomes may function as a female has not been observed. It appears to be established that sex-reversal may occur in birds: but here again only a change of the female into the male appears as a possible consequence of disease or of experimental excision of the reproductive organs.

Until comparatively recently it was widely held, and the idea still crops up in popular literature, that sex is determined solely by the conditions under which the embryo develops. Individuals consequently claimed that the human mother, by suitable food and mode of life, could at will produce children of a prescribed sex. Enough is now known to demonstrate the falsity of such claims. What emerges from present knowledge and investigation is that, in sex as in other aspects of his physical organisation, man belongs to the system of animate nature, alike in its uniformities and exceptions.

Super-sexes.

Associated with inter-sexes are super-sexes whose existence has emerged from modern biological investigation.

We have previously stated the general law that, for each species of organism, the number of chromosomes in the cells of the organism is constant. But a study of biology teaches that Nature is so prolific of new ventures or experiments that few biological laws are without exceptions. In recent years, in a large number of species, individuals have been discovered which have three, four, five, ... times the haploid number of chromosomes. Such individuals are called triploid, tetraploid, ... and in general polyploid. A large number of modern varieties of flowers and plants are polyploids. Triploid hyacinths are replacing the older types as the bulbs of commerce. In the cultivated varieties of chrysanthemum a Japanese investigator has found extensive polyploidy. Our cultivated roses present a somewhat perplexing problem, as they are most certainly hybrids derived from probably three different stocks. But many of the cultivated varieties are polyploid types.

Animals no less than plants can be polyploids. They usually differ less from the normal than do mutant types. Speaking generally, we can say that, while haploids are not as vigorous as the normal types of the species, tetraploids and the like are above the normal in the appearances of physical well-being which can be observed.

Sex in connection with polyploidy is naturally of interest. Suppose that we have an organism in which the sex-mechanism is of the human (X, X)—(X, Y) type. Let a denote a typical non-sexual chromosome of such an organism. Then its normal (diploid) genetic structure will be denoted, if it is a female, by

$$\Sigma(2a) + 2X;$$

and, if it is a male, by $\quad \Sigma(2a) + X + Y.$

In these formulae $\Sigma(2a)$ stands for the whole group of paired non-sexual chromosomes. One a comes from each parent; and we do *not* assume that the individuals of a pair of a's have exactly the same properties: such a pair can be 'heterozygous'.

Apparently super-sexes and inter-sexes alike arise when the chromosomes 'go wrong' at one of the divisions associated with the ripening of the cell which precedes the fusion of the gametes.

Suppose, for instance, that in the female gamete the two X's stick together. Normally, as we have seen, one is cast away. If, however, both are retained, we shall get on fertilisation individuals given by one or other of the formulae

$$\Sigma(2a) + 2X + X,$$
or $\quad \Sigma(2a) + 2X + Y.$

The super-female with three X's has been obtained by Morgan in *drosophila*. She is, as is to be expected, abnormal. "She is sluggish, her wings are short and often irregular, and she is sterile." The individual whose genetic composition is $\Sigma(2a) + 2X + Y$ is an abnormal female.

A triploid form of *drosophila* has been found whose genetic composition is $\Sigma(3a) + 3X$. This is a practically normal female. The individual with the formula $\Sigma(3a) + X + Y$ is a super-male.

How far such aberrant sexual forms exist in the mammals is not known. Probably they can be produced artificially. Whether, like inter-sexes, the super-sexes ever occur in humanity is an interesting question. It may be that super-sexual aberrations are lethal, so that, when the chromosomes thus 'go wrong', the individual dies. It may be, on the other hand, that they produce lethargic individuals who are classed as degenerate types. And it is just possible that among super-female human types we must place such famous women of history as Helen of Troy and Cleopatra. Speculation is vain.

§ 349. *Parthenogenesis.*

In some primitive organisms reproduction occurs simply by 'budding': the fusion of two cells is not a necessary preliminary to the formation of a new individual. In many relatively advanced forms of life, and especially among the insects, reproduction from unfertilised egg-cells is common. Such parthenogenesis can co-exist, or alternate, with reproduction as a result of sexual union.

Presumably there is no reason in the nature of things why a virgin birth should be impossible. Granted that an egg-cell receives some stimulus which leads it to begin the process of cell-division and that the egg-cell is also in a suitable environment, a new individual may well be formed from it. Investigation into such matters reveals the prodigal resourcefulness of Nature. A few instances may be given. Flies of the genus *miastor** consist of winged males and of winged females. Fertilised eggs (or eggs which are believed to be fertilised) develop into maggots. These maggots are not invariably transformed in due course into adult flies: but they can, as maggots, produce eggs which will develop into another generation of maggots: and this process of parthenogenesis, or rather of paedogenesis, can with the appropriate environment go on indefinitely. Let the environment be suitably changed and a generation of maggots will turn into flies. We then get once again winged males and winged females: from these forms a new generation arises by normal sexual union. Experiments seem to shew that the maggots which are the offspring of any particular maggot are all males or all females. Thus apparently male maggots can reproduce their kind by paedogenesis! Nature's resourcefulness could hardly go farther.

Haploid males and diploid females.

As another example of parthenogenesis we may take the rotifer. A female rotifer, according to Whitney, can reproduce her kind by parthenogenesis indefinitely. When her eggs develop, no chromosomes are discarded; and therefore the same number of $2n$ paired chromosomes

---

* *Vide* T. H. Morgan, *loc. cit.* p. 270.

occurs in her parthenogenetic daughters as in herself. Let now the environment be suitably changed (and a change of diet appears to be adequate) and a new type of female emerges. If this female is not fertilised, she produces eggs smaller than the parthenogenetic eggs. These eggs will also develop parthenogenetically; but half the chromosomes will be discarded in such development; and, as a result, a male emerges with only n chromosomes. This male, which has only half the normal number of chromosomes in any one of its cells, is termed, as has been said, a haploid. If, on the other hand, the new type of female is fertilised by such a male, the haploid sperm-nucleus will unite with the nucleus of the egg (which is now haploid owing to the discarding of half the chromosomes). In consequence, a fertilised 'winter' egg with the full number of chromosomes results. This, in due course, hatches into a female with $2n$ paired chromosomes; and she can again reproduce her kind by parthenogenesis. Thus by a process of evolution the rotifer appears to have eliminated normal (diploid) males and to use the haploids that remain merely as an adjunct to parthenogenesis.

Artificial parthenogenesis.

When compared with such abnormalities on the part of Nature the successes of biologists in producing parthenogenesis artificially seem meagre. But it is on record that, by puncturing an unfertilised frog's eggs and developing them in saline solution, frogs have been produced. Some of these were decrepit but others reached sex-maturity. Goldschmidt examined one such ripe male cytologically and found that it had the diploid number of chromosomes (26). Other investigators, who do not seem to have been numerous, have, on counting, found fewer chromosomes. Dürken after careful investigation concludes that, even though the chromosome number be haploid to start with, the diploid number appears in these frogs as development goes on*. Such experiments are notable because the frog, as an amphibian, is higher in the scale of evolution than any creatures in which parthenogenesis is known to occur in the course of nature.

§ 350. *Ants, bees and wasps.*

Sexual conditions in ants, bees and wasps are similar to those which we have described as existing among the rotifers; and among the more organised of these insects they are made the basis of their amazing 'civilisation'.

* I owe this information to Professor Sir J. Arthur Thomson of the University of Aberdeen.

Ants, bees and wasps are all closely related. From the fossil evidence there seems to be no doubt that ants evolved from a generalised wasp-like form in Mesozoic times, possibly during the Cretaceous era or earlier. A few species of fossil ants have been obtained from Eocene deposits and many specimens are found in amber of the Lower Oligocene and Miocene. Though these belong to extinct species, they seem to have been as specialised as any existing forms. We may take it then that the ants arrived at an equivalent to their present degree of specialisation at least fifty million years ago. In other words, they have had about fifty times as long a period of time as man in which to perfect their social organisation. Several facts of observation suggest that the evolution of bees and wasps is more recent. For instance, in the ants the two female types, queens and workers, differ markedly, in that normally the former are winged and the latter wingless. Among social bees and wasps, however, the worker resembles the queen in having wings: the differentiation which, as we imagine, will ultimately cause her to discard them has not yet taken place. There are wide divergences among different species of ants, bees and wasps. For instance, many kinds of bees and wasps have no social organisation. In the more primitive ants, moreover, many colonies are small and there is little divergence between 'queen' and 'worker'. But the more 'civilised' ants shew astonishing developments. Not only are the workers quite different from the queens, but they themselves shew signs of dividing into two castes, 'workers' and 'soldiers'. These ants have become increasingly vegetarian, though their ancestors, like the wasps, must have been carnivorous. Moreover, colonies of ants exploit one another. Some have become grossly parasitic and have even lost their workers, members of a conquered species serving as their slaves.

§351. *The termites.*

But of all the insects some species of termites, or so-called white ants, appear to have reached the highest degree of civilisation. The termite appears to be white because it has no light-proof pigment in its skin: it lives away from daylight in nests which in South America are at times as much as 20 feet high and contain millions of individuals. In these nests, as in those of certain species of true ants, there are fungus gardens in which are grown mushrooms treated in some unknown way so as to produce tumours which form nourishing food. On this food the king and queen feed and also the young termites; but it is not given to the workers or soldiers. Even more surprising than the communal mushroom gardens is the fact that the termites appear to have domesticated other insects, as we have domesticated cattle. In their nests are "extraordinary beetles found nowhere else, in which the huge and greatly modified abdomen grows out into bizarre projections from which exude food material that is licked off by the termite proprietors". In some species of termites the queen is a pathetic figure with enormously enlarged ovaries: she is said to be able to lay eggs at the rate of over a thousand a day for a period which may extend to ten years. Such specialisation has its counterpart in other members of an advanced termite community. There is little cause for surprise that an authority like Holmgren finds in such termites a highly developed nervous organisation coupled with signs of general degeneration. They are probably over-specialised and likely to vanish in the evolutionary struggle of the future.

§ 352. *The advance of social organisation among the bees.*

The various species of bees differ enormously in their habits. The most primitive type of bee makes a small hole in the ground, puts into it a little pollen and honey, and then deposits in the hole an egg: from this egg there will come in due course a small grub to feed on the food provided. At the other end of the scale of social organisation we have the honey-bee, with its amazing perfection of social organisation in the hive, familiar to all through the writings of naturalists like Fabre and men of letters such as Maeterlinck. The hive of a honey-bee will, when in full strength, contain a queen, some 2000 drones and some 30,000 workers. As is well known, the queen alone produces eggs. Those which are deposited in queen-cells and worker-cells are fertilised at the time of their deposition: those placed in the drone-cells are unfertilised. As the fertilised eggs ripen they are all left with the haploid number (that is, half the normal number) of chromosomes. These combine with the haploid number in the sperm-nuclei to give the normal (diploid) number of chromosomes alike in 'queens' and 'workers'. The differences between these two forms of the insect appear to result entirely from the way in which the young are fed: the workers are undeveloped females which cannot be inseminated by the drones. These latter, the drones, are haploid results of parthenogenesis.

With the bees, as with the rotifers, the difference between female and male seems to depend, not on sex-chromosomes, but on whether in the cells of a particular individual there is present the normal or only one-half of the normal number of chromosomes. We are left wondering whether the more usual sex-mechanism has passed into disuse. It is, to say the least, improbable that the production of males by a normal process of fusion of gametes never existed among insect forms from which the honey-bees have been derived. Be that as it may, the fact remains that such a process gives equal numbers of male and female offspring and there seems no way of altering this equality. But the method of production of males, now invariable in the hive, means that the honey-bees can arrange to have that particular balance between the sexes which they may think desirable! So perfect is their social organisation that the destruction of young (which is usually enormous among organisms where the female lays a large number of eggs) has been brought to an end. Only one female in 10,000 is needed as a parent: hence other females by suitable food are changed from parents to workers! In humanity by improved social organisation the destruction of young life is being lessened, so that the pressure of population is now becoming heavy. Our eugenists would have us breed strongly from good stocks and so arrange matters that human beings belonging to inferior stocks should leave no descendants. Unfortunately, however, humanity does not seem sufficiently plastic to allow of the artificial production of such a differentiation as that of 'queens' and 'workers' in the bees. But we have only just realised the existence of mutant forms and the possibilities which they offer of developing new human types are entirely unexplored. Many close observers of the fossil record have concluded that, when genetic variations begin, they tend to continue in the initial direction*. Sir Arthur Smith Woodward, for instance, states that "when any kind of animal shews a tendency to change in some particular part, the degree of this change increases in successive generations, especially if the change at first gives it some advantage". If this conclusion could be applied to humanity we might, by exploiting some favourable sequence of mutations, produce a whole series of changes which shewed humanity to be unexpectedly plastic. Such possibilities are by no means fantastic: but they belong to the future. At present we have to admit that the bees, by good luck or by good management, can produce queens or workers or males at will: the fact that we have no such capacity means that our social organisation is relatively immature.

It may be added that, among many species of bees and ants, the

---

* This question is discussed, and the idea rejected, in § 397. But conditions which allow the persistence of a mutation will probably be favourable to other, and more pronounced, mutations of the same type.

workers occasionally lay eggs. These, being unfertilised, become haploid males. But among certain species, alike of ants and bees, workers can apparently produce normal females at times: in such cases the unfertilised egg must retain all its chromosomes in the process of cell-division. We cannot understand the cause of this exceptional and unexpected fact. We gain nothing by stating that the higher insects have a surprising sexual plasticity. But we are led to wonder why such plasticity does not occur among the mammals.

§353. *Instinct and intelligence.*

It is well known that, in M. Bergson's opinion, the ways of ants and bees cannot be described as intelligent. Their ways are, he asserts, instinctive; and, moreover, instinct and intelligence differ in kind and have evolved on different paths. It is a pity that we cannot get the ants' reply to the philosopher's calm assumption of superiority. We may grant that, in certain aspects of the behaviour of the social insects, there is, as Professor Sir J. Arthur Thomson says*, "an adjustment of means to ends which certainly does not rest on a basis of individual experience". Purely instinctive activity would presumably be in no degree conscious. But the behaviour of hive-bees under exceptional circumstances shews that their instinctive behaviour is not unaccompanied by intelligence. I personally doubt Bergson's sharp separation of intelligent from instinctive behaviour. Instinct develops when we have thoroughly learned a lesson, e.g. to drive a motor car; and also when, in our hereditary make-up, we carry knowledge which our ancestors have been able to transmit. But we need intelligence to learn a lesson, and without intelligence we can hardly acquire new knowledge to hand on to our descendants. Both instinct and intelligence are, I would maintain, different aspects of the mental development of the organism in which they are manifest.

The salt of life.

The social life of the higher bees and ants cannot fairly be disparaged as merely instinctive. But, in the apparent absence of any progressive development, it is depressingly sterile. The short hard lives of the 'workers', and the monotonous reproduction of the same circumstances year after year, might well lead the insects to echo the Psalmist's words: "How short my time is! Wherefore hast thou made

* J. Arthur Thomson, *The System of Animate Nature.* 2 vols. Williams and Norgate, 1920, vol. I, p. 210.

all bees for nought"? Human life is saved from futility, so far as existence on earth is concerned (and the question of life after death does not
enter into any analogy), by our progress in knowledge and in mastery
of our environment. If it were stagnant, a mere repetition century after
century of stereotyped activities, it might be like that of the higher
insects and shew a monotonous and even exasperating perfection. But
when students of political development claim that the final outcome
of the better social organisation of man desired by left-wing reformers
would be an unendurable gynaecocracy of maiden aunts, such as exists
in the hive of the honey-bee, they forget that the salt of human life
consists of man's apparently inexhaustible curiosity. If perfection of
social organisation eliminated all our philosophers, inventors and men
of science, we might well deplore the fate for which we seem compelled
instinctively to strive. But we have far to go and much to discover
before we can attain to the level of social evolution reached by the
higher insects: and we are so made that, when we shall have reached
such a stage, we shall have passed far beyond it. For, in truth, we cannot draw an exact parallel between the higher insects and ourselves.
Without any bias born of self-esteem we may affirm that we are far
more highly organised and with far greater potentialities than the
'civilised' insects; but we must also admit that we are as yet at a less
advanced stage of development.

§ 354. *The Virgin Birth.*

For a generation a common subject of controversy between modernist
and traditionalist theologians has been the Virgin Birth of Jesus Christ.
Modernists have argued that the story, which is only to be found in the
introductory chapters of the first and third Gospels, is not a statement
of fact. It represents, they say, a popular attempt to explain the
spiritual excellence of One Who was rightly and naturally revered
by the early Christian community. The introductory narratives of
Matthew and Luke must be dated at least eighty years after Jesus was
born. They reflect, as do New Testament narratives in general, the
outlook of a community which had not realised the invariable character
of those natural sequences which form the 'laws of Nature' investigated
by the modern man of science. The traditionalist replies that the Virgin
Birth was at all events congruous with the fact of the Incarnation:
that the public announcement of it was unlikely to have been made
before the death of Mary, the mother of Jesus: and sometimes he adds
that such a birth 'broke the entail of sin'. A critico-historical examina-

tion of the story would be foreign to these lectures; but its biological associations may be briefly considered, as by theologians they are usually ignored.

I have, personally, little doubt that biological research will in due course prove a human virgin birth to be possible. Probably the individual so produced would be haploid, with but half the normal number of chromosomes, and the chances are that its sex would be male. But whether haploid or normal, male or female, it would vary little from the normal mental and emotional make-up of the human race. What exactly is meant by 'breaking the entail of sin' I do not know: my imagination fails when a metaphor derived from our land laws is applied to a mixture of biology and theology. But there is no reason to believe that a human being produced by parthenogenesis would lack normal appetites and passions. Biological parallels indicate that, if haploid, such an individual would probably be of sub-normal physical development. I do not personally think that such development could be regarded as 'congruous with' the Incarnation, though Rendel Harris in an ingenious investigation* has adduced some evidence to shew that Jesus of Nazareth was below normal height. It may be added that, if the story of the Virgin Birth be rejected, Jesus will remain, as St Mark implies, the son of Joseph and Mary. We should then know of nothing in His ancestry to explain the moral ascendancy and religious genius which were undoubtedly His. These qualities might be held to result from a dominant mutation: and if all mutations are to be regarded as manifestations of the creative activity of God, the spiritual excellence of Jesus would be from God. As these lectures clearly shew, I personally do not doubt that God acts in and through the evolutionary process; and between such a mode of Divine action and the assertion of the divinity of Christ I see no necessary opposition.

There are some who may shrink from any such investigation of the Virgin Birth as I have indicated. For my own part I am convinced that we must abandon the practice of arguing *in vacuo*, as it were, for such a mode of argument was the typical vice of medieval scholasticism. On the basis of observed facts of Nature, and by arguments drawn from such analogies as come within the range of our observation, we must approach all problems which present themselves. I would add that reverence and truth can always be combined, unless the object of our reverence should happen to be untrue.

* J. Rendel Harris, "On the Stature of our Lord", *Bulletin of the John Rylands Library, Manchester*, vol. x, 1926, p. 112.

Lecture xiv

THE EVOLUTION OF ANIMALS
AND MENDELISM

THE EVOLUTION OF ANIMALS

§ 355. *Evolution and religious prejudice.*

There are in modern Christendom two curious types of degenerate religious thought which are widely prevalent. One is a refusal to admit the truth of man's evolution from lower forms of life. The other is a belief that a spiritual presence can be attached to, or reside in, inanimate objects. The refusal is, in essence, a mistaken attempt to assert the dignity of man. The belief is a survival of primitive religious credulity.

Man's dignity needs no defence save such as is provided by his conduct. He is what he is, whatever be his origin. Whether he has evolved from an anthropoid ape or was specially created in the image of God, his present faculties, aspirations and achievements determine his worth: and from them we must argue as to his destiny. Gradually these considerations have become plain to most educated men. As we lament the ignorant opposition to evolution manifested even to-day in the Roman Catholic Church and among Protestants in certain backward States of the American Commonwealth, we may remember with pride that many British religious leaders refused to join in ignorant denunciation when *The Origin of Species* was published in the year 1859, and that by the decision of Anglican clergymen Charles Darwin (1809–1882) was buried in Westminster Abbey.

Much of the continuing opposition to the doctrine of evolution is due to defective education. Ignorance and religious prejudice are congenial bedfellows. Evolution, moreover, is not a fact of observation: it is a conclusion reached by coordinating a whole series of facts, the significance of which, for the most part, only experts can appreciate. Because we cannot see evolution taking place, those who have no scientific imagination must be guided by authority as they accept or reject the idea. The authority of tradition, conservative and reactionary, usually rests with organised religious bodies. But the authority of knowledge ultimately triumphs in a healthy progressive community. Should Western Civilisation decay, then all forms of scientific knowledge will gradually be ignored as superstition combines with degenerate religion. But, though such mental and emotional deterioration was marked in the decline of Graeco-Roman civilisation, there seems to be no good reason why we should yet expect it in Europe.

§ 356. *The nature of species.*

We have said that the arguments in favour of the doctrine of evolution are indirect. Human life is too short for us to be able to see the making of new species. Perhaps we ought rather to say that the process of evolution is too slow for man to be able to observe it in those living forms which naturally attract his attention. A close study by experts of insects, which have very brief lives and in which the generations succeed one another rapidly, should ultimately reveal the making of species. Work such as has been done by Morgan and his pupils with *drosophila* and by H. S. Jennings with *difflugia corona* needs but a little extension to shew us that the evolution of new species is still taking place. Meanwhile, as every horticulturist and breeder of animals knows, new varieties within species are constantly being produced.

There is at least the possibility that in man at the present time we can observe a significant evolutionary change, inasmuch as, in many persons, the wisdom teeth fail to cut the gums and are consequently for such persons 'vestigial organs'. If this change establishes itself generally, man will only have altogether twenty-eight teeth. He will thus have gone farther along a path already traversed some little way by his recent ancestors. The short-nosed monkeys of South America which have thirty-six teeth undoubtedly represent a generalised form from which the anthropoid apes emerged. The latter, and man with them, have thirty-two teeth. Whether in humanity a further reduction will ultimately be established it is impossible to say. The Australian duck-billed platypus has no teeth; but in their place it has developed hard plates which crush the insects, snails and so forth on which it lives. These plates are gums which have hardened. None the less, teeth appear for a short time in the gums of the young platypus. They are vestigial organs discarded in adult life. Man is the most advanced, and the duck-billed platypus is probably the most primitive, of living mammals. Will extremes meet as man loses his teeth?

Species are usually defined as groups of animals which are fertile when mated with one another, but which are either infertile or produce sterile hybrids when mated with other species. Yet though such a definition is useful it is, like most statements that can be made with regard to animate nature, not free from exceptions. For instance, according to Bateson, hybrids between dogs, wolves and jackals are fertile. "Many species of *anatidae* cross and produce fertile hybrids. The pintail duck and mallard will breed together, though the fertility of the cross is sometimes partial. Dürken cites a fertile female cross between a male goose and a female swan*." On the other hand, every horticulturist knows that crosses between artificially produced varieties of the same species of plant can be infertile. A familiar example is the primrose, on which there are two forms of flower. One has tall stamens and a short pistil, and the other short stamens and a long pistil. Pollen taken from short stamens and placed on a short pistil produces vigorous seeds. Equally satisfactory results can be obtained from long stamens and a long pistil. But if pollen from stamens of one length be placed on the other length of pistil, the resulting seeds are 'few and feeble'. In connection with such relative infertility, we must remember that much evidence goes to shew that sexual reproduction is easily disordered: it is delicate rather than strong and many physiological (and psychical) factors easily interfere with it. When varieties begin to differentiate themselves from the norm of a species, effective barriers to reproduction arise. Naturally the existence of such barriers aids in the formation of new species.

We thus reach the conclusion that a species is not always a naturally defined unit. We can have groups of animals and plants so large and diverse that, while an expert would hesitate to assign adjacent individuals to separate species, yet the extreme members of the group can hardly be ranked as mere varieties of the same species. In Nature intermediate forms often perish in the struggle for existence; and for this reason the resulting divergence gives what can conveniently be classed as independent species. After all, the essence of the doctrine of evolution is that new varieties are constantly being produced and that, by a process of continuous change, they create new species. A species is thus an artificial mental construction which is for practical purposes useful because it corresponds in a very large number of instances to a natural group. When such correspondence does not exist, differences of opinion as to classification will shew themselves. The growth of

---

* I owe these references to Professor Sir J. Arthur Thomson of the University of Aberdeen. He pointed out to me that Darwin's cautious statement ("it has lately been asserted") that hare and rabbit will produce fertile offspring is erroneous. *Vide The Origin of Species.* Murray, 1889, p. 240.

knowledge within a century can be well exhibited by contrasting two statements by men as great as Linnaeus (1707–1778) and Huxley (1825–1895). The former believed in the immutability of species and stated, in words which have been often quoted, that "the number of species is as many as the different forms created in the beginning". Huxley, in the year 1880, fully recognised the difficulty of the position which had then arisen and expressed the view that "sooner or later" we should have "to give up the attempt to define species".

§ 357. *The main arguments for evolution:* (1) *The geological record.*

What are the main arguments for evolution? First, we would put the fact that the geological record cannot be understood save in the light of some doctrine of evolution.

When modern men first realised that in the rocks there were remains of animals that had been entombed in sediment deposited by water, they naturally assumed that they had discovered confirmation of the biblical story of the Flood. This theory of the origin of fossils proved untenable when the different strata in the earth's crust were explored and it was found that in them there were markedly different types of fossilised animals and plants. A theory of catastrophic deluges, always followed by new creations, was devised to account for the new discoveries. When, however, it had become necessary to postulate twenty-seven such catastrophes and when, even so, it appeared doubtful whether more were not required, a 'uniformitarian' theory became obviously necessary. The possibility that earth's fossil history was due to slow physical and organic changes became the more probable as men became familiar with two facts. On the one hand, slow movements in the earth's crust can produce upheavals or subsidences as effectively as violent volcanic action. On the other hand, species in successive geological ages shew evidence of a type of progress as to which it can be fairly said that continuity and development are more obvious than arbitrary change. One of Lyell's great services to science, as we have already said, was that he clearly demonstrated that the record of the rocks could be explained by small causes effective over vast periods of time. Older catastrophic theories resembled Ptolemaic astronomy. The increase of knowledge led to such an elaboration of theory that the whole became incredible.

§ 358. *The main arguments for evolution:* (2) *The evidence from embryology.*

Darwin himself believed that the science of embryology furnished the strongest arguments on behalf of evolution. It is, in fact, quite impossible to explain the amazing series of changes through which the embryo of one of the higher animals passes, as it develops from the fertilised cell, save on the assumption that "it is climbing up its own ancestral tree". The embryo passes through stages which correspond, more or less closely, with the adult life of remote ancestors. Haeckel (1834–1919), in the year 1866, expressed this fact in the words "Ontogeny is a short recapitulation of phylogeny", a sentence which, when it is understood, is admirably expressive. Of course, many phenomena to be observed during the growth of an embryo are mere adaptations to the form of life which it is forced to lead: they could never have been present in adult animals. For instance, the human embryo develops from its belly a mushroom-shaped organ or sucker, called the placenta, by which it is enabled to draw nourishment from the mother. But no ancestor walked about in adult life with such an appendage. It is necessary sharply to separate such 'secondary' embryonic developments from the 'primary' developments which recapitulate ancestral history. When this is done, the latter developments give valuable information. For instance, the ascidian or sea-squirt has chosen such a type of adult life that it resembles a sponge: its youth over, it attaches itself to a rock and becomes enveloped in a gelatinous external skeleton which serves as a sort of filter. It was classed as a mollusc, until Kowalewsky, in the year 1866, shewed that the young possess the notochord, tubular nerve-cord and gill-slits of the typical vertebrate.

Speaking generally, we may say that every higher animal begins as a fertilised egg, which undergoes a series of divisions which lead to the formation of a hollow sphere, the blastula. The blastula resembles a very primitive organism which, coloured by chlorophyll, is to-day to be found in our ditches. In the next stage of development one end of the hollow sphere is, as it were, pushed in and a two-layered embryo, the gastrula, is formed: it has the shape of a hollow cup. The gastrula can be compared to a simple sponge or hydroid. From the gastrula stage the different great branches, or phyla, of the animal world follow different paths. We may, because it is to us of primary interest, very briefly describe the vertebrate path. As a vertebrate develops from the gastrula stage the inside of the cup gradually becomes the gut or, more accurately, the alimentary canal. At the same time a plate of superficial cells on the outside of the cup rolls up, as it were, to form a tube. Then the front of this tube swells out to form the brain and the rest of it forms the spinal chord: thus brain and nervous system are at first mere thickenings of the outer skin. Meanwhile, below the nerve plate and above the alimentary canal, a ridge of the inner skin forms the notochord, a sort of tissue-scaffolding which ultimately enables the organism to develop a backbone. This ridge becomes surrounded by segmented cartilage which is ultimately changed to bones. These bones in man fuse together, five at a time, so as to become the vertebrae. At one stage in the life of all vertebrates the cavity behind the mouth and nose is pierced on both sides by gill-slits between which arterial arches run. These gill-slits in fishes enable the blood to be oxygenated at the gills. In air-breathing vertebrates the gill-slits, though they are always formed for a short time in the embryo, are subsequently transformed in ways which differ in different types of animals.

Perhaps no phenomenon in the whole of embryology is more impressive than the fact that the human embryo even now passes through a stage which can only be explained as a still-persisting record of the time when man's distant ancestors passed from the water to the land. The human embryo at this stage is extraordinarily like a tadpole: and in the development of both there is a fantastic resemblance. The head of the embryo has a mouth resembling that of a shark and the nostrils are, as in the shark, connected with the edges of the mouth by grooves. In fact, the shark and the dog-fish are survivors, with relatively few modifications, of the early vertebrates; and hence the dog-fish is sometimes studied because it affords "a good ground-plan of human anatomy and physiology". All vertebrates, from fishes up to man, have a stage in their embryonic life when they have not only gill-slits but also "five or six pairs of aortic arches, a simple tubular heart with one auricle and one ventricle, a notochord and a primitive type of kidney". The human embryo develops first the primitive type of kidney which exists in the lower fishes. At a later stage there appears a more advanced type like that of a frog. Finally, there is produced the type of kidney which is to be found not only in other mammals but also in reptiles and birds. A pair of kidneys of the latter type alone survives in the adult human being.

As a study of the unexpected, and a living record of evolutionary changes in the long distant past, embryology is a most fascinating branch of science. A few facts concerning human embryology will further illustrate this statement. When the limbs of the human embryo first grow from the trunk it resembles a four-footed animal, with fingers and toes webbed like those of a dog. At this stage it develops a tail which survives in rudimentary form even in the adult. Normally our tails are invisible, but sometimes, by an unwelcome mutation, a child is born with a short visible tail. Later in its growth the human embryo is completely covered with hair which resembles that of an ape. Even at birth the big toe of a baby is opposed to the others as in the ape; and, if the infant be held on its feet, its legs curve inwards. The legs of the ape curve in the same way in order that it may the better press with its feet against the tree up which it desires to climb.

To elaborate such facts would be to write a treatise on embryology. They are of course absolutely inexplicable save on the assumption that the embryo, as it develops, describes the evolutionary path of successive types of ancestors. Moreover, the pedigree thus suggested agrees markedly with that which we should naturally construct from our knowledge of the fossil record.

§ 359. *The main arguments for evolution: (3) The existence of useless organs.*

It has been said that man is a museum of useless antiques and, though the statement is a gross exaggeration, it is a fact that in his body there are a number of organs, possibly as many as one hundred, which are useless. Such are usually called vestigial organs, as they are relics or vestiges of a past which man has outgrown. These organs serve no useful purpose: at times they are harmful. Their presence in the human body can only be explained by the doctrine of evolution. Each recalls a time when some ancestor of man, suited to a different kind of life, needed the organ of which the utility is now ended.

The best known of all such organs in man is the appendix. In some herbivorous mammals the appendix is relatively large and elaborate: situated, as it is, at the junction of the large and small intestines, it seems to play an important part in digestion. In monkeys and in anthropoid apes it is relatively small, as in man. Apparently it has become entirely useless in humanity; and, as we all know, it readily becomes a centre of intestinal imflammation. The existence and cause of appendicitis are singularly difficult of explanation by those who contend that man was specially and directly created by God.

A second example of a vestigial organ in man is the little ridge of whitish tissue which can be found in the angle of the eye adjacent to the nose. This ridge is the remnant of a third eyelid, the so-called nictitating membrane. It is functional in many mammals and, passing under the two outer lids, it serves to cleanse the eyeball. A third example of a vestigial organ in man is the group of muscles which once served to enable some ancestor to move his ears. Some among us can still use some of these muscles; and many a boy, by reason of such prowess, has won the respect of his schoolfellows. But, though a dog normally adjusts his ears that he may the better detect slight sounds, man has lost the habit. In man the muscles of the external ear are now useless relics.

Nature provides elsewhere more striking examples of vestigial organs than any to be now found in man. As all know, the whale is a mammal: a warm-blooded creature protected, like a successful channel swimmer, by a thick coating of tissue. It breathes air and can store a large quantity of purified blood for use while beneath the sea. Its single pair of flappers correspond to the hands of a man: but there is no sign of hind limbs. When, however, a 'whalebone whale' is carefully examined, there is found embedded in the flesh an isolated group of bones which corresponds to a rudimentary pelvis and hind legs. This group of bones is a most astonishing vestigial organ. It may be added that when the mammalian affinity of the whale is investigated by the 'blood test', the swine appears to be its nearest living relative. When I was a boy I learned, as part of a widely believed folk-lore, that a pig when it tries to swim cuts its own throat: I have heard this belief used to vindicate the truth of the story of the Gadarene swine. It appears, however, that in a distant past era a mammal, not wholly unlike a pig, did learn to swim and became a whale!

One or two other examples of vestigial organs may be given, as they serve forcibly to emphasise the fact of evolution.

The snake is a legless reptile. But in the python on each side of the vent there are small claws. These are supported by a rudimentary internal skeleton and are clearly relics of the hind legs of some four-legged ancestor.

We have already said that the tail in man, which still exists under the skin as the lower end of the vertebral column, is a vestigial organ. Abnormal human beings, 'throw-backs' in which the tail appears, are very rare. They may be likened to similar 'throw-backs' in horses, in which two useless but not entirely rudimentary toes appear, one on either side of the 'toe' on which the horse runs. This 'toe' is, of course, the horse's hoof. Normally the rudimentary side toes exist as slender splint-bones on each side of the horse's 'leg'. As was implied in § 328, the fossil record in America reveals three-toed horses alike in the Oligocene and in the Miocene epochs. From the earliest Eocene comes the fossil of a four-toed ancestor of the modern horse.

In New Zealand there is a strange bird, the kiwi, which can run rapidly but cannot fly. It has a thick coat of feathers which somewhat resemble hair; and, beneath them, are very small, absolutely useless, wings.

Most air-breathing vertebrates have two equal lungs, placed symmetrically in the body. But in some snakes only the right lung is really efficient, the left lung being small and practically useless. In the viper this secondary lung has vanished, save that a small protuberance which represents it can be detected: only the one lung remains. Exactly analogous is the ovary of the bird. Speaking generally it may be said that in the females of most vertebrates the ovaries are symmetrically placed, as are also the passages (oviducts) through which the eggs pass. But in the birds the left ovary alone is functional, the right exists as a useless relic. Unless the doctrine of evolution be accepted, all the facts relating to vestigial organs—and we have merely given a few striking instances—are incapable of a reasonable explanation.

§ 360. *The main arguments for evolution:* (4) *The geographical distribution of animals.*

A minor but none the less effective argument for evolution is supplied by the way in which varieties and species of animals, alike living and extinct, are and have been distributed. All evidence which can be obtained goes to shew that, when a species of animal or plant is isolated by geographical barriers, it begins what may best be described as a course of independent evolution. Just as a breeder artificially eliminates from animals characters which he desires to suppress and thereby produces new varieties, so Nature produces new types by the steady pressure of a particular environment on an isolated group of animals.

Whatever the proximate *cause* of evolution—and this as yet unanswered question will be discussed later—there is no doubt that the *direction* of evolutionary change is largely determined by environment. Let an organic group be placed in a new environment where it can maintain itself in isolation from the rest of its kind and in a comparatively short space of time, even as historical time is reckoned, changes in it will become obvious. Isolation is necessary lest crossbreeding with another group, in which different characters have found favourable opportunity of development, should mask the consequences of the influence of the environment.

It must be remembered, moreover, that in any particular region the environment, in so far as it affects any particular species, is constantly, even if slowly, changing. Dry land becomes swamp and conversely.

Forests grow or are destroyed: climate consequently changes. Fauna and flora are never stable. What Darwin called 'natural selection' is always at work, eliminating the less fit and keeping the changing species adapted to its environment with a closeness which might almost be termed accurate.

We have already, in § 326, referred to one of the most striking instances from palaeontology of evolution in isolation. When the land-bridges across the Mediterranean sank, elephants were left on some of the islands which were formed, Malta, Sicily, Crete, etc. The animals were necessarily prevented from wandering far afield and from breeding freely outside each island group. As a result they degenerated, became dwarfs and finally disappeared.

Another example is afforded by the northern immigrant mammals in South America. As we have said in a previous lecture, North and South America were separated, from the Eocene until the late Miocene, by a great belt of sea. At the period of separation there were, alike in the Middle West of the United States and in Patagonia, large accumulations of sediment in which the mammalian fauna of North and South America respectively are well preserved. In the middle Miocene the separation of the two continents had been so prolonged that their fauna were entirely different. Because of the Alaska land-bridge the fauna of the United States at that period consisted essentially of Old World mammals. When the Isthmus of Panama rose above the sea there was a natural infiltration of some of these northern mammals into South America. Some of their descendants, especially certain beasts of prey and deer, still remain in South America. But, since they crossed the Isthmus, they have so changed that they must now be placed not merely in different species but in different genera from their northern cousins.

A standard example of the way in which geographical isolation leads to new varieties at the present time is given by Gulick's investigation of snails in the Sandwich Islands. These snails live in dark damp forests: they cannot survive the dry glare of open country. Consequently they form a large number of isolated communities. Every valley has a variety of snail which differs slightly from that in the neighbouring valley: and between widely separated valleys there is a marked difference of type.

Enough has been said to shew that the geographical distribution of animals can be explained if the theory of evolution under the influence of a changed or changing environment be accepted. If this theory be rejected we have an array of facts of which no coherent explanation can be given.

§ 361. *Missing links.*

While the cumulative evidence for the fact of evolution is overwhelming, it must be admitted that the fossil record has so far failed to reveal certain important links in the evolutionary chain. Popular attention has been almost exclusively directed to the fact that there is but meagre evidence for the transition from an anthropoid ape to primitive man. When, however, the statement is made that no 'missing link' has ever been found, those who make it are guilty of exaggeration amounting to misrepresentation. Dubois' *pithecanthropus erectus* (§ 409) is a true missing link with semi-human, semi-anthropoid characters so apportioned that even experts differ as to whether it should be classed as ape or man. As we shall see in Lecture XVI, there are other remains of fossil men with markedly simian characteristics. Further, the physical differences between man and the anthropoids, even when they are most definite, are relatively slight. In fine, there is substantial evidence for the evolution of modern man, *homo sapiens*, from an apelike stock: and no palaeontologist doubts but that in due course such evidence will be largely increased by further discoveries.

But, while the details of man's origin from the anthropoids are either known or can be safely surmised, there are other origins of which nothing is known and with regard to which surmise is purely speculative. We have seen that, when the fossil record begins in the early Palaeozoic era, the great divisions among the invertebrates are already well established. Eight of the nine great phyla, which are the primary divisions of the animal kingdom accepted by zoologists, seem to appear suddenly in the Cambrian period: and six of these can certainly be found in the earliest Cambrian strata. Most phyla, it is true, are represented by somewhat lowly forms; but the trilobites, which are so characteristic and so numerous, are relatively high in the evolutionary scale. The phyla range from sponges (porifera) and jelly-fish (coelenterata) through worms (annelida) to higher groups like the arthropoda (which include insects, crustacea and spiders) and the mollusca (which include shell-fish and squids). It must have taken hundreds of millions of years to establish these great phyla; but there is no fossil evidence of the manner in which development took place. All that we can say is that the oldest fossils which have been preserved shew that the higher invertebrates must have had a very long evolutionary history during which they did not, in all probability, secrete lime and so left no bony remains which could be preserved for our observation. Doubtless further investigation of the embryology of the invertebrates will tend to establish relationships between some of the great phyla or between the classes or orders within them: but of the actual history of primitive evolution no records remain.

§ 362. *The origin of the vertebrates.*

It might reasonably be expected, however, that there would be fossil evidence shewing how the vertebrates arose from some invertebrate stock. This, the most sought after of all missing links, has not yet been discovered. Naturally, diligent search has been made: probably every palaeontologist dreams that one day he may discover some transitional form and become famous. In the meantime speculation rests upon a most meagre basis of fact. There appear to be two rival theories. According to the generally accepted view the vertebrates (or, if we include more primitive types, the chordates) are allied to the echinodermata (star-fish and the like), inasmuch as in both "the middle layer of the three primary cell-layers arises from out-pockets from the primitive gut". The echinodermata have a complete digestive tube surrounded by a spacious secondary body-cavity. Their skeleton consists of calcareous plates embedded beneath the skin: it is not a secretion from the external surface of the skin. On the other hand, arguments have been brought forward to shew that the chordates were derived from the arthropoda and, in particular, from some form resembling the fossil éurypterids. In support of this contention it is pointed out that both vertebrates and arthropoda are many-jointed animals, with a not wholly dissimilar apparatus for movement and a complex head which has apparently in each case been built up of parts originally independent*. Those of us who survey from outside the rival arguments probably conclude quite unintelligently that we are nearer crabs than star-fish: and it would appear that this conclusion finds some little support in recent discoveries. The earliest chordates so far discovered appear to be fish-like forms from Silurian and Devonian rocks in Norway, Scotland, Spitzbergen and Russia. These *ostracoderms*, as they are called, "foreshadowed the higher vertebrates, including man, in the ground-plan of their organisation". They had the notochord above

---

* The theory that the vertebrates are descended from an arthropod stock was advocated by W. H. Gaskell (1847–1914) in his book, *The Origin of the Vertebrates*, published in the year 1908. Gaskell's skilful advocacy, however, failed to convince the majority of his fellow-experts.

the primitive alimentary canal and above the notochord was the central nervous system: a similar arrangement, as we have seen, is found at an early stage in the human embryo. Forms which still survive practically unaltered in such primitive vertebrates as the existing lancelets (*amphioxus*) of shallow seas are distantly connected with the ostracoderms: what palaeontologists desire to find is a synthetic invertebrate form from which both *ostracoderms* and *amphioxus* evolved. Should such prove to be a sort of eurypterid, the connection between vertebrates and arthropods would be established. Most probably it will be found to be allied to the echinoderms.

The first Silurian chordates were already highly evolved; and, before the end of the Devonian, fishes had appeared with the main vertebrate characteristics. Some of them closely resembled modern sharks and dog-fish which, as we have seen, are primitive but characteristic vertebrate types. Thus in Devonian animals of rather more than 300 million years ago* there can be found an anticipation of human digestion and circulation and even, to some extent, of the processes of human respiration and reproduction. Moreover, from these ancient vertebrates we can trace, or infer, the gradual sequence of change that has led to ourselves.

§ 363. *The transition to the amphibians and thence to the mammals.*

Inference predominates in regard to the change which led from the fish to the earliest amphibians. There seems to be little doubt but that from some lobe-finned externally armoured fish of the Devonian the first land-living vertebrates arose. We should find it very hard to believe experts who told us that fishes became air-breathing land animals, were it not for the fact that the same almost miraculous transformation takes place under our eyes when the tadpole becomes a frog. Without doubt the first fishes to emerge from sea to land went back to the water to cradle their young.

The strong-jawed ganoids which are thought to be ancestral to the late Devonian or early Carboniferous amphibians had an internal skeleton: their fore-paddles were attached to bones corresponding to our shoulder and collar-bones and the hind-paddles were supported on a long plate with a vague likeness to the lower bars of the human pelvis. They must have had, in addition to gills, lungs adapted for air breathing. Further, when they tried to make progress over mud and earth they must have used their fore- and hind-paddles to push themselves along. These

* We take, in accordance with our general custom, Holmes' estimate as reduced by Jeffreys.

paddles consisted of bony rods arranged fanwise: we naturally surmise that their new use caused them to break into segments* and so to form primitive fingers and toes. In this picture of transition there is more conjecture than we could desire: but there is nothing unsupported by processes to be observed elsewhere in evolutionary development.

What is of interest is that in many of the earliest air-breathing vertebrates we find five digits alike on hands and feet. Possibly there had been seven digits in the first land vertebrates from which we are derived: but, if so, the digits outside the thumb and a little finger (or great and little toes) were speedily reduced to mere vestiges. To-day we use the decimal system of numeration because of structural changes developed by amphibians of the early Carboniferous some 300 million years ago. In many respects a duodecimal system would be more convenient; and it would be in common use if only our early Carboniferous ancestors had preserved six digits on hands and feet. The dead hand of the past is far-reaching.

As was indicated in § 321, experts are not agreed as to the passage from amphibian to reptile. Some think that it is known with singularly satisfactory completeness. Without doubt fossil forms exist as to which only the expert can say whether they are rightly to be classed as amphibians or reptiles†. One such, *seymouria*, is usually regarded as a particularly satisfactory transitional type, a generalised reptile from the Permian rocks of Texas.

We have previously, in § 323, described the reptilian origin of the birds, for which the evidence is conclusive.

We have also briefly discussed the evolutionary development which led from the reptiles to the mammals. Of course the chief differences between these two animal types are due to the fact that the mammal nourishes its young before and after birth, while the young of a reptile are hatched from an egg. The mechanism of the mother is profoundly altered by this change; but, as the alteration is almost entirely limited to the soft parts of the organism, it cannot be observed in fossils. Thus fossil differences between mammals and reptiles are relatively few. They are, in fact, structural improvements which affect mainly the teeth, jaws and skull. In the mammals developments resulting in greater simplicity are noteworthy.

---

* The language is, of course, popular and inexact. More accurately, germinal changes which led to segmentation were preserved by natural selection.

† See, for instance, R. Broom, *The Origin of the Human Skeleton*. Witherby, 1930, pp. 20, 46.

§ 364. *The moral significance of the development of the herd-instinct.*

It is impossible to read any zoologist's account of the distant ancestry of humanity without being somewhat surprised by the ferocity of some of the forms on which he fixes particular attention. We have already said that the shark affords an excellent ground-plan of the development of which man is a product. When, however, the evolution of mammals in the Permian epoch is under consideration, a group of 'fierce carnivorous' theromorphs is found to be specially important. Finally, a discussion of man's kinship with the great anthropoids leads to the conclusion that the gorilla is his nearest cousin. We should not expect that sharks, fierce carnivorous theromorphs and gorillas would be associated with the development of the animal in which moral aspiration and spiritual understanding are supreme. Man is, in fact, as surprising as the appearance of a medieval saint in a family of ruthless banditti. Doubtless the medieval saint was not perfect; but neither is man. None the less, he is far removed from shark and gorilla. There can, however, be little doubt that his moral sense is geologically a very late development. In part it is a concomitant of the growth of his brain. We are forced to assume that this growth gave him a truer understanding of the Universe, and significantly it seems to have led *per se* to an understanding of ethical values. But we must also allow that pity, affection and all the qualities associated with social solidarity, seem in part to have resulted from the relative physical weakness of man face-to-face with the great carnivora. That he might survive in the struggle for existence he was forced to develop the herd-instinct; and from it came the herd virtues.

The way in which the herd-instinct has arisen merits reflective attention, for it can be ultimately traced back to the evolution of modern grasses. Every writer on evolution repeatedly finds it necessary to insist that the development of plants and animals has proceeded step by step and that there has been close correlation between changes in the two realms of animate nature. Nowhere is the correlation more marked than between the grasses and the herbivorous mammals. We have seen that the modern grasses and cereals only made their appearance in the late Eocene. They flourished during the Oligocene and have since become dominant in the world. They share this supremacy with the modern forest trees. Now one result of the creation by the grasses of great prairies was the evolution of herbivorous mammals. These quadrupeds perforce became migrants as they followed their food through the changing seasons. On them the carnivora preyed. In self-defence they developed horns and hoofs. Primarily they relied on speed to escape from their foes; but—a much more significant and important change—they also combined for defence by corporate action. In the struggle for existence there was evolved the herd with its instinctive unity of thought and feeling when danger is at hand, with its ready obedience to a leader. Certain tree-living mammals allied to the insectivores found the need and value of similar unity. They were early primates, physically somewhat feeble creatures. Their descendants developed, with growing brains, a quick intelligence. Gradually in a semi-arboreal existence they copied, unconsciously or more probably consciously, the mass-action tactics developed on the prairies. From such a beginning came man's social solidarity: on it no small part of his ethical altruism has been reared.

§ 365. *Mind versus material protection.*

It is interesting to observe that man has emerged triumphant among the mammals, which during the Tertiary era have dominated the earth, although he is physically a weak creature. Apart from his intelligence and his capacity for combined action he would be found an easy prey by most of the carnivora. But it is not an exaggeration to say that the causes of his triumph had been foreshadowed in earlier periods of geological history. We have several times indicated that types of evolutionary change similar to one another have been manifested at different epochs of terrestrial history in widely divergent animals. One seductive and ultimately always fatal path has been the development of protective armour. An organism can protect itself by concealment, by swiftness in flight, by effective counter-attack, by uniting for attack and defence with other individuals of its species and also by encasing itself within bony plates and spines. The last course was adopted by the ganoid fishes of the Devonian with their shining armour. Some of the great lizards of the later Mesozoic were elaborately encased. Some Tertiary mammals, especially in South America, were immense and bizarre creatures: and one wonders how long a period of evolutionary history was needed for them thus to arm themselves. Always the experiment of armour failed. Creatures adopting it tended to become unwieldy. They had to move relatively slowly. Hence they were forced to live mainly on vegetable food; and thus in general they were at a disadvantage as compared with foes living on more rapidly 'profitable' animal food. The repeated failure of protective armour shews that, even at a somewhat low evolutionary level, mind triumphed over mere matter. It is this sort of triumph which has been supremely exemplified in man.

MENDELISM

§ 366. *Mendel's work and its significance.*

We will now assume that we have given arguments adequate to establish the doctrine of evolution. Species are not immutable. As the generations pass, new varieties arise. As these varieties diverge more and more from ancestral types and from collateral branches, new species are brought into being. With increasing differentiation we can get new genera, new families and so forth.

It is, however, one thing to say that such and such changes must have taken place, but quite a different thing to be able to explain the cause of change or even to describe the machinery by which it was effected. In the next lecture we will discuss the *machinery* of evolution. But here and now we pass to consider certain results, obtained in the experimental study of inheritance, which are known as Mendel's laws.

Gregor Mendel (1822–1884) was a monk, and afterwards abbot, of an Augustinian monastery at Brünn. "A young mathematician, whose statistical interests extended to the physical and biological sciences", he made a systematic study of inheritance in edible peas and published his conclusions in the year 1865 in the transactions of the local Natural History Society. The brilliant Dutch botanist de Vries thirty years later reached similar conclusions as a result of crossing evening prim-roses. When he searched through the literature of the subject he found that Mendel had to a large extent anticipated his own results, although what the older man had discovered had lain unnoticed. Mendel's most important paper was recovered in the year 1900.

The outstanding value of the researches initiated by Mendel is that the laws of heredity can be investigated by experiments which yield *numerical* tests. Biological science is largely descriptive and in it the accurate conclusions of the physical sciences are therefore not easily reached. But, since Mendel made his discoveries, a method has been available by which numerical results can be used to control genetic theory. For this reason Mendel's researches deserve the epithet epoch-making.

§ 367. *Mendel's fundamental experiment.*

Mendel crossed a tall variety of edible pea with a short variety. Each variety was such that it bred true to itself: it was, in fact, a pure strain. The hybrids resulting from the cross, which are denoted by the symbol

F_1, were all tall. When they were allowed to self-fertilise, their offspring, denoted by the symbol F_2, were tall and short in the ratio of 3 talls to 1 short. (It should be said that such a ratio as 3 : 1 is only an approximation to the truth. If the generations F_1 and F_2 consist of but a few individuals, the final ratio of talls to shorts may diverge somewhat from the ratio which is reached when a large number of individuals is considered.) Now if the tall variety of pea contains an element in the nucleus of its germ-cell which makes the plant tall, and if the short variety contains an element which makes the plant short, we may conjecture that the hybrid must contain both these elements, inasmuch as they appear in the F_2 generation. Then, inasmuch as all the hybrids are tall, we must assume that the factor for tallness *dominates* that for shortness or, in other words, short is *recessive* to tall.

Mendel saw that the ratio 3 : 1 which appears in the second generation can be explained by a quite simple hypothesis. Suppose that in the pure tall strain there is a pair of like elements corresponding to tallness, and that in the pure short strain there is similarly a pair of like elements corresponding to shortness. Further, suppose that, in the F_1 hybrid, the tall and short elements are both present, though separated, in the germ-cell. In fact, we suppose, if t and s stand for the tall and short elements respectively, that we may denote the original pure strains by t, t and s, s respectively, and the F_1 hybrid by t, s, this latter association being the result of sexual fusion. Then, in the F_2 generation, we get four equally probable possibilities of association through sexual fusion. They will be:

$$t, t; \quad t, s; \quad s, t; \quad s, s.$$

Because t dominates s, three of these possibilities will be tall and only one short. We have, in fact, the observed ratio.

Mendel next put his hypothesis to a test which confirmed it with singular elegance. He crossed the hybrid F_1 with the original short variety of pea. Now the hybrid can be denoted by the formula t, s. The short variety will, as we have seen, be denoted by the formula s, s, which indicates that it is a pure strain. Hence the results of the new cross will be represented by the equally probable forms:

$$t, s; \quad t, s; \quad s, s; \quad s, s.$$

We shall thus get an equal number of shorts and (impure) talls. Mendel's experimental results confirmed this expectation: tall and short varieties were equally numerous.

§ 368. *Mendel's first law.*

We thus reach a conclusion which is an example of what is sometimes called Mendel's first law and may be stated fully as follows.

In the germ-cell of the hybrid of the edible pea there are two linked or associated elements which correspond to tallness and shortness respectively. In a pure tall strain both the associated elements correspond to tallness: in a pure short strain both elements correspond to shortness. All hybrids are tall; but a tall hybrid differs from a 'pure tall' in that in its germ-cell there is one element of each type. Moreover, when these elements are paired in the hybrid F_1, neither contaminates the other. They separate out cleanly in the 'pure talls' and 'pure shorts' of the generation F_2.

The results obtained for the edible pea are typical of a general law of inheritance. With certain limitations, which we shall indicate, they apply to any organism provided that, in place of tallness and shortness, we take any pair of associated characters which in the organism appear as alternatives. Such associated characters are, for example, brown eyes and blue eyes in man. Suppose that pure blue and pure brown strains mate. Then, speaking generally, the eyes of the children will be all brown, for brown is dominant to blue. But if two brown-blue hybrids mate, the number of their children with brown eyes will be, on an average, three times the number of the children whose eyes are blue.

At this early stage of our exposition it is well to emphasise a fact which modifies—some would say vitiates—practically all statements which can be made as to Mendelian inheritance. This fact, on which we have previously insisted when discussing parthenogenesis, is Nature's prodigious resourcefulness. In the domain of heredity it is rarely possible to make any general statement which must not be qualified by exceptions. Hence all statements are, in the absence of explicit assertion to the contrary, to be regarded as but first approximations to the truth. Doubtless Nature's apparent waywardness will, on further investigation, prove to be largely reducible to subordinate laws modifying the general conclusions of present Mendelian theory. But it is probable that, when such subordinate laws have been discovered, there will still remain exceptions to them. In fact, the progressive study of heredity will consist of a series of successive approximations to the truth: and it may be that the series is without end.

The warning just given applies to the inheritance of brown eyes and blue eyes in man. To a first approximation the two types of eyes form a simple pair of associated Mendelian characters, in which blue is recessive to brown. But recent investigators have found relatively small, but none the less significant, departures from strict Mendelian inheritance. Winge states that when blue mates with blue, some 2 per cent. of brown eyes unexpectedly appear, together with about half as many eyes which must be classed as bluish or greyish green. Similarly, when blue and brown mate, though the numbers of brown and blue eyes in the offspring are approximately equal, there are some 1·5 per cent. of greenish eyes. But it is in connection with the mating of blue eyes with brown that the most significant departure from Mendel's law appears, for it becomes evident that the inheritance is to some extent 'sex-linked'. When the father has brown eyes and the mother blue, equal numbers of sons have blue and brown eyes but many more daughters have brown eyes than blue. When, however, the father has blue eyes and the mother brown, there is a marked excess of blue-eyed sons and daughters, the ratio of brown to blue being roughly the same in each sex. Evidently blue and brown in eye-colour in humanity result primarily from a pair of associated characters such as those discovered in Mendel's fundamental experiment: but other subordinate factors, some of which somehow depend upon sex, modify the simple law.

It should be further observed that associated characters are not always dominant or recessive, one to another. In the F_1 hybrid they may, in fact, produce a new character; and it is probably true to say that in a hybrid pure dominance and pure recessiveness are alike rare. But, whether the alternative characters act in this way or not, there is a clean separation of the corresponding germinal elements in the F_2 generation. For instance, there are pure strains of fowls with 'rose' combs and 'pea' combs respectively. If they be crossed, the F_1 hybrid has a 'walnut' comb. But, from the F_1 generation, by mating its members with one another, there will result rose, walnut and pea combs in the ratio of $1:2:1$. This result corresponds exactly to what happens when black and white (or accurately white with greyish splashes) fowls are mated to produce blue 'Andalusians'. If the blue Andalusians be mated, one-half of the offspring are like the parents; but the rest in equal proportions are black and white.

The inheritance of factors which thus separate out cleanly from a hybrid is sometimes called *particulate* or *factorial* inheritance.

§ 369. *The law of independent assortment.*

Results similar to those of Mendel's primary experiment are sometimes obtained when more than one pair of associated characters is in question. Mendel crossed pure strains of peas of which the seeds were yellow and round with pure strains of peas of which the seeds were green and wrinkled. Yellow and green form a pair of associated characters; and likewise round and wrinkled form such a pair. The offspring F_1 of the cross were all yellow and round. When they were self-fertilised, their offspring F_2 were yellow-round, yellow-wrinkled, green-round and green-wrinkled in the ratio of $9:3:3:1$. Mendel's explanation of these ratios can be readily obtained. Let us denote the elements by the letters y, g, r, w. Then in the F_1 generation we have the pairs of associated elements

$$y, g$$
$$r, w.$$

Now, if the four elements giving rise to the four different characters assort themselves at random, we shall have in the F_2 generation sixteen possibilities given by the table

yr yr	yw yr	gr yr	gw yr
yr yw	yw yw	gr yw	gw yw
yr gr	yw gr	gr gr	gw gr
yr gw	yw gw	gr gw	gw gw

If y dominates g, and r dominates w, we see that these possibilities correspond to the ratios found experimentally. From the experiment it is clear that the whole of the germ material derived from a particular parent does *not* act as a single unit. The characters of the 'yellow-round' parent are, as the diagram shews, distributed among the offspring. In the belief that such results were invariable, Mendel formulated his second 'law of independent assortment'. The associated elements yellow and green on the one hand, and the associated elements round and wrinkled on the other hand, assort themselves at random, as though neither pair was in the presence of the other.

§ 370. *Linkage-groups.*

Four years after Mendel's paper was rediscovered two Cambridge investigators, Bateson (1861–1926) and Punnett, found that experimental results did not always confirm the law of independent assortment.

For instance, there are sweet peas with purple flowers and long pollen-grains which can be crossed to others with red flowers and round pollen-grains. In the result purple and long tend to come out together and so do red and round. Now-a-days such characters are said to form a 'linkage-group'. Knowledge of such groups has been enormously extended by the intensive study of the banana-fly, *drosophila melanogaster*, made by Morgan and his pupils. They find that, in *drosophila*, there are four pairs of linkage-groups into which some 450 'mutant' characters are now known to fall. One of these pairs of linkage-groups, in which there are some 200 characters, has a definite relation to sex: the corresponding characters are said to be *sex-linked*.

The characters associated in a linkage-group do not always come out together in successive generations. Sets of these may be interchanged with their associates, but they remain united more often than they thus interchange. When interchange occurs 'crossing-over' is said to take place.

We have perhaps now said enough to make intelligible

§ 371. *Morgan's restatement of Mendel's laws of inheritance**.

The characters of an organism correspond (though a one-to-one correspondence must *not* be assumed) to certain elements, or factors, which are associated in pairs in the germ-cell from which the organism is derived. In sexual fusion of germ-cells only one element from each parental pair enters into the corresponding pair in the derived germ-cell. In a pure stock the elements of an associated pair are identical. A hybrid results from the mating of parents with associated elements different from one another. But when the different elements of an associated pair are thus associated in the hybrid they do not contaminate one another. For this reason pure stocks can be bred from hybrids. This fact of non-contamination is sometimes called Mendel's first law: or (not very happily) the law of the purity of the gametes.

We can have in a (compound) hybrid several, or many, associated pairs of elements, each pair being composed of two different elements derived from an opposition of characters in the parents. These pairs sometimes assort themselves at random as though the others were not present. Mendel thought that this fact was invariably true; and hence he framed his second law of independent assortment. But often sets of characters and corresponding elements in the germ-cell form 'linkage-groups'. If two characters are in the same linkage-group the corre-

* T. H. Morgan, *The Theory of the Gene*. Yale University Press, 1926, p. 25.

sponding elements in the germ-cell are so united that, when they enter a hybrid together, they tend to come out together in the next generation. In general, therefore, there are in an organism only as many groups of characters which assort at random as there are linkage-groups for that particular organism. Nevertheless, at times an orderly interchange takes place between sets of different elements in two associated linkage-groups. 'Crossing-over' is then said to occur. For instance, let associated pairs of different elements in two associated linkage-groups be

$$A, a; \ B, b; \ C, c; \ \dots \ L, l; \ M, m; \ \dots.$$

Then the associated linkage-groups may be written $ABC\dots LMN\dots$ and $abc\dots lmn\dots.$ Normally these groups will enter and leave a hybrid together. But when 'crossing-over' occurs the emergent groups of characters may correspond to linkages of elements $ABC\dots lmn\dots$ and $abc\dots LMN\dots$ respectively. Furthermore, it has been observed that crossing-over may occur several times between the same pair of associated linkage-groups. Finally, it may be remarked that, if the linkage-groups of elements formed linear sequences with the elements at definite relative distances apart and if 'crossing-over' were (as one imagines it must be) purely a matter of chance, then the number of times that crossing-over occurred between two definite elements would indicate the distance between them; and distances, as so calculated, would confirm one another by arithmetical addition and subtraction. Experimental evidence bears witness to the fact that linkage-groups are thus *linearly* arranged.

Inasmuch as the number of pairs of linkage-groups corresponds, so far as observation has gone, with the number of pairs of chromosomes in the nucleus of the germ-cell, it is natural to assume that *the elements are 'genes' arranged in linear order at loci or particular places on the chromosomes.* If this is true, the chromosomes will constitute linkage-groups and paired chromosomes will be associated linkage-groups. In short, the experimental study of heredity initiated by Mendel and the physiology of sexual reproduction disclosed by cytology confirm one another in a remarkable way. As Fisher puts it, "the conceptual framework of loci must therefore be conceived as made of several parts, and these are now identified, on evidence which appears to be singularly complete, with the dark-staining bodies or chromosomes which are to be seen in the nuclei of cells at certain stages of cell-division*". The

---

* R. A. Fisher, *The Genetical Theory of Natural Selection*. Clarendon Press, Oxford, 1930, p. 9.

microscopic difficulties associated with the investigation of phenomena within the nucleus of the cell are great. Much, moreover, remains to be learned with respect to many matters such as, for example, the machinery by which the number of chromosomes in a species changes as it changes into another species. But already a whole series of hopeful investigations is foreshadowed: of them it will certainly be possible to say that they enhance the marvel of the mystery of life.

§ 372. *Mutant characters.*

Mendel's work, as we have seen, rests upon the fact that the same species may have different characters which alternate with one another. Such characters are, for example, the tallness and shortness in the edible peas with which Mendel made his fundamental experiments. We have seen that these characters correspond, either closely or loosely, to associated or paired genes. In the fertilised germ-cell from which the individual takes its origin all the chromosomes are paired. This is true even of the sex-chromosomes of the male in species which have the human sex-mechanism, if we regard (X, Y) as a pair. The chromosomes constitute linear linkage-groups of genes and, lying along each pair of chromosomes other than the pair which includes the male sex-chromosome, are the paired or associated genes. In a pure strain each gene of a pair exactly resembles its fellow; the pairs are termed *homozygous*. But, in a hybrid, the two genes of the pair which correspond to the different characters of the parents are themselves different: the genes will be *heterozygous*. How comes it, we naturally ask, that associated or paired genes become different from one another? In other words, how comes it that different characters arise, so that new varieties of a species are formed? This question will be discussed subsequently. At present we content ourselves with saying that new characters, corresponding to changes in the nucleus of the germ-cell, do suddenly appear and are called *mutant characters*. They are the results of *mutations*. They may be produced by changes in a single gene or by changes in a number of genes; and when so produced, they will form heterozygous elements in pairs of chromosomes. If the mutant character shews itself in the hybrid, it is a dominant mutation. When such a mutation results from the change in a single gene, the corresponding mutant gene is dominant over its associate. If the mutant character does not shew itself in the hybrid, the corresponding mutant gene is recessive to its associate. It should be added that we may have, of course in different organisms, several mutations associated with the same gene. In other words, more than a single mutation may occur at the same locus. Such mutations are then said to form *a series of allelomorphs*. In *drosophila melanogaster* no less than eleven eye-colours have been observed as alternatives to the red eye of the wild fly. It is important also to state that no instance is known where a mutation has simultaneously occurred in each gene of an associated pair.

New inheritable characters may also result from the 'crossing-over' of parts of associated chromosomes, and from irregularities of cell-division which increase or decrease the number of chromosomes. Such causes of new characters we may class as *changes in the gross morphology of the chromosomes*.

Mutations, and more extensive chromosome changes, are the expression of the inherent instability of living matter. In fact, heredity and instability are correlative factors in life. Each checks and limits the other. By virtue of heredity species have relative permanence; but because of instability, new varieties constantly arise and in due course give birth to new species.

Everyone knows that, in animals and plants bred under artificial conditions, new characters constantly arise. Many of these characters are passed on to succeeding generations by inheritance. Such must correspond to changes in the germ-plasm: we have reason to believe that usually* they are, in fact, the result of chromosome changes, and in particular of point-mutations which may, of course, when they are recessive, have occurred many generations before they are observed. But also there is abundant evidence, according to Morgan and a growing majority of naturalists, that mutants arise similarly in wild races living under natural conditions. Most of such mutations doubtless produce weaker individuals which are less fitted to survive than the types to which they are alternates. Individuals shewing such mutant characters are therefore quickly eliminated under wild conditions. But if the mutant characters chance to have greater survival-value than the old types, they will persist. Owing to different local conditions one of the two alternate types may do well in one area and the second in another: we should thus get the different varieties of the same species, which are often to be found in adjacent areas separated by some barrier which the species cannot cross.

* We must not rule out the possibility that inheritable changes, which are not transmitted by Mendelian laws, result from other differences (as to centrosome-structure and so forth) in the germ-cell.

§ 373. *The contrast between Mendelian and blending inheritance.*

As Fisher has pointed out*, Mendel's studies were of paramount importance in that they put an end to that belief in *inheritance by blending* which was assumed by Darwin and apparently by all his contemporaries and predecessors. It was perhaps natural to assume that, when parents had contrasted qualities, the children should inherit the mean of the contrasts. But we might have expected that such an assumption would have been challenged, inasmuch as it presents grave difficulties even to casual observers. Children of the same parents differ widely. On the blending theory one must hold that mutations occur with practically every child. Further, on the same theory, all mutations will be rapidly brought back to the mean; and the greater part of the amount of variation, which at any time is present and inheritable, will be of quite recent origin. Still further, such a blending theory fails entirely to account for that likeness in some feature, of a child to one of its grandparents, which can so often be observed.

It is, therefore, surprising that no abstract thinker was led to abandon the idea of blending and to replace it by a theory of the existence of alternate genetic elements. As each parent contributes to the genetic outfit of the next generation, it would then have been necessary to assume that the individual had pairs of genetic factors, each parent contributing one element from each pair in the sexual fusion of the male and female reproductive cells. Obviously when two different elements formed a pair, either their conjoint action might produce a result intermediate between that of either, or the influence of one might quite overshadow the other. By means of such a *particulate* theory of inheritance (the inheritance of one or other of two factors) the likeness of child and grandparent is at once explicable. Further, the persistent variability of races is explained without postulating constant mutations. Old mutations, more or less completely hidden as recessives, merely await favourable mating that they may at length shew themselves. Without experiment the conception of linkage would not have emerged. But the superiority, as an abstract scheme, of a particulate theory of inheritance would quickly have become manifest.

Fisher has worked out the relative mutation-rates which the two theories of blending and of particulate inheritance require. He finds that the mutation-rate needed to maintain a given amount of variability is, on the particulate theory, *many thousand times smaller* than

---

* *Loc. cit.* pp. 7, 8.

that which is required on the blending theory. Full recognition of this fact will make clear how much less perplexing now are many questions which seriously troubled the pre-Mendelian biologists. For instance, there is no reason to assume that the mutations which man observes and uses in domestic animals are of recent origin. We need no longer, therefore, speculate as to the rapid influence of an artificial environment in producing mutations. Similarly, speculations as to the effect of use and disuse in producing genetic changes can be set aside. Attention must now be concentrated on the effect which natural selection will have in increasing or diminishing the number of individuals in whom a particular mutation exists. It might be thought that a recessive mutation would not cause the individual in whom it exists to be in any way affected by natural selection. But, as we have already said, very few mutations are pure recessives. Most have some slight effect on the organism in which they exist; and, as we shall see in the next lecture, even so slight a selective advantage or disadvantage as 1 per cent. would rapidly modify the genetic constitution of a species.

§ 374. *Mutations in humanity.*

Mutations of course occur in humanity. Many are trivial and pass unnoticed. Inherited idiosyncrasies with regard to teeth are good examples of such trivial mutations. But more serious mutations are not uncommon. In civilised countries their results are usually concealed by those individuals and families in which they shew themselves. Naturally men and, perhaps more especially, women do not care to reveal an abnormality or defect. The extent to which mutations occur and are inherited is not therefore generally recognised. Few know that among European races at least one man in twenty-five is colour-blind or that club-foot has a frequency of about 1 in 1500. Among typical abnormalities which almost certainly arose originally as mutations we may mention, in addition to colour-blindness and club-foot, haemophilia or 'bleeding', and albinism. But some characters which are now general and serve to differentiate various races of mankind are probably the result of dominant mutations: for instance, the white skin of the European races is probably the result of a mutation which occurred or recurred in a yellow-skinned people. It should be noticed that there is clear evidence from *drosophila* that the same mutant character may arise independently any number of times. But recessive mutant characters in humanity shew themselves far more often than might be expected if each appearance were due to an independent mutation.

With regard to them we may say that, if a recessive character can be discovered to have appeared in ancestors or collaterals, it has probably been latent; such a character, of course, must meet its like in mating before it can shew itself. For instance, albinism is, speaking generally, a recessive character in man. Normally, human albinos only arise when, in each parent, albinism is latent. It may be latent in each case through long inheritance: in one or both parents it may be latent owing to a recent mutation.

Some writers contend that the artificial conditions of civilised life are the main or even the sole cause of the numerous congenital deformities and abnormalities which occur in humanity. But studies of native peoples who have not advanced beyond a primitive stage of civilisation make it clear that inheritable variations from the normal occur among them with the same frequency. Inasmuch as among primitive races an endeavour is usually made to suppress the more noteworthy abnormalities by infanticide, it is somewhat surprising that abnormalities among such races are as numerous as investigation proves them to be.

Mutations occur persistently, in fact, alike among savage and civilised men, among other mammals and, so far as investigation has gone, among all lower forms of life: they are, as we have said, the raw material of evolution. But what seems to emerge from our present knowledge is that there is a far greater percentage of *dominant* mutations in humanity than in, say, *drosophila*. In the latter, according to Gates*, "only about a dozen dominant mutations have appeared among some 300, all the rest being recessive, and they are equally uncommon in other organisms". This apparent difference between man and other animals is almost certainly illusory. The simplest human pedigree will reveal a dominant mutation: a recessive can only be discovered by much more elaborate pedigree evidence which is not easily obtained.

Often, in man as in other species of animals, the Mendelian ratios do not shew themselves. Some writers think that environment, including external conditions which possibly cause physiological changes, must be assumed to exercise a disturbing influence. It is just possible that, owing to such causes, some abnormalities tend to become less pronounced in successive generations: but any particular character whether normal or abnormal, may, and usually does, depend in varying

* R. Ruggles Gates, *Heredity in Man*. Constable, 1929, p. 24. This book contains a valuable summary of our present knowledge and I am much indebted to it.

degrees upon a large number of factors in the germinal constitution of the individual. Almost certainly there exist, even in apparently uniform stocks, large collections of recessive mutations of which the effects, where they can be observed, are slight. Some of these may influence a noteworthy mutation to a slight extent with the result that natural selection acts strongly (as we shall see in the next lecture) in eliminating those individuals in which the abnormal character corresponding to the mutant gene is most apparent. In this way mutations, so slight as to be almost undiscoverable, act as modifying factors in causing an abnormality to become less conspicuous as a result of selective breeding for a number of generations.

It may be safely said that the apparent failure of Mendelian ratios, whenever it shews itself, will not be due to some fundamental flaw in the particulate theory of inheritance. It will probably result from the fact that the number of mutations which are of influence in our particular investigation is larger than we assume and their interaction more intricate than we recognise.

A similar kind of explanation will probably be found to be satisfactory as regards another perplexing fact. What is apparently the same abnormality may be inherited in quite different ways in different families. In one case it may be recessive, in another dominant and in yet a third 'sex-linked'.

Club-foot, for instance, is an inheritable defect. When it is inherited, it is apparently sometimes a dominant and sometimes a recessive. Possibly further study will shew that defects of quite different origin have the same general appearance; and thus dominant and recessive types of club-foot will be clearly distinguished. It is, however, equally likely in our present state of knowledge that other genetic factors combine to reveal or to hide the presence of the club-foot mutation.

All three possibilities of inheritance are believed to shew themselves in connection with a condition in which the eyeball is exceptionally small. The defect may appear in different degrees of intensity. Sometimes the individual affected is blind: sometimes vision is subnormal. Further research may shew that there are, in fact, at least three different types of microphthalmia which have different modes of inheritance. More probably it will reveal the presence of other genetic factors, one or more being possibly in a sex-chromosome, which modify the effect of the primary dysgenic microphthalmic mutation.

Occasionally dominance and recessiveness are variable or even alternate in the same pedigree. No satisfactory explanation of such variability has been given; but the existence of modifying factors will probably be found to be the cause of the irregularity.

§ 375. *The persistence of mutations in humanity.*

The scientific study of mutations in man is so recent that the persistence of such mutations from generation to generation through the centuries can only be established in exceptional cases: and these naturally must relate to dominant mutations. One such, given by Miller in the year 1915, is interesting. The descendants of a Dr Little, who emigrated to Canada from Carlisle about the year 1824, have had through four generations a white lock of hair on the forehead. Dr Little's mother had this white fore-lock; and she could trace her descent through the Percys and Mortimers to Edward III. The investigation of this mutation in recent generations shews that it behaves as a simple Mendelian dominant: on the average half the children of a parent shewing the defect reveal it and it is never carried through a parent who does not shew it. It must, of course, be regarded as a form of albinism. In connection with the pedigree, the interesting fact emerges that the white lock goes back to the Percys and that, after Harry Hotspur was slain at Shrewsbury in the year 1403, his wife is said to have given birth to a son bearing a white patch on his forehead. Here, then, we may reasonably conclude that we have a mutation which has been dominant for at least five centuries.

An anatomical defect, which is likewise a Mendelian dominant, was described by Drinkwater in the year 1917. There is historical evidence to shew that it also has been inherited through at least five centuries. The defect is called symphalangism. In the middle-finger of both hands one of the joints is thickened so as to be but slightly movable while, alike in the ring-fingers and little-fingers of both hands, one joint has become rigid, the bones which it ought to join being fused together. The man in whom it appears to-day is descended from John Talbot, first Earl of Shrewsbury. The Earl was killed near Bordeaux in 1453 and buried in a tomb at Whitchurch in Shropshire. In the year 1874 his tomb was opened and repaired. The skeleton was identified by the fractures to skull and thigh which are known to have caused Talbot's death. The finger-bones of the skeleton shewed the defect which exists in his descendant to-day. It is said, moreover, that in the effigy on the tomb the medieval sculptor faithfully recorded in stone the thickening of the joints which must have persisted in different descendants until now. The particular defect of stiff fingers with enlarged joints is a mutation that can be readily observed. Other families in America are known to have it, and the speculative conclusion has been reached* that they too derive from the Talbot who finds a place in Shakespeare's *Henry VI*. We may add that the occurrence of a dominant mutation is probably a surer witness to descent than a pedigree granted by the College of Heralds.

§ 376. *Sex-linked defects.*

Colour-blindness† and haemophilia are of special interest to humanity as they are sex-linked defects: they are, that is to say, defects which arise in, and are carried by, the X sex-chromosomes. The inheritance of 'bleeding' is a matter of popular knowledge, inasmuch as the defect occurs in one of the royal (or more accurately quasi-royal) families of Europe. 'Bleeding' does not normally shew itself in the female; but she can transmit it to her sons. Curiously, a similar sex-linked dysgenic mutant was discovered by Morgan in *drosophila*: it is known as 'white-eye'.

Let (X, X) and (X, Y) be the pairs of sex-chromosomes in the female and male respectively of humanity. Suppose that a sex-linked mutant arises so that the chromosomes of the male become (X_m, Y). X_m in humanity may correspond to 'bleeding', in *drosophila* to 'white-eye': in these cases X_m is recessive to X.

In the first generation which results from the mating of a normal female (X, X) with a mutant male (X_m, Y), we get either (X, X_m) or (X, Y). Of these the former is a female in which the mutant is recessive: the latter is a normal male.

We must notice particularly that (X, X_m) is an apparently normal female, carrying latent within her the dysgenic mutation.

If now this female (X, X_m) is mated with a normal male (X, Y), we get either (X, X) or (X, Y) or (X_m, X) or (X_m, Y). Of these the first two are normal female and normal male: the last two are a female in which the defect is latent and a male in which it appears. Thus all the daughters are apparently sound, but half the sons suffer from the disease.

If a defective male were to be mated to a female in which the defect was latent we should have a combination of the chromosome pairs (X, X_m) and (X_m, Y). This combination would yield

$$(X, X_m) \quad \text{or} \quad (X, Y) \quad \text{or} \quad (X_m, X_m) \quad \text{or} \quad (X_m, Y).$$

* See Gates, *loc. cit.* pp. 152, 154.

† We refer to the common type of colour-blindness in which red and green cannot be distinguished from one another.

The third of these would represent a female in which the defect was apparent. Thus 'bleeding' can theoretically shew itself in a female.

There is still some doubt as to whether homozygous female 'bleeders', haemophilics of constitution (X_m, X_m), actually exist. Certainly, in the majority of cases, such are non-viable: in other words, individuals carrying the condition degenerate as embryos or perish soon after birth. Yet in this respect Nature shews her abhorrence of rigid law or, at any rate, her apparently inexhaustible capacity for producing the unexpected. Though the dysgenic mutant of constitution (X_m, X_m) is normally lethal, so that such individuals die, and though therefore female bleeders ought not to exist, yet a case is on record* of a woman who almost certainly had haemophilia in a reduced and sub-lethal form. We may add that, although 'bleeding' is sex-linked, so that no heterozygous woman shews the defect as it occurs in man, yet some women 'carriers' shew the presence of the latent trouble by the fact that their blood coagulates slowly. Normally blood will coagulate in some five or six minutes: in a carrier it may need a much longer time. Some women carriers, moreover, shew that they are abnormal in that bluish marks will follow a quite slight blow, a mere 'tap'. Although the investigation of haemophilia of recent years has been active, much more research is needed before conclusive results can be formulated exactly. There are several conditions which may be varieties of haemophilia; and their diagnosis, classification and manner of inheritance are still undetermined.

It has been said that red-green colour-blindness resembles haemophilia in that it is a sex-linked dysgenic mutant which appears normally only in the male. It is recessive in the female and is due to a defective gene in the X-chromosome. A heterozygous mother of constitution (X, X_m) will, if married to a normal male, transmit the defect to half her sons. A homozygous woman carrying the defect will be of the genetic constitution (X_m, X_m). Such women are, of course, much more rare than abnormal men. Red-green colour-blindness in men is so frequent that in Europe one twenty-fifth part of the male population suffers from the defect. It appears, however, that only ·1 to ·5 per cent. of the women have the same defect.

Recent research has demonstrated that the common red-green colour-blindness is but one of a number of analogous deficiencies of sight which occur in humanity and that it can itself be split up into different types of defect. Possibly not all of these conditions are sex-linked Mendelian recessives. At all events some apparently authentic

* See Gates, *loc. cit.* p. 207.

pedigrees reveal unexpected types of inheritance, at present inexplicable. Further, the statistical averages of colour-blind persons are unsatisfactory. If some 4 per cent. of the men are colour-blind, it would be expected that only ·16 per cent. of the women would have the defect: yet in Central Europe more than twice as many women exhibit it.

§ 377. *Mental mutations in humanity.*

There is no reason to think that the inheritance of mental characters in man follows laws different from those which govern the inheritance of physical characters. The researches of Karl Pearson and his pupils, published in the year 1904, shewed that the resemblance between parents and offspring is as marked for mental as for physical traits. Since then various careful enquiries have been made and an almost identical correlation for mental and physical inheritance has been established, so far as adequate psychological tests can be made. Heredity and not environment will determine in great measure both the physical and the mental nature of an individual. A series of injuries may, of course, damage the mind as they may damage the body; but what a child may become under fairly normal conditions is effectively determined by his germinal constitution. An inherited physical weakness or tendency to functional disorder may be to some extent overcome by appropriate physical treatment. Inherited mental tendencies may equally be inhibited or encouraged by suitable training. But it is doubtful whether the most careful treatment, physical or mental, will do more than affect the preponderance of fairly well-balanced alternatives. Unless, for instance, a boy has inherited some mathematical ability it will be impossible to make a mathematician of him. No training will develop beyond a definite natural limit the intelligence of a mentally defective child.

Among mental defects which are inherited, by far the most important are feeble-mindedness and insanity. Almost certainly under each of these names there are classed a whole series of types of defect. The types of feeble-mindedness appear to form a graded series; but various kinds of insanity differ markedly alike in their manifestations and in the period of life at which they appear.

§ 378. *Feeble-mindedness.*

Feeble-mindedness is, in essence, a condition of arrested or primitive mental development: the adult only reaches the mental condition of a child maybe of three, or maybe of ten, years of age. Insanity, on the other hand, may result from the abnormal working of a highly developed mental organisation. Thus, as has often been said, genius is closely akin to insanity.

It is well known that a high percentage of the feeble-minded become insane and that not infrequently children of the feeble-minded are insane. But, none the less, between genius and feeble-mindedness there is nothing in common. As Gates* has well said: "It is impossible to graft genius on to feeble-mindedness, and the loss of a whole feeble-minded stock would not involve the suppression of a single genius". This truth cannot be too strongly emphasised. One argument commonly used by those who object to the sterilisation of the feeble-minded is that thereby we might destroy some potential genius. But *by no possibility can a feeble-minded stock produce a genius:* the argument consequently is worthless.

We have said that the different types of feeble-mindedness appear to form a graded series. Such appearance of grading probably conceals the existence of types of defect which correspond to different mutations. Quite possibly, also, a single mutation which behaves in inheritance as a simple Mendelian recessive is modified by other factors which vary with varying types of the disorder. Further research will doubtless lead to modifications and developments of our present knowledge. But as a first approximation to the truth we may assert that some severe types of feeble-mindedness in humanity are due to a single defective gene which is a recessive in inheritance. The defect has probably arisen repeatedly as a mutation from the normal. When, however, it shews itself afresh in a child of apparently normal parents, we must not, in general, assume that a fresh mutation has occurred; but a recessive character in each of the parents has revealed itself because it is homozygous in the offspring.

Because of the importance of the subject we will give in some detail the argument that certain types of feeble-mindedness in humanity behave as though due to a simple Mendelian recessive.

Suppose that F denotes a chromosome carrying the gene for feeble-mindedness and that N represents the associated normal chromosome. Then, if N be dominant to F, $\overset{+}{(NF)}$ may be taken to represent an apparently normal woman in which feeble-mindedness is recessive. $\overset{\nearrow}{(FF)}$ will represent a feeble-minded man.

The offspring of such a pair will be either NF or FF. Hence from

* See Gates, *loc. cit.* p. 272.

such a pair we may expect to have an equal number of feeble-minded and apparently normal children.

Now the American investigator Goddard, in his book on *Feeble-mindedness* published in the year 1914, recorded that 42 matings of this character produced 144 children, of whom 71 were feeble-minded and 73 apparently normal. The approximate equality of these numbers is thus in accordance with expectation, if feeble-mindedness be a simple Mendelian recessive.

It appears from Goddard's enquiries, however, that the mating of a feeble-minded woman $\overset{+}{(FF)}$ with $(NF)^{\nearrow}$, an apparently normal man in whom feeble-mindedness is recessive, gives a larger number of feeble-minded children than would be expected. Out of 193 children which resulted from such unions, it was found that 122 were feeble-minded and that only 71 were normal. Until further research has supplied a reason for this fact, it must remain as a warning against over-confident statement.

On the other hand, when both parents are feeble-minded, practically all the children shew the defect, as would be expected from the mating of $\overset{+}{(FF)}$ with $(FF)^{\nearrow}$. Thus, according to Goddard, out of 476 children of parents, both of whom were feeble-minded, only 6 were normal: and it is, of course, quite possible that these were in each case children of other than the nominal father.

There is thus strong evidence* that, to a first approximation, some types of feeble-mindedness are due to a single defective gene which is normally a recessive. But, though normal mental capacity may thus be dominant to mental deficiency, it would appear that the dominance is often incomplete: in other words, even average mental power is not to be expected in an individual in whom there is latent feeble-mindedness. I would add that investigations made at Rostock by Reiter and Osthoff and published in the year 1921 shew that some types of feeble-mindedness are associated with dominant heredity factors. Lenz† believes that in the less severe types the heredity is usually dominant.

Most probably, certain kinds of 'dullness' are to be distinguished from true feeble-mindedness. The full significance of the endocrine glands and their secretions has still to be discovered; but atrophy of the thyroid is certainly accompanied by a dull mental state. Quite

---

* The representative character of Goddard's work has been challenged by more recent investigators.

† Baur, Fischer and Lenz, *Human Heredity*. Allen and Unwin, 1931, p. 431.

possibly the so-called 'Mongolian idiots', which usually appear in good middle-class families, are due to hypothyroidism. Whether this particular condition is inherited or accidental is in dispute.

The conclusions which we have reached, tentative though they are, are sufficient to make it clear that mental defectives should not be allowed to have offspring. The feeble-minded, as compared with men of genius, are disastrously fertile and are increasing in Great Britain and elsewhere at a rate which gives cause for grave anxiety: in England they already number from ·8 to ·9 per cent. of the population*. Under the harsher social conditions of even a century ago they would have often been eliminated in the struggle for survival. Now-a-days at great expense to the community they are preserved; and, though the more gravely defective individuals are permanently segregated, many feeble-minded who are classed as high-grade mental defectives are allowed to produce offspring which are alike a burden to the State and a menace to racial soundness. It is, of course, true that from a feeble-minded parent, who may be assumed to have no sound chromosome in the homozygous pair, an apparently normal child can be born if the other parent be normal. But this is no reason why mental defectives should be permitted to have offspring. Yet it is still sometimes advanced as an argument by medical men in important official positions. Such a type of argument, in the light of present knowledge, betrays lamentable ignorance: those using it have done much to impede eugenic progress. We cannot, of course, prohibit the marriage of persons in whom feeble-mindedness is recessive: but if, whenever the defect appears, we do not permit it to be handed on to another generation, we shall prevent its present rapid spread. There is no doubt that in Great Britain at the present time mental deficients are breeding much faster than more valuable stocks. If the process were to continue for many generations the result would be disastrous to the mental soundness of the race.

Evidence, moreover, is accumulating to shew that often, even when the mutant recessive gene which appears to cause severe feeble-

* The *Royal Commission on the Care and Control of the Feeble-minded* (1904–8) estimated that the feeble-minded in England and Wales were 4·6 per thousand of the population. The *Report of the Mental Deficiency Committee* of the year 1929 was disquieting in that the probable incidence then seemed to be 8·56 per thousand. The figures will be found with some comments on p. 76 of Parts I and II of the *Report*: the conclusion that these figures must correspond to an actual increase in mental deficiency is reached after a discussion on pp. 31–8 of Part III of the *Report*.

mindedness is present as a heterozygote, the individual is harmed. The gene, in fact, like many mutants, does not normally behave as a pure recessive. This is expressed in a striking manner in the *Report* to which reference has just been made*. Suppose that we could segregate as a social group all the families in England to which children are born with an inherent incapacity for mental development. The group would include "a much larger proportion of insane persons, epileptics, paupers, criminals (especially recidivists), unemployables, habitual slum-dwellers, prostitutes, inebriates and other social inefficients than would a group of families not containing mental defectives". In fact, most of the families so collected would belong "to the lowest 10 per cent. in the social scale". They are genetically unsound and their elimination is the most fundamental, urgent and perplexing of our social problems.

One defect of English law in regard to feeble-mindedness has been several times brought to my notice. In England a woman, of course, has a right to be married by banns in her parish church and the parish priest may not refuse to 'call' her banns. What is he to do if an application is received for the marriage of a feeble-minded woman, who usually has money or the expectation of money? He can protest to her parents or to her intended husband; yet, if his protests are disregarded, he must be a party to action whereby feeble-minded children are only too likely to be brought into the world. It is even doubtful whether, as yet, public opinion would be with him were he to refuse to call the banns on the ground of the woman's defect. It is certain that by so doing he could expose himself to the risk of a lawsuit alleging libel. Our civilisation is still imperfect.

§ 379. *Insanity.*

Our present knowledge of the inheritance of the different types of insanity is unexpectedly meagre. It is known that a tendency to insanity 'runs in families': that it is often associated with a highly developed nervous organisation: and that it may shew itself in different forms in different individuals of the same stock. It is also known that, in individuals with a predisposition to it, insanity can result from a mental shock. War-time investigation of 'shell-shock' by Rivers and others revealed something of the psychological machinery

---

* *Loc. cit.* Part III, p. 80. It should be observed that there is also the possibility that, owing to selective mating, the 'lowest ten per cent.' carry numerous dysgenic mutations.

by which such psychoses are produced*. But why particular individuals are liable to 'shell-shock', while others are apparently immune, is unexplained: we should naturally expect that the former class carry a mutant 'shell-shock' gene.

A common form of insanity called *dementia praecox* appears to be separable from types with other symptoms. It normally shews itself in or soon after adolescence and is characterised by melancholia and other morbid emotional conditions. It appears disastrously in successive generations in certain families. But the law of its inheritance has not been determined. There is evidence that it is at times associated with some biochemical defect. The latter may be a consequence of two, or even more, dysgenic mutations affecting endocrine glands.

A somewhat rare form of disease known as Huntington's chorea is important as giving information as to the way in which one type of insanity is inherited. Described by Huntington in the year 1872, it has been exhaustively studied, especially in America. It normally shews itself by nervous tremors which appear in middle or late life; and it is not seldom accompanied by progressive mental deterioration, which may end in a suicidal form of insanity. It is inherited as a dominant condition. Unfortunately, different pedigrees give different numerical results, and possibly different varieties of the disease have not been properly distinguished. Some investigators conclude that the inheritance is that of a single Mendelian dominant. Others argue that two or more independent dominant factors must be present.

Now-a-days the vigorous predestination of Calvinistic divines is out of fashion. But a knowledge of Huntington's chorea suggests that their doctrine, however depressing, was not untrue to some facts of human life. A child is born into one of the choreic families. He lives a normal and healthy life. His value to the community is recognised by his social success. He marries and has children who seem to be normal. Apparently he may look forward to an old age of honourable ease. But in late middle life tremors begin to shew themselves in head and hands and feet. Then the mind begins to degenerate. Suicidal tendencies appear. The end is the private lunatic asylum. In his germinal constitution the man carried the defect which almost certainly some of his children will inherit. Such a life-history is surely a terrible example of predestination and is not easily combined with the facile optimism now popular among some religious teachers.

* See, for instance, W. H. R. Rivers, *Instinct and the Unconscious*. Cambridge University Press, 1920.

§ 380. *Lethal mutations.*

Recent research has tended to emphasise the importance of lethal and semi-lethal mutations. By far the largest class of mutations consists of those which are lethal recessives. Such cannot, of course, be directly observed; but their existence can be inferred as they disturb the frequency-ratios of other factors.

If a defective gene be completely recessive it has no effect when present as a heterozygous factor: if it be dominant and similarly present the effect may be slight. But in either case if it be present as a homozygous factor the consequences may be disastrous.

We have seen that there is reason to believe that, when haemophilia is homozygous in a woman, it is usually lethal.

Short-fingeredness is inherited as a simple Mendelian dominant. A type of brachyphalangy in Norway, described by Mohr and Wriedt in the year 1919, is known to have been inherited for five generations. In one case intermarriage of two persons, each shewing the defect, produced a female child apparently homozygous in the defective gene. The child was a cripple lacking fingers and toes: she failed to develop and died when a year old. It is hazardous to draw wide-ranging conclusions from a single case; but it is a natural inference that in this instance a particular defective gene which produces a slight abnormality when present in one chromosome of an associated pair may become semi-lethal when present in both chromosomes of the pair. Experts have reached the conclusion that most so-called dominants are lethal when homozygous.

Hairlessness in rabbits is a simple recessive. Individuals in whom the corresponding factor is homozygous die soon after birth.

The Japanese Yamane has in recent years described a remarkable malformation in the horse. When the defective gene appears in both members of the associated pair of chromosomes there is no passage from the upper part of the alimentary canal to the large intestine. Consequently the foal dies a few days after birth. The defect was recessive in a prize stallion introduced into Japan some forty years ago. It has now spread extensively among Japanese horses.

Several lethal and sub-lethal mutations exist among the highly-valued Holstein-Friesian cattle. Their existence is a source of anxiety to breeders and an indication that methods of breeding adopted in the past will have to be changed in the future. Too often, when some exceptionally fine stallion or bull has been produced, it is so extensively

BST

used in breeding that any dangerous recessive it may carry makes an appearance repeatedly in the herds derived from it.

§ 381. *Inbreeding.*

Such facts of heredity shew that the popular prejudice against inbreeding has some foundation. That this process can continue for generations without ill-effects is shewn by the royal marriages of ancient Egypt wherein brother might unite with sister. There is no biological harm apparently, even in such close unions, provided the stock is sound. But, if the stock carries recessive dysgenic characters, these will appear in due proportion, whereas in outbreeding they would remain latent unless, by some relatively unlikely chance, there was union with a stock in which the same dysgenic character was recessive.

§ 382. *Can dysgenic mutations be reversed?*

Of great interest is the question as to whether mutations can be reversed. Is it, in fact, possible that a second mutation can take place in a gene whereby the original influence of the gene on the organism is restored? Only recently has an affirmative answer been given to this question. Some might contend that such an answer was never in doubt, inasmuch as cultivated plants and animals in which artificial characters have been produced by selective breeding will usually revert to wild types if allowed to do so. But in all probability such reversal is produced by the gradual elimination in successive generations of individuals in which the mutant gene occurs. The wild types are the fittest to survive and therefore, if there is any individual carrying the non-mutant gene, its descendants will emerge successfully from the struggle for existence.

Conclusive evidence as to the existence of reverse mutations has come from the experimental production of mutations by means of radiation of short wave-length. If either male or female reproductive cells are treated with X-rays, or with the γ-rays resulting from the disintegration of radium or with the β-rays (which, it will be remembered, are high-speed electrons), alike mutant genes and chromosome breakages and displacements are produced*. It may be inferred that the so-called cosmic rays, discussed in § 300, will have, to some extent, the same effect.

* A valuable *résumé* of recent work is to be found in a paper "Radiation and Genetics", by Professor H. J. Muller, *American Naturalist*, vol. LXIV, May–June, 1930. I have to thank Professor Julian Huxley for calling my attention to this paper.

A specific example will illustrate the nature of recent discoveries. In *drosophila* there is a sex-linked recessive mutant known as 'forked'. In it the bristles of the head, thorax and scutellum are shorter, more twisted and more heavy in appearance than in the wild fly. Of course these peculiarities only appear in the homozygous female: the heterozygous females which carry the 'forked' X-chromosome are indistinguishable from normal wild flies. Muller and Patterson have of late carried on experiments on a large scale, working at the same time with X-rayed flies and with controls which were not X-rayed. They found no 'forked' mutations in the controls; but irradiation gave eight mutations from forked to non-forked and eight from non-forked to forked. "Most of the mutations from non-forked to forked occurred in treated non-forked genes that had themselves arisen under X-ray treatment by mutation from forked to non-forked, so that the induced mutations are clearly reversible." It was proved that the mutations actually occurred at the point in the sex-chromosome which is known to be the locus of the forked gene: further, they were not due to the production of genetic modifying factors such as sometimes arise and have been appropriately called suppressors or mimics.

§ 383. *Mutations and short-wave radiation.*

The point-mutations, or mutations of a single gene, which arise as a result of the use of short-wave radiation do not apparently differ in any way from the similar mutations which occur in nature. Such radiation, it is true, also produces changes in the 'gross morphology' of the chromosomes: the latter are often broken and dislocated so as to produce bizarre monstrosities. But what are apparently quite normal point-mutations regularly arise from short-wave irradiation of the germ-cells.

Moreover, Hanson, using radium, found that the frequency with which mutations were produced was directly proportional to the energy absorbed, the latter being measured by the induced ionisation. Further, Oliver, and subsequently Hanson and Heys, using X-rays, have obtained the same result and also have shewn that the mutation frequency is independent of the wave-length of the X-rays used. If we recall what was said at the beginning of Lecture IX, we are led to conclude that the radiation which is used liberates electrons by the laws of the quantum theory, and that mutations are produced when such electrons hit the chromosomes in the nucleus of a germ-cell subjected to irradiation. Apparently point-mutations and chromosome dislocations are produced by direct electron hits: it appears also that indirect effects are absent. Attempts have been made to discover whether there are other agencies than radiation which cause mutations. Probably a rise of temperature increases to some extent the natural mutation-rate; but no other known agency save irradiation appears to affect it. We ought, however, to say that the natural mutation-rate appears to be by no means constant. It should be added that no associated conditions have been found which appear to affect the mutation-rate due to irradiation.

Of course the question at once arises as to whether such mutations as occur in Nature are due to the 'cosmic' radiation of high frequency which penetrates all terrestrial organisms. In popular language, did Millikan's cosmic rays (§ 300) turn monkeys into men? The answer appears to be a decisive negative. If all the spontaneous mutations which occur in *drosophila* were due to natural radiation, such radiation would have to be a thousand times as intense as it is. (It will be recalled (§ 190) that the intensity of radiation of energy-density E is Ec, where c is the velocity of light.)

It has been suggested that possibly radio-active elements exist in the germ-cell and that they are the cause of natural mutations. We know, for instance, that potassium exists in protoplasm and that it is faintly radio-active. Amost certainly, however, no such concentration of radio-active elements is to be found in germ-cells as would produce more than a quite inappreciable percentage of the mutations which occur in Nature.

Obviously the discovery that radiation of high frequency will produce mutations, apparently indistinguishable from those which occur under natural conditions, is of the highest importance. The limits to its practical utility none can foresee. What its consequences will be in the realm of biological theory we cannot say: the first effect is sheer bewilderment. Spontaneous point-mutations and more complex chromosome changes are without doubt the raw material of evolution. In them we get as near as we can go to ultimate creative activity. Yet they can be produced artificially by a process which seems to be simply the bombardment of the nucleus of the germ-cell by electrons. That such electron-bombardment would damage the chromosomes and produce lethal mutations is intelligible. But that an electron-hit, a chance smash, should produce colour-blindness or its reverse is incredible. We can understand that a shell fired into a motor-car factory would wreck it. But the shell also seems able at times to turn the machinery for making a Ford into that which will produce a Rolls-Royce and *vicê versâ*. Our present ignorance is most intriguing.

§ 384. *The sexual cycle in animals and plants.*

Between those animals and those plants which propagate by union of male and female reproductive cells there is a fundamental similarity with respect to the sexual cycle. We have seen that, if the possibility of an absent sex-chromosome be ignored, the number of chromosomes in the nucleus of the cell of any particular species, whether it be of animal or plant, is constant. Alike in animals and plants, moreover, such chromosomes exist in pairs, of which one is received from each parent. Thus the normal or diploid number is always even. But at the time of fertilisation the normal number must be reduced to one-half by some ripening process and so must become haploid; otherwise as a result of sexual fusion the number of chromosomes in the offspring would be double that of the parents. Now in certain of the more primitive plants, as we have seen in § 333, the haploid stage consists of a prothallus which produces eggs and sperm-cells. This (gametophyte or gamete-producing) stage alternates with a diploid (sporophyte) stage which sexually produces spores. These spores in turn give rise to male and female haploid plants; and thus the cycle is continued.

In those flowering plants which are monoecious or hermaphrodite, pistils and stamens grow on the same plant. The latter carry the small male spores and the former the large female spores. From such spores by fertilisation a seed is produced from which a new generation arises.

When the plants of a species are of two sexes, the sexual union of its reproductive cells, the female ovule being fertilised by the male pollen, leads to a striking similarity with the reproductive process of the higher animals. In fact, alike in mammals and plants, not only is the chromosome number constant but, when reproduction takes place by sexual fusion, there is an alternation of the haploid with the diploid stage in each sexual cycle.

§ 385. *Has the sex-mechanism arisen independently in animals and plants?*

The natural conclusion to be drawn from this striking similarity is that sexual propagation preceded the separation of the animal and vegetable kingdoms. But there seems to be no evidence for this conclusion and its truth is denied by many experts. Such would contend that sexual reproduction has arisen independently among animals and plants. They hold that all reactions of animal and plant to a particular environment in which development takes place will be parallel or, to use a technical term, homoplastic. Some contend that, by virtue of such homoplasy, the same mechanism of sexual reproduction may have arisen more than once, not only in animals and plants but even in distinct families of each. If such be indeed the fact, there seems no reason why, by virtue of such homoplasy, the same type of evolution should not have been repeated. Thus to take an extreme possibility, man might have been evolved from the anthropoids on two or more occasions, distinct in time and place. Similarly, civilisation might have developed independently, though on exactly parallel lines, in different regions of the earth. Yet there is little conclusive geological evidence that any species has twice arisen in the evolutionary series*: and Elliot Smith and his pupils deny that any so-called 'psychic unity' has led to the separate origin of similar types of culture.

Undoubtedly the same sort of adaptation to environment has arisen more than once in biological history. The leaves of the extinct race of gymnosperms known as *cordaiteae* were, from the standpoint of structural engineering, built according to a plan used in similar leaves of certain existing monocotyledons. Such modern and totally unrelated species as *cactuses* and *euphorbias* are strikingly alike: but the resemblance is a consequence of the fact that each lives in arid localities. Similar instances can be multiplied. Yet it may be held that the more fundamental changes which made the decisive stages of evolution were never duplicated, because, though identical mutations and chromosome changes may have arisen in different ages, they only once arose in an environment favourable to their permanence. The theist will regard God as the Creator both of mutations and of environment. Probably he will not be in error if he likens Him to the great creative artist whose supreme achievements are unique.

§ 386. *The future of the evolutionary process.*

When we reflect upon the evolutionary history of animals upon the earth we cannot, because we are human, easily refuse to regard man as the crown and final end of the process. Yet obviously the most complex, efficient and beautiful monocotyledons, such as cereals and orchids, are not the end of the evolution of plants. They may fitly be ranked as

---

* Mr A. T. Hopwood of the Department of Geology, British Museum, informs me that there is evidence that certain *gryphaeae* (the 'devil's toe-nails' of our peasantry) arose more than once as modifications of a form of oyster.

Nature's present masterpieces in the vegetable kingdom. Yet they are, we must surely admit, but episodes. Supreme types to-day, fifty million years hence they may well have become extinct: or they may then be represented by forms which will be able to make no claim to supremacy. So surely will it be with man. He, too, is but an episode in terrestrial evolution. Fifty million years hence further specialised and more highly developed human types may dominate this globe—did not horses multiply and develop for forty million years in North America? But as the millions of years go by, so too, if we may judge the future by the past, will humanity as we know it ultimately yield place to some other animal form*. What form? Whence evolved? We cannot say. But some Cosmic Intellect, watching the mature capacities of this unknown form, will almost certainly judge it to be more highly evolved, of greater value in the scheme of things, than ourselves. On earth man has no permanent home; and if, as I believe, absolute values are never destroyed, those which humanity carries must be preserved elsewhere than on this globe.

* As shewing the divergence of opinion to which our present ignorance leads it should be stated that, in the opinion of an expert palaeontologist such as R. Broom, "evolution has practically finished and cannot be repeated unless all higher life is wiped off from the earth and a new start made from the very beginning". We may urge in reply that to prove a negative is notoriously difficult; and, when that negative limits Nature's amazing resourcefulness, it may well be doubted.

Lecture xv

THE MACHINERY OF EVOLUTION

§ 387. In this lecture we shall propound and endeavour to answer a perplexing question: by what process of action and reaction has evolution come about? In other words, what is the machinery by which, relatively rapidly or by the slow aggregation of small changes, first new varieties and then new species have been made, so that there has arisen the amazing diversity of living forms which are, or have been, on the surface of the earth?

Charles Darwin's achievement.

It has been our primary object in the previous three lectures to shew that there can be no doubt as to the fact of evolution. The careful arguments marshalled by Charles Darwin and the knowledge of animate nature accumulated since his day have finally convinced all qualified biologists that species are not immutable. Henceforth educated men will agree that the constitution of organisms is not something permanent. Organisms were not directly created by God in the forms in which we know them; and they are not incapable of change. As the generations of living creatures pass, new varieties develop; and, as the process of change continues, new species arise. By this process the multitudinously diverse forms of life to be found upon the earth have come from one or more primitive organisms. Among these diverse forms of life is man himself: he is not a special creation but a product of evolutionary change, an anthropoid who differs physically from the gorilla and the chimpanzee mainly in the size and complexity of his brain. His mind is a derivative of the mind of some ape-like being: his moral qualities existed in rudimentary form in its tenderness and self-regardless care for offspring. The same power and process which shaped elephant and tiger, horse and deer, shaped man also. He is one of a group of placental mammals which diverged from some lowly form, a common ancestor, when the terrestrial reign of the great reptiles was coming to an end.

Others before Charles Darwin had put forward evolutionary theories. He himself wrote* that "Plato, Buffon, my grandfather (Erasmus

* In a letter to Lyell, March, 1863.

Darwin), before Lamarck and others, propounded the *obvious* view that, if species were not created separately, they must have descended from other species ". Lamarck (1744–1829), in a series of works published during the Napoleonic wars and ending with one published in the year of Waterloo, upheld "the doctrine that all species, including man, are descended from other species* ". But what before Darwin had seemed a more or less plausible hypothesis became, through his researches and arguments, an accepted theory. He convincingly demonstrated the fact of evolution and deserves his assured place among the immortals because of the vast significance of his addition to human knowledge.

As is well known, Darwin held that natural selection constitutes the main machinery of evolution. The recent mathematical investigations of R. A. Fisher, continuing important researches initiated by others, have strikingly vindicated his intuition. But, before this vindication, Darwin's fame was secure: and attempts on the part of ecclesiastical partisans to obscure the greatness of his achievement are merely deplorable.

§ 388. *The fact of variation.*

Obviously species could not change but for the fact of variation. Graham Kerr† describes this fact by stating that "the power of heredity is not sufficient to control the instability of living matter so completely as to ensure that the offspring shall be an exact replica of the parent, or of the mid-parent, or of the racial mean ". Such variations as apparently arise from the instability of living matter may be conspicuous, when they are popularly termed 'sports'. But, as we have learned from the researches initiated by Mendel, 'sports' may not indicate any failure of heredity; and such a term as 'the racial mean' is a survival from the time when inheritance by blending was assumed to be normal.

In discussing variation we first define inheritable qualities as those qualities of an individual organism which are the direct and necessary consequence of the properties of the fertilised germ-cell in which it originates. Such must be sharply distinguished from non-inheritable qualities of the organism. The latter are due to the influence of, or to accidents within, the environment in which the organism has existed from the moment of fertilisation.

---

* The words are those of Darwin himself; and come from the historical sketch which appeared in later editions of *The Origin of Species*.
† J. Graham Kerr, *Evolution*. Macmillan, 1926, p. 135.

Alike conspicuous 'sports' and smaller unexpected variations in the characters of any particular organism are normally due to strict Mendelian inheritance. It is true that each inheritable departure from the normal represents the result of some past mutation or other change in the germ-cell: but we must bear in mind the fact that such a mutation may have occurred in a far-distant ancestor.

§ 389. *Fluctuation.*

Often, however, minor variations from the normal are not due to a mutation, either recent or in a long-past generation. They result from the favourable or unfavourable influence of the environment; and it is convenient to speak of them as *fluctuations*. For instance, it is certain that, of two 'identical' or 'mon-oval' twins, one brought up with an abundant supply of good food and in healthy surroundings will normally be heavier and more healthy than one half-starved in a slum. In such a case the divergence between the two individuals constitutes a fluctuation. In a pure stock fluctuations will vary from the mean by excess or defect: they may be regarded as chance failures to achieve the mean. Moreover, they will be exactly analogous to the failures of a marskman to hit the bull's eye of a target. When we take a large number of shots at a target and make a curve in which the abscissa represents the divergence from the centre of the target and the ordinate the number of shots with that divergence, this curve will be the *curve of error*, or curve of probability. In a pure stock fluctuations in individuals which correspond to such a curve almost certainly will have their origin in the accidental circumstances of the environment: we should not expect that any one of them would necessarily result from some mutation in the fertilised cell from which the new organism took its origin.

De Vries and his followers were the first to make a sharp distinction between mutations on the one hand and those fluctuations on the other hand which correspond to the curve of error. We repeat that mutations are changes in germinal material and may therefore be inherited; but fluctuations are changes in the individual which have no correspondence with any changes either in the fertilised cell from which it takes its origin or, as we shall see, in the reproductive cells which it carries.

§ 390. *Natural selection.*

Darwin's theory of evolution by natural selection can be simply stated. He observed that, while the number of individuals of any species is roughly constant in a given area, the number of eggs and young is normally so great that it would lead to an enormous population-increase were not a large proportion destroyed.

A single female of the ling, for example, is stated to produce some twenty-eight million eggs. The ling is an edible fish resembling cod. If no eggs or young were destroyed, the sea in a brief time would be packed tight with ling. Another instance of potential population-increase is worth giving. A pair of song thrushes begin to breed when the partners are about a year old. They produce under normal conditions eight young a year and they continue to breed for some ten years. It is easy to calculate that, if all the young survived to full maturity, a single pair would have produced by the end of their lives some twenty million birds. In thirty years from the time that the first pair started to breed the earth would be covered a hundred thousand times over with thrushes which everywhere touched one another!

Necessarily, therefore, there is 'elimination of the less fit'; or, as Herbert Spencer (1820–1903) put it, 'survival of the fittest'; or, in Darwin's somewhat awkward phrase, 'natural selection'. Field naturalists who are familiar with the intensity of the struggle for existence, as it can be observed especially in the tropics, have long been agreed that natural selection has been of paramount importance in guiding evolutionary change. Environment on earth is constantly changing. Any change in an organism which fits it a little more advantageously to exist under new conditions will, by the operation of natural selection, be preserved. Such organic changes will in the long run produce new species.

But how overwhelming is the strength of natural selection has only been realised comparatively recently as a result of applying statistical mathematics to biological problems. As we have just said, it clearly appears in conclusions reached by R. A. Fisher*, who has greatly extended the work of earlier investigators†.

Suppose that by a selective advantage of 1 per cent. we mean that organisms owing to a gene-mutation have an expectation, of offspring which shall reach maturity, which is 1 per cent. greater than if the mutation had not occurred. Then a single such mutation has a chance of about 1 in 50 of establishing itself and sweeping over the entire species‡. The mutation cannot occur with any great total frequency before this

* In the volume *The Genetical Theory of Natural Selection*, to which reference was made in § 371.
† Recent work by Professor J. B. S. Haldane should also be mentioned.
‡ *Loc. cit.* p. 78.

sweeping success is rendered certain. The odds, according to Fisher, are over 100 to 1 against the first 250 mutations of such a favourable type all perishing.

On evidence which is none too satisfactory, Fisher estimates that mutation-rates, in such organisms (including man) as have been investigated, are of the order of 1 in 100,000 or possibly of 1 in 1,000,000. In a species in which a thousand million individuals come to maturity in each generation, a mutation, with a frequency-rate of one in a million, would easily establish itself in the first generation if it had a selective advantage of merely 1 per cent.: it would then in due course sweep over the whole species. Now such a selective advantage is very small, probably far too small to be directly observed. None the less its strength is so great that even the sceptical must be forced to allow its effectiveness. In short, 'natural selection', combined with even very slow mutation-rates, suffices to explain the origin of species.

§ 391. *How does variability arise?*

We are thus led to the enquiry as to how or why those favourable variations arise which not only the better fit an organism to its environment but also are inherited by its descendants? Because such variations are inherited they must obviously correspond to changes in the reproductive germ-cells. What excites such changes? We have already seen in § 383 that mutations can be artificially produced by the use of short-wave radiation; but at the same time we recorded the opinion that such radiation as is always present at the surface of the earth would have to be a thousand times as intense as it is known to be to produce the mutations which occur in Nature.

Lamarck believed in the inheritance of acquired characters*. He thus held that the individual, in fitting itself blindly or consciously to its environment, acquired new characters which could be transmitted. Probably most Lamarckians would say that inheritance of new structural modifications due to habit is a secondary matter. What is primary and essential is the inheritance of stored memories which habits imply. Some neo-Lamarckians contend that the sustained endeavour of the organism creates habits and thereby impresses memories on the germ-plasm. Thus it is, they conclude, that characters, acquired by what Lloyd Morgan calls a hormic process, are inherited. The inward urge (*hormê*) drives the organism forward to its end.

* By acquired characters we mean characters other than those with which the organism begins its existence, whether the latter are or are not due to mutations. Some writers confuse the issue by claiming that characters which result from mutations are acquired.

But belief in the inheritance of acquired characters can be held without thus deeming it the result of an urge on the part of the organism. It may be postulated that there is in the germ-plasm or reproductive cells of the organism some change, an 'engram', fashioned in the course of its history and retained as a sort of structural or functional modification. This is substantially the mnemic theory of R. W. Semon (1859–1919). He argued that the immediate physiological effect due to the stimulation of irritable organic substance is but half the problem presented by observed facts. "The other and distinctive half of the mnemic problem underlying the problems of memory, habit and heredity, is the effect which remains in the stimulated substance after the excitement produced by the stimulation has apparently ceased*." The capacity for such after-effect of stimulation Semon called the *mneme*. Its result, which is the enduring though primarily latent modification in the irritable substance produced by a stimulus, he called an *engram*.

Semon assumed that, when a new character appears in the body of an organism, some new engram is added to the cell-nuclei of the part affected by the new character. He also postulated that this change tends to spread throughout the body, even to the reproductive cells, and that it produces in them a possibly faint copy of the original engram. Semon, however, felt it necessary to allow that efficient engrams could only be impressed on the reproductive cells slowly and by prolonged action. Among English botanists Sir Francis Darwin (1848–1925) accepted Semon's theory. Charles Darwin himself, probably because of his acceptance of blending inheritance, felt forced to postulate that acquired characters can be inherited.

§ 392. *Weismann's position.*

On the other hand, A. Weismann (1834–1914) argued cogently that characters acquired during the lifetime of the individual are not inherited. Weismann was probably the greatest German biologist of the generation which came immediately after Darwin. His denial was based chiefly upon zoological evidence; and the fact that, in animals, germ-cells are segregated at an early stage of the existence of the organism greatly influenced him and those who accepted his views. But it has to be admitted that, in plants, such early segregation does not occur. The tissues of plants which are ultimately to be differentiated as germ-cells may therefore be affected by the environment of

* R. W. Semon, *The Mneme*. Translated by L. Simon. Allen and Unwin, 1921, p. 12.

the organism: and thus influences which lead the organism to acquire new characters may produce corresponding changes in the reproductive cells. For this reason Lamarckism, speaking generally, has proved more attractive to botanists than to zoologists.

Weismann's arguments were strong. The reproductive cells of an animal are, as he urged, apparently derived by simple fission from the originating fertilised cell of the mother: all available evidence points to the fact that they are not in any true sense a product of the animal in which they exist. That animal is merely a vehicle, a strong-box, in which they are preserved to become in due course parent-cells of a new generation.

I suppose that we are all instinctively Lamarckians, just as in philosophy the natural man is a naïve realist. What we have created in ourselves, so the possibly unformulated argument runs, we ought to be able to hand on to our descendants. It is unjust if a man cannot do what he will with his own. We bequeath our property to our children, why then should we not be able to bequeath our personal qualities? A vague sense of 'the fitness of things' strongly predisposes us to accept some form of Lamarckism. It is then a high tribute to Weismann's clear and effective presentation of his case that he persuaded the great majority of zoologists to abandon the Lamarckian theory.

§ 393. *Criticisms of Lamarckism.*

There are certain 'obvious' arguments against Lamarckism. We do not expect, when a limb of an individual has been amputated, that a similar defect will appear in his children. Circumcision has been practised among the Jews for a hundred generations and no inherited effect has been produced.

Now in reply to such contentions it is justly pointed out that changes of external form may be ineffective to cause changes in the germ-plasm, but that nevertheless more far-reaching physiological changes affecting the metabolism or secretions of the body might have such consequences. Such 'obvious' arguments as can be derived from mutilation will not convince the physiologist that the germ-cells are absolutely stable and that they live a life apart from the common life of the organism. He is right in refusing to allow that a general negative can be established on so limited a basis.

Of course, a single indubitable example of Lamarckian inheritance would destroy Weismann's doctrine. Yet it is singularly difficult to get any convincing example of the fact that acquired characters are inherited. It is true that among the mammals diseases in the mother can affect her offspring; but this is due to the fact that before birth the embryo is, in a sense, parasitic on the mother. Through the placenta the causes and consequences of disease, toxins and anti-toxins, hormones and the like, can be transmitted between mother and offspring. For instance, an infant will sometimes secrete milk, the 'witches' milk' of the midwife. The cause, without doubt, is the influence of the so-called *corpus luteum* which causes milk to be secreted in the mother and, through the placenta, has in a limited degree the same influence on the child. Such facts are not examples of true inheritance, for they are not due to properties of the fertilised germ-cell from which the offspring derives its existence.

It can, however, be stated confidently that there is some interaction between the reproductive germ-plasm and the body-cells of the organism within which it is contained. We cannot otherwise explain the undoubted fact that, when the generative glands are removed by operation or destroyed by disease, the consequences to the organism are often marked. But we cannot go further and state that characters acquired by the organism are transmitted through the germ-plasm to the next generation. We need definite proof in some particular instance before we can make such a statement; and such definite proof is not forthcoming.

§ 394. *Dürken's experiments.*

Neo-Lamarckians challenge the statement that proof of the inheritance of acquired characters is not forthcoming: and adduce experiments of Dürken, Kammerer and others as affording satisfactory evidence. It appears that Kammerer was deceived by an assistant whom he employed and that, on discovering the fact, he committed suicide. We need not therefore consider his experiments, the more so as the argument against them, were they true, would be that which is fatal to the better attested work of Dürken.

Dürken worked with caterpillars and pupae of the common cabbage-white butterfly. Usually the pupae are of a colour which ranges from almost pure white to dirty grey. Under natural conditions some 4 per cent., however, are 'albinos': they have no pigment in the skin and appear to be bright green in colour because the green blood of the pupa shews through.

Dürken took the eggs of butterflies living under normal conditions and from these eggs reared (1) caterpillars in orange light. He found that he thus obtained a high percentage of green pupae. He then picked out the green pupae and took the eggs of the resulting butterflies. Some of these eggs he reared (2) in orange light, when they produced an even higher percentage of green pupae. Others of these eggs he reared (3) in bright light and others (4) in darkness. In each case he obtained a much higher percentage of green pupae than would be obtained by rearing wild unsorted caterpillars in bright light or darkness respectively. It appears then, as the Lamarckians claim, that the green colour which the pupae acquire by being reared in orange light is inherited by a large percentage of caterpillars.

But fatal criticism can be brought against this conclusion. Not all caterpillars respond to the orange light. Probably, therefore, the wild caterpillars are not genetically homogeneous. Some have responsive genes or groups of genes in the chromosomes of their germ-cells: others have not such genes or, if they exist, they are recessive. Dürken in his experiment (1) apparently segregated the more responsive caterpillars. This selected group would therefore naturally shew in experiment (2) that it was a specially responsive group. Similar responsiveness would equally be manifested in experiments (3) and (4).

Equally damaging criticism can be brought against all experiments with organisms which are not proved at the outset to be genetically homogeneous. If the stock at the beginning was a mixture, experiments which sort out the mixed material will of necessity appear to prove the inheritance of acquired characters.

§ 395. *Johannsen's experiments: fluctuations are not inherited.*

There are certain experiments with genetically homogeneous material, carried out originally by Johannsen in the year 1910 and confirmed by other investigators, which are of the highest importance. They shew that *fluctuations are not inherited.*

Suppose that the stock with which we experiment is pure, and by this term it will be recalled that we mean that the members of each pair of associated genes in the nucleus are identical. Suppose further that, as we breed from the stock, there are no sudden changes in the genes or, in other words, that no mutations take place. Then there will be, at most, fluctuations in the stock whereby individuals will differ from one another; and, in particular, individuals will be larger or smaller than the mean. Now it might be thought that by breeding from larger individuals we could get a larger race and that smaller individuals would similarly give us a smaller race. Yet, however we choose the individuals from which we breed, the same differences from the mean size of this stock appear in the next generation.

Johannsen, in his brilliant investigation, worked with the scarlet-runner or princess bean. This bean reproduces by self-fertilisation and so a 'pure line' can be obtained in which each plant is homozygous. The beans which come from any plant of such a pure line are of somewhat different sizes: their difference from the mean corresponds to the curve of error or curve of probability which we described in discussing the fact of variation. Johannsen found that, working with the offspring of a particular bean, it made no difference, if environmental conditions were unchanged, whether large beans were selected and sown generation after generation or whether small beans were similarly chosen. The final result was a crop of beans with an identical distribution of size. As regards size, in fact, the same sort of a group of beans resulted whatever selection process was used in obtaining them. In short, the fluctuations were not inherited. They were not due to changes in the germ-cell; and continued selection of extreme fluctuations had no effect in changing the inheritable factors carried in the germ-cell.

Similar work has been done by Jennings* and others with *paramecium*, a primitive unicellular slipper-animalcule which reproduces by division. All have found that specimens of this infusorian varied in length but that selection failed to produce a breed of individuals longer or shorter than the mean. Agar worked with *simocephalus*, a small water-flea which reproduces itself parthenogenetically. Here again the size of the shell of this little crustacean cannot be altered by repeated selection in successive generations.

These experiments on a plant, a uni-cellular 'protist' and a small crustacean make it certain that fluctuations are not inherited. Most emphatically then, the slight variability of an organism, which results from environment in the widest sense of the term, is *not* the raw material of evolution. In so far as Darwin made the contrary assumption, he was in error. The raw material of evolution consists of sudden changes in the chromosomes of the germ-cell.

There is, however, a fact complementary to the experimental results just cited, to which attention should be called. If we improve the environment of an organism, we can alter the distribution of its natural fluctuations. Thus good air, good food and healthy exercise will

---

* Baur gives an excellent account of experimental work on *paramecium* and its theoretical consequences in Chapter II of the volume *Human Heredity*, to which reference has already been made in § 378.

undoubtedly produce a human population of larger size and better physique than the normal of the race. But, let the descendants of this better type be bred under slum conditions and a change to a human type below the normal will occur. Environmental conditions can thus affect variation within the limits within which a population can naturally fluctuate.

Morgan* states these important conclusions in words well worth transcribing. "Selection cannot cause a group (species) to transcend the extreme variations that it naturally shews. Rigorous selection can bring a population to a point where all of the individuals are nearer to the extreme type shewn by the original population, but beyond this it cannot go. Only by the occurrence of a new mutation in a gene, or by a mass-change in a group of old genes, is it possible for a permanent advance—a step forward, or backward—to be made."

§ 396. *Further arguments against the inheritance of acquired characters.*

We saw in the last lecture that Mendel's theory of heredity assumes, as one of its fundamental postulates, the stability of some element of inheritance which we may think of as a gene. In a hybrid, in which two different but associated elements of inheritance, or genes, are yoked together in the same germ-cell, experiment proves that neither is affected by the other. For example, by mating hybrids pure strains can be recovered. We may recall that there is in Andalusian poultry a pure strain of white (with greyish splashes) and also one of black. When the two strains are mated, 'blue' birds result. If two of these 'blue' birds are mated, the offspring will be pure black, pure white (with greyish splashes) and blue in the ratio of 1:1:2. The purity of the resulting black and white can be confirmed by many experimental tests. It shews that, when black and white genes exist as associated partners in the same germ-cell, neither is contaminated by the other.

Now this complete separation of the different genes in the hybrid would be impossible if the characters of the hybrid could affect its germ-cells. The hybrid has acquired the 'blue' character. If an acquired character could affect the germinal material, this 'blueness' would surely affect the genes especially associated with colour. Yet such a consequence would invalidate the basal postulate of Mendelism.

The only way in which this argument can be rebutted is to postulate that white represents a mere absence of a gene. Then obviously we may argue that black cannot influence an absent gene and that an absent

---

* T. H. Morgan, *The Theory of the Gene.* Yale University Press, 1926, p. 289.

gene cannot influence one which is black. The hybrid will be 'blue' as a sort of intermediate colour between black and absence of black. Bateson, in the year 1914, elaborated the idea that mutations are due solely to complete or partial losses of genes. On this theory all changes in germ material are due to successive losses from the genes present in the original stock; and those who believe that mutations are the raw material of evolution find themselves confronted by the paradox that the whole evolutionary process has been due to successive losses from some original (and surely very full!) storehouse. Bateson's hypothesis in the light of our present knowledge is a *jeu d'esprit*. It cannot be maintained: there can be brought against it evidence which in the aggregate is conclusive.

If, however, the instance of Andalusian poultry is regarded as in-decisive as against Lamarckism, an experiment of Morgan with *drosophila* can hardly fail to carry conviction.

Morgan obtained a mutant stock of *drosophila* termed 'eyeless'. In it the eyes are smaller than the normal and are often absent altogether. But, as the age of the culture increases, a curious effect shews itself. The flies which are hatched, after breeding in the stock-bottles has taken place for some generations, tend to have eyes and increasingly large eyes. Good eyes are here apparently a positive character ac-quired in the course of a number of generations, possibly—so the con-tention might run—as the result of an inward urge for light on the part of the organism. Like the dying Goethe the flies demand 'more light'. The process seems admirably to give the sort of evidence which the Lamarckian requires. But further experiment ruins his hopes. For let the late-hatched flies be mated to unrelated wild stock and then from the offspring let the mutant type be extracted by inbreeding. We get again flies of the original 'eyeless' type!

What has happened is clear. The original culture was variable in its genetic make-up. In the competition for existence in the stock-bottle, those types of flies were successful whose genetic qualities modified the violence of the eyeless mutation. A gradual selection of these modifying factors led to flies which had increasingly satisfactory eyes, though the flies contained unaltered the mutant 'eyeless' gene.

397. *The raw material of evolution.*

We can then confidently reject Lamarckism. We can, while satisfied that mutations due to changes in the genes of the germ-cell are the raw material of evolution, assert that there is no evidence that such mutations arise in Nature from any but the most exceptional circumstances in the life-history of the individual in which they first appear. Among such exceptional circumstances we must include irradiation and, as some believe, the use of poisons (including possibly alcohol) by which mutations are said to have been artificially produced.

Some who retain belief in Lamarckism argue that mutations practically always result from artificial conditions of life: and that any which arise in Nature are such a handicap as to give the unfortunate individual in which they occur no chance in the struggle for existence. In reply it may be admitted that just possibly mutations are more numerous when the organism is subjected to an abnormal or unhealthy environment. An unhealthy environment may have an influence similar to, but less violent than, high-frequency radiation. Certain experiments of Tornier with Chinese carp seem à priori to warrant this conclusion. If it is a fact, it will be of immense significance; but at present it is merely a possibility which cannot be summarily dismissed. On the other hand, there is no truth in the statement that mutations do not occur freely under natural conditions; and it is also untrue that such mutations as occur in Nature are invariably variants from the normal so extreme as to injure the chances of survival of the individual.

There is, in fact, growing agreement among geneticists that the more intently any particular group of organisms is studied the more numerous are the mutant characters discovered within it. Further, most of the mutations thus discovered consist of small deviations from the normal. Yet these deviations are not fluctuations due to environmental conditions. They are modifications consequent on changes in the genes. So-called 'sports', or extreme departures from the normal, are not of a different character from small variations when such small variations are due to changes in the germ-cell. Moreover, both the 'sports' and the small genetic variations are inherited according to the same laws.

We have several times drawn attention to the fact that a small abnormality in an organism may be due to a combination of several genetic mutations. It should also be carefully noticed that what may naturally be regarded as the change in a single gene does not affect only one character of the individual; more usually it affects a whole group of characters. And, further, there is the correlative fact that the change in a gene does not merely lead to changes in the structure or form of the organism: it may equally have physiological consequences which affect the secretions or metabolism of the organism and so may profoundly influence its activity, fertility and length of life.

If either the structural or physiological consequences of a mutation or more complex chromosome change, slight though they may be, enable an organism to fare better in the struggle for existence, individuals carrying the mutation or other nuclear change will survive. In this way new races will be produced and ultimately new species will arise.

But it would appear that at the present time we have no certain knowledge whatever of the cause of natural mutations. As was stated in the last lecture, we can apparently produce artificially, by irradiation, mutations exactly similar to those which arise in Nature; and it seems as though such changes in the germ-cell as lead to these artificial mutations are due to impacts in the nucleus of electrons liberated by the high-frequency radiation. But why electron-hits should have such an effect is at present totally inexplicable.

We have already emphasised that the rate of production of natural mutations is, though variable, normally slow. Possibly not more than one mutation normally occurs in a hundred thousand organisms. Probably also a large proportion of the mutations which arise in Nature are lethal. Many others, though not actually lethal, are disadvantageous, so that the organism in which they arise is gravely handicapped in the struggle for existence. If the handicap is but slight, modifying factors may gradually, in the course of a number of generations, turn the mutation, when it only exists in one of the pair of associated chromosomes, into an almost pure recessive so that the organisms which carry it may survive. For this reason there are doubtless in all stocks large numbers of heterozygous mutations. In fact, experts agree that the great bulk of the physical and mental defects of man and of other animals are recessive.

Mutations which are recessive when heterozygous are often lethal when homozygous. When, though homozygous, they are not lethal they will normally be a handicap to survival. Thus organisms which carry such homozygous mutations will not flourish in Nature; but from the corresponding heterozygous stocks man can create, in stock-yards and gardens where natural selection is not allowed free play, new varieties of domestic animals and plants.

We have said in § 383 that the rate at which mutations are produced may depend slightly on the temperature of the environment in which the organism is placed. But, though observation has not yet led to certainty, it does not seem to be accelerated by drugs, or (in spite of the belief mentioned above) by poisons in non-lethal doses, or by overfeeding or by any increase in the metabolic rate of the organism. The belief, previously mentioned in § 352, that a *direction* of mutational change can be established in a particular stock of organisms is apparently without foundation. Most certainly the actual direction of evolutionary change is not shewn by the kinds of mutations which occur in any species. As Fisher* says, were it so, "the evolutionary prospects of the little fruit-fly *drosophila* would be deplorable indeed". He adds that in man striking recessive defects, such as albinism, deaf-mutism and feeble-mindedness, must have occurred in the comparatively recent past. If it were true that they indicate the direction of human evolution, acute pessimism would have to dominate our expectations as to the future of humanity. Fortunately such pessimism is unnecessary.

It is to be regretted that we cannot so far discover, either within the organism in some inward urge, or in the conditions of its life, any reason why mutations or more complex chromosome changes should occur. We must be content for the present to say that such genetic changes, the raw material of evolution, do arise in all living things; but we know not how or why.

§ 398. *Genetic variation the vehicle of emergence.*

We have reached the conclusion that the creative activity to be observed in evolution is primarily manifested through the changes which arise in the chromosomes carried in the reproductive cells of organisms. Such creative activity, by the agency of natural selection, has produced from relatively few primitive organisms, or possibly even from a single primal form of life, the immense range of plants and animals which now cover the earth. In particular, man himself is one of its products.

Now, all our observation leads us to the belief that the Universe (including the realm of organisms) is a unity. Moreover, there is within terrestrial evolution such progressive development as would appear to indicate that the unity was planned for a definite end. The Source of the unity cannot conceivably be inferior to the products of its activity. If we apply the term God to this Source, we must ascribe to Him at the very least personality such as we observe in man. If this line of argument be accepted, the unity of the Universe and, in particular, of the realm of animate nature upon earth will be the consequence of God's

* R. A. Fisher, *loc. cit.* p. 18.

creative activity; and such activity will be primarily manifested as regards terrestrial life in the genetic variations which are the raw material of evolution.

We do not, of course, postulate a 'supernatural' origin for these variations*: we merely say that in them there is the creative activity which expresses God's plan and that, in the present state of our knowledge, they are ultimates which we cannot get behind. Probably if we could probe further into the secrets of creation, genetic variation would appear to be part of a mechanism. But analysis of the mechanism would disclose the fact that it was a sequence of which a completely satisfying cause could not be discovered. In the end it would be necessary to say, 'things happen so, we know not why'.

For instance, if, as is most unlikely, it could be proved that all mutations were due to chromosome changes caused by electrons freed by cosmic radiation, we should not know why such a physical process could produce such a biological change. When we reflected that by such changes man with his mental and spiritual development had been evolved from primitive organisms, the belief that cosmic radiation was a reasonable cause would have to be dismissed as ludicrous. It seems likely that, whenever we discover fairly complete sequences in Nature, they will appear to be mechanisms; and that invariable sequence, or 'law', will conceal the emergence of such higher manifestations of Reality as result from, or are associated with, the sequences.

§ 399. *Evolution the result of external creative activity.*

The idea that in evolution we have a self-acting mechanism, by which from inanimate matter man with his emotional and mental life has been produced, seems to me unworthy of serious consideration. Further, we have discovered no reason to believe that the evolutionary process, even in its higher stages, results from some urge within the organism. That God exists only within the process and that He is, as it were, in the making as the process continues is, therefore, a belief not supported by any biological evidence which we can get. The natural conclusion from the evidence now available is that God exists apart from His creation: that He is primarily transcendent and only immanent to a very limited degree in so far as His creatures share His nature and serve His plan.

The fancy that God is in the making as the evolutionary process

* The dualism of 'natural' and 'supernatural' is fundamental in Catholic theology. It is examined and rejected in § 448 *infra*.

continues seems to me essentially pre-Copernican or, at any rate, pre-Brunonian*. It ignores the probability, reached in Lecture XI, that there are in our galactic universe tens of thousands of other planets where life exists and that, for the most part, the evolutionary process upon them must be immeasurably in advance of the stage which it has reached upon earth. If God only realises Himself within an evolutionary progress, then elsewhere He has reached a splendour and fulness of existence to which earth's evolutionary advance can add nothing.

I repeat that such evidence as we can get from the natural sciences seems to lead clearly to the belief that the cosmos, and also the progress of which earth has been the scene during the last thousand million years or more, are alike due to the creative activity of a God Who is transcendent and to Whom we must ascribe at least such qualities as constitute personality in man. We lack alike the knowledge and the imagination which would enable us to say how much more we ought to add if we would describe the fullness of His being.

§ 400. *Is God's creative activity non-moral?*

There is thus, if our arguments be sound, no reason to think that the fact of evolution leads necessarily or plausibly to atheism. It does not, in my opinion, lead naturally to pantheism. Since the Churches felt it necessary to come to terms with evolution, both facts have been re-iterated, almost *ad nauseam,* by theologians and professional apologists. But the grave difficulty to which I feel forced to direct attention has hardly yet come above their horizon. I could wish that this difficulty did not intrude itself or that I could pass it by. The latter alternative is forbidden, inasmuch as in these lectures I take the world as revealed by natural science and consider its spiritual interpretation with the absence of bias shewn by men of science in their special investigations.

The difficulty to which I must allude can be briefly stated. The whole process of evolution is founded upon genetic variations. In these variations we approach, as nearly as is at present possible, God's creative activity. By mutations in the genes, together with more complex chromosome changes, it would appear that God has fashioned the entire development of life upon earth: by such mutations and changes He has created man. But such genetic variations, as judged

* As we saw in Lecture X, it seems established that Giordano Bruno first concluded that there exist innumerable other worlds than ours.

by our ethical standards, are non-moral. Good and bad arise alike. On the one hand a mutation can arise from which comes some vision of supreme beauty:

> And like a skylit water stood
> The bluebells in the azured wood.

On the other hand, the mutation may equally be the precursor of a series leading to the formation of some loathsome parasite. In humanity evil mutations are certainly not rare: it is, as we have seen, practically beyond doubt that certain forms of feeble-mindedness and also horrible physical defects have originated as mutations. Moreover, the same evil mutation may arise repeatedly.

Theologians have often been hard put to it to account for the existence of evil in humanity. So long as belief in Eve's wrongdoing in the Garden of Eden lasted, a theory of the inheritance of Adam's guilt was put forward as a satisfactory explanation. That theory must now be consigned to oblivion, inasmuch as the story on which it rests is obviously folk-lore. Since its overthrow certain theologians have resuscitated the theory of a pre-mundane 'Fall', some outburst of insurgent evil that took place before the world was made. This 'Fall', we are told by one sponsor, was 'the assertion' of the individual against 'the unity' and 'could not have taken place on the present globe'. The theory is only worth mentioning as illustrating the way in which educated men, when in difficulty, will turn anew to myths that seemed long dead. Of course such play of fancy is useless in serious theological reconstruction.

Our present difficulty is not merely that in humanity sin exists. There is a far more fundamental source of perplexity in the fact that the whole process of creation now appears to be non-moral. There is no evidence to lead us to infer that variations in the genes are directed towards ends which in our judgment are good. In such variations there seems, in fact, to be no ethical quality whatever. They have led to odious parasitism, to the carnage of the jungle, to the microbic diseases which cause such suffering to humanity, to those animal appetites which are useful in the struggle for survival and are the basis of sin in man. This, the immoral, brutal, lustful side of creation is as characteristic as the parental self-sacrifice, the adventurous curiosity, the instinct for truth, the enthusiasm for righteousness, the beauty of form and the physical well-being which equally result from the evolutionary process.

No 'revolt of angels', no theory of a 'Fall', will account for such facts.

In the end all attempts to take from God responsibility for the nature of His creatures must fail. An Hebrew Psalmist* in a flash of insight recognised this truth: "The lions roaring after their prey do seek their meat from God". I can see no reason to deny that the evolutionary process is as clear a revelation of God's creative activity as we can have. Its apparently non-moral character must be with His permission. For some unknown reason He permitted death, disease, struggle, the instincts which have led to selfishness and lust in man, because He willed that higher moral, intellectual and emotional development which in man is such an unexpected outcome of the process.

§ 401.   *Man and the cosmic process.*

We must allow, as a fact, that Christians share the perplexity acknowledged by Huxley † when in a still-remembered Romanes lecture he spoke of war between man and the cosmic process. Mr H. G. Wells was trained as a biologist and is most certainly gifted with exceptional imaginative understanding. Significantly, when he attempted in the year 1917 to fashion a theology in *God the Invisible King,* he felt forced to postulate two Gods. One of these is the God within humanity, virtually the Christ-Spirit: the other is the Veiled Being, the inscrutable Power behind creation. Personally I do not think that Wells' solution is satisfactory: it creates a dualism and leaves the relation between Christ-Spirit and Veiled Being a complete enigma. But it was an honest attempt to solve a problem which professional Christian theologians have of late practically ignored.

I personally would emphasise that we cannot postulate that God resembles His creative process in being Himself non-moral: to do so is to leave the moral nature of man unexplained and inexplicable. We cannot deny that the highest consequence, so far, of the progressive development of terrestrial life is civilised man with his ethical sensitiveness and his increasing regard for ideal goodness. Man, so far, is God's finest achievement upon earth: and the best that is in man, we are forced to assume, must reveal, as fully as we can know it, God's nature.

So, as I see the situation, we are confronted by a dilemma from which there is, at present, no escape. Verbal dexterity and the skilful use of those evasive phrases which are too common in modern theology might

* Psalm CIV, verse 21.

† W. R. Inge says (*Outspoken Essays,* Second series, Longmans, 1922, p. 7): "The dualism which naturalism had hoped to remove reappears in the war between man and the cosmic process, which Huxley, hardly knowing what he did, proclaimed in his famous Romanes lecture". I am inclined to think that Huxley realised alike the necessity and the implications of his statement.

seem to offer escape to some: but to the man of science evasion is high treason against truth. We must apparently allow that genetic variation, the raw material of evolution, seems to be as often for worse as for better: if it is good, it is also evil: it leads alike to progress and to degeneration. And yet from the evolutionary process, thus morally blind and blundering, comes man, in whom the Christ-Spirit represents the perfection which we feel forced to ascribe to the Creator as we postulate that He is the source of goodness, beauty and truth. The Christ-Spirit is as real as the process of which it* is apparently the climax. To deny its existence would be to ignore all that is finest in our civilisation.

§ 402. *The sternness of God.*

But while we rest uneasily in a perplexity from which we cannot escape, we may well reconsider certain oft-repeated statements. The sentence 'God is Love' comes from a writer who can be identified with the author of the Fourth Gospel. To use it without qualification is to ignore the sternness of much of the teaching of Jesus. As He likened God to a Father in Heaven, He did not intend that Christians should think of Him as an indulgent autocrat or mere good fellow. God demands from man willing obedience to the purpose of his creation; and this purpose, according to Jesus, is the growth within and through us of the Christ-Spirit. Failure, He repeatedly told His followers, means punishment; and, most certainly, such is the law of evolution where the animal that fails is punished by swift destruction.

But, while to this extent biological knowledge corroborates the teaching of Jesus, we cannot go farther and assert that God, as revealed in the evolutionary process, is a Father. The Christ-Spirit must be of God; and, if it also reveals God, then God is our Father. But belief in the Fatherhood of God is primarily a religious intuition and, as such, not to be reached through biological theory. The place of religion in human thought and, in particular, its association with value-judgments, we shall discuss in Lectures XVIII–XX.

§ 403. *The genetic process and predestination.*

The evolutionary process, if its source is, as would appear, in genetic variation, is disconcerting in several ways and, in particular, as we suggested in the last lecture, because it seems to re-establish predestination. The physical and mental (and, presumably in man, moral) qualities of an individual organism are established at the beginning of its existence as soon as half the parental chromosomes have been

* One may speak in the neuter of the Christ-Spirit, without necessarily denying to 'it' personality or 'super-personality'.

rejected in the fusion of the reproductive cells. Equally early, it would seem, there occur those genetic changes, if any, which cause the organism to escape the outcome of strict inheritance.

Doubtless, within the framework thus constructed, there is opportunity for fluctuation, strictly limited opportunity for the expression of free-will in man and of such measure of freedom as animals possess. But one does not gather grapes of thorns or figs of thistles. From the lunatic one does not expect reasonable behaviour nor from the feeble-minded decency and restraint. Once the fusion of the reproductive cells has taken place the framework of life is apparently determined.

> The Moving Finger writes; and, having writ,
> Moves on: nor all your Piety nor Wit
>   Shall lure it back to cancel half a Line,
> Nor all your Tears blot out a Word of it.

Omar's lines, as Fitzgerald gave them expression, are an exaggeration; but they are nevertheless unpleasantly near the truth. The man or woman in whom a markedly dysgenic mutation is dominant is, without exaggeration, a hopeless problem. Even the one in whom such a mutation is recessive is a menace to humanity, for in half his descendants it will persist; and, whenever the opportunity for the recessive mutation to become homozygous may occur, there will be produced a faulty human being who had better never have been born.

There is apparently no 'cure' for a dysgenic mutation. Nature's way, God's way, of dealing with such is elimination by an environment which automatically tests and destroys. We know too little of the higher insects to be able to say whether they destroy their unfit with the ruthlessness of Nature. There is, however, no evidence that dysgenic mutants flourish among them. It is, if we may judge from observations of geneticists on other species, very unlikely indeed that such mutants do not arise: and, if they do, we must conclude that they are deliberately killed. It appears that there are in humanity mutant stocks of which it can be said with literal truth that their members are 'predestined to condemnation'. When men generally awake to this knowledge, what action will they take with regard to such wretched beings? Will the Christ-Spirit within us forbid their destruction? Will the same Spirit compel us to foster them and to allow them to reproduce their kind? The practical dilemma arises because God, the Creator, Guide and Lord of Evolution, seems to us so different from the Spirit which guides conscience and, as Christians believe, flamed out with matchless splendour in Jesus the Christ.

Lecture xvi

MAN'S ORIGIN AND PAST

§ 404. *Man's place among the Primates.*

Man belongs to the Primates. They are the 'first' among the mammals; and the word is due to Linnaeus. The Primates are differentiated from other mammals by the fact thay they have a skull, large in relation to their size, which contains a highly developed brain; they have also fore-limbs which can grasp and which end in hands with flat nails, teeth adapted to a mixed diet (partly animal and partly vegetable) and two mammary glands on the breast.

Man is, of course, a product of the Mammalian era, one of a group of anthropoids with thirty-two teeth, differing from the rest of the group mainly in the superior size and quality of his brain. In all physical essentials there is much less difference between man's brain and that of a gorilla than between the brain of a gorilla and that of a lion. From the time of its appearance the group of Primates to which man belongs is always, as the Abbé Breuil says, linked to a definite fauna, constituted by forms of which modern representatives are the elephant, hippopotamus, horse, stag, bear, hyaena, lion, cat and so forth. The anthropoids and these other forms were evolved simultaneously. The evolutionary changes by which they were produced probably began in the later Mesozoic era. The mammals became the dominant feature of life upon the earth at the beginning of the Tertiary era some sixty million years ago. Since that era began there are good fossil records of the development of some of the great mammalian orders; but, unfortunately, those of the Primates are meagre.

§ 405. *The earliest Primates.*

Near the beginning of the Eocene, which is the first period of the Tertiary era, the precursors of the Primates seem to have appeared in North America. They are represented by archaic forms allied to the insectivores. These primitive tree-shrews were small: one especially interesting skull is barely an inch in length. Subsequently, in the Middle Eocene, there appeared in the United States ancient forms allied to living lemurs and to the tarsier of the Malay Archipelago. Such forms seem to have resulted from the evolution of the earlier types. No trace of a Primate has been found before the Mid-Eocene in any other part of the world, so that, pending further discovery, we may suppose that the Primates originated either in North America or in some northern Americo-Eurasian region.

In the Mid-Eocene deposits of France remains of generalised lemurs have been found. Similar remains became abundant in Europe in the Upper Eocene and in the Lower Oligocene periods. But, by the time of the Upper Eocene, the lemuroids and allied forms had disappeared from North America. We may with some confidence postulate a two-fold migration of primitive Primates from what seems to have been their original home in North America: some went *via* the Alaska land-bridge to the Old World and others simultaneously passed through the isthmus of Panama to South America. In South America the Primates seem to have lost four pre-molar teeth in all and, as Boule* says without flattery, to have "increased their brain-box at the expense of their face". They became one group of the flat-nosed monkeys.

§ 406. *The development of the Primates.*

Elsewhere the primitive Primates spread, flourished and developed. The meagre record of their past was a disappointment to all geologists until, in the year 1910, Schlosser confirmed a prediction made by C. W. Andrews some ten years previously and found the remains of several Primates at Fayum in Egypt in Oligocene deposits. Remains of three species, all of small size, were discovered. Two bear some like-ness to Eocene lemurs of the United States: one resembles an early flat-nosed monkey of South America. The importance of the discovery may be indicated by the statement that it proves that in the Oligocene there were in Egypt generalised forms of true monkeys, and one of them might even be a very primitive anthropoid ape.

It will be remembered that the Oligocene period was followed by the Miocene. Now all over Europe Miocene deposits have yielded fossil monkeys having distinct affinities with modern forms. But the most interesting deposits of this period which have so far been discovered are in the Sivalik Hills, lower outlying slopes of the Himalayas in Northern India. These beds have been known for forty years to be rich in fossil vertebrates; and, in 1912 and subsequently, Pilgrim found in them remains of apes of high significance. The deposits range from Mid-Miocene to Upper Pliocene: they shew that during this period

* Marcellin Boule, *Fossil Men*. English translation. Oliver and Boyd, 1923, p. 80.

"Asia was inhabited by anthropoid apes with characters diverging in all directions and perhaps in a certain degree...towards the human type*". Among the fossil fauna of the Sivalik Hills are dog-faced monkeys, sacred Indian apes, short-tailed baboons and various genera of anthropoid apes. One of these, *dryopithecus*, is represented by three species. It was a synthetic form now extinct which has also been found in Europe; and it seems to have had in certain of its branches close affiliations with modern chimpanzees and gorillas. Other branches of *dryopithecus* and a genus named *sivapithecus* by Pilgrim seem, from the fragmentary jaws and teeth which are known, to be a transition between the anthropoids and man.

§ 407. *Man's emergence.*

There is no doubt that out of such a process as can be traced in the Sivalik fossils man emerged, one of the latest of the Primates, a new-comer among the mammals. Thus, as the great theologian Hort† (1828–1892) said a generation ago, man with his whole mental and spiritual nature has been derived through various steps from lower beings having no such nature, and those probably in turn from inorganic bodies.

Compared with such a still-existing form as *lingula*, the lamp-shell, man is a thing of yesterday. When the great saurians of the Lias were lords of the earth, his ancestor was some precursor of the archaic tree-shrew which we have described, a small generalised mammal, precariously maintaining, not a place in the sun, but an unobtrusive existence. Further, it is clear from what we have previously said in §§ 324, 325, that many highly-organised mammals were developed in the Tertiary era before some rudimentary Primate shewed the promise of that brain development which makes man supreme upon earth.

Man is not particularly remarkable for his physical organisation. Many of the cat tribe can be justly held to be his superiors in purely animal qualities, in coordinated physical skill, grace and strength. But in man the anterior portions of the frontal lobes of the brain have in the process of evolution become exceptionally large. In particular, there has been a great development of, and increased complexity in, those parts of the cortex which form the so-called zones of association: these are 'the intellectual centres and true organs of thought'.

* Marcellin Boule, *op. cit.* p. 88.
† F. J. A. Hort, *The Way, the Truth, the Life.* Macmillan, 1897, pp. 187, 188.

No one who gives any intelligent consideration to the problem of man's origin will imagine that there must be some single 'missing link' between man and the apes. The obvious truth is that there must be a whole series of intermediate forms between modern man and the generalised stock from which both man and the anthropoid apes have emerged. We must expect, moreover, to find intermediate forms belonging to collateral branches. Apes, in some ways more highly developed than living forms, which nevertheless left no descendants: primitive sub-men who ultimately failed in the struggle for existence: such would be among Nature's unsuccessful essays in the production of humanity.

§ 408. *Where and when did man emerge?*

Where and when did man begin to be? What was the course of his development? To the second of these enquiries we can give some answer, but of the first, to which we shall return more than once, our ignorance is almost absolute. We have previously insisted that few animal bones find at the animal's death a resting-place favourable to their preservation as fossils. Further, of such fossils a singularly small proportion is likely to be discovered by men in digging the soil or quarrying the rocks of the earth; and, of such as are discovered, geologists will see but a relatively small number. Hence it may be said that fossil remains of an animal will not normally be found in any region save in rocks laid down at, or after, the time when it had become abundant in that region. No human remains have been found in Western Europe in geological formations earlier than the Pleistocene: but that fact does not imply that man did not exist in these regions at an earlier time. The truth is rather that almost certainly man was here in earlier ages and that he was then a migrant from regions where at a still earlier period his characteristic development had begun.

We must admit that, in comparison with the help which palaeontology gives in reconstructing the ancestral history of the horse or of the elephant, it offers but feeble aid to the discovery of man's evolution. Our difficulty is that we do not know where those decisive changes took place which separate man from the anthropoids. Did primitive hominians emerge in Southern Asia or in Africa? Most experts are now agreed that the balance of probability inclines to Asia. Darwin*, whose scientific flair no naturalist would despise, suggested that the development took place in Africa. He wrote: "In each great region of

---

* Charles Darwin, *The Descent of Man*. Murray, 1890, p. 155.

the world the living mammals are closely related to the extinct species of the same region. It is therefore probable that Africa was formerly inhabited by extinct apes closely allied to the gorilla and chimpanzee; and as these two species are now man's nearest allies, it is somewhat more probable that our early progenitors lived on the African continent than elsewhere". Yet Darwin felt it necessary to add: "But it is useless to speculate on this subject . . . there has been ample time for migration on the largest scale".

Some palaeontologists of distinction maintain that during Mid-Tertiary times a continent extended from East Africa over India through Java to the Philippines; and that in this area, since broken up by subsidence, man's origin must be placed. We have already insisted that, since the middle of the Tertiary era, the geography of the world has changed remarkably. To some extent the changes must be a matter of conjecture, inasmuch as we can have no direct knowledge of the strata in land now beneath the sea. But when in the course of geological exploration we find over a large area, now broken up in many ways, sedimentary rocks everywhere containing fossils of the same or of closely allied species of marine animals, we can be sure that all parts of the area were simultaneously under water when such animals were living. So also when in different regions we find the same fossil fauna in corresponding deposits, we can conclude that there must have been free connection between these regions when such a fauna was alive. Co-ordinations of this nature indicate that changes in the geography of the world even since man's first appearance have been more extensive than we are apt to assume. It is perhaps worth while to repeat that England was united to the Continent until comparatively recently, if we think in terms of geological time. If, as can no longer be doubted, man was living before the Mid-Pleistocene, he could have migrated on foot to our country.

The higher Primates, as we have seen, emerged with and belong to a characteristic fauna. The majority of modern animals belonging to this fauna were differentiated during the Miocene period. Though many Miocene genera are now extinct, some still survive. In the Miocene anthropoid apes were numerous. It is, therefore, possible that some primitive man or sub-man existed then. During the succeeding Pliocene era almost all modern genera were represented: it is, therefore, more than possible, it is even probable, that man had then appeared. But, apart from inferences drawn from man's spread as a primitive tool-using animal over a large part of the surface of the globe in the early Pleistocene, we have no knowledge of his existence before, at the earliest, late Pliocene times.

§ 409. *The Java ape-man.*

The earliest quasi-human remains known to us were discovered by Dubois, a Dutch army doctor, in the year 1890 at Trinil, in the island of Java. They were scanty: a skull-cap, a femur (thigh-bone) and two teeth. Apparently the geological formation in which they were found was either the Upper Pliocene or the Lower Pleistocene. As these two formations lie one above the other there is not really much dispute as to the geological age of *pithecanthropus erectus,* for thus the animal to whom they belonged has been named. Experts differ as to how he should be classified. Speaking generally the Germans regard him as a giant anthropoid, the British class him as definitely human, and the Dutch claim that he is a true missing link. Who shall decide when there is such divergence? His skull indicates such a brain development as is almost human. Probably he had already begun to speak in some sort of way, if we may judge from " a localised and precocious expansion of those areas of the brain " where man appreciates the meaning of sounds used as speech*. The femur indicates that *pithecanthropus* had the capacity to walk and to stand upright: it is almost human. Perhaps we may fairly conclude that the Java ape-man was a sort of *homme manqué,* a sub-man, not one of our ancestors but a shoot lying between the branches that led respectively to modern anthropoids and to modern men.

§ 410. *The Piltdown remains.*

We may speculate that from the South Asiatic continent sub-men migrated with the contemporary associated mammals to Europe. They possibly came *via* the Mediterranean area. At any rate the Piltdown remains found by Dawson and Woodward in the Weald of Sussex in the year 1912 would appear to be in age not very much later, relatively speaking, than the Java remains. Of the Piltdown man broken fragments of a skull were discovered together with the right half of a lower jaw and two teeth. The skull is singularly thick, but has such a well-developed frontal region as to suggest that it belonged to a primitive race of *homo sapiens.* The jaw, on the other hand, is absolutely simian. So striking is the contrast between skull and jaw that many experts

---

* The quotation is from G. Elliot Smith, *The Evolution of Man.* Oxford University Press, 1924, p. 84.

hold that they belonged to a man and an ape respectively. To the mathematician, who knows that independent probabilities must be multiplied together, the chance is infinitesimal that the only man found in England in a particular geological formation should have left his skull close beside the jaw of the only known ape of the same formation. In spite of expert incredulity, skull and jaw must belong to the same individual; and they point to the existence of a type of man with such characters that he cannot be ancestral to any other known type with the possible exception of the recently discovered Pekin man. It may be added that with the Piltdown remains worked flints were found. Thus at a remote period of the Pleistocene a sub-man was a tool-using animal: he dressed flints in the Sussex weald.

§ 411. *Pekin man.*

At Chou Kou Tien, twenty-five miles from Pekin, there are important Early Pleistocene deposits which have of late been investigated by the Geological Survey of China. In them there were found, as was announced in the year 1926, two fossil human teeth which, in the opinion of some experts, might have belonged to a creature somewhat resembling the Java ape-man or the Piltdown man. Another tooth was found a year later; and, finally, in the year 1928 and subsequently numerous remains of a primitive variety of the human family were discovered. Fragments of two jaws, one that of an adult and the other that of an infant, were first investigated. Portions of brain-cases were embedded in a stony matrix from which their separation was a long and difficult task. When they could be examined Elliot Smith was led to conclude that Pekin man was more primitive in type than any other known human fossil. It is too early to say whether this opinion (which contradicts an earlier verdict of Davidson Black) will be accepted by other experts, but already it is clear that the discovery of Pekin man is of the highest importance. He belonged to "the upper part of the Lower Pleistocene"; and, though he therefore lived long before Neanderthal man of the Mid-Pleistocene, he was "probably capable of articulate speech". Possibly, however, he was somewhat later in date than Piltdown man; discoveries of the year 1931 go to shew that his tools were of a crude Chellean type and that he knew the use of fire. If we are convinced that primitive flint instruments of the Pliocene have been discovered by Reid Moir in East Anglia, we must allow that those who made them preceded Pekin man by a long period. The jaws of Pekin man undoubtedly belonged to the human brain-cases discovered

34-2

in the same deposit. Yet they have the ape-like characteristics of the Piltdown jaw. They therefore confirm the conclusion that the latter jaw belonged to the Piltdown skull: it is sub-human and not simian.

Any statements at present made must be subject to revision; but it would appear that at epochs in the Early Pleistocene three sub-men, the only ones at present known to have existed at so remote a period, were at extremities of the Eurasiatic land-mass as far removed from one another as Sussex, Java and Pekin. Curiously, the men of Sussex and Pekin resembled one another more closely than they resembled the man of Java. The three types differ so extensively from one another that the stock from which all three were derived must have been sub-human in the Pliocene period; and the development by which they were produced probably proceeded within the Eurasiatic land-mass in some centre not yet discovered. It may yet appear that the intelligent guess is correct which places the centre in some inland basin of Central Asia to the north-east of Tibet.

§ 412. *Heidelberg man.*

Possibly cotemporaneous with Piltdown man was the Heidelberg man whose jaw was found in sands at Mauer, a few miles south-east of Heidelberg, in the year 1907. These sands are rich in fossils. In them are found ancient elephant, Etruscan rhinoceros, a primitive horse, archaic lion and wild cat. These are the typical mammalian fauna of the Early Pleistocene which we have learned to associate with the bones of fossil men of early types. The species or genera from which they were derived constitute one part of the mammalian *souche* from which man sprang. The jaw, the only fragment of Heidelberg man which was discovered, is horribly heavy and chinless, but its dentition is human and not simian. Probably Heidelberg man left descendants who for long survived: there are at any rate close affinities between him and Neanderthal man. Probably stone tools of the types known as Chellean and Acheulean (we cannot say which: the former were the earlier) were made and used by Heidelberg man.

§ 413. *Neanderthal man.*

With the beginning of the Mid-Pleistocene period we reach an era when human fossil remains become relatively extensive. Neanderthal man appears in the last great interglacial phase of European climate; and his existence continued until the last great glacial phase. During the latter era of cold he was a contemporary of the mammoth, the woolly rhinoceros and other fauna adapted to semi-Arctic life. Associated with him are flints characterised as Moustierian, typical specimens of which are carefully dressed by chipping on both sides. Some of his flints were apparently used as scrapers and piercers; and he even appears rarely to have used bone tools. The name of this race of men is due to the fact that in the year 1856 a skull-cap and some other bones were found in the Neanderthal valley near Düsseldorf. Some forty analogous discoveries in all have been made: and among them there are fossils of some fifteen well-preserved individuals. Even the amateur can recognise at a glance a Neanderthal skull. The forehead recedes: over the eyes there are heavy arches and the jaws are massive and strong: there is more chin than in the Mauer jaw, but less than we find in the negro and therefore much less than in the modern European. The skull of Neanderthal man had a capacity which on the average seems to have been equal or somewhat superior to that of the lowest of living races: but casts of the interiors of typical skulls indicate that the convolutions were simple and coarse.

Neanderthal man was uncouth and unattractive, if we may judge by the opinions which experts have formed of his appearance. Sufficient is known of his remains to make the description given by Elliot Smith* not wholly imaginative:

His short, thick-set, and coarsely built body was carried in a half-stooping slouch upon short, powerful, and half-flexed legs of peculiarly ungraceful form. His thick neck sloped forward from the broad shoulders to support the massive flattened head, which protruded forward, so as to form an unbroken curve of neck and back, in place of the alternation of curves which is one of the graces of the truly erect *homo sapiens*. The heavy overhanging eyebrow-ridges and retreating forehead, the great coarse face with its large eye-sockets, broad nose, and receding chin, combined to complete the picture of unattractiveness, which it is more probable than not was still further emphasised by a shaggy covering of hair over most of the body. The arms were relatively short, and the exceptionally large hands lacked the delicacy and the nicely balanced co-operation of thumb and fingers which is regarded as one of the most distinctive of human characteristics.

It may be added that Neanderthal man was probably black-skinned and that it is unlikely that he has left descendants†. At all events the pure Neanderthal stock has vanished from the earth. Some anthropologists‡ insist that from his appearance we can deduce "the pre dominance of functions of a purely vegetative or bestial kind over the

* Elliot Smith, *loc. cit.* pp. 69, 70.
† This is contested by some anthropologists of distinction.
‡ Marcellin Boule, *op. cit.* p. 238.

functions of mind ". Others, however (and among them H. Breuil), say that his intellectual faculties are not in doubt: he had a knowledge of fire: he hunted the largest of contemporary animals: his skill in shaping flints had reached a high degree of perfection. Moreover, this species of man, in whom so many simian traits survived, appears to have buried his dead and therefore probably had some 'psychical preoccupations*'. When the last glacial phase reached its maximum he retreated before the lengthening Alpine and Scandinavian glaciers and sought shelter from the cold in caves from which we disinter his remains.

§ 414. *The coming of* homo sapiens.

And then suddenly, side by side with Neanderthal man, there appeared in Western Europe other human types. They seem to have come first from the south and then, as the climate improved, from the east. These men of the Reindeer Age†, later Palaeolithic men, were of distinct races, but were all potentially ancestral to modern men. At last *homo sapiens* had arrived. Where he arose we cannot yet say; but a recent discovery associates him with Africa.

In the year 1913 H. Reck discovered at Oldoway, Tanganyika, a skeleton of *homo sapiens* in an undisturbed deposit. The condition of the bones was similar to that of the animal bones in the same bed; and a large proportion of the latter belonged to species now extinct. Reck's discovery suggested that *homo sapiens* was already to be found in Central Africa in the Lower or Lower Middle Pleistocene era. Further investigations towards the end of the year 1931 have confirmed this unexpected fact. In deposits, where the fossils shew a high percentage of extinct forms including a *deinotherium‡*, tools of a Chellean or Acheulean type, which in Europe preceded the Moustierian culture of Neanderthal man, were apparently used by *homo sapiens*.

Wherever *homo sapiens* was evolved he was, when he arrived in Spain and Southern France, represented by such differing types, that

* The Neanderthal skeleton, found in the year 1908 at La Chapelle-aux-Saints in a layer containing dressed flints of typical Moustierian forms, had been buried in a shallow trench hollowed out of the marly floor of the cave. The man to whom the skeleton belonged was, moreover, sufficiently 'civilised' to have suffered in gums and teeth from pyorrhoea, though not from caries.

† It should be distinctly understood that reindeer bones are numerous in earlier Moustierian deposits. But the animal had become very abundant in the later Palaeolithic era and it was all-important in the life of the Reindeer Age races of humanity.

‡ A form nearly related to the elephant and mastodon, though with tusks in the lower and not in the upper jaw: it is common in certain Miocene deposits.

we must assume his origin in some series of mutations which occurred long before we find him in Western Europe. Between the new-comers and Neanderthal man there seems to have been no fusion. Possibly the two types were mutually infertile: perhaps in Western Europe the older sub-men were exterminated with cold determination by the invaders.

The new races were, as we have said, distinct. Among them were negroids such as were discovered in the lowest deposits of the Grimaldi cave near Mentone. Of this race, if we may judge by skeletons and statuettes, the women were of the South African Bushman type. There were also the Cro-Magnons, who probably flourished in most regions at a later period than the negroids and whom we may, with a high degree of probability, assume to have been white. Of them de Quatrefages said that "in this savage contemporary of the Mammoth, the skull presents in a high degree all the characters regarded as indications of an intellectual development of the most advanced kind". The Cro-Magnons survived during the Neolithic era; and experts believe that to-day their descendants can be found in the Dordogne region of France and throughout Spain. Probably also the type is preserved in the Kabyles of Algeria and in the Guanchos of the Canary Islands. A third race, that known as Chancelade man, was cotemporaneous with the Grimaldi negroids and the Cro-Magnons. Its kinship with the Eskimos seems definitely established. Possibly when the reindeer retreated to the Arctic regions Chancelade man followed the animal, which still supplies many of the Eskimos' needs.

§ 415. *The men and culture of the Reindeer Age.*

All the races which were the first representatives of modern men in Western Europe belonged to the late Palaeolithic culture. Their flints, though shaped with great dexterity, were not polished. They were skilled hunters. They could sew hides. They used ornaments, necklaces of teeth, bracelets of shells and so forth. They had tamed the dog. They buried their dead, often smearing the body with haematite, the iron-ore which coloured red the bones and surrounding earth. Most remarkable was their artistic skill. The Reindeer Age was of long duration, and during it art, like industry, evolved. At its beginning we get the greater number of sculptures: at its end the finer and more numerous engravings. But all who have studied this art, so apparently isolated in humanity's progress, have been surprised by its unexpected skill and by the sheer beauty of line that is not seldom found.

The men of the Reindeer Age are thought to have come into Western Europe twenty or thirty thousand years ago. Whence? Probably from Africa; but to Africa ancestors must have gone from sources which hitherto have remained undiscovered. The affinities of the different types of Reindeer men were apparently with the black, white and yellow races respectively, so that they belonged to the three great existing divisions of humanity. Thus, at a time thrice as distant as the beginning of written history, the Neanderthal sub-men with their simian characteristics were disappearing from Western Europe and were being replaced in these regions by the diverse groups which to-day form humanity and are classified as varieties of *homo sapiens*. Probably at that time some of these races had already reached their present habitat. The Australian aborigines, who seem to have been akin to the Chancelade race, had quite possibly, if we may judge by the Talgai skull*, reached Australasia. When the Grimaldi negroids lived in Southern France their cousins, the Bushmen, may have reached South Africa: between the Aurignacian cave-paintings and the wall-engravings of the Upper Palaeolithic in Spain on the one hand, and similar productions of ancient art in South Africa on the other hand, there is a likeness upon which all observers insist. The fact that such diverse groups formed the men of the Reindeer Age shews that the mixture of races in Western Europe twenty thousand years ago was, if anything, worse than it is now. At the present time, at all events, the black and yellow strains seem to have been largely bred out of the population, probably under climatic influences. If, however, we begin to speculate as to the length of time necessary to produce the various invading races of the Reindeer Age, we see that we must assign to *homo sapiens* an antiquity measured in all probability by hundreds of thousands of years. It is plausibly conjectured that all these races separately developed their different characteristics in a relative isolation enforced by sea, desert or forest. They probably sprang from a single mutating group of sub-men who had established themselves in an environment favourable to the development and permanence of further mutations. Their original habitat was a sort of focus from which sub-human types were first sent out. Subsequently, truly human types emerged and, as groups of these developed in isolation, there were fashioned distinctive races which

---

* This skull, though found in Queensland in the year 1884, was only described and critically examined in the year 1914 and subsequently. A primitive palate and very large canine teeth connect the proto-Australian owner of the skull with the anthropoid apes.

were ancestors of modern Australians and Bushmen. After these primitive varieties of *homo sapiens* were established, other races appeared which, developing under varied conditions, have formed the main human stocks of the world of to-day.

§ 416. *The differences between Palaeolithic and Neolithic culture.*

The Upper Palaeolithic culture of the Reindeer Age endured for long. Ultimately it was succeeded in Western Europe by that Neolithic culture which seems to have been an almost universal phase in human progress. The differences between the Palaeolithic and the Neolithic are many and important. In the former stone implements were flaked and there was no pottery: in the latter there was a polished stone industry and both the making of pottery and the weaving of cloth had begun. Later Palaeolithic man was of a contemplative mind and, though his religious ideas seem to have been primitive, his temperament was markedly artistic. Neolithic man had the practical utilitarian mind: his artistic skill and feeling were rudimentary: his religion was already complex, his burial rites elaborate.

§ 417. *Iberians and Nordics.*

Probably a somewhat long period intervened between the Palaeolithic and the Neolithic; it may be that there was a time of decadence of the older races followed by the irruption of new human types. Among the latter we must almost certainly include long-headed men, of small stature, with long faces, represented to-day by the Iberian race of ethnologists. Probably the culture of this widespread 'Mediterranean' race was that which we know as Neolithic. This culture seems to have begun in Egypt some eighteen thousand years ago, in Crete a few thousand years later and in Western Europe some seven or eight thousand years ago. It endured until the Metal Age came in with the discovery of copper some five thousand years before the Christian era. These numerical estimates are of necessity conjectural; but what we have said shews that, until practically the Christian era, civilisation was developed in the east and spread gradually to the west. Probably this was the case even with the Aurignacian culture of the Upper Palaeolithic negroids: experts still hope to find somewhere in the east, and not far from the Mediterranean, the same sort of culture associated with the fauna of a warm epoch preceding the last great glacial phase. But though there is some reason to think that Neolithic culture was spread westward by the advancing Mediterranean race, it gradually passed from them to other people. It seems as if, at the very end of the last glacial epoch, the Caspian Sea shrank to its present dimensions and the Arctic glaciers to the north of it withdrew, so that what had been an impassable barrier (possibly in part of forest) between Asia and Europe ceased to exist. The result was that, apparently in Upper Palaeolithic times, new races entered Europe from Central Asia to be ancestors of the modern Nordic men: at all events Nordic types are found in early Neolithic burials. At the end of the Neolithic period it is possible to recognise in contemporary tombs and burying-places the three main racial types of modern Europe. There were then in existence the Iberian, the Nordic and the Alpine stocks, mixed at times with the *débris* of older races. Occasionally we seem to find the three races fused with one another; but on the whole each is dominant and distinctive in its own areas.

§418. *The cradle of humanity.*

It may be asked whether there was not more than one focus where man was made and from which the various species and races of men were diffused. Apparently there was only one such focus, situated either, as has been suggested, in Central Asia, north-east of Tibet, or, as Elliot Smith suggests, near the Caspian Sea, or in that Indo-Malay continent which has since been broken up by subsidence. Of such a matter we cannot speak with confidence, for, as we have said more than once, our ignorance of the beginnings of humanity is vast. But such meagre evidence as we have indicates that at first sub-men, and later the primitive races of *homo sapiens*, came from one and the same region. Of the extinct races of sub-men the known traces are so fragmentary that argument is precarious. But primitive races, Australians, Bushmen, Patagonians and the like, which have been well called living fossils, have been, as it were, pushed by more highly developed peoples to the regions farthest removed from the focus which is commonly postulated.

There seems to be no doubt that neither man nor the higher primates existed in America before the last glacial epoch. When its glaciers re-treated, yellow-skinned invaders from Asia penetrated *via* the Behring Straits and gradually made their way over the whole continent. But, in America, there was at an earlier period no ape-like stock throwing out branches in various directions: there was no focus of creation and diffusion of men. The earliest human remains and tools found there seem to belong to the Upper Pleistocene and may well represent the civilisation of backward races thrust from Asia across the land left by the retreating glaciers at the beginning of our Neolithic era.

Australia is likewise impossible as the source of humanity. We have already said in § 324 that at some period before, or cotemporary with, the beginning of the Tertiary era it became practically isolated from the rest of the world. On it there were imprisoned the fauna and flora then dominant throughout the world. In isolation this fauna and flora pursued each its own evolution in a significantly specialised direction. There resulted giant marsupials and other characteristic animal types, but nothing like that richly varied mammalian fauna which arose elsewhere during the Tertiary era and to which man belongs. The peoples whom we term Australian aborigines are descendants of immigrants during the late Pleistocene.

Why could not the Australian continent in the long Tertiary era have produced in its independent isolation an evolution leading up to man? To this question, which is of the highest interest, we can give no answer. We can indeed reiterate that the development of man does not present itself as an isolated effort of Nature. In the Lower Eocene the Primates diverge from a group of related animals: but at the same time other members of the group begin to shew differentiation towards other orders of mammals. In fact, the formation of the Primates was but one of a number of cotemporaneous divergent differentiations leading to carnivores (such as the lion), hoofed quadrupeds (such as the horse), elephants, rodents (such as the rat) and so forth. Of all the orders that thus arose the Primates had the most splendid efflorescence, because of the development of brain and coordinated nervous system which in the end produced man. But this whole mammalian development appears to have been unique: it happened once and once only. Out of a particular combination of circumstances, some conjunction or series of conjunctions of environment and mutations, the Primates emerged: on this earth of ours the necessary combination has never recurred.

§ 419. *The antiquity of man.*

How long is it since man began to be? No question is more natural and yet no answer that may be given fails to excite the wrath of most of our experts. The fact is that we have no data on which to base a decisive answer. The end of the Palaeolithic era was marked by the retreat of the glaciers and was followed by the hiatus which preceded Neolithic culture in Western Europe. This epoch may probably be dated ten or twelve thousand years ago. But even this estimate is disputed: some would divide the figures by half and others would multiply them by five. The fact is that the rate of deposition of silt varies enormously, as does also the rate at which rivers hollow out the valleys in which they flow: yet by such measurements the date of the final retreat of the Western European glaciers must be determined. We may add that estimates of the duration of the Neolithic era are only made relatively possible by the fact that during the whole of it the geography and climate of Western Europe have changed but little. When, however, as in earlier epochs, we have to allow for totally different climatic conditions, and for land and water distributions unlike anything that we have now, the problem of lapse of time becomes virtually insoluble.

If it were possible to relate the different glacial epochs of the past to astronomical variations of known length the problem might be solved. But there seems to be no reason to assume that the epochs in question are connected either with variations in the eccentricity of the earth's orbit or with the precession of the equinoxes. Such assumptions have frequently been made *faute de mieux*. But the reason for the wide changes of temperature which England, for instance, has experienced is unknown. That there should be fossil sub-tropical flora in Greenland and none the less a certainty that France has in the past suffered the rigours of a sub-Arctic climate may perhaps be explained by a shifting of land-masses over the face of the earth. Wegener, as we stated in § 321, suggested that the continents may, as it were, float over the core of the earth, drifting slowly as the centuries pass. The idea seems fanciful. But the surface land-masses are composed of less dense material than the core of the earth. If they were not rigidly joined to the core on which they rest they would be subject to tidal friction, which acts as a sort of brake. Many a problem of zoological distribution now solved by the assumption of land-bridges of vast size would, on Wegener's hypothesis, admit of simple explanation: and the glacial epochs would cease to be wholly perplexing*. But weighty arguments can be advanced against Wegener's theory.

It is certain that the antiquity of man must be great. Though no human fossils can with confidence be assigned to a period before the Early Pleistocene it is, as we have seen, reasonable to assume that the differentiation which led to man began in Mid-Tertiary times. If the rude eoliths of the so-called Chellean period were actually made by man, he was already a tool-using animal at the end of the Pliocene.

* A critical *précis* of various theories of climatic variation on the earth's surface will be found in Appendix D, pp. 262–267 of H. Jeffreys, *The Earth*. Cambridge University Press, 1924.

Now there is no doubt that the growth of human culture has proceeded at a rapidly accelerated pace. Take, for instance, the developments of the Metal Age. Copper was apparently first discovered in Egypt (others held that it had an Asiatic origin) some five thousand years before the Christian era. A millennium and a half later bronze, an alloy of copper and tin, was known in Egypt.

Iron appears to have been known in the same country before the alloy was made: but it was not until about 1400 B.C. that in Egypt iron came into general use. The story of David and Goliath seems to shew that the Hebrews had had no iron weapons when they invaded Palestine about 1100 B.C.; but the Philistines, probably sea-roving invaders who preserved fragments of the dying Cretan culture, by means of iron weapons conquered the country which to-day bears their name. These Philistines were non-Semites and may even have been Aryans. At all events the Iron Age has been held to correspond "to the maximum expansion of the Nordic race". By 500 B.C. the use of iron had spread over the whole Mediterranean area.

Simultaneously with this development there arose a knowledge of gold which ultimately led to ability to extract it from gold-bearing quartz-reefs. In the search for gold there was a widespread diffusion of Egyptian culture: and the ancient mines of Rhodesia shew that the Egyptian or Semitic prospector was little less shrewd than the man of our own time, whom he possibly anticipated by two and a half or three millennia. Thus all the evidence that we have points to a relatively speedy development of distinctive Metal Age culture. Yet even more rapid has been the building up of the Electrical Age in which we are living: Faraday's fundamental discoveries were made in the year 1831.

As we go back, however, progress becomes more gradual; and, as we return in imagination to the Lower Palaeolithic and preceding ages, we must assume that for vast stretches of time the conditions of human life were almost stationary. With man, as with biological evolution itself, the initial stages, now hidden from us, were by far the longest. An incredibly slow preparation preceded a development that became, or so it seems to us, increasingly rapid in its final stages. If then popular scientific writers claim from one to three million years for the development of man from the first animal in whom distinctively human rationality shewed itself, there is no good reason to dispute their assertion. It is indeed as satisfactory an estimate as can be made in our present state of knowledge. It is similarly possible that the Java ape-man lived half a million years ago.

§ 420. *The evolution of human intelligence.*

But it remains to be said that the dawn of human rationality is an event hard to describe with any definiteness. Since psychology was emancipated from theological prejudice, the barrier formerly thought to exist between the mental processes of man and those of 'the beasts' has largely vanished. It is now recognised that in each there is the same type of mechanism. The mental evolution of man has been a continuous process which began before, and has continued since, the differentiation of the Primates: it is, of course, a concomitant of the associated development of the nervous centres. Equally, in the mammalian orders which developed concurrently with the Primates, there has been an evolution of intelligence.

Moreover, as we have seen in § 353, it is impossible to place human reason in sharp opposition to animal instinct. Instincts are hereditary habits from which man himself is not wholly exempt. They have their origin in reactions which a particular species of animal has found satisfactory and, with regard to many of which, individuals of the species may therefore be supposed to have originally exercised some low-grade process of thought. The human brain is larger and finer than that of the anthropoid ape and man's intelligence is more powerful than that of his simian cousin: yet the same sort of psychic machinery produces comparable results. And if we could get back to the time when man first began to diverge from the anthropoids, the gap which now exists, broad and deep, between the lowest savages and the most intelligent of living apes would be found to have closed up.

Darwin taught us conclusively that the theological doctrine of the special creation of species must be abandoned*. It is equally a result of his carefully marshalled observations that belief in the special creation of human reason cannot be maintained. The human mind with its distinctive qualities and faculties came gradually into being. Its development and existence represent a phase of emergent evolution. The power of man to frame abstract concepts and to argue about them has no parallel on earth; but none the less we must insist that the intellectual processes of man are not in their essential nature distinct from those of the lower animals.

* It is well known that A. R. Wallace (1823–1913) who, concurrently with Darwin but independently of him, put forward the theory of natural selection, thought it insufficient to account for the development of man and, in particular, of his mental powers and moral sense. Wallace's belief that man's creation resulted from some special supernatural interference with the course of Nature is, however, unnecessary.

§ 421. *The development of brain and speech.*

Where man is supreme is in his power of coordinating and of reasoning with regard to sense-impressions. It is doubtful whether his senses themselves are as well developed as those of many other animals. The dog has a far more sensitive sense of smell than any human being. The eye of the vulture is a more perfect instrument than the eye of a man. But, when once impressions from the external world have reached the brain by means of the senses, man can on the whole use them far better than any other animal. This is because the central portion of the cerebral cortex, the neo-pallium, which contains the association-centres, has reached in man a quite remarkable development. Its various parts are linked to one another, and to other parts of the brain, by an inconceivably fine and complicated network of nerve fibrils.

Such a development accounts for the extended use which man makes of speech. The lower animals are not entirely without the gift of speech. They have what we may rightly describe as an elementary language. The hen calls her chickens to food or warns them of danger. A dog will ask unmistakably for a door to be opened and will give a satisfied bark of thanks. But in man the evolution of the organs of speech has been accompanied by the power of finely discriminating between the various sounds which the human voice can make. The result on man's mental evolution has been enormous. Language enables us to describe experience in great detail: it also allows the comparison and discussion of different types of experience to take place. It has thus tended to free man from subservience to the automatic reflexes which constitute instinct and to permit him to substitute new types of action determined by reason applied to experience. The growth of intelligence in man has thus gone *pari passu* with the extended use of language. We may speculate that primitive man differed from his ape-like progenitors by slight changes in brain and vocal chords. Increased brain power enabled him to use his greater power of speech: but in return the faculty of speech made possible that development of intelligence which separates a Newton from an ape.

§ 422. *The faint dawn of civilisation.*

Written history carries us back at most some six or eight thousand years. Behind its beginning lies the pre-history of humanity, the long period when mankind was in the making. Of man's thoughts, feelings and aspirations during the vast earlier stages of his development we know nothing. We can guess but little. What mental processes occur within the brain of the gorilla or the chimpanzee? He who would give a definite answer would have little on which to base his rashness. Until Neanderthal man appeared in Western Europe we have no hint of the psychical life of humanity save such as is given by the practice of burial (if it existed) and the use of very primitive tools. In Neanderthal man the anterior region of the frontal lobes of the brain was ill-developed and we may therefore conclude with confidence that his intellectual powers were small. Experts agree that he had but a rudimentary capacity for speech. Yet, as we have said, he could fashion carefully dressed flint implements, some of them of fine quality: he could make scrapers and piercers; and, above all, he and Pekin man before him knew how to make fire.

Tools and fire are distinctively human achievements. They lie at the basis of human invention and discovery. Together they constitute an advance as marvellous as any of the modern inventions which they have made possible. Earlier sub-men made and used many primitive tools; but Neanderthal man, sub-man though he was, laid in Europe the firm foundations of human material civilisation. Yet even if he buried his dead, as is highly probable, we are at a loss to know with what thoughts or hopes the rite was accompanied.

§ 423. *The Reindeer Age civilisation.*

It is not until we reach the Upper Palaeolithic, when the new races of the Reindeer Age came to supplant Neanderthal man, that we get plain indications of the psychical development of humanity. They are twofold in their nature. In the first place, we have the actual paintings and sculptures, the wall-engravings and statuettes, left by the new races. The earliest period of this art is termed Aurignacian and the latest Magdalenian. Probably, as we have already said, the artists were in the earliest period negroids and in the latest yellow men. Yet there was a vague unity throughout the whole era. The artists of the different races lived where the reindeer flourished. Some among them observed accurately and drew, with exquisite feeling and delicacy of line, red-deer and reindeer, bison and mammoth. Probably their decorated caves served as sanctuaries, and it is natural to associate the ornament with primitive magic.

The strong sexual interest plain in many of the statuettes may be taken to exemplify an association of magical and religious beliefs with fecundity. We are probably not mistaken if we see behind them those cults of vegetation and fertility which are widespread, not only among primitive but also in somewhat civilised races such as the Jews before the Exile and the Carthaginians before their overthrow by Rome.

Moreover, some of the sculptures of the men of the Reindeer Age give evidence of funeral rites and of the worship of the dead*. The dead, as was stated in § 415, were often buried in red ochre: and possibly the practice (the red blood is the life) points to a belief in, or at least a hope of, a continued existence of the deceased.

Such are the direct hints that we get of the psychical states of the earliest representatives of modern man that have been discovered. But there are also what we have called the living fossils of the men of the Reindeer Age. In the Australian aborigines, the Bushmen, the Eskimos and certain primitive peoples still to be found in odd corners of the world, we get races which are, as we have seen, apparently closely allied to the earliest representatives of modern man in Western Europe. Moreover, when first discovered they were at a stage of civilisation not far removed from the Upper Palaeolithic. By examining the beliefs and customs of these primitive races field-anthropologists, we have reason to think, can give us an insight into the sort of religion to which *homo sapiens* had risen when first he came to Western Europe.

Naturally, we must not assume too exact a mental similarity between living races and those removed from them by possibly fifteen or twenty thousand years. We must also be careful not to assume as indigenous those religious practices or beliefs which may have been derived from, or coloured by contact with, more developed races. The investigator, moreover, may most easily be led astray by putting his own interpretation on the practices which he observes in primitive races or by introducing his own ideas into statements made by their members. He has continually to remember that humanity in its mental growth has passed through stages through which the normal European child passes before adolescence. Just as in his physical development man climbs up his own ancestral tree, so also the expanding mind of the child recapitulates in a general fashion the mental progress of the human race. A study of the child-mind is a useful corrective to the unduly logical schemes of thought which some anthropologists still continue to attribute to primitive man.

§ 424. *Characteristics of primitive religion.*

It must be allowed that such evidence as we can get tends to shew that the religion of primitive man, if we may use the term in its widest

---

* Marcellin Boule, *op. cit.* p. 258.

reference, was not a markedly attractive development. We cannot, in the first place, doubt that in rites connected with the bounty of Nature, the fertility of animals and the renewal of vegetation, sex-emphasis was unpleasantly prominent. There are writers who contend that phallic worship is not primitive, but a semi-civilised development. Such writers, or some of them, also postulate a primitive monogamy rather than the highly probable matriarchal condition of early human society. The picture they present is, as far as we can see, more roseate than true. A second feature of early religion is its childishness. In totemism, whatever its social value, there is a mass of make-believe that suggests a child's game. Thirdly, throughout primitive religion we get magic. In theory we may separate religion from magic. It is doubtful, as we shall see, if primitive man ever made the separation: at any rate, as every close observer knows, the vitality of magical beliefs in present-day religion is great.

§ 425. *Animism.*

When Sir E. B. Tylor (1832–1917) laid the foundations of modern anthropology he suggested that at the basis of primitive religion there lay a belief in spiritual beings. Such were, he held, either supernatural in origin or the disembodied spirits of dead ancestors or heroes. These beings were deemed to be potent for good or ill and necessarily therefore were to be placated or adored. Now undoubtedly the *animism* constituted by beliefs of this kind has influenced religion at certain stages of its development. To men with no highly developed logical processes the disappearance of personality at death must have suggested its survival in some immaterial form: dreams and visions would give substance to such speculations. But it seems to be clear that Tylor greatly exaggerated the contribution made by animism to primitive religion. In fact, primitive man was a more practical creature than animism would suggest.

§ 426. *The practical nature of primitive magic and religion.*

Religion, we must emphasise, grew out of human needs: it was not a product of man's idle speculation, but was his response to the troubles and difficulties of life. Magic had a similar origin.

Consider, for instance, the place of magic in the life of primitive man of the Upper Palaeolithic. It was no substitute for his knowledge, his nascent science. He was skilful in making a fire, in hunting, in shaping and using rudimentary tools. Primitive man to-day shews equal skill over the wider range of achievement corresponding to the Neolithic era of human history. But Palaeolithic man was by no means master of his environment; and to an individual or a tribe, gravely limited in capacity to subdue Nature, occasions are constantly coming when such knowledge and power as exist are inadequate. Fear or desire, human feeling at its strongest, then creates the occasion for magic. There *must* be some way out of the *impasse*; the logical processes of primitive invention have failed: illogical belief has its opportunity. Magic derives strength from the instinct that 'where there's a will there's a way'. But the way is not that of thoughtful endeavour: it is the way of the charm or the spell. We shall unjustly underrate our far-distant ancestors if we deny to them knowledge based on clear and accurate observation. They had a realm of behaviour based alike on empirical knowledge and on confidence in reason: and into this realm magic did not enter. But to control the mischances of human existence, such as famine, bad hunting, fire and storm, man's knowledge was of no avail: so he turned to magic.

Every student of childhood must have observed how complete is the child's acceptance of magic. A fairy story, with spells that produce the most amazing changes, he accepts with grave enjoyment: but let the writer's fancy depart from apparent seriousness and his youthful reader's resentment is quick. Strongly rooted in the mind of the race are beliefs that once in all probability held undisputed sway and even now revive when emotional disturbance permits.

§ 427. *The relation between magic and primitive religion.*

What is magic? It is a sort of pseudo-science, knowledge of the rite and spell by which the course of Nature can be controlled. It rests upon belief in a mystical, personal or impersonal, power which the magician can control. If there be a charmed object the power conveys virtue to the object. The power is conveyed by the spell, by use of the right formula. 'Open sesame': the formula is the central essential feature of the magical art. And the right formula is a secret known only to the elect, or capable of effective use only by those who are in the right succession by birth or due initiation. Behind the formula lies the myth, the story which accounts for its existence. The great hero, the magic which he discovered when his safety was menaced, his triumph: such are enshrined in the racial traditions which constitute among savages an orthodoxy more stringent even than that which the Roman Church imposes upon its clergy.

The magic is believed: why? Often enough it must fail. But it is a curious characteristic of the human mind that one positive, or supposedly positive fact, is remembered as against a score of negative disappointments. The rare coincidence, the occasional happy chance are, in fact, sufficient to maintain credulity. It must also be remembered that in primitive communities the professor of magic is usually one of the natural leaders of the tribe: he is, that is to say, a man of exceptional personality. The prestige which he gains by successful leadership attaches to his magic and thus tradition is enforced by what is believed to be contemporary experience.

If it be objected that, when all is said, we can only bring forward the most flimsy reasons why primitive men should have allowed magic so extensive a realm, the answer must be that man is only slowly becoming a reasonable creature. In modern civilised communities belief in magic is widespread: unreasonable credulity is much stronger in most religious bodies than their representatives are prepared to admit. But in fairness we must state that among the non-religious magic flourishes with equal vigour: no one would assume that the presence of a mascot on a motor-car meant that its owner was especially religious.

Primitive religion, like magic, is concerned with the unknown, the incomprehensible, with the vague Power or Powers which influence human life, thwarting or aiding man's endeavours, giving or withholding what he desires. By magic man seeks to control the forces around and above him, to deflect the course of Nature, to compel the unknown Powers to obey his commands. In religion, on the other hand, the belief that such compulsion is possible is set aside and ideas of entreaty, supplication, propitiation come to the fore.

Sir J. G. Frazer, generalising from unequalled knowledge, separates magic from religion by finding in the former the idea of direct control and in the latter the propitiation of superior beings. Thus in Frazer's view religion is subsequent to animism: it is a consequence of the rise of belief in disembodied spirits, ancestors, gods or demons. The borderline between magic and religion is, however, difficult to draw. Belief that god or demon can be influenced by ritual or spell, or by right modes of worship, is essentially magical and yet it is also religious. Magic is non-rational pseudo-science which may, according to the claims of its exponents, work directly or because some Power is thereby induced to take action. We had perhaps better say that the distinction, between being able to set impersonal forces at work and being able to persuade a Power to take action which leads to the same desired end, constitutes the difference between secular and religious magic.

§ 428. *Primitive religion and totemism.*

Religion itself is not easily defined, and primitive religion differs notably from the developed religions of civilised communities. In primitive races, behind the ritual which centres naturally upon death and to a lesser extent upon the other critical stages of human life, there lie cloudy mental processes compact of imagination, fear, desire and hope. Perhaps some of these processes hardly deserve the name of mystical feeling. If, however, we employ this term we can say that primitive religion is made of ritual and mystical feeling. It endures because it becomes a cohesive social force. The ritual which surrounds death and the beliefs which gradually attach to the ritual are valuable in so far as they prevent the disintegration of a group which loses an important member. By means of tribal ritual, loss can become an occasion when social bonds are strengthened by a ceremony for which all unite.

It is highly probable that, in primitive religion, ritual precedes belief and that beliefs survive largely because they have an obscure practical value. Only so can we account for totemism and its vagaries. As we read accounts of it, it seems a gigantic growth of childish make-believe complicating human existence by senseless interference. Yet it appears to represent a definite stage in human evolution. Not only does it exist among the Australian aborigines from whom we get our fullest knowledge of it, but clear traces of it can be found in the pre-dynastic civilisation of Neolithic Egypt and probably indications occur in the so-called Azilian period (between the Upper Palaeolithic and the Neolithic) of Western Europe.

Frazer defines totemism as "an intimate relation which is supposed to exist between a group of kindred people on the one side and a species of natural or artificial objects on the other side, which objects are called the totems of the human group". As a rule the totem object is some animal or vegetable, of special use or value or interest. It is held in reverence by the clan of which it is the totem: if it is edible, they will probably not eat it; and invariably they attach to it some special significance in regard to their own welfare.

Totem lore would fill a large volume: it has, indeed, filled many a one. What is its true place in the mental development of humanity? It is easy to see the value of a totem as the badge of unity of the clan;

but some anthropologists assert that the survival value of totemism is due to the fact that it tended to preserve food supplies. They argue that, if a number of groups with different totems each sought to increase the multiplication of the associated species of animal or vegetable useful for food, a check would automatically be placed on that improvidence which is all too common among primitive races. But, even so, it is difficult to understand why animals useless for food (the serpent which Moses lifted up in the wilderness was possibly a totem), or more especially artificial objects, should be adopted as totems unless we have here a purely fanciful extension of a useful cult.

§ 429. *The development of primitive religion.*

What emerges, or seems to emerge, from such information as to the working of the mind of primitive man as we can get is that he was not in any sense a potential philosopher: he did not try to find a logically coherent metaphysical scheme by which his own existence and the world in which he found himself might be explained. He sought practical ends such as sufficiency of food, the well-being and increase of his tribe, and control over the mischances to which he was exposed. Naturally he turned to magic when knowledge and skill failed him. Naturally his religious development attached itself to the reproductive processes of the animal and vegetable kingdoms which were to him alike so inexplicable and so important. Naturally he came to associate the crises of life, and especially death, with a public ritual which acquired a quasi-mystical significance; and, as fancy played in a region specially suited to its exercise, animism came into existence. Thus arose the emotionally valuable belief that the dead hero was not wholly lost but that his spirit lived on. Further, it was natural to assume that fertility was produced by goddesses and would be increased by their worship. So a pantheon, attested by myth, was gradually formed. A vague belief in some sort of human survival after death probably arose early in man's mental development.

Few, however, will be convinced by the arguments of those who would have us accept a stage of primitive monotheism when worship of the All-Father of the tribe was central in its religion. Equally, it seems clear that there was no necessary connection between primitive religion and moral progress. Of course, the religion and the morality of a tribe were alike part of its tradition. A fierce orthodoxy guarded both; and, as parts of the same system, they could not be mutually independent. But there is no reason to think that crude religious speculation contributed to moral progress. On the contrary it is probable that the religious myths and beliefs of primitive man were often a barrier against, rather than an incentive to, ethical advance. In fact, not until after the dawn of written history do we get, and especially in ethical monotheism, a type of religion which shelters and creates moral ideals.

Primitive morality was but a system of rules of conduct found by experience to be of value, or at any rate not injurious, to the welfare of the tribe. In them room had to be made for the animal appetites of individuals, and also for occasional licence as a relief from labour and its monotony. So even when religious beliefs were no longer rudimentary, gods were jealously tribal and gross orgies were countenanced by religious teachers. To-day in Southern India and elsewhere many religious practices are morally debased: and when so-called civilised nations go to war they entreat their God, as though He were a tribal deity, to avenge Himself of their enemies. The immoralities and hatreds and puerilities which enter into primitive religion have not been entirely rooted out even from the more advanced peoples of the world: they are dormant and still dangerous.

We may emphasise in conclusion that we do not impugn the substantial value of the higher forms of religion or of morality by admitting the lowly origin of both religion and morality. By their fruits ye shall know them, not by their roots. So William James urged when contending that religious experience was not to be despised because of the pathological manifestations sometimes associated with it. The criterion by which we judge an object must be the value of the finished product: its origin is almost entirely irrelevant. Eight hundred million years ago the ancestor of the modern leader of thought and aspiration was a worm in the sea-mud. Fifty thousand years ago another ancestor's religious and ethical ideals were a jumble of fancies and superstitions and ritual acts, many of them childish and some disgusting. We do not judge the man by the worm nor his creed by its primitive beginnings. That the process of development has been surprising and its beginnings amazingly unpromising we admit. Why God should have chosen so to act, so to use evil and to bring good out of evil, we cannot say. But we must accept the present no less than the past; and those of us who believe in ethical monotheism claim that it must be judged by its present value to humanity and by the extent to which it gives a reasonable picture of the cosmos. I personally do not doubt that ethical monotheism both explains and encourages the development of the highest faculties of man.

Lecture xvii

SCIENTIFIC THEORY AND THE 'REAL' WORLD

§ 430. *Introduction.*

Throughout our previous enquiry we have assumed the existence of a world presented to us in experience, and also that the human mind is adequate not only to perceive such a world but also to create sciences capable of describing it. We have never suggested any doubt as to whether the world which has been described is the world which actually exists. We must now discuss this and cognate questions.

Our senses give us a continuous stream of impressions which we regard as coming from a world external to ourselves. We think that we perceive physical objects in this world. From our perceptions we form concepts which we may elaborate into theories. How far do these concepts and theories, or such of them as other men also form, give us knowledge of a 'real' world? Further, what exactly do we mean when we talk of such a world? How far can science give us knowledge of reality; or does it entirely fail to give us such knowledge and merely describe phenomena arising in consciousness? Another problem is equally important and difficult. We commonly assume that the physical and biological sciences are built up by mind as it observes changes in matter. Are matter and mind two disparate entities? If so, how can they interact? As we attempt to answer such questions we enter the realms of psychology and philosophy.

It must be admitted that the average man of science has an instinctive dislike of metaphysics. He is irritated by the suggestion that his own assumptions, which seem to him entirely reasonable, may not be able to survive critical examination. He is aware, moreover, that the philosophers have not reached any generally accepted conclusions comparable to those which form the established 'truths' of scientific theory. He wrongly concludes that in philosophy no progress has been made, for he is ignorant that many seductive paths to error have been closed. Not seldom he asks, somewhat impatiently, that he may be preserved from 'word-spinning' and 'logic-chopping' as he continues his researches, confident that he is discovering 'causes' which account for change in a 'real' world. His use of such terms as 'cause' and 'real' shews, of course, that he has his own primitive metaphysics. He may well take to heart William James' aphorism: "metaphysics means nothing but an unusually obstinate effort to think clearly".

Every educated man knows that the uncriticised beliefs of 'common-sense' have been responsible for much ignorant dogmatism. Controversy has made all familiar with the fact that religious teachers have often advanced claims that cannot be substantiated by critical enquiry and that their own undoing has been the result. It is also true, however, that similar claims which will not survive critical investigation have been, and still are, sometimes advanced by scientific experts. Such claims do harm to good feeling and lessen the respect in which science should be held. If by an examination of fundamentals we are led to realise the extent to which both religion and science rest on faith and are a reasonable interpretation of experience, we may hope that the hostility between them which has been too frequent in the past may change to that sympathetic understanding which ought to exist between the different loyalties of the human spirit.

§ 431. *Naïve realism: physical realism.*

The ordinary assumptions as to the ultimate nature of things, accepted by men who have given no critical attention to metaphysical questions, are said by philosophers to constitute naïve realism. We are all familiar with this standpoint. Fundamental in it is the belief that we live in a world of things that can be touched, tasted, heard and seen; that these things are real in the sense that they have an existence independent, not only of me and my experience, but of all men and of their experience. Further, these real things are made of matter, various forms of which have the qualities which we perceive. Material substance, the essential foundation of material objects, is thus the primary reality of the Universe. Mind is quite different from matter and is somehow not as real, though it is through mind that we understand what matter is. We can see the greater permanence of matter by the fact that, when animals die, the mental part of them perishes but the matter which forms their bodies endures. Such, in brief, is naïve realism. I need not describe it further, for it is a philosophy which at some period of our lives we have all accepted.

Physical realism, the uncritical metaphysics of the trained man of science, has much in common with naïve realism. It differs in that those who accept it explain that physical science demonstrates that things are not what they seem. Solid matter, for instance, is an aggregate of protons and electrons which occupy little of the space through which the matter appears to extend. But the protons and electrons are thought of as being fundamentally real. It is admitted that some of the qualities of things, such as the colours of objects, are in part at least contributed by our minds, but it is assumed that other qualities belong to things in themselves. The physical realist also tends to regard mind as something which is not real, in the sense that matter is real. Matter, in fact, is usually held to possess the permanent substratum of substance which is wholly lacking to mind. Often the naïve realist and the man of science who is a physical realist accept the materialist position. They then regard the mental or psychical as an epipheno-menon, a mere derivative of the physical, a sort of by-product of certain material changes which take place in the brain.

§ 432. *Individual experience.*

We can only determine whether physical realism gives an adequate picture of reality by examining the process by which we gain knowledge of the external world. Now, as James Ward (1843–1925) has well said, "all we think and feel and do, all our facts and theories, all our emotions and ideals and ends", may be included in the one term, experience. Consider a particular concrete experience. In it there will be a subject to whom the experience comes: the subject is, as it were, the centre of the experience. There will also be an objective factor in the experience: we say that the experience is constituted by the perception of an object by the subject. But such perception will not be a mere act of cognition. The activity of the subject in experience is always synthetic. Sensa-tions are not to be likened to a patter of disconnected atoms received by the subject: they are changes in the *continuum* which is the objective domain of perception. The subject-object relation which thus con-stitutes experience is, moreover, a unity. It cannot be separated into two parts. We do not know what a subject would be without objects or what objects would be without a subject. Experience is, in fact, a continuous process in which subject and object are invariably corre-lated. It is, in addition, an activity in which not only cognition but also feeling and practical interests are normally involved. Such duality of subject and object in the unity of experience is vastly different from the Cartesian dualism embedded in popular thought. In the latter dualism, mind and matter are supposed to be entirely distinct and independent: and we cannot even faintly understand how any relation between the two can be established.

§ 433. *Collective experience: public knowledge.*

The axioms and postulates on which different kinds of philosophy are based differ because some, which it seems necessary to accept, result from a choice between alternatives; and men differ as to how far the alternatives by which they are confronted are likely to be true. We cannot even prove certain premises which are generally admitted alike by philosophers and 'ordinary people'. For instance, we all believe in the existence of other centres of consciousness, other subjects, than ourselves. But if a man were to declare himself a solipsist and to say that he had only knowledge of his own mental states and that they gave him no reason to believe that others similar to himself existed, his view could not be shewn to lead to any logical contradiction. Yet in metaphysical theory, as in practical life, we all reject solipsism; and we justify our rejection by the fact that public knowledge exists as the result of what we believe to be the experience of other subjects.

We can best approach the problem of the nature of public knowledge by considering what happens when a group of men see what in popular language we call a common object, such as the moon. Does each man see the same moon? The answer, to one way of interpreting an ambiguous question, is in the negative, inasmuch as each man's experience is unique. But, as the men discuss their experience, they convey to one another what is common to the experience of them all. More than this they cannot convey, just as we cannot convey to a colour-blind man the distinction between red and green. The experience of the moon common to all the group leads to the formation of a concept. Thus from intercourse between subjects we get the concept of the moon, the moon which is not the particular object of some specified consciousness but an object for human consciousness in general. It must, however, be distinctly recognised that, though this conceptual moon is not the object of individual experience, it is not independent of collective experience. We have no right to conclude that the moon of public knowledge exists apart from perceiving minds: if we believe that the moon has such an existence 'in itself', the belief will be the result of an act of faith.

We have, at this stage of our enquiry into the foundations of knowledge, two related pairs of terms. In my perception of the moon there is a duality in unity, the subject and object of individual experience. But in addition to this pair of terms there is the moon as an object when collective or universal experience is the subject. The latter conceptual moon is reached by the use of reason. Similarly, every material object is, in fact, made by the individual subject from a synthesis of sense-impressions and of memories of such impressions. When the object is taken out of the subject-object relation of actual experience we get a construct which in popular thought is assumed to have a real existence apart from the perceiving mind. When such constructs as are made by different subjects are compared and the differing elements in them are eliminated, a conceptual object is created which satisfies the collective consciousness of mankind. This object, à fortiori, is deemed to have a real and independent existence. Thus arises the dualism of matter and mind which dominates popular belief.

§ 434. *The synthetic activity of the intellect.*

Before considering the legitimacy of such popular belief we would point out that the comparison of subject and object in individual experience with subject and object in universal experience is of primary importance. As the processes of reason operate in making synthetic constructs from individual experience, mere passive reception is associated with feeling and will. It is such constructive activity which enables us rightly to use perception and makes possible the intercourse between different subjects from which public knowledge results. The more we reflect upon the part which mental processes take in framing the constructs which we call material objects, the more are we led to see how much truth there is in a famous paradox of Kant: "the intellect makes Nature, though it does not create it". We are also compelled to appreciate Kant's claim to be the Copernicus of philosophy, because he was the first to maintain that "objects conform to the principles of our intelligence, not our intelligence to the independent nature of things". In other words, man's understanding makes Nature in its formal or intelligible aspect.

We have, in fact, no knowledge save that given in experience: and experience is a mental process. Even Huxley* (1825–1895) acknowledged this truth: in the year 1886 he declared that for half a century he had held that "the arguments used by Descartes and Berkeley, to shew that our certain knowledge does not extend beyond states of consciousness", were "irrefragable". A thinker of a very different school, Edward Caird†, emphasised the same standpoint in the paradox: "All ignorance of the object is ignorance of the self, all develop-

---

* T. H. Huxley, *Collected Essays.* Macmillan, vol. IX, 1894, p. 130.

† Edward Caird, *The Critical Philosophy of Immanuel Kant.* 2 vols. Maclehose, vol. I, 1889, p. 423.

ment of consciousness is also a development of self-consciousness ". Such views of the nature of our knowledge of the physical world are so contrary to ' common-sense ' that we find it hard to appreciate them: but until we make such an inversion of ordinary prejudices as they necessitate we cannot begin to understand the function of scientific description.

No one, of course, will deny that intercourse between subjects enables us to transcend the limitations of solipsism. The subject of collective experience is the subject of individual experience when the latter participates in all that other subjects are able to communicate. Thus intelligence at its highest, intelligence which is self-conscious, forms the intelligible world; and apart from such intelligence this world would not exist. What would exist we cannot say: the answer depends, as I believe, on the extent to which the consciousness of man resembles that of God. We may not assume that the collective experience of humanity exhausts all possible experience. For we may be, and in all probability are, so limited that we are incapable of experiences which would be possible to self-conscious beings of greater mental range and power: our inability to perceive radiation except such as happens to be of wave-lengths within the range of light and heat is significant of human limitations. Yet even the trained metaphysician sometimes writes as though he had forgotten that we cannot pass outside what we may term the extended solipsism of human consciousness in general.

§ 435. *The Newtonian philosophy.*

Galileo (1564–1642) and Newton (1642–1727) laid down the principles of mechanics before the significant developments of modern philosophy which we owe to Berkeley (1685–1753) and Hume (1711–1776). Though the laws of motion which are fundamental in the Galileo-Newtonian scheme now seem to us simple, their long-delayed discovery was a great triumph of human thought and was naturally associated with metaphysical reflections as to space, time and matter. Newton's discovery that the law of gravitation was the key to the motions of the solar system gave immense intellectual prestige to all his writings. Hence the thought of his own era was profoundly influenced by his metaphysical views, and his religious opinions commanded respect. The profession of atheism in the seventeenth century was dangerous and therefore the semblance of orthodoxy in that age may be deceptive; but there is no doubt that Newton was sincere when he maintained a steady belief in God*. At

---

* It seems, however, to be established from his papers that he was an Arian, rather than an orthodox Trinitarian, Christian.

the end of the *Principia* he concluded that "the whole diversity of natural things can have arisen from nothing but the ideas and will of one necessarily existing being, who is always and everywhere, God Supreme, infinite, omnipotent, omniscient, absolutely perfect". Elsewhere, in the *Opticks*, he speaks of "a powerful ever-living Agent who being in all places is more able by his will to move the bodies within his boundless uniform *sensorium*".

Such belief in God did not commend itself to some of the leaders of scientific thought in the nineteenth century, but Newton's other metaphysical assumptions were, until recently, accepted by most men of science. Now, in the Newtonian philosophy the visible world is supposed to consist of material bodies which have an existence, independent of one another, in a space which is absolute and independent of bodies within it. Changes in these bodies and in their relative positions take place in time; and such time is supposed to be absolute and to flow uniformly at a rate undisturbed by any relative motions of such bodies. If we combine the law of gravitation with belief in physically real and independent bodies we get the mechanical theory of the Universe, an abstraction of the highest utility which to men of science has only lately begun to seem inadequate because relativity denies one of its postulates and quantum phenomena find no natural place within it.

Bishop Berkeley, to whom some would give the first place among post-Renaissance philosophers, initiated scepticism of one aspect of this Newtonian philosophy when he urged that percepts constitute the whole reality of material objects. All that we can directly perceive consists of 'impressions received by our souls': and in the impression itself there can be nothing from which we can learn of its source in a material world. Thus Berkeley could write* in *The Principles of Human Knowledge* (1710): "It is indeed an opinion strangely prevailing among men, that houses, mountains, rivers, and in a word all sensible objects, have an existence, natural or real, distinct from their being perceived by the understanding".

Hume carried such scepticism farther when he urged that the existence of the perceiving soul which Berkeley had allowed was equally an unjustifiable inference. What we know is actually limited to sensations together with the way in which they follow one another and are associated. In opposition to Hume's contention we can urge that, as we have previously said in describing individual experience, sensations are not like disconnected atoms. Kant (1724–1804) took a step of

---

* See Berkeley's *Works* (cited in § 110). Vol. I, p. 157.

fundamental importance when he pointed out that each element of experience is actually linked up to other elements. The self-consciousness of experience arranges its elements in order of time and distributes them in space. Thus the spatio-temporal ordering of experience is part of human perception and the synthetic activity of the subject of experience is a psychological fact to be set against Hume's scepticism.

On the whole Kant's influence tended to perpetuate the Newtonian standpoint. Only quite recently has belief in absolute space and in absolute time been abandoned by men of science: and even now that belief in the independent existence of material bodies which is the foundation of classical mechanics persists. Yet, even granting the existence of 'things in themselves', material bodies or atoms cannot have absolute independence inasmuch as matter corresponds to a warping of space-time and each particular space-time curvature warps, albeit ever so slightly, the whole of space. As has already been made clear in these lectures, Einsteinian relativity has destroyed certain assumptions of the Newtonian scheme. But it is probable that an even more wide-reaching revision of Newtonian concepts will be made when the full consequences are seen of the knowledge that the physical Universe is a linked system in which no bodies are, in the Newtonian sense, independent.

§ 436. *Space and time.*

The belief that space is an objective reality, existing in itself independently of experience, is still common. It has a long history. In antiquity Democritus seems to have held that "the real basis of things consists of atoms and void". His view came through Epicurus to Lucretius who, in his famous poem *De Rerum Natura*, says*: "all nature then, as it exists by itself, is founded on two things: there are bodies and there is void in which these bodies are placed and through which they move about". We have seen in § 83 that Henry More, the Cambridge Platonist, held a doctrine which affirmed the spiritual nature of space: its "infinite extent will seem to be something divine". And from this region of opinion Newton accepted a belief in absolute space. For him infinite space is, as it were, the sensory of God†. "God, by continuing to be always and everywhere, constitutes duration and space."

* Lucretius, *On the Nature of Things*. Munro's translation. Deighton Bell, 1886, p. 10.

† This notion received the approbation of Addison (*The Spectator*, No. 565, 1714): "The noblest and most exalted way of considering this infinite space is that of Sir Isaac Newton, who calls it the *sensorium* of the Godhead".

Berkeley appears to have been the first modern philosopher effectively to challenge belief in the external reality of space. He declared it to be simply the subjective result of sensations of sight, touch and movement. Absolute space, he said roundly in the year 1721*, is "mere nothing (*merum nihil*)". Leibniz (1646–1716), like Berkeley in the next generation, regarded space as subjective but differed from him in thinking that it was constituted by the objective order of 'things in themselves'.

Kant, as was mentioned in §142, regarded space and time as necessary forms of perception, imposed by the perceiving mind. Thus "the statement that all things exist in space and time is, for Kant, a statement about the nature of our perception and not about the things perceived". But while he held that space is subjective, he differed from Berkeley in thinking that geometrical axioms are prior to all experience. The view of Leibniz he found unsatisfactory for he held that we can have no knowledge of 'things in themselves'. For Kant geometrical axioms were principles, antecedent to all experience, given by *à priori* intuition. It was, as we have seen, the work of certain great mathematicians of the nineteenth century, Gauss, Lobatchewsky and Riemann, to shew that such intuition was not always trustworthy. They made it evident that active experience is itself the basis of geometry: our experience is not conditioned by geometrical intuitions. Space is not prior to, or independent of, our experience of the objects which in common speech are said to be contained within it.

Similar conclusions apply to time. From activity and change we derive our idea of time. Events are not contained in absolute time. In fact, time resembles space in that it is given in experience. Neither time nor space is separately given; and together they cannot be properly said to belong to the subject apart from the object nor to the object apart from the subject. They are not objective realities independent of experience: neither are they, either singly or together, constructs made by the subject prior to experience. We do not start with empty space and time and fill them with bodies and events. Since Einstein gave us the special theory of relativity we have learnt that Newton's belief in uniformly flowing time must be abandoned. Space and time, as we have seen in Lecture V, have been fused into the 'four-dimensional manifold' which we call space-time. Yet what has just been said of space and time severally is true of space-time. *It is not an objective reality independent of experience: nor is it a pre-existent*

* See Berkeley's *Works* (cited in § 110). Vol. III, p. 93. [*De Motu*, § 53.]

continuum in which the events of Minkowski's world make the Universe and its history. It is a construct derived from the collective experience of humanity.

We have previously insisted on the fact, of which Kant first saw the decisive importance, that sensations are not atomic: acts of perception are not isolated like rain-drops. Now into the most simple perception space and time enter: psychical activity is synthetic and thus space-time enters into all interpretations of experience. Hence it would seem, as Kant would have held, that space-time is, as it were, a projection outwards of the forms under which we necessarily interpret experience. The forms are the same for all men and hence the perceived world seems to be the same for all. It is this agreement which leads to the mistaken belief that space-time is objectively real. From the view that time is a form under which, owing to the nature of perception, our conscious experience is arranged, Kant concluded that time-relations are within consciousness. Perception is, therefore, not a mere occurrence in time, but time-relations are included in perception. Or, to put the same thing in other words, time is not something within which mind exists: it is an expression of mind itself. Our modern knowledge that space and time form a single continuum leads to the conclusion that space-time is an expression of mind. Thus, though mind does not create the world, it gives to it the form which we know. What the appearance of the world would be to a being with a different kind of perception we cannot say.

J. S. Haldane* insists that, in the world of spiritual interests and values, we do not get events separated from one another in space and time. The Newtonian idea of bodies isolated in space and time is only an abstraction from reality useful within the limited range of physical investigation. Haldane urges further that "the parts and environment which participate in life are inseparable in space". If I understand him aright, he concludes that when we pass to biological enquiries we find ourselves unable to understand life because we believe that things must be separated in space in the manner postulated by Newton. For this reason such ill-defined concepts as 'vital force', entelechy and so forth are often introduced to make up for the inadequacies of the Newtonian scheme. But even the biologically interpreted world is an imperfect abstraction, since in it there is no place for consciousness. We must not strip away the psychological aspects of experience as we interpret the

* J. S. Haldane, *The Sciences and Philosophy.* Hodder and Stoughton, 1928, p. 228.

BST

36

world; and, if we do not make this error, our understanding gives us a spiritual world, the events of which are inseparable from one another in space and time. It is this latter world of interest, values and responsibilities which is the best construct from sense-impressions that we can make.

Of course, if we believe in the objective reality of space-time, such a real ground of existence will form a bed of Procrustes which all our interpretations of the world must be made to fit. But we have argued that such a belief is erroneous and that space-time is merely a form under which, owing to the nature of perception, our experience is arranged. Haldane rightly insists that spiritual concepts transcend this form: but the difficulty of his, to me, most attractive philosophy is that the limitations of our mental processes make any concrete application of Haldane's spiritual or biological interpretation appear necessarily to belong to a world ordered in space and time. If I may anticipate conclusions—for which I shall argue at a later stage of this enquiry—I would say that we cannot hope to understand the world as it exists in the thought of God save by transcending perception in space-time. Unfortunately, such transcendence is beyond the present powers of humanity.

§ 437. *Realism and Idealism: moderate realism: theism.*

Our analysis of experience has shewn us the fundamental character of the subject-object relation. We cannot go beyond this relation without making some sort of assumption and the precise assumption which we make will determine the metaphysical system which we accept. Berkeley is typical of the left wing of the Idealist school. For him, apart from percepts (or ideas as he calls them) there is no material reality. His view, as we shall see shortly, fails to do justice to the objective unity of experience. For Idealism in general, material things only exist in so far as they form an element in the experience of some conscious subject. Thus Idealism does not separate the object out of the subject-object relation and therefore does not regard an object as existing apart from that relation.

Those who reject Idealism lay stress upon the certain fact that physical percepts are not produced by the perceiving mind. If such percepts were subjective in origin, public knowledge would be impossible. The possibility of 'intersubjective intercourse' makes it clear that the raw material of physical perception is independent of the individual. There is, in fact, an element in our physical experience which we cannot regard as originating with ourselves. All such considerations lead plausibly to Realism, to the assumption that the element in physical experience which is independent of the individual subject has a real and independent existence. This element, it is argued, is not merely a co-factor in the subject-object relation: it can be separated out of it both in logic and fact.

Naïve realism passes at once to a dualism of matter and mind. The object is matter: the subject is mind. But how mind perceives matter remains unintelligible. In fact, when the unity of experience has been thus sundered, it is impossible to unite its parts. It ought, however, to be emphasised that the object, when taken out of the subject-object relation, need not be assumed to be physical: it might be psychical.

Kant in his synthetic philosophy postulated two orders of objects. The one order consists of objects *extra nos*, or external phenomena. The other consists of objects *praeter nos*, or 'things in themselves'. Of the latter we cannot have knowledge. But they apparently originate experience: they may also be regarded as objects for beings whose intelligence differs from, but is more far-reaching than, our own. If, however, things in themselves set experience going, we ought to be able to deduce something as to their nature. In short, Kant's assumption is not free from serious difficulties. There is much to be said for the view accepted by J. S. Haldane that "'the things in themselves' of Kant's conception are nothing but the ghosts of the Newtonian physical reality".

As we have just stated, all forms of critical realism assume that a reality exists apart from the subject-object relation, and that in some way it affects our perceptions. In scientific realism this reality is supposed to be given by the constructs of scientific theory. In critical realism it is not normally or of necessity identified with such constructs.

My own position, as I said in the first lecture, is usually, but not with strict accuracy, termed that of moderate realism. I hold that from the subject-object relation it is possible to separate out objects which have a real and independent existence because they exist in the Mind of God. Thus, as W. R. Inge says*, God is the only 'conscious subject' necessary to the existence of the world. I conceive that our minds do not create the world inasmuch as it has its being in God: it would be what it is were there no finite centres of consciousness such as ourselves in the Universe. But we contribute something—how much we do not know —to the making of the world as it appears in the concepts which

* W. R. Inge, *Outspoken Essays, Second Series*. Longmans, 1922, p. 19.

constitute our public knowledge. Thus the world *as we know it* has not an independent objective existence.

My own 'moderate realism' may be called Realism, inasmuch as it assumes that it is possible to separate out objects from the subject-object relation of our experience. Further, it is monistic (in one sense of this variously used word), because it postulates that God and the world constitute a unity, though a duality in unity similar to that of our experience, a duality in which God and the world are subject and object. Yet I do not think that we can rightly say that God is the only reality. The world presented to us in experience has, I hold, a reality derived from God: it is dependent upon Him for its continued existence. But the fact of evil and our freedom alike make it necessary, as I believe, to assume that the world has a certain measure of independence given to it by God. What we call matter will have this derivative reality and relative independence: but it does not follow that in matter there is a real substratum called substance. What matter is 'in itself' is a puzzle: it may be psychical or merely a manifestation of psychical activity. We have seen in §142 that in the conceptual scheme of modern physics matter seems to have been reduced to geometrical form which is capable of relative motion.

The moderate realism which I have put forward assumes the existence of a Universal Mind which I have termed God. The existence of God as thus postulated I hold to be necessary for many reasons, of which the chief is indicated in the following argument. All our experience goes to shew that there cannot be, as Ward* says, "bare subjects lying in wait for objects, nor objects that by definition never are positively objects". Yet the objectivity of the world is for a single finite mind intermittent; and the totality of finite minds is not sufficient to maintain it. We are thus, if our basis be sound, led to the conclusion that such objectivity is only constituted by a Universal Mind for Whom all objects are always present. Though this particular standpoint and argument do not appeal to 'the man in the street', yet the more closely they have been examined the more have they commended themselves to leaders of philosophic thought. Thus Hastings Rashdall, the greatest English philosophic theologian of the present century, could write†:

* James Ward, *Naturalism and Agnosticism.* 2 vols. Black, vol. II, 1899, p. 129.

† See his article, 'The Ultimate Basis of Theism', in *Contentio Veritatis* by 'Six Oxford Tutors'. Murray, 1902, p. 21.

We cannot understand the world of which we form a part except upon this assumption of a Universal Mind for which, or in which, all that is exists. Such is the line of thought which presents itself to some of us as the one absolutely convincing and logically irrefragable argument for establishing the existence of God.

If now it be agreed that God is the Universal Mind in Whom and for Whom all that is exists, we need to explain the relation of finite minds to Him. Our enquiry began with the individual as the conscious subject of experience; and we reached public knowledge by coordinating his experience with that of other subjects. Each one of us as an individual thus belongs to 'the many': interaction with others is a primary factor in our mental lives. But the world as it exists for the many is a Universe, not a Multiverse. There is, in fact, a unity of being to which the many belong and there is a unity of ends to which their diverse strivings lead. This unity must be God, "the ultimate source of their being and the ultimate end of their ends*". We who constitute the many exist *in* God and, in so far as we are fellow-workers with Him, in seeking the Good we exist *for* God. But unless our daily experience is an illusion we are free spirits: we have some power of choice between different courses and that power enables us to create means to the ends which we seek. It is, then, natural to think of God not only as having intelligence and will but also as having created us for His own ends—ends which are the reason for the existence of the world. Of course such creation, if only because of the measure of freedom in ourselves with which it is associated, implies self-limitation on the part of God. It is in fact true, as Spinoza said, that all determination implies negation. The omnipotence which Christian theism ascribes to God is an assertion of the fact that He is not limited from without; but God's omnipotence is not power to change the impossible into the possible. We may add that the fact of God's self-limitation offers a partial explanation of the problem of evil. If there were no evil in the world we should be, in effect, not free spirits but automata.

In thus briefly outlining my philosophical position I do not pretend that I have a final explanation of the Universe which completely suffices for myself and should satisfy every reasonable man. I feel, however, that the conclusions I have set out, and for which I shall argue, are the most satisfying that we can reach; and they are none the less worthy of respect in that they have behind them the intellectual and moral weight of the Christian tradition.

* James Ward, *The Realm of Ends*. Cambridge University Press, 1911, p. 442.

§ 438. *A possible cosmos of monads.*

As a pendant to the philosophical scheme outlined in the previous paragraph, I would mention as an attractive possibility certain speculative ideas suggested by the Monadology of Leibniz. We cannot pretend, as was pointed out in § 420, that our minds differ *in toto* from those of 'the lower animals'. Animals, at least from the amoeba upwards, are to some extent psychical beings; and it may even be true that mind is inseparable from life. Moreover, we cannot say at what stage, if any, the organic passes downwards to the inorganic. It is possible that Spinoza was right when he wrote that "all individual things are animated, albeit in divers degrees". We have seen in §§ 168, 169 that the phenomena of radio-activity seem to imply some power of choice on the part of individual atoms. They may indeed be, not the manufactured articles of Maxwell, but psychical elements: and the laws of radio-active decomposition may be merely statistical averages such as we are familiar with in life-insurance tables.

If such a view of the material world is correct, all objects in it may be built up of primary psychical units or monads, each of which uses such freedom as it possesses to endeavour to maintain or to improve its position in the world. Complex organisms such as ourselves will not merely be complex physico-chemical mechanisms. They will result from the organisation and co-operation of monads; and thus we should have a clue to the apparently incomprehensible phenomena of response and automatic adjustment that the physiologists investigate.

Such a theory of monads is worthy of serious consideration. It gives an interpretation of the process of evolution which satisfies our instinctive desire for continuity; and it makes that process not a mere unfolding but a true epigenesis or creative synthesis resulting, at any rate in part, from the co-operation or conflict of free agents. Such creative activity on the part of monads, either singly or in organised groups, is not incompatible with theism if with James Ward we agree that "the total possibilities, however far back we go, are fixed; but within these, contingencies, however far forward we go, are open*".

Perhaps the best verdict on Monadism is that of William James†: "Speculative minds alone will take an interest in it; and metaphysics, not psychology, will be responsible for its career. That the career may be a successful one must be admitted as a possibility—a theory which

* *Loc. cit.* p. 315.
† William James, *Principles of Psychology.* 2 vols. Macmillan, vol. I, 1890, p. 180.

Leibnitz, Herbart and Lotze have taken under their protection must have some sort of a destiny ".

§ 439. *Cause.*

The notion of cause is derived from our own activity. By our volition we can (or we think that we can) cause things to happen: we can produce effects. This notion of cause and effect we transfer to the physical realm. We think of some event or process as being the cause of some other: the first is regarded as an active agent which compels the effect which we observe. In this kind of thought there is a naïvely anthropomorphic interpretation of Nature. We imagine the existence in the inorganic realm of some compulsion similar to that which we ourselves exert as conscious beings. When an effect is produced by an active agent it is convenient and usual to speak of efficient causation. Cause in the popular sense can then by contrast be used to express the fact that some particular condition results from a group of antecedent conditions. For instance, when there is the conjunction of a lighted candle and a mixture of coal-gas and air, an explosion takes place. We then say that the light has caused the explosion. But the phenomenon is an example of invariable sequence. No active agent is necessarily involved: the effect is not due to efficient causation.

One of Hume's great contributions to thought was to make clear that we do not get efficient causation in the physical realm. When we consider the operation of causes we are never able, he says*, to discover any power or necessary connection, any quality which binds the effect to the cause and renders the one an infallible consequence of the other. We only find that the one does actually, in fact, follow the other.

Notwithstanding Hume's teaching, the belief that efficient causes could be discovered in the inorganic realm lasted long among men of science. The mutual attraction of material bodies was conceived to be caused by a force inherent in matter. It was possible to measure the effect of this force; but the force itself, the cause of the attraction, was regarded anthropomorphically as a sort of desire on the part of matter to draw other matter towards itself†.

---

* Hume, *Enquiry Concerning Human Understanding.* Sect. VII, Pt. I. See, for instance, *The Philosophical Works of David Hume*, edited by Green and Grose. 4 vols. Longmans, vol. IV, 1875, p. 52.

† One can find this idea in Copernicus' epoch-making *De Revolutionibus Orbium Coelestium* of the year 1543: "I think that weight is nothing but a certain natural appetite with which the Divine Architect of the Universe has endowed pieces of matter, so that they unite in the form of a globe".

Only gradually has it become clear that organised science consists of descriptions of the regular sequences of Nature. Its 'laws' do not imply the existence of efficient causation within any non-psychical realm; and no such efficient causation can be discovered. Similarly, in the observed sequences of Nature and in the so-called laws of Nature there is no logical necessity. Such logical necessity only exists in the realm of thought. In this realm, of course, it may link together concepts which correspond to observed phenomena. But laws of Nature are descriptions of uniform sequences: they are not self-existent and no inherent necessity attaches to them. According to Kant*, "so far as cause and effect have any possible interpretation in terms of experience, they mean regular constant sequence of events in time, and nothing more".

Among the modern men of science who have cogently argued in favour of the point of view just adumbrated, Mach deserves especial mention. A characteristic passage may be quoted from an address given in the year 1894†:

It is said, description leaves the sense of causality unsatisfied. In fact, many imagine that they understand motions better when they picture to themselves the pulling forces; and yet, *the accelerations*, the facts, accomplish more, without superfluous additions. I hope that the science of the future will discard the idea of cause and effect, as being formally obscure; and in my feeling that these ideas contain a strong tincture of fetishism, I am certainly not alone. The more proper course is, *to regard the abstract determinative elements of a fact as interdependent*, in a purely logical way, as the mathematician or geometer does. True, by comparison with the will, forces are brought nearer to our feeling: but it may be that ultimately the will itself will be made clearer by comparison with the accelerations of masses.

Mach's ideas run counter to the general belief that it is the duty of science to 'explain' Nature. What science does is to frame conceptual schemes which are agreeable to human reason. But sequences can be rational for us even though we do not import into them the notion of efficient cause or imagine that they can be represented by some mechanical model. Belief in the utility of such models was general in the nineteenth century. Thus Lord Kelvin said: "I never satisfy myself till I can make a mechanical model of a thing. If I can make such a model I can understand it". Not unnaturally he complained that he could not "get the electro-magnetic theory of light". May it not, how-

* R. Adamson, *The Development of Modern Philosophy*. 2 vols. Blackwood, vol. I, 1903, p. 200.

† Ernst Mach, *Popular Scientific Lectures*. Translated by T. J. McCormack. Open Court Publishing Company, 1895, p. 253.

ever, be argued that, though mechanical models are familiar, they are not especially intelligible? All observed sequences are facts of experience. None can be explained, for neither logical necessity nor efficient causation is applicable to them. They are simply familiar or unfamiliar.

When sequences which we at first think strange cease to surprise us, a feeling of comparative ease of mind simulates understanding. From such sequences we build conceptual schemes. These schemes must logically cohere with others which we have been led to form; and in this way the Universe is felt to be capable of description by rational schemes. In this connection we may again quote Mach's words. In an address* given in the year 1882 he said:

> Those elements of an event which we call 'cause and effect' are certain salient features of it, which are important for its mental reproduction. Their importance wanes and the attention is transferred to fresh characters the moment the event or experience in question becomes familiar. If the connection of such features strikes us as a necessary one, it is simply because the interpolation of certain intermediate links with which we are very familiar, and which possess, therefore, higher authority for us, is often attended with success in our explanations. That *ready* experience fixed in the mosaic of the mind with which we meet new events, Kant calls an innate concept of the understanding.

We have admitted that science has rightly discarded the notion of efficient causes. Such do not enter into her descriptions of Nature. But we must not therefore conclude that cause must be banished from Nature. Whenever conscious agents are active, efficient causes exist. The typical scientific scheme is a construct of the mind from which efficient causes are eliminated because variations due to individual activity are excluded. If God were an efficient cause in Nature His action would not necessarily be uniform; but such action of His as was not uniform would lie outside the realm to which our scientific schemes apply. Furthermore, we should assume that any observed uniformity of sequence did not directly imply His causal control, whereas from the standpoint of theism He is the cause of all the sequences which we observe. In brief, science is ideally an elaborate network of uniform sequences which form a single continuous whole in which there is no element of contingency, nothing casual or fortuitous. Moreover, the conception of efficient cause lies outside the realm of science because the man of science picks from the apparent chaos of Nature orderly sequences and, without pretending to say why such sequences exist, formulates corresponding laws.

* Ernst Mach, *loc. cit.* p. 198.

§ 440. *Substance.*

An important factor in naïve realism is belief in substance as the permanent substratum of things. Material substance is thus thought of as the essential foundation of material bodies: it is, as it were, a thing in itself which carries the various properties or qualities by which in perception we separate one object from another.

In medieval ecclesiastical philosophy the doctrine of substance was accepted; and a distinction between the substance and the properties or 'accidents' of material things was used to explain and defend the doctrine of transubstantiation.

Locke (1632–1704), in his famous *Essay concerning Human Understanding*, which first appeared in the year 1690, accepted and criticised the concept of substance*.

When we talk or think of any particular sort of corporeal substances, such as horse, stone, etc., though the idea we have of either of them be but the complication or collection of those several simple ideas of sensible qualities, which we used to find united in the thing called horse or stone; yet, *because we cannot conceive how they should subsist alone, nor one in another*, we suppose them existing in, and supported by, some common object; which support we denote by the name substance, though it be certain we have no clear or distinct idea of that thing we suppose a support.

As it became clear that at all events some qualities of material bodies were not independent of the percipient, a division into primary and secondary qualities was made. The primary qualities were supposed to belong to the object itself: among such were extension and motion: these, like substance itself, were asserted to be independent of the percipient. On the other hand, colour, smell and sound were deemed secondary qualities which, as we should now say, resulted from the interaction of subject and object in the subject-object relation. The distinction between primary and secondary qualities has gradually proved untenable and belief in the existence of substance has worn away with the advance alike of the analysis of perception and of modern physical theory.

We can say with confidence that the only things of which we have positive knowledge are subjects with intrinsic qualities. Kant, who accepted the idea of substance, denied that substantiality could be predicated of the conscious subject of experience. Leibniz, among others of his predecessors, had argued in favour of the substantiality of the soul: he thus postulated a permanent substratum for the conscious

* John Locke, *An Essay concerning Human Understanding.* Ed. A. C. Fraser. 2 vols. Clarendon Press, vol. I, 1894, p. 395 [Bk II, Ch. XXIII, § 4].

individual, and in this way established the immortality of the soul. Such a proof of the doctrine of immortality was of little value inasmuch as atoms were equally believed to possess a substantial basis and thus to have a like immortality. But there is no justification for the belief that the unity and continuity of the conscious individual who is the subject of experience are due to the existence in him of a permanent substratum of which thought, will and feeling are properties. The activity of a conscious individual shapes, as we say, his character; and because such activity is continuous it leads to the continuous change and development of psychical qualities. All consciousness is thus dynamic, but substance is essentially a static conception.

Yet it might be argued that precisely in matter we need to postulate such a static substratum as substance is defined to be. To that argument it may be replied that substance is never given in experience. It could not be so given, for it is incapable of being directly perceived. We reach the concept of it by stripping away in thought all the properties of material objects. In the end there is nothing left for perception: what remains is a mere logical abstraction. I would remind you that we cannot have knowledge of a thing unless it changes or produces changes in other things. It was pointed out in a previous lecture that we only see an object when light is producing complicated changes in its surface atoms; and this is but one illustration of the general truth that the properties which we attribute to things result from the changes which occur in them. Thus substance, if it existed, could not possibly enter into experience; and the concept appears to be the result of some instinctive but imaginary need. As a concept, moreover, it deserves the judgment passed by Berkeley on the similar concept of absolute space: "its attributes are negative, it is mere nothing". With this conclusion Hume would appear to have been in substantial agreement. In a short essay, *On the Immortality of the Soul*, not published until after his death, he wrote: "But just metaphysics teaches us that the notion of substance is wholly confused and imperfect; and that we have no other idea of any substance, than as an aggregate of particular qualities inhering in an unknown something". Hume concluded that "matter, therefore, and spirit, are at bottom equally unknown".

Mach's attitude towards the notion of substance may be seen by a quotation from the address* of the year 1882 which has just been cited.

In mentally separating a body from the changeable environment in which it moves, what we really do is to extricate a group of sensations on which our

* Ernst Mach, *loc. cit.* p. 200.

thoughts are fastened and which is of relatively greater stability than the others, from the stream of all our sensations. Absolutely unalterable this group is not. . . . But because we can separate from the group every single member without the body's ceasing to be for us the same, we are easily led to believe that after abstracting all the members something additional would remain. It thus comes to pass that we form the notion of a substance distinct from its attributes, of a thing-in-itself, whilst our sensations are regarded merely as symbols or indications of the properties of this thing-in-itself. But it would be much better to say that bodies or things are compendious mental symbols for groups of sensations—symbols that do not exist outside of thought.

In denying the existence of substance we do not of necessity take the pure phenomenalist attitude of Berkeley's idealism and deny the existence of matter. Matter is, in a sense, the logical residuum of corporeal bodies: but it is not a permanent substratum devoid of qualities. It has the primary quality of inertia which gives us the quantitative measure of the mass of a material body. Kant held that unity of consciousness, and therefore experience itself, were only possible through some permanent or enduring phenomenon which serves as a substratum to changes in the objects of perception. Further, he attributed quantity to such substratum or substance and said that in all change the quantity of substance in Nature is neither increased nor diminished*. Here we have a view which seems to adumbrate the principle of the conservation of mass now subsumed under the more inclusive principle of conservation of energy.

Doubtless, after all that we have said, there will be those who assert that, if the objective existence of matter be granted, we must allow that it has substance. They will urge that there *must* be behind it some permanent substratum. At the present day those who have this instinctive feeling must hope to find their substratum in the protons and electrons of physical theory. Yet the whole trend of modern physical speculation is not favourable to such hopes. If protons and electrons can annihilate one another to form radiation, the substance postulated must be a substratum of the energy, dissociated from matter, of which radiation consists. Our instinctive need of a substratum for such energy is not strong. If, however, matter is rightly regarded as but a symptom of the curvature of space-time, then, as was suggested at the end of Lecture VI, we seem to have reduced matter to geometrical form without substance, unless indeed we regard space-time as substantial;

* See Immanuel Kant's *Critique of Pure Reason*. Translated by F. Max Müller. Macmillan, 1907, pp. 149 and 773. That Kant regarded matter (or mass) as a substance may be inferred from a statement as to the weight of smoke (*loc. cit.* p. 151).

and I do not see what arguments can be advanced for such a view. In short, the concept of substance can profitably be excluded alike from physics and psychology. It will remain as it were petrified, in the obsolete theology of transubstantiation.

The present tendency to return to this dogma, which is to be observed in the Church of England, is an interesting example of how beliefs, well below the general level of culture of a community, will revive at periods of religious decay and moral disorder. It is true that to-day in the Church of England belief in transubstantiation will, as a rule, be formally repudiated and replaced by an assertion of the Real Presence of Christ attached to, or inherent in, the consecrated elements of the Holy Communion. Nevertheless, the Roman Church is still committed to the view that the substance of the bread and wine is in consecration annihilated and replaced by a spiritual presence. Perhaps we can allow that Roman theologians have a better case than their Anglican imitators, in that a bad theory is better than none at all. But that a spiritual presence should appear in, or instead of the 'substance' of, an inanimate material object as the result of certain acts and words of a priest is incredible. Naturally, every experimental test* fails to reveal it. With this fact we can conjoin the truism that a spiritual change which no one has the spiritual capacity to perceive belongs to the realm of mythology. Fortunately, this particular revival of obsolete theology in defence of superstition is unlikely to hamper scientific investigation. What Hobson† calls "medieval prejudices relating to occult properties of supposed substrata behind phenomena" can in the future be ignored. Religion and science interact in other and more vital ways.

§ 441. *Phenomenalism.*

Increasingly those men of science who explore the foundations of scientific theory accept what is known as phenomenalism. Historians of philosophy trace the origin of this view of scientific knowledge to Protagoras; but in modern times Bishop Berkeley, in a number of works and especially in his *New Theory of Vision* (1709), first advanced considerations which have led to the adoption of the phenomenalist standpoint.

Rival doctrines of space were of primary importance in this development. For Kant, as we have seen, space was a subjective form of perception and geometrical axioms were intuitive. Thus for him these

---

* Such tests must, of course, be psychological and not chemical.

† E. W. Hobson, *The Domain of Natural Science*. Cambridge University Press, 1923, p. 64.

axioms had a transcendental nature and were independent of the presentations of space given in experience. The influence of Kant's synthetic philosophy has been deservedly great, and during the larger part of the nineteenth century his views of space commanded general assent. But gradually, as we have seen, it became clear with the rise of non-Euclidean geometry that Berkeley was right in regarding our spatial concepts as the result of experience. These concepts have taken shape because of the interaction between man's psycho-physiological organisation and his environment.

Those who accept the phenomenalist position urge that by reason of a similar interaction the whole of scientific theory has been established. We observe phenomena which are, as we believe, derived from physical processes. What is common to all our observations we usually assume to belong to the processes themselves. But this assumption is unnecessary. All that is necessary is that from common knowledge derived from perception we should frame simple concepts. Such simple concepts, by the synthetic activity of the mind, are then built into schemes to represent such classes of sequences among phenomena as are regular and admit of precise description. We thus get scientific theories. Phenomenalism insists that into such theories only those assumptions or distinctions should be introduced which make some difference to observable phenomena.

For a full discussion of all that is implied in phenomenalism the writings of such men as Kirchhoff, Mach and Karl Pearson should be studied. It may here be remarked that strict phenomenalism cannot be established. We must admit that it is of the nature of an unattainable ideal, inasmuch as we contravene its fundamental principle in rejecting solipsism and assuming the existence of other observers, other subjects of experience, than ourselves. Most certainly we cannot deny that if such assumed observers were mere phantoms the fact would make no difference to observable phenomena.

Though strict phenomenalism is unattainable, a scientific theory constructed, so far as is possible, on a phenomenalist basis will eliminate unnecessary and possibly erroneous assumptions. Those who create or use it will not assert that its concepts are real entities. Natural science, in fact, is neutral in the dispute as to whether 'things in themselves' give rise to percepts or whether *per contra* percepts constitute all that is real in material objects. Science has no need of the assertion that the distinctions which our psychical organisation leads us to make correspond to similar distinctions in the objective continuum. Our working hypothesis is merely that from experience we can separate out sequences to form the conceptual schemes which we term scientific theories. These theories must be logically coherent and they must adequately represent what is observed. They must also have a predictive power. They will then give us such understanding of some particular range of perception as we can hope for. They will not in themselves enable us to solve ultimate philosophical problems, though those who consider such problems will be the more advantageously placed for their task in that they will have organised conceptual schemes on which to base argument.

Yet no scientific theory will enable us to say, for example, that genes are 'real' or that Bohr's or some alternative theory of the atom is 'true'. The gene is a mental construction which summarises what we believe to be a group of observed facts. Thus we think of a gene as a particular chromosome-locus where a change can take place which affects in a definite manner certain characters of the organism derived from the germ-cell containing the gene. We may picture a gene as merely a complex chemical molecule; but, in doing so, we create a concept which does not hint at the reason of the manner in which the gene acts. If the 'real' is for us rational, such a gene is not 'real'. Similarly, Bohr's model of the atom is a mental construction designed to summarise certain observed facts. At present the model is inadequate, inasmuch as we have to postulate behaviour which is irreconcilable with Newtonian dynamics. When we are able to build up a scheme of infra-atomic mechanics which explains all the observed facts, alike of infra-atomic and of ordinary mechanics, we shall rest satisfied. But whether the scheme will be 'true', in that it will express what happens in an assumed objective continuum, is not a problem for scientific investigation.

It should be added that a great part of the domain of experience does not yield percepts that can be combined into scientific schemes. We have good reason to believe that increasingly particular domains of Nature can be widened so as to be included in such schemes; but we have no reason to assume that in the end all the processes of Nature will be even theoretically united into a single coherent theory.

§ 442. *Materialism and agnostic naturalism.*

We will for the present forbear to ask whether the popular dualism of mind and matter is erroneous. We do, however, assert that both psychical and physical factors are present in experience: and it is natural to enquire as to whether one or the other is primary. Assuming for the moment that it is legitimate to use the term Nature for that which is non-psychical, ought we to regard Spirit as derived from Nature or Nature from Spirit? Expressing ourselves in the language of common use, we ask whether mind or matter is the fundamental reality? The materialism of the naïve realist asserts that matter is the primal real substance. The agnostic naturalism of such men as Huxley and Spencer asserted the primacy and independence of matter regarded as a phenomenon. Ward gave the following description of such naturalism*:

Nature, to which we entirely belong, is an unbroken continuity of necessary causes, and of these our mental conditions are simply the inefficient symbols. We have no knowledge how these symbols are connected with those causes, but we are confident that volitions do not enter into this chain of causation at all.

To shew that this description does not misrepresent the position we may cite Huxley's words†:

If these positions (Huxley's own) are well based, it follows that our mental conditions are simply the symbols in consciousness of the changes which take place automatically in the organism; and that, to take an extreme illustration, the feeling we call volition is not the cause of a voluntary act, but the symbol of that state of the brain which is the immediate cause of that act. We are conscious automata, endowed with free will in the only intelligible sense of that much-abused term—inasmuch as in many respects we are able to do as we like —but none the less parts of the great series of causes and effects which, in unbroken continuity, composes that which is, and has been, and shall be—the sum of existence.

Agnostic naturalism may not unfairly be described as a refined type of materialism. It differs from materialism in that it regards matter as "a name for the unknown and hypothetical cause of states of our own consciousness"; but it assigns to this unknown cause primacy and independence. Further, in this philosophic system it is assumed that all the changes of the unknown and hypothetical cause can be arranged in a single deterministic scheme, an elaborate series of sequences such that the whole aggregate of conditions at any time determines the conditions at any subsequent time. Concomitant with such material changes as occur in certain nervous centres of conscious beings is an

* James Ward, *Naturalism and Agnosticism*. 2 vols. Black, vol. II, 1899, p. 212.

† T. H. Huxley, *Collected Essays*. 9 vols. Macmillan, vol. I, 1894, p. 244. These words of Huxley are quoted alike by James Ward (*loc. cit.*) and by William James (*Principles of Psychology*. 2 vols. Macmillan, vol. I, 1890, p. 131). The latter also gives a quotation from W. K. Clifford to shew that his position was substantially the same. James' criticism takes the form of an ironical account of the origin of Shakespeare's *Hamlet*.

epiphenomenon called consciousness. It does not effect the sequences, though we may fancy that it does. We believe that our wills have effects in the material world, but the belief is an illusion: the sequence which immediately leads to the so-called effect is accompanied by the epiphenomenon which we misinterpret as a cause of the change. Such, in brief, are the fundamental postulates or principles of agnostic naturalism.

The points of view described by the terms materialism, agnostic naturalism and mechanistic determinism are variations of a metaphysical standpoint which is especially common among students of science. This standpoint was subjected to damaging criticism by James Ward in his Gifford Lectures on *Naturalism and Agnosticism*, published at the close of last century. As a result one often finds an assumption in the literature of religious apologetics that such a standpoint is no longer intellectually respectable. Now naturalism is not without its internal contradictions, and I personally think that fatal objections can be brought against all positions to which it is allied. But it must be remembered that no metaphysical scheme exists against which arguments of weight cannot be adduced: and the contempt with which naturalism is sometimes treated is unfair.

A primary objection to it is that in it matter is regarded as a something inferred from perception and that mind is regarded as an epiphenomenon supervening on material change. Yet all that we know of material change is given by the sequences of phenomena perceived by mind. Thus we have the postulate that mind is the mere concomitant of inferences from its own perceptions. Using slightly different language we may say that the sequences of physical change, which in natural science are represented by deterministic schemes, are psychical events and the schemes are psychical constructs. That the interaction of hypothetical "things in themselves", assumed to be the origin of these psychical constructs, should give rise to all psychical activity, including that by which such interaction is assumed to be perceived, may well be doubted. Assuming that such doubts can be resolved or safely ignored, we will pass to further considerations of the naturalistic standpoint. But before we do so we will briefly recall some historical landmarks in the theory of mechanistic determinism.

§ 443. *Mechanistic determinism.*

The mechanical theory of the Universe or, as its principle is sometimes called, mechanistic determinism, represents a belief which has been widely held by men of science. It owes much to the brilliant success of that determination of motions of bodies comprising the solar system of which Newton laid the foundations in the *Principia*. Fitly, one of the best descriptions of the character and range of the mechanical theory of the Universe is due to the great mathematician and astronomer Laplace (1749–1827): it comes from the beginning of his *Philosophical Essay on Probabilities*, first published in the year 1812*.

We ought to regard the present state of the universe as the effect of its antecedent state and as the cause of the state which is to follow. An intelligent being who at a given instant knew all the forces animating Nature and the relative positions of the beings within it would, if his intelligence were sufficiently capacious to analyse these data, include in a single formula the movements of the largest bodies of the universe and those of its lightest atom. Nothing would be uncertain for him: the future as well as the past would be present to his eyes.

Laplace adds that "the human mind in the perfection which it has been able to give to astronomy offers a feeble suggestion of such an intelligence". E. du Bois-Reymond (1818–1896), in a famous address at Leipzig in the year 1872, *On the Limits of Natural Knowledge*, described the possibilities of the world-formula of Laplace. The intelligent being, able to construct and use the formula, he assured his hearers, would tell us who was the Man in the Iron Mask and when England should have burnt her last piece of coal. Of only one problem should we be ignorant—the explanation of consciousness.

The enthusiasm of du Bois-Reymond represented the apotheosis of the Laplacean world-formula. Many students of science and others were captivated by the belief that every process of change in the whole realm of Nature could be exhibited in some scheme fashioned by the methods of rational mechanics. But the critical investigation of recent decades has made the mechanical theory of the Universe seem less probable to modern men of science than to their predecessors of the nineteenth century.

Some adverse considerations may be briefly stated. In the first place mechanistic determinism took its rise from the fact that in experience we can delimit approximately isolated regions in which sequences of events can be described by a finite formula. But such regions are never absolutely isolated: the known formula is thus only approximate. We may speculate that it can, however, be included in Laplace's

* See *Oeuvres Complètes de Laplace*. T. VII. Gauthier-Villars, 1886, p. vi. This volume of the complete works is a reprint of the 1820 edition of the *Analytical Theory of Probabilities*, to which the *Essay* served as an Introduction.

hypothetical world-formula. But, as we do so, we assume that all experience can be exhibited as ordered sequences, an assumption for which there is little justification in our present knowledge. Further, the world-formula would have to be finite in the sense that into it there would enter only a finite number of functions each of which is determined by a finite set of rules. If the cosmos is itself finite we can postulate the existence of such a finite formula on the assumption that conscious beings cannot alter the course of Nature; but in an infinite cosmos the existence of any such formula would be very doubtful. Further, it should be observed that Laplace's formula has such a character that the future can be determined by a knowledge of the past alone. Now deterministic schemes can be formulated in which the future cannot be determined simply by a knowledge of the past. In these schemes, as Hobson* points out, there is a ground more general than the principle of causation; and if any such scheme is possible in Nature, Laplace's intelligent being would not be able to discover it.

Once again, though Laplace spoke of cause and effect, he had in mind the sequences of the perceptual world. The notion of purpose did not enter into his scheme and indeed it cannot enter into any world-formula. Such a formula must be imagined as a system of functional equations and must of necessity be purposeless. Yet we have seen that it is hardly probable that biological evolution can ever be so presented as to dispense with the notion of purposive activity. Though natural selection be a purely mechanical process, and though the alleged tendency of an organism to diverge still further in a chosen direction of change might be, were it true, a persistence analogous to inertia, yet the origin of mutations seems to be an effect of efficient causation. At any rate mutations due to changes in the genes represent, so far as our present knowledge goes, contingency and not uniformity. If, as most biologists would probably assume, laws regulating the production of mutations will be ultimately discovered, we shall be confronted by what are in a final analysis inexplicable sequences behind which we must postulate purposive activity. It seems impossible that uniformities of this type could be included in any such general formula as we reach in rational mechanics.

But the final argument against mechanistic determinism is the existence in the world of conscious beings with freedom of action. Such freedom must be an illusion and mental process must be a purely

* E. W. Hobson, *The Domain of Natural Science.* Cambridge University Press, 1923, pp. 84, 85.

secondary consequence of mere sequences of physical change, if the mechanical theory of the Universe is valid. There can on this view be no meaning in reason, no pursuit of truth or goodness; and all talk of high aspirations and ideal standards of conduct must be idle.

Of course, those who accept mechanistic determinism are not discouraged by such conclusions. They set aside as mistaken all the inward experience which from hour to hour of our waking life negatives the notion that we are conscious automata. They act thus because they would have us believe that, in extracting merely quantitative aspects of natural phenomena and building them into a scheme of relations, we can reach all that is fundamental in such phenomena. But why should all the qualitative aspects, which are perforce ignored, count for nothing? We can give no quantitative measures of the things that matter most in human life: they will not therefore enter into Laplace's world-formula: to that extent it cannot fail to be defective.

When Laplace wrote the statement which we have been considering, he had in mind such laws as the laws of mechanics formulated by Newton and made by him fundamental in determining the motions of the planets. To this type Einstein's relativity formulae belong. But the discovery of entropy in the middle of the nineteenth century led to the notion of statistical laws: of such the second law of thermodynamics is the outstanding example. Into this second class of laws the idea of probability enters. Such laws are true, not absolutely, but because the chances of their failure are infinitesimal. It may be that for this reason they differ profoundly from the laws of Newton. On the other hand, the uncertainty-relations of Heisenberg suggest that the Newtonian laws themselves are essentially of the statistical type and that they are true, not of individual particles, but of large aggregates for which the probability of their failure is negligible. Laws reversible in time, like those of Newton, cannot adequately describe the progress of our Universe. Whether statistical laws such as the second law of thermodynamics, which must also enter into any description, give an opportunity for the free exercise of human activity we shall consider in § 445.

§ 444. *The problem of consciousness: psycho-physical parallelism.*

The origin and explanation of consciousness are among the most perplexing of all problems. All origins are shrouded in mystery. But what consciousness is, whence it has come and why it ends, these questions leave some of us the more bewildered the more we think of them.

Somehow or another consciousness is associated with the brain; and the association of special regions of the brain with definite mental processes has been established with considerable accuracy. The statement that "the brain secretes thought as the liver secretes bile" was probably intended by its author* to be somewhat impertinent. Though it be agreed that mental changes are invariable concomitants of physical changes in the brain, there is no analogy between a material substance such as bile and an imponderable like thought. Invariable concomitance can hardly coexist with absolute independence: there must then be some relation between physical and psychical processes in a conscious organism. On the dualistic assumption that matter and mind are absolutely disparate the problem presented by invariable concomitance is intractable. But, however we approach it, it is singularly difficult. As William James† said: "The ultimate of ultimate problems, of course, in the study of the relations of thought and brain, is to understand why and how such disparate things are connected at all".

Psycho-physical parallelism is the doctrine that there are two disparate series in consciousness. One series is physical, such as a physicist or physiologist examining the brain would investigate. The other series is psychical and a psychologist could describe it. The two series are said to proceed step by step, to correspond element to element, though the detailed nature of such correspondence is hard to define. Which of the two series is primary? It is certainly difficult to imagine that the mental state comes first and affects the associated physical change in the brain. If the blood supplied by the heart to the brain is not oxygenated complete loss of consciousness is rapid. Three or four deep breaths of pure nitrogen will produce complete loss of consciousness, presumably because the brain ceases to function as a physiological organism. Thus mental activity must apparently be secondary to physiological. If then one or the other of our two series must be primary, we seem forced to assume that the physical series is fundamental and that the associated psychical series is derivative. If further we believe that the physical realm is a determinate mechanism we are forced to believe

* Karl Vogt appears to have coined this phrase. But, before him, Cabanis (1757–1808) declared that "impressions arrive at the brain and make it enter into activity just as food, falling into the stomach, excites it to secretion". Huxley ascribed to Cabanis the actual words of Vogt. (*Vide* Huxley, *Hume.* Macmillan, 1879, p. 80.)

† William James, *Principles of Psychology.* 2 vols. Macmillan, 1890, vol. I, p. 177.

that successive elements in psychical experience belong to a deterministic system. In this way naturalism arose.

Psycho-physical parallelism thus compels the belief that we are conscious automata. Our thoughts must be determined by equations similar to, but more complex than, those which give changes in the motion or temperature of bodies. Our belief that we have freedom of choice must be an illusion. If molecular changes in the brain are the causes of states of consciousness, the feeling of volition is not the cause of a voluntary act: it is merely a symbol of that state of the brain which is the immediate cause of the act. Consciousness is but an epiphenomenon of the organism.

We need not repeat the objections already urged against such a standpoint. We may ask, however, why if the physical series is complete in itself, mental states should be produced by such a series. How can one of the products of a complete system be something outside itself? And we cannot too often urge that, if we are not efficient agents who can cause things to happen, purposive activity is an illusion; and spontaneity must then be banished from the psychical realm. But we are sensitive; and as we receive impressions we act with definite ends in view. These truths surely are fundamental in experience: there can be nothing more fundamental, more real, than such knowledge. If any theory demands that we shall discard such primary factors in experience, we must conclude that the theory is at fault.

Where then is psycho-physical parallelism at fault? I would reply that the error in it lies in the dualism of mind and matter on which it is based and against which we have previously argued in our analysis of experience. Mind and matter are not two disparate substances: but the physical and psychical series are two aspects of a single process. Neither series is primary: neither can be regarded as the cause of the other. So much would appear to be certain. But unfortunately we must admit that, of the nature of the fundamental process in which thinking is correlated to brain-changes, we are wholly ignorant.

§ 445. *Freedom and natural law.*

We have now given reasons which lead to the rejection of psycho-physical parallelism. If we were to assume that there are two independent series of concomitant changes, one psychical and one non-psychical, experimental evidence would appear to forbid the belief that the psychical is primary; and belief in the primacy of the non-psychical would lead to the conclusion that we are but conscious automata for whom ideal aims are but vain words and reason without meaning. We affirm therefore that the psychical and the physical are two aspects of some unknown unity. But we are then forced to admit that it is difficult to see how any scheme in which this unity is involved can on its physical side be deterministic. Apparently 'mind' or the psychical must interfere with mechanical 'laws' and thus destroy the generally assumed independence of the physical world.

Experimental science gives no evidence of the existence of such interference. The law of conservation of energy appears to be accurate when living beings are included in any finite region to which it is applied. Now it is quite possible that mental processes do no work when they interfere with a physical system; and thus mental decisions will not upset the principle of conservation of energy. But, none the less, if a mental decision has any effect at all in the physical cosmos, the dynamical equations of that conceptually isolated part of the cosmos in which the decision takes effect will be changed. In other words, the established laws of dynamics as applied to the region in question will be at fault. Somewhere or another there will be an action to which there corresponds no reaction; and, consequently, Newton's third law of motion will not hold good.

We seem compelled to conclude that our experimental science is in error and that sooner or later we shall discover that conscious beings can interfere with those formulations of experience which we term natural law. Schemes based upon such law are merely descriptive. All that has actually been established is that, in Hobson's words, "tracts of phenomena can be found which are sufficiently represented for certain purposes by means of deterministic schemes". The mind chooses tracts which can be thus represented. Its schemes are not arbitrary, for they are prescribed by experience. But by the very act of choice the mind brings its own desire for simplicity or continuity into the laws which it frames. It is therefore highly probable that the physical world is more varied and less calculable than we force it to appear to be in our conceptions.

Laplace told Napoleon that in his (Laplace's) system of the world there was no need for the hypothesis of God. We may add that in that world also there is no place for the creative activity of man. The mechanistic scientist of the nineteenth century, in fact, made a paradise of intelligibility from which he necessarily excluded himself.

But while I believe that all such contentions are sound, it must be emphasised that we have no evidence that volition can interfere with the working of a mechanical system which includes a conscious being. Until such evidence can be discovered we have no conclusive answer to those who assert that human consciousness is but a by-product of processes of change in the physical world which it is powerless to influence. In §227 we referred to the possibility that the Heisenberg uncertainty-relations offer a loophole through which volition can enter to modify the rigidity of the dynamics of physical systems which include a conscious being. The Heisenberg relations undoubtedly shew that, in regard to such ultimate entities as electrons, we cannot observe the present without changing it. A complete knowledge of the present state of the Universe would include the determination of the positions and momenta of all the particles within it. Such knowledge cannot be obtained; and the fundamental assumption of Laplace's scheme of mechanistic determinism set out in §443, though it seemed reasonable when it was enunciated, cannot rightly be made.

Those of us who are convinced that the freedom of the will is not illusory are naturally sure that some loophole for volition will be found; and the idea that a few units of action may be all that are required to operate some highly important switch within the mind is attractive. If all dynamical laws are statistical, an operation involving merely a few units of action *might* escape from their control. But I doubt whether physiologists are in a position to say that important decisions of the will can be made, and be made effectual, by minute transfers of action. If, however, such a physiological fact be true, there seems the possibility of a mechanism by which statistical laws might be evaded. But perhaps it is better merely to say that the Heisenberg uncertainty-relations reveal the existence of a region of indeterminacy within which some principle, at present unknown, may operate to produce, when consciousness is present, effects which would not be observed in the inorganic realm.

Perhaps, however, the formidable difficulties, which arise when we set natural law in opposition to human freedom, are of our own making. We discover natural law not because Nature is obviously an orderly system but because we labour and struggle to extract order from the chaos of experience. Natural law is a result obtained when man works towards an end. Thus what is primary in scientific discovery is our mental activity: the physical world is raw material. We have hitherto only succeeded in thus imposing law upon a small fraction of Nature's domain: by far the greater part has not yielded to our endeavour. Thus the belief that the Universe is a single realm of law remains a hope and a desire, an unconfirmed hypothesis. We make it because we are driven to such an action by our own interest for law and order, by the fact that our own experience is a unity. Because we are children of Nature, because our spirit is somehow akin to the Spirit for Whom and in Whom Nature exists, we may hope to succeed in our endeavour and to some extent to justify our belief that the unity of Nature is the counterpart of the lesser unity of our individual experience. But the scientific schemes which we postulate are obtained by eliminating the individual. To get them we smooth out that which separates any unit from its type. If there is in Nature some efficient cause, which would shew itself by producing varieties and breaking free from uniformity, such efficient cause will not be apparent in the conceptual schemes which we impose upon Nature. Thus efficient causes must lie outside our schemes: if they were active we should eliminate their presence as we search for law and orderly sequence. In short, we cannot expect to find Creative Mind in Nature as she is presented in our scientific textbooks, since all that implies spontaneity and creative freedom has been set aside.

Suppose that in describing a community we were to ignore all departures from regular routine, all idiosyncrasies of individuals. Suppose further that we paid comparatively little attention to anything which was a quality incapable of numerical measurement. Would our description be adequate? Could we from it infer the presence of man's spiritual activity? We are certain that any inference from so inadequate a representation would be unsatisfactory. If it were a logically justifiable conclusion it would be superficial. As we sought for fuller understanding we should have to introduce the spontaneity and spiritual values ignored in the imperfect description. Now the world of scientific description is similarly an imperfect picture. Only as we recognise the reason for its imperfection do we understand why we cannot derive from it that sense of the presence and power of the Spirit which religion finds in the world.

Lecture xviii

GOD AND OUR BELIEF IN HIS EXISTENCE

§ 446. *Scientific experience: general conclusions.*

In the last lecture we made an analysis of experience in order to ascertain how far science could be assumed to give us knowledge of the 'real' world. We reached the conclusion known as phenomenalism. The data of perception are presented to the conscious subject. He by the synthetic activity of his mind creates from uniform repetitions of like-nesses a conceptual scheme which represents some particular sequence or class of sequences. The conceptual schemes of science are satis-factory in so far as they faithfully represent what is observed. Their practical utility lies in their predictive power: they enable us to antici-pate what will happen from particular conjunctions of objects or, if we prefer so to say, in consequence of events in the objective continuum. But these schemes do not give us knowledge of a world of 'things in themselves' lying behind phenomena, though the orderly synthesis which science makes of certain types of phenomena may guide the metaphysician in his search for reality.

We have had occasion repeatedly to emphasise that science is public knowledge. The perceptions of the individual are not accepted un-critically. They are compared with the perceptions of other subjects of experience and what is common to all is made the basis of scientific theory. Without 'intersubjective intercourse' the various branches of science could not have been established.

Furthermore, science is not based upon the alleged existence of special faculties of perception in particular individuals or groups. Theoretically all normal men and women can perceive the phenomena from which the conceptual schemes of science are constructed. Such persons may need special training and it may be necessary to provide elaborate instruments for their use. But any normal individual pro-perly trained and using the appropriate instruments should obtain the common experience on which scientific theory rests. This statement, it will be noticed, conceals the assumption that scientific experiments can be repeated indefinitely. We postulate that we have merely to arrange anew a particular conjunction of objects and then at any time identically similar impressions will be received by a normal observer.

Such an arrangement, which *exactly* repeats one previously made, is, it must be admitted, an ideal which is unattainable: yet, as we approximate to it in experiments in which our numerical results are such that we can eliminate variation by statistical averages, we find our postulate the more exactly confirmed.

§ 447. *Experience and 'Spiritualism'.*

Alike the man of science and the cautious ordinary citizen tend to be critical of any alleged experience which does not depend upon conjunctions admitting of indefinite repetition or which demand supernormal perceptive power on the part of its subject. The evidence on which the faith commonly called Spiritualism is based is thus deemed inadequate by many who would welcome evidence for the survival of personality after bodily death. At *séances* scientific uniformity of repetition cannot be ensured: the spirits who are supposed to give information seem to be at times capricious. Mediums, moreover, claim to possess and to exercise super-normal powers, whereby they receive messages which others cannot get in the same way. In consequence of these facts Spiritualism cannot be regarded as a branch of scientific knowledge. There may in the medium be super-normal qualities of consciousness and especially a power (probably spasmodic and irregular) of intuitive perception of what is passing in the minds of others who are in his presence. This power, if it exists, will be a development of the herd-consciousness of gregarious mammals. With it there may possibly be associated some tendency to dissociation of personality which causes the medium to imagine that the results of telepathic perception are communications from the spirit-world. And unfortunately, as the history of the spiritualist movement shews, there is always the possibility of fraud and fraudulent assertion.

No one but a foolish dogmatist would deny that abnormal types of perception may exist in particular individuals. Such types of perception are fit material for psychological investigation. But any analysis of the more obscure processes of the human mind is necessarily difficult and conclusive results are not easily reached. Some may think that Spiritualism is not worthy of mention in these lectures. But I have felt it important to emphasise the wide difference between the types of experience on which science and spiritualism are respectively based. Midway between them lie the various types of experience commonly termed religious. They will form the topic of my next lecture.

§ 448. *The dualism of natural and supernatural rejected.*

Our discussion of the relation between scientific theory and the 'real' world was intended to achieve two ends. In the first place, we sought to shew that science must renounce all pretensions to metaphysical dogmatism. Secondly, it was desirable to point out that each of the main metaphysical positions rests upon some postulate, acceptance of which requires faith, and that none fails to give rise to special perplexities. We have urged that in science the phenomenalist attitude towards knowledge ought to be accepted. Yet none the less, though in consequence science must not claim to explore the domain of reality, it can influence metaphysical assertions. The classical example of such influence is afforded by the way in which non-Euclidean investigations have upset Kant's view of geometry: another example, of which the metaphysical consequences are still undeveloped, is given by Einstein's union of space and time into a single continuum. In fact, science provides metaphysics with material for examination and for argument; and at times new material will serve to correct unsound judgments. Science is towards metaphysics in the position of a servant: but of a servant alike independent and indispensable.

The continued existence of the various metaphysical schools to which we referred in the last lecture shews that no arguments for a particular position can be deemed decisive. On the other hand, we may fairly claim to have shewn that the case against mechanistic determinism and all allied positions which assume the primacy of matter is very strong. We pleaded in favour of a monistic* view of the cosmos: it is rightly to be regarded as a unity, but as a duality in unity in which Universal Mind or Consciousness is the subject and the world of our intermittent perception is the object in the fundamental subject-object relation. This position admittedly rests upon a postulate, an affirmation of faith, that such a relation of the world to Universal Mind is necessary, inasmuch as an object without a subject is unthinkable. On this view such finite centres of consciousness as we ourselves are replicas in very limited modes of God Who is Universal Mind. His relationship to the world reappears in a very partial form in the subject-object relation of our own experience. Such an assumption and argument serve as our chief intellectual basis for the existence of God.

* We use the terms 'monism' and 'monistic' in reference to the standpoint of the text. There is an alternative use in which all things are regarded as parts of a single real being: of this latter character is Spinoza's monism.

We assume, then, that God or Universal Mind is ultimate reality and that the world, represented to us by phenomena, exists for Him. 'Things in themselves', which give rise to phenomena, have at most a derivative and not an independent existence. With this conclusion few, if any, Christian philosophers would quarrel. But many would not like to affirm the logical corollary that the Catholic dualism of natural and supernatural cannot be maintained. Whether we regard God as immanent or transcendent or as transcending the differences implied by these words, the whole realm of Nature derives its existence from Him. It is, therefore, subject to His guidance, the domain of His activity. God has not withdrawn from Nature to revisit it at intervals when His presence is shewn in supernatural interventions. The reality behind those sequences from which we derive our laws of Nature exists in Him: in popular language the laws are His laws. To believe Him to be in the habit of breaking or suspending such laws is to put an end to any science of Nature. It is true that we accept a view of the Creative Activity of God which, in James Ward's phrase, "lets contingency into the very heart of things". But the contingency is not that of chance, of spasmodic interruption: it is shewn especially in the emergence of new types and higher values in biological evolution. In that domain of science there exist law *and* development, uniformity *and* freedom; and they form a system in which there is, as it seems to me, an inner unity. But there is in it no dualism of natural and supernatural. However grave be the difficulties raised by the problem of evil, we must affirm that the whole of creation is a revelation of God. The dilemma of § 401 confronts us again. In spite of the arguments which then seemed persuasive, we must now affirm that, when viewed in all her aspects, Nature is not to be likened to a blind giant, irrational, purposeless, knowing neither good nor evil, against whom man must wage war. She is God's process; and we are children of her womb, brought forth by the divine plan that we may become sons of God.

In view of the problems to be discussed in the next lecture it is well now to say that no right understanding of any type of religious experience can be reached unless at the outset the naïve dualism of natural and supernatural is set aside. The mystic is not one who has received a supernatural gift of perception. On the contrary, mysticism is profoundly natural. Mystics are of many races and different creeds; and whether their experience is, or is not, rightly interpreted as direct apprehension of God or of Supreme Reality, there is no reason why we should suppose it outside the realm of the natural.

If we must make contrasts within experience, the right opposition will be between the natural and the spiritual*, which will correspond to the dualism of matter and mind in Cartesian philosophy. But just as we have insisted that such a dualism is erroneous, so we ought to assert that the separation between the spiritual and the natural is artificial. Man's spiritual understanding is a part of his natural endowment, one result of the evolutionary process by which he and, be it remembered, so lowly a product as the grass of the field have been created. Whatever be the experiences by which man reaches, or is believed to reach, God, they are natural experiences. Man's apprehension of the moral law and his pursuit of truth are as natural as his bodily appetites. We admit that these latter appetites are earlier products of the evolutionary process, while man's spiritual faculties are of comparatively recent origin. But neither can be rightly thought of as being 'above Nature'.

The dualism of natural and supernatural starts, in effect, with the concession, possibly unavowed, that Nature is subject to the sway of mechanistic determinism: it then attempts to correct this false view by introducing supernaturalism. Against false assumption and mistaken correction we protest. Freedom and law actually coexist in the world. To think that God cannot combine them into a single scheme is to doubt that the world is the realm of His activity.

§ 449. *Emergence.*

As we reject dualism, we think of the Universe as a unity in which the physical, the physiological and the psychical each has its place in a single divinely planned order. Science boldly makes a reconstruction of earth's past and, from such evidence as remains, describes how at successive epochs of time new phenomena have emerged. The doctrine of emergence has assumed great importance in the writings of Professors Lloyd Morgan and Alexander. It implies a monistic view of the cosmos and gives what most of us feel to be a satisfactory description of the development of life upon the earth. But it *explains* nothing. We remain ignorant as to *why* what a moderate realist would call different kinds, and successively higher values, of reality have in turn appeared in orderly succession. I think that such a statement is true even of Alexander's important and suggestive philosophy†.

Alexander assumes that space-time is real. He postulates that in

---

* This is the contrast which St Paul makes in the familiar passage of Scripture, 1 Cor. xv, usually read at the burial of the dead.

† S. Alexander, *Space, Time, and Deity.* 2 vols. Macmillan, 1920.

the first place the physical arises from some concretion, as it were, of space-time. Then from a highly developed complexity of physical structure life emerges. Subsequently with a development of physiological structure mind emerges. From primitive mind self-consciousness with its power of conceiving and using abstract ideas has emerged. Continuously there is what Alexander calls a *nisus* towards deity, deity being the next stage higher in the emergent process. Alexander thinks of the process as self-evolving and argues that something essentially new appears at each stage. To many of us such creative activity as he describes calls for Creative Spirit. To those who accept mechanistic determinism something of the nature of a miracle must apparently occur at each stage.

Alexander's philosophy is not a mechanical theory of the Universe; but J. S. Haldane does not hesitate to say that he postulates that a miracle occurs when, for instance, organic coordination appears where it was formerly absent. Haldane himself would have us understand that, at the beginning of the evolutionary process, all that subsequently appeared was present *in embryo*, as it were. Thus the physical, he urges, is an abstraction from reality in which the coordination characteristic of life has been ignored because it is not so obvious as in what we call living organisms. Similarly, Haldane asserts that the interest and values of conscious behaviour are equally without beginning. So he is led to liken Alexander to a conjuror who produces rabbits from a hat*: "The rabbits are real enough, and not shams, but in reality they were there from the beginning".

Now, if what we call matter be a sign of the warping of space-time, the physical might emerge from it, as Alexander describes, provided we have at the outset both geometrical form and Creative Activity; but I cannot see how we can avoid postulating some Mind in which the form exists and some Principle or Power which, as it were, makes it concrete. Haldane's belief that our 'Newtonian' ideas of matter are an inadequate abstraction is probably true. But there is a vast difference between such organised interaction as we term physiological and any rudiments of it that can be observed in what we call inanimate matter. In fact, this gulf is so profound that, to my thinking, we must make the further postulate that it is bridged by Creative Mind†. When,

* J. S. Haldane, *The Sciences and Philosophy*. Hodder and Stoughton, 1928, p. 261.

† Even if the existence of elementary monads be admitted, Creative Mind would appear to be necessary for their organisation.

further, Haldane suggests that the interest and values of conscious behaviour are without beginning on an earth which was once incandescent matter, the need of Creative Mind to bring the actual out of the potential (if indeed the potential was present) becomes even more necessary.

Those who hold that the whole of Nature is the realm of Spirit or Cosmic Consciousness will need neither miracle nor the supernatural. They can say that some part of Spirit's creative process may be represented by regular sequences of events. But they must admit that no such representation of the other part is at present possible. Whether it will ultimately become possible we cannot say. To know all might be to find all regular. But a regular sequence which produced self-conscious beings from molten rock in a couple of thousand million years must needs have been guided and developed by the Creative Activity of God unless we are to accept it as an unintelligible fact. Thus I would contend that emergence describes the process by which the Creative Process of God reveals His activity more fully at successive stages of earth's history. There is the promise of life and even potential consciousness in inanimate matter, because such matter exists in and for God, and because the kind of use which He would make of it was immanent in it when it began to be. Without Him it would have been nothing: all its properties and potentialities are from Him and it is His Spirit which gives them actuality. The origin of matter, like the cause of events, is the will of God.

§ 450. *Purposiveness in emergence.*

I personally, as I have indicated, am inclined to believe that, however far investigation and experiment enable us to extend our regular sequences or laws, we shall always find irregularities remaining. Such phenomena as seem to escape from the reign of law will point directly to a contingency in Nature analogous to, but transcending, human creative activity. Yet, as was made clear in § 302, I am far from basing on such irregularities my plea that emergence is due to Spirit as Creator. I would rather urge that in the whole process, however we may be able to describe it, there is purpose. Moreover the sequences only continue to exist by virtue of the Divine Will dominant in creation. In apparent irregularity we seem forced to postulate creative activity; but such activity on the part of God exists equally in sequences which seem to us alike natural and inevitable. Their appearance of 'inevitableness' may be and, as I hold, is merely a consequence of the fact that we are familiar with them.

We have given, as I believe, good reasons to reject the mechanistic theory that we are but conscious automata. In ourselves there exists self-directing purposive activity. It is of primary importance in our lives: by its use or misuse a man's value in the scheme of things is determined. We may not deny the existence of some more primitive kind of purpose in animals lower in the scale of life than ourselves. It may even be nascent in the vegetable world and potential in inanimate matter. But can there be such manifestations of purpose unless the whole scheme, within which they exist and emerge, is itself purposeful? The enquiry is central in the Teleological Argument which we must shortly consider.

§ 451. *The existence of God.*

Desire to have some absolutely convincing proof of the existence of God is no new thing. Various arguments for Christian theism have come to us from medieval scholastic theologians. At intervals they have been examined, criticised, modified. In addition to the argument already advanced in § 437, three forms of 'proof', the ontological, the cosmological and the teleological, are fundamental. The fatal defects in all were exposed by Kant; but most Christian thinkers would argue that at all events the cosmological and the teleological arguments can, in Inge's words*, "be restated so as to have great value". Few Christian theologians, however, would claim that such arguments are absolutely conclusive and the majority regard the so-called ontological proof as unsatisfactory. The psychologists for the most part agree with William James (1842–1910) "that feeling is the deeper source of religion and that philosophic and theological formulas are secondary products, like translations of a text into another tongue".

Yet it is most doubtful whether the course of thought during the last quarter of a century has justified James' further statement that "the arguments for God's existence have stood for hundreds of years with the waves of unbelieving criticism breaking against them, never totally discrediting them in the ears of the faithful, but on the whole slowly and surely washing out the mortar from between their joints†". I would, on the contrary, argue that an increased recognition of the

---

* W. R. Inge, *Outspoken Essays, Second Series.* Longmans, 1922, p. 14.
† William James, *The Varieties of Religious Experience.* Longmans, 1912, p. 437.

important place which mental constructs occupy in physical theory, coupled with an understanding that thought, will and feeling cannot be wholly sundered from one another, has produced a widespread conviction that Theism and science will in the end form a harmonious unity, and that the growth of our knowledge of Nature will strengthen belief in the existence of God. We may at present fail to make a satisfactory intellectual synthesis, but we may expect that more, and not less, success will result from progressive effort.

§ 452. *The ontological argument and its rejection.*

I think, however, that the so-called Ontological Argument must be abandoned. This 'proof' is an attempt to shew that God exists by considering merely the content of the conception of God. It was first advanced by Anselm (1033–1109). Rejected by Aquinas (*ca.* 1225–1274), it was stated in a modified form by Descartes and finally subjected by Kant to criticism so damaging that most philosophers have since been content to set it aside.

Anselm's contention may be briefly summarised. He urged that by God we mean "that than which nothing greater can be conceived". This phrase has a definite meaning: hence God exists *in intellectu,* as a mental construct. But, if God only existed thus *in intellectu,* and not as an object, we could think of something greater than God: we could, in fact, think of a being who was also real. We should thus reach a contradiction. Hence God, as thus defined, cannot be conceived as non-existent. Thus God must exist.

Objections rise at once. So much, we feel instinctively, cannot be so readily proved. If God, as Anselm defines Him, exists *in intellectu,* this only means that we can understand the meaning of the statement 'God exists'. But there are many propositions whose meaning we understand which none the less are false. Anselm, as was pointed out by his contemporary Gaunilo, a monk of Marmoutier, ought to prove that no one can see that the statement has a meaning without also seeing that it is true. This he does not do.

Descartes (1596–1650) restated the ontological argument in a slightly different form. By God, he argued, we mean a being perfect in every way. But existence is an attribute of perfection. Therefore the being who is perfect in every way must exist. Thus God exists. Existence, in fact, is implicitly contained in the very conception of God.

As against Descartes' argument Kant urged that existence was not rightly to be regarded as an attribute or predicate. He maintained further that the proposition 'God exists' could only be derived from the concept of God if existence had already been included in that concept. Though he was willing to admit that the idea of a Supreme Being might be most useful, yet because it was merely an idea it could not possibly extend our knowledge of "what exists by means of itself alone".

If the ontological argument were satisfactory, a purely *à priori* proof of the existence of a Supreme Being would be possible. We must, in the light of the history of philosophy, admit that such an *à priori* proof cannot be found. "Our knowledge of God is of the nature of a valid inference."

§453. *The cosmological argument.*

Perhaps the argument for God's existence which at first sight is most alluring is that known as the cosmological. It has a long history, which may be traced backwards through Aquinas to Aristotle. Briefly the argument runs that the world results from a chain of cause and effect, each link being the effect of the previous link and the cause of that which follows. As we proceed backwards we shall arrive at a First Cause which must be God.

The argument is open to serious objection. There is the logical flaw that we assume an invariable sequence of cause and effect and yet get to a First Cause which is not an effect. Further, there is no reason why we should not have an indefinite regression. Still further, even though God be the ground of their existence, it is most doubtful whether anything resembling efficient causation can be imported into sequences investigated by science: yet, if the First Cause be equated to God, it must be efficient. Thus William James spoke none too strongly when he said that "causation is indeed too obscure a principle to bear the weight of the whole structure of theology". In brief, the cosmological argument in its old form is derelict.

It is a singular fact, as we have seen alike in §187 and towards the end of Lecture XI, that speculations based on the second law of thermodynamics seem to re-establish the cosmological argument with the utmost directness and simplicity. The organisation of the energy of the cosmos is always diminishing. Such degeneration of energy is the source of all that makes our physical existence not merely pleasant but possible. As a result of it there will finally be in the cosmos no organised energy capable of doing work. In the beginning there must have been a maximum organisation of energy; and, if the cosmos is finite, that beginning must itself have been remote from us by a measurable interval of time. In fact, there was a time when God wound up the clock and a time will come when it will stop if He does not wind it up again.

Against this thermodynamical argument we can bring no valid objection: but it is characteristic of the temper of our era that few theologians of eminence are willing to sponsor it as it stands. We have the instinct that God is not outside the cosmos as the householder is outside his clock. Further, if the cosmos were 'wound up' once, the same phenomenon can, we may imagine, happen again. Such winding up will then shew itself as an element in a regular sequence. By such speculative considerations we set aside a good argument, at present unanswerable. As I have said, it is by a sort of instinct that we reject a cosmological proof of God's existence based on the second law of thermodynamics. Personally I think such an instinct sound. A purely transcendent God, to Whom the cosmos (ourselves included) is related as watch to watchmaker, does not accord with our general outlook.

The sort of cosmological argument to which we are naturally led by modern knowledge and speculation we have already indicated. Natural Science could not exist were it not that domains or tracts of the objective continuum which is presented in experience can be described by schemes agreeable to human reason. There must then be, as the ground of the objective continuum, a reality which is for us rational. In other words, if we use the term Nature to express what I should call the derivative reality manifested in phenomena, we may say that Nature is informed by some principle which for minds built like our own is rational. Thus Nature and man form a unity, so that schemes which describe the ordering of Nature are akin to the processes of our thought. The rational Principle of Nature will be God, Who pervades every part by His continuous activity; and, though such a God is by no means necessarily the God of the Christian religion, other considerations, associated especially with the Moral Argument which we shall shortly consider, indicate that such is His character.

The main defect of this modern cosmological argument is that it assumes that the whole of Nature can be described by rational schemes such as have, in fact, been only obtained for very restricted domains. It may be that ultimately Nature will be found to consist of a single system of rational schemes; but those who hold this belief cannot prove that it is true. Perhaps we must be content to say that there is a ground of unity between Nature and human reason; and its existence suggests that man's thought and the Spirit active within or through Nature are not alien from one another.

§ 454. *The teleological argument.*

The Teleological Argument for God's existence used to be based on what were supposed to be manifest evidences of purpose and design in Nature. The human eye, for instance, had been made for a definite end: in it there was clear evidence of purpose; design, purpose and end pointed to an intelligent Creator. The argument from design was used, in a manner which gradually came to be considered alike crude and unsatisfying, by William Paley (1743–1805) in his *Evidences of Christianity* (1794), a famous book that for long was a compulsory subject of study in the preliminary examinations of the University of Cambridge. In consequence the argument by which the existence of the watchmaker was inferred from the watch became a standard object of scorn to clever undergraduates. All know that there are defects in living organisms: that the eye, in particular, is by no means a perfect piece of mechanism*. And such defects might not unjustly, before the working of the evolutionary process was understood, have been held to point to a bungler rather than to an omniscient and 'omnipotent' Creator. Moreover, in its old form the theory postulated a relation between Creator and creature analogous to that between potter and vessel: it was congruous with the belief that mind in man was disparate from Universal Mind. Thus it led naturally to the sort of Deism which is opposed to the view that God is continuously active within His creation, and it did not satisfy man's instinct that it is possible to attain to some measure of communion with God.

But the final collapse of the old argument from design came with the acceptance of the principle of evolution. No longer can we imagine the benevolent Deity making an animal in every way fitted for its place in creation. In place of such a picture we have the conception of the apparently fortuitous appearance or reappearance of a vast number of inheritable variations. Some of these enable the animal in which they are manifested to survive more easily in its environment. Such are inherited by individuals which successfully maintain themselves in the struggle for existence; and thus gradually new types of structure and new biochemical rhythms are established. In this way, apparently, chance joins hands with instability to create; and the struggle for

* As to this fact, Darwin quotes Helmholtz, "whose judgment no one will dispute", in *The Origin of Species*, 6th ed. Murray, 1889, p. 163.

survival eliminates. Hence Darwin could write: "There seems to be no more design in the variability of organic beings, and in the action of natural selection, than in the course which the wind blows*". We have previously indicated the way in which Darwin's views have been modified by the work of biologists since *The Origin of Species* was published. Incidentally it was made clear that such alterations have certainly not ousted 'natural selection' from its place of primary importance in the evolutionary scheme. Moreover, the ruthlessness of natural selection does not obviously point to benevolence in the Creator and Guide of evolution; neither can we easily regard it as purposive. Thus the old teleology has perished.

None the less it is possible to argue that, if we widen our survey so as to include the whole evolutionary process, we shall find evidence of purpose due to Creative Mind. In the first place evolution is not a mere unpacking: in the process there has been actual change. New things have emerged. Even if we were to accept Haldane's contention that there is elementary life in what we term the inorganic world, we could nevertheless urge that the change which leads to distinctively biological organisms is so significant that we can truly assert that something new has emerged in the process. Furthermore, as Boutroux† (1845–1921) has well said:

Whether in our means of knowing, of noting, of representing, of arranging things, or in Nature itself, science, at the present time, no longer sees anything quite stable and definitive. Not only is a purely experimental science, by definition, always approximative, provisional, and modifiable; but, according to the results of science herself, there is nothing to guarantee the absolute stability of even the most general laws that man has been able to discover. Nature evolves, perhaps even fundamentally.

There are, of course, those who would contend that if we accept the notion of such radical change we must abandon the idea of natural law. But Boutroux with admirable cogency maintains that "although evolution be radical, it is not conceived, on that ground, as arbitrary and scientifically unknowable. If the remotest principles of things are transformed, that very transformation must obey laws which are analogous to immediately observable laws, to experimental laws".

* See Francis Darwin, *Life and Letters of Charles Darwin*. 3 vols. Murray, 1887, vol. I, p. 309. The words appear in the chapter in which the development of Charles Darwin's religious opinions is described. They are an extract from a part of the autobiography, written in the year 1876, a few years before Darwin's death.

† E. Boutroux, *Religion and Science in Contemporary Philosophy*. English translation, Duckworth, 1909, p. 357.

Now such a radical process of evolution entirely transcends in significance the mechanism of natural selection, which is a mere apparatus for adapting a changing organism to a changing environment. We obviously need to fix attention on the ultimate origin of all changes rather than on secondary interactions. That origin cannot at present, at all events, be placed within any mechanistic scheme; and indeed, as has been argued in § 443, Conscious Purpose seems the only adequate way of accounting for evolution and its consequences. Among such consequences we must place the growth in animals of mental activity and of mental power during the evolutionary process and, finally, the development of self-consciousness in man. That such a reality as human self-consciousness should have emerged without the operation of Creative Mind is incredible: we cannot explain the higher by the lower. We have seen reason to hold that by our volition we can influence the course of Nature for ends which we choose. There is then no reason to regard as an unjustifiable assumption the belief that a single Creative Mind behind phenomena has purposively contrived the process upon earth of which man is the present culmination.

§ 455. *Faith in God.*

What does faith in God imply? Most people would probably answer that such faith means belief in the existence of some Being who created the world. But such a faith cannot possibly satisfy us. Our faith must be faith in One Whose primary attributes are Goodness, Beauty and Truth. It must be associated with belief in an eternal spiritual world, the perfect archetype of that Kingdom of God upon earth which in our highest moments we desire to set up. The God Who emerges from reflection upon scientific theories is an abstraction because such theories are themselves obtained by ignoring all that is individual and much of that which is qualitative in experience. Scientific speculation, in so far as it leads to a God, leads merely to One Whose will is the cause of events. We infer that He is the Mind from Whose creative activity all that lies behind phenomena derives such reality as it possesses. We may thus reach, though we cannot go much further than, a somewhat colourless Deism or pantheism unless we pass beyond the boundaries of scientific enquiry.

It would, however, be wrong to imply that such scientific enquiry is without its own values. In it truth is supreme; and thus the God inferred from science is intolerant of falsehood and superstition. There is, moreover, an aesthetic element in scientific theory. The mathe-

matician shapes his symbols and polishes his formulae until they take
to themselves a satisfying beauty. Thus the God inferred from science
has a power which is both harmonious and beautiful: He is not some
rough uncouth giant, though such a being would be fit to represent the
psychical aspect of the blind forces of Nature. Nevertheless, though
all values are not excluded from the realm of scientific enquiry, the fact
remains that good and evil find no place in scientific schemes; and
therefore no arguments strictly based upon such schemes can lead to
a God Whose goodness draws us to Himself. Yet unless we can think of
God as a Father, responsive to our struggle to overcome evil and ready
to aid us by some measure of communion with Himself, He is not the
object of religious aspiration but merely the end of a limited range of
speculative enquiry.

§ 456. *The natural sciences and qualitative judgments.*

As a preliminary to the argument to which we now proceed we repeat
that scientific investigation, considered apart from the spirit in which
it is carried out, ignores practically all those aspects of experience which
cannot be weighed or measured. Judgments that are qualitative and
incapable of justification by quantitative arguments have little place
in scientific schemes. Hence we cannot expect that the conclusions of
natural science will form a complete basis for metaphysical speculation.
It is true that such conclusions give us reasons why we should postulate
that the world owes its existence to Creative Spirit. But no investigation which ignores moral values can possibly lead to Christian theism
or, indeed, to any satisfactory understanding of the ground of reality.
We therefore proceed to consider* briefly what philosophico-religious
outlook is made probable by an examination of man's moral consciousness and its judgments.

In so doing we pass outside the domain assigned by their sub-title to
the present lectures. We need not hesitate so to act inasmuch as the
spiritual interpretation of biological evolution, when attention is concentrated on genetic change and the struggle for existence, becomes,
as we have seen, profoundly disturbing by reason of its apparently
non-moral character. Yet the mere mention of such a character shews
how difficult it is to avoid importing ethical considerations into our
estimate of the evolutionary process. Assuming that the process is
due to some Creative Spirit, Whose continuous activity pervades the

* Throughout the ensuing paragraphs I have made use of W. R. Sorley's
valuable *Moral Values and the Idea of God*. Cambridge University Press, 1918.

world, we are compelled to consider the significance of the realm of moral values if we would understand aright the nature of this Spirit.

§ 457. *Individuality, value and quality.*

The natural sciences, as we have often said, are concerned not with individual things or processes but with properties of groups or aggregates. Their propositions relate to sequences derived from observations in which differences between individuals are ignored. Now Ethics predicates value; and value-judgments relate to the individual. Hence Natural Science by its inherent limitations cannot investigate such things as the worth of a statesman or the significance of a hero: it cannot even measure the joy of scientific discovery or compare, save inadequately, different flowering-times of human genius. Values lie outside its scope; and, in particular, moral judgments belong to other regions of investigation than those which the man of science explores.

We all know vaguely what we mean by 'value' and 'quality': the notions are too fundamental to admit of satisfactory definition. Value is an estimate of worth: a scale of values serves to measure our appreciation of the way in which some particular quality is manifested in different objects. An important distinction between qualities and values needs to be emphasised at the outset. Qualities may belong to concepts which have no actual existence; but ethical and aesthetic values belong only to things which either exist or are assumed to exist.

We have seen that the descriptions of natural science do not imply existence. But as soon as we bring in the notion of value we pass beyond description and so outside what is strictly the realm of science. Natural science deals with relations between concepts: and concepts as such have no ethical value, inasmuch as there cannot be moral worth in what is purely a mental construction. For instance, we cannot give a value to the abstraction which we term justice: what we value proves on reflection to be a relation existing between human beings. Hence we cannot say that justice is good; but we can predicate goodness of just actions or just men.

§ 458. *The rise of moral consciousness.*

There seems to be no doubt that the moral consciousness arose at a comparatively late period in the evolutionary process. It may exist in rudimentary form in some of the lower animals, but it is only to be found in a developed form in civilised man. Activity in elementary organisms seems to be largely the result of mechanical reflexes. At a higher stage pleasure is a motive of action: and this stage undoubtedly preceded the rise of the feeling of moral obligation. But we cannot therefore assume it possible to derive moral consciousness ultimately from the desire for pleasure. Morality requires us to choose between things that please and even at times to forgo our strongest desires. Subsequent to the time when the activity of low-grade consciousness had pleasurable sensations as its end there took place a process of mental development by which man was led to find what, as we shall try to shew, is rightly described as *objective validity* in ethical principles. In this last significant stage of biological evolution something new emerged: we may term it the recognition of the moral law. Its ultimate origin is not directly apparent; and he who seeks to investigate the source of its existence must enquire at the same time into the ultimate origin of life and of mind.

There are, of course, those who would say that our moral consciousness has been formed by the necessities of social order and that it is ultimately a product of man's reaction to his environment. The argument runs that, for his own well-being, man had to create both the family group and tribal organisation, and that the needs of such organisation led to the establishment of what we now regard as ethical principles. We cannot but allow that in such contentions there is an element of truth. Morality is most certainly the result of a process of development. Moreover, the conduct and principles of men have changed with the growth of civilisation. It is by the growth of understanding, by reflection upon the world in which he finds himself, that man has been led from grossly imperfect moral judgments to a more adequate appreciation of the moral law. But we cannot therefore deny the objectivity of such judgments as have been, or shall be, finally reached.

Science equally results from individual reflection and social organisation; but the objectivity of the 'laws' which it frames is shewn in their predictive power. We do not assume that such laws in their present form are final, but they represent our more or less imperfect understanding of objective truth. Thus we cannot deny that there is an objective element in science, and equally we are not able to deny that moral principles are objective. The subjective apprehension of facts does not make them relative to the observer, and similarly the subjective appreciation of values affords no reason for the belief that they are relative to changing human standards. The historical process by which man has become aware of values can be described in rough outline; but we must not confuse this process with the construction of the values themselves. Man in his development has merely discovered morality. Thus he has not created ethical principles though he has increasingly taken them to be criteria by which conduct is regulated.

§ 459. *Ethical judgments.*

The discovery of the moral law has been a slow progress. It began when elementary moral judgments were applied by the family or tribal group to particular actions and issues. But even the formation of such judgments was not immediate, for it was the outcome of a critical examination of intuitive judgments of value made by individuals. Such are analogous to the judgments of sense-perception in natural science. What we term moral intuitions are immediate consequences of perception and not results of reasoning. Now it is obvious that such immediate judgments may be erroneous. How are we to eliminate this possibility of error? We must answer that the critical examination of its moral experience will in the end enable humanity to discover the moral law. In accordance with this postulate we construct an increasingly perfect system of ethical principles by a process of critical analysis which continuously removes the contradictions which arise from the different judgments of individuals. In the end we shall reach a system of moral principles which is objectively valid.

When we say that a particular moral judgment is objectively valid we mean, in the first place, that it is more than the expression of opinion of a particular subject who judges: it is, in fact, independent of the person by whom the judgment is made. He does not express an opinion, but states a truth which he has come to apprehend. In the second place, the objective validity of ethical judgments may be contrasted with the objective character of 'laws of Nature'. The latter are relations between concepts derived by 'intersubjective intercourse' from sense-observation. Ethical judgments are similarly derived by 'intersubjective intercourse' from the perceptive judgments of value made by individual subjects. Yet they apply not to concepts but to things which either exist or are assumed to exist. They are thus implicated in reality. In fact, as James Ward says, "validity implies reality and is otherwise meaningless".

It is thus apparent that a moral judgment, by its very nature, claims to be objective. It measures, as it were on an absolute scale, the value to be found in some person or process or in some relation between persons. It does not purport to be the private opinion of the subject who forms the judgment. It arises, of course, in his mind; but it has a universal nature because all who judge correctly will, it is assumed, reach the same conclusion.

Complexity with regard to ethical judgments arises in part from the fact that estimates of good or evil cannot be reached by any process resembling addition and subtraction. We cannot judge a man save by considering his actions in relation to those general principles of his life of which they are the outcome. The whole man considered as a moral being is more than the algebraic sum of his parts. Similarly we cannot estimate the value of a race or an epoch by a mere process of enumeration. We must think of the elements of morality in any such case as uniting to form an organic whole, some unity which resembles an organism rather than an aggregate. As we learn to appreciate such organic wholes our moral experience grows. With its growth we are enabled more and more completely to see ethical principles as a system. We thus reach the idea of the Absolute Good; and, though our comprehension is never perfect, our discovery of the objectively valid moral order becomes progressively the more complete.

Our conclusion that moral values are objectively valid is strengthened by the fact that truth has a similar character. Thus neither truth nor moral value is merely subjective. Furthermore, our belief that truth is absolute can be readily seen to be fundamental. For if it could be proved that truth had only significance for some individual, the proof would be itself a truth and its significance would therefore be similarly limited. Thus the assertion that truth has no objective validity carries within itself its own denial. From such considerations there arises the situation, embarrassing to the sceptic, that if all truth be relative the scepticism which denies the existence of absolute truth is itself relative. In brief, doubt of the absolute value of truth destroys itself. We cannot use a similar argument to demonstrate that goodness is absolute; but goodness and truth are so allied in their nature that belief in the absolute value of the one predisposes to belief in the absolute value of the other.

§ 460. *The realms of Nature and of moral order.*

I have now tried to state why we ought to believe that there is in the world an objective moral order, a realm which would correspond to our intuition if all our moral judgments were perfect. This realm claims our allegiance: we experience the claim in the imperative demands of our moral consciousness. We do not deny that our moral apprehension is normally imperfect. Such imperfection arises for the most part from conflict between different ethical loyalties. Nevertheless conscience demands obedience to the moral law as that law presents itself to us. Now we also belong to the realm of Nature, the realm which the natural sciences describe. We have seen reason to deny that this realm is a closed mechanism, but we have to admit that it is a realm in which evil is persistent. Are the two realms, the realm of moral values and the realm of Nature, such that we can believe that both belong to a single scheme of creation? Is our experience of life such that Nature gives a domain suited to the attainment of goodness? These enquiries are of profound importance: and the answers, which do not seem to me to be in doubt, determine the character of our belief in God.

I say that the answers are not in doubt because I can neither believe in a dualism which sets the realm of Nature against the realm of moral law nor can I accept a naturalism for which moral law is, in effect, an illusion. Our experience is a whole and the contradictions within it must be due to imperfect understanding.

Many of these apparent contradictions vanish when we postulate that life is given to man that he may become good rather than happy. We cannot pretend that the course of Nature has been so adjusted as to enable us to be comfortable: the world most certainly was not created by an all-powerful Being Who desired as His chief end the happiness of man. But none the less it may be argued that the misery and suffering of the world increase the goodness within it. As humanity, in its evolution from some ape-like stock, has fought against a hostile environment its powers have grown. Conflict and endurance and even, by its tonic quality, the bitterness of failure have increased man's value in the scheme of things. The character of the individual is often strengthened by suffering and the saint not seldom has passed through much tribulation. Hence, in spite of the evil within Nature, her realm may rightly be judged to be one in which moral values are realised. It is thus possible to argue that the two realms of Nature and moral purpose belong to a single scheme: and that the God of Nature is also the Source of the moral values of which we are conscious.

§ 461. *The moral argument for God's existence.*

The considerations which have now been advanced enable us to reach the Moral Argument as it has been formulated by Rashdall. He says*:

---

* Hastings Rashdall, *The Theory of Good and Evil.* 2 vols. Clarendon Press, 1907, vol. II, p. 212.

An absolute Moral Law or moral ideal cannot exist *in* material things. And it does not exist in the mind of this or that individual. Only if we believe in the existence of a Mind for which the true moral ideal is already in some sense real, a Mind which is the source of whatever is true in our own moral judgments, can we rationally think of the moral ideal as no less real than the world itself. Only so can we believe in an absolute standard of right and wrong, which is as independent of this or that man's actual ideas and actual desires as the facts of material nature. The belief in God, though not (like the belief in a real and an active self) a postulate of there being any such thing as Morality at all, is the logical presupposition of an 'objective' or absolute Morality. A moral ideal can exist nowhere and nohow but in a mind; an absolute moral ideal can exist only in a Mind from which all Reality is derived*. Our moral ideal can only claim objective validity in so far as it can rationally be regarded as the revelation of a moral ideal eternally existing in the mind of God.

Rashdall goes on to say that we may, perhaps, be able to give some meaning to Morality without the postulate of God, "but not its true or full meaning".

§ 462. *The absolute values.*

We have shewn, to those who regard the foregoing arguments as satisfactory, that we may claim objective validity for goodness and truth; and similar arguments can be applied to establish the objective validity of beauty. For this reason goodness, beauty and truth are termed absolute values. They are absolute because by reason of their objective validity they are independent of their apprehension by, or manifestation in, individuals. In fact, Pringle-Pattison (1856–1931) rightly maintained that "all claims on man's behalf must be based on the objectivity of the values revealed in his experience and brokenly realised there. Man does not make values any more than he makes reality".

We conceive then that absolute values are attributes of God. Some idealist philosophers hold that therefore they have a real existence apart from their manifestation in the concrete and especially in human activity. Yet others would contend that, as abstractions, absolute values belong to a different order from that of real existence. We have suggested that they do not exist but that they are valid of reality, so that we can say that the real world is a world of values. It is in fact impossible to think of an existing world without valuation. If value-judgments did not apply to the existing world, if they were not judgments of existence, they would be meaningless.

* "Or at least a mind by which all Reality is controlled." Rashdall's footnote.

Thus, even though we do not hold that absolute values have a real existence, we must believe that existence and value belong to the same realm and have the same ground. On this basis Sorley* builds Christian theism. He says:

The order of nature and of finite minds, as we know them, do not manifest ethical values with any exactness or purity; in their existing nature they are out of harmony with the moral order. But harmony may be reached if it is allowable to assume purpose in the world and freedom in man. Nature can then be regarded as an appropriate medium for the realisation of value by minds finite but free. The harmony is a relation which stands in need of realisation; and the purpose of realising it requires consciousness in the ground of reality as a whole. This ground or principle of reality will therefore involve the will to goodness as well as intelligence and power; and this is what we mean by God.

Inge would claim objective reality for Absolute Values. They "exist in their own right": and "the ultimate identity of existence and value is the venture of faith to which mysticism and speculative idealism are committed". The difference between the standpoints of those for whom absolute values do or do not exist is unimportant provided that those who deny their existence believe them to be valid of reality. But the difference is fundamental between those who contend, as we have argued, that the real world is a world of values, and those, on the other hand, who separate reality from value. The latter normally accept some form of naturalism in which psychical facts are mere epiphenomena, by-products of physical change. Of course, they who deny the objectivity of moral values do not ignore the fact that in perception we continuously make value-judgments. But I would reiterate that no theory which regards such judgments as merely subjective is satisfactory. Our ethical principles are not merely our own. We may differ as to what is the right course of conduct in certain circumstances. But the difference will arise from a conflict between different ethical loyalties and not from dispute as to whether ultimate principles are good or evil. The moral law is universal, although it may be imperfectly apprehended by even the highest in moral attainment. Yet as we reflect upon experience, and criticise in intersubjective intercourse the results of our reflection, we get an ever fuller apprehension of the moral order. We thus discover that which is objectively valid.

We may now sum up our conclusions by saying that any faith in God that is worth having will be based upon the intuition, derived from and

* W. R. Sorley, *Moral Values and the Idea of God.* Cambridge University Press, 1918, p. 487.

confirmed by all rightly interpreted experience, that the values of Goodness, Beauty and Truth are of supreme importance in the cosmos. They are not merely regulative principles which we infer from experience, and not merely abstractions which indicate the purpose of types of human aspiration which we agree to admire. They are absolute and not relative. They are valid as attributes of God. We cannot create them save that, as we grow aright, they are manifested in us. Religious understanding asserts that this trio of values is of the highest significance in our experience. Our actions embody or exemplify them imperfectly: they reveal the Divine nature. God, in fact, is the Source of beauty and truth and, also, He is good.

Lecture xix

RELIGIOUS EXPERIENCE

§ 463. *Normal religious experience.*

However emergence be interpreted it has led to man as we know him; and man, as we have seen, by some necessity of his being gives values to the various parts of his experience. These value-judgments form his character and shape his activity because they determine the ends for which he works. We have, moreover, argued that the values which are thus important are not merely abstractions derived from man's interests and desires. They lead to standards and principles which for the right-minded man have a compelling power: in fact, as humanity's valuation of experience develops, it increasingly harmonises with the truth of things.

From our attempts to give meaning to human life we are thus led to believe that goodness, beauty and truth express the fundamental nature of the cosmos or, in other words, the character of God. God is absolute; and they also form absolute standards. Thus the perfect spiritual world is the world where these values are perfectly manifested. For civilised men and women the religious view of the cosmos is based upon belief in the validity and sovereignty of these values as attributes of God; and normal religious experience among ourselves comprises those aspects of our ordinary activity which lead to such belief and enable us through the influence of such values to feel that which we interpret as God's presence in our lives.

Thus I would say that religion is, in Baillie's words, "a moral trust in reality" and that the religious life is the life fashioned by true value-judgments and elevated by the spiritual power which they possess or reveal. In thus describing 'normal religious experience' there are many whose criticism I shall incur. Some will contend that a much wider definition is needed if we would indicate the character of that widespread and variable factor in human nature which we term the religious sense. 'Fellowship with the unseen' or 'a relation towards what is deemed divine' have been, with much justification, put forward as definitions which best indicate the nature of religion.

Now, as we saw in Lecture XVI, primitive religion has often been a non-moral mixture of myth, magic and ritual. Often enough such religion has consisted largely of attempts to appease angry deities or to establish some close bond with a tribal god. Even to-day in India foul immorality is at times associated with temple worship; and thus a form of degraded religion persists which has a long and painful history and of which we get plain evidence in the older books of the Bible.

But, while we need wider definitions of religion in studying primitive peoples or decadent reversions to the past, we can for practical purposes, in making religion and religious experience an object of scientific study, limit ourselves to such expressions of the religious instinct as occur in civilised peoples. We must, in the celebrated phrase of William James, already quoted in § 429, judge religion by its fruits, not by its roots. What religion has been as man has slowly emerged from the beast is of little account. But we ought carefully to investigate what religion is now, among the races who represent the best of human civilisation, if we would discover its true place in human life and measure its power to shape the future of man's thoughts.

I have spoken of normal religion as an aspect of our ordinary activity. I need not defend the statement in so far as it assumes the generally accepted fact that man is a religious animal. In due course we shall have to consider mystical states which are abnormal or, perhaps more accurately, super-normal. But, in connection with the distinctions implied by the terms normal and super-normal, we must admit that it is virtually impossible accurately to grade the different conjunctions of feeling and thought which are to be found in the religious life of man. What we can say confidently is that the normal manifestations of the religious instinct which exist among ourselves are, as compared with those of savage peoples, of a relatively advanced type. The normal channels of religious understanding are familiar as they appear in our churches and chapels and sunday schools. The supernormal are rare, though perhaps not so rare as is commonly supposed. Any of us may exceptionally find some super-normal channel open for our enrichment, and to the great mystics a fullness of religious insight thus comes often. But there are probably no gaps in the scale of religious experience. From the elementary motions of conscience in the child to the rapture of the third heaven experienced by St Paul* there is probably a steady ascent.

* The language of 2 Cor. xii. 2 is slightly ambiguous; but all commentators seem to agree that the reference is to St Paul himself.

§ 464. *Prayer.*

Among races in our own stage of civilisation normal religion and normal religious experience are always associated with prayer. In prayer the individual seeks God, tries to know His will, and to understand His government of the world. Though different individuals differ widely in the requests which they think it right to make, all who pray intend in some way or another to seek God's aid.

Prayer in its most general sense includes religious meditation and may therefore be described as the attempt to gain inward intercourse or communion with the Divine. Sabatier has described it as "religion in act". Prayer is, in fact, both the central and the highest act of worship. It is far more than mere petition, quite other than a substitute for the magic spell to which Wundt and divers anthropologists would assign its origin. There is no doubt that in magical formulae the names of powerful spirits are used as spells: quite possibly the conventional way in which Christians end their prayers has association with such usage. But always in religious practice an examination of origins is likely to mislead. Though much of the past is retained in formula and act, the ancient significance of that which is thus retained has probably in many cases passed away. Thus the prayers of the educated religious man in Western Europe have little in common with the crude petitions and elaborate spell-casting of the Australian aborigine.

There is, however, it must be acknowledged, as regards their attitude towards and use of prayer, a vast difference between individuals of various degrees of mental and spiritual development who may co-exist in the same community. With some men meaningless formulae may be of value in creating what Pratt* calls a "prayerful attitude of mind". With others a customary attitude of reverence may be an important means towards the same end. The set formula and the conventional posture are established in the public worship of many communions. But probably the private individual, whose religious life is mature, more often prays in spirit than with the set formula; and such a one acquires the habit of 'entering into himself', whatever may be his physical surroundings, when a few moments can be snatched for the desired meditation. For some, as for F. W. H. Myers (1843–1901), prayer may thus become 'an attitude of open and earnest expectancy' associated with largely indefinite theological beliefs. Yet all who use prayer would probably say that by it they draw spiritual energy as from some inexhaustible reservoir.

* J. B. Pratt, *The Religious Consciousness.* Macmillan, 1921, p. 316.

Is such a conviction well-founded? And, if so, may we go further and affirm that God answers prayer? We may not doubt that men get satisfaction from prayer, for otherwise they most certainly would not pray. But, of course, it is possible that the satisfaction which men find in prayer is deceitful.

§ 465. *Does God answer prayer?*

The most diverse opinions exist as to how far God answers prayer. Among those who pray regularly one can meet with few who are unable to give some significant example of an answer to prayer. Yet, no doubt, a hostile critic would reply that the unanswered prayers are forgotten or, at any rate, uncounted; and that, if they were remembered, the answered prayers would be no more than the doctrine of chances would require. Against such contentions may be set many extraordinary achievements. One of the most famous is the life-work of George Müller of Bristol, who died in the year 1898. "His intensely private and practical conception of his relations with the Deity", says James*, "continued the traditions of the most primitive human thought." Yet for his charities he raised, exclusively by prayer, as he believed, nearly a million and a half sterling: the story is completed by the fact that he died worth a hundred and sixty pounds. Many of us hesitate to use, or at any rate to speak of our use of, prayer in this way. Yet there are many of us, I am sure, who believe that dramatically through prayer we have had some tangled perplexity resolved. The suddenly gained confidence that some particular course of action is right has thus led many a man forward to high achievement.

I myself, of course, have no doubts as to the value of prayer. A merely mechanical theory of the Universe I reject. God rules the world: the laws of Nature are His laws and in no way constrain His freedom. Thus there is no reason to believe that God cannot grant favourable answers to the crudest petitionary prayers: our experience alone can determine whether He thus acts as we seek His aid. I should even hesitate to affirm dogmatically that petitions for rain or fair weather were necessarily unavailing: until we have proved that the physical cosmos is a closed system, there is no theoretical reason why God should not hearken to such prayer. I would pray for a friend's recovery from sickness with the knowledge that such prayers are often of no avail and yet with hope that God in His goodness would grant my petition. With

* William James gives some account of Müller in *The Varieties of Religious Experience*. Longmans, 1912, pp. 467–71. Other accounts are numerous.

great confidence would I pray for strength against temptation, whether I myself or some other was in need.

But it must never be forgotten that in petitionary prayer we primarily seek to know God's will. Jesus with His matchless religious understanding put the petition 'Thy will be done' in the only set formula which He gave to His followers. To learn God's will, and to accept it with a submission in which there is no resentment, form a chief object of prayer. There are times when religious leaders organise prayer for a particular public purpose, fail to obtain their desire and, in consequence, shew marked irritation. Such have forgotten the teaching of Christ. God's kingdom will not come as we expect or by such means as we would employ. 'Think that ye may be mistaken' is a useful reminder to self-confident men who would dictate to their Creator.

To a man whose creed is agnostic naturalism prayer is, of course, an absurdity. But I have previously insisted (§ 443) that such a man, if consistent, would similarly dismiss as idle all our ideals and aspirations. We repeat that if, as we have seen reason to believe, the Universe is ultimately a unity, spiritually guided and controlled, the limits to what can be obtained by prayer are theoretically non-existent. Such limits must be determined practically, as from experience we find how far God in His wisdom is willing to act as we desire.

Yet petitionary prayer, as we have said, is not prayer at its highest. There are types of meditation to which prayer leads which belong to the highest regions of religious experience. In them there comes an overpowering conviction that God is near. When we descend from the heights we know that inwardly and spiritually we have drawn strength from God: we have experienced His love: we are the better for having realised His presence. Such moments come seldom and are quite possibly much rarer than many sermons would lead us to expect. But they are not the fictions of myth-making piety, and I cannot believe them to be merely vivid and beautiful daydreams. Yet who can prove the reality of spiritual grace? If at times we think that we can see its effect in the lives of men, and if then its fruit is of great excellence, we must be content.

§ 466. *Conversion.*

No account of religious experience could pretend to be complete if it omitted to describe that spiritual crisis known as conversion. This revolution in the soul stands in marked contrast to that gradual recognition of the divine source of the moral law which we have termed normal religious experience. It is more akin to mystical experience in its suddenness and in the way in which the memory of it remains precious throughout life. But it is a less profound psychological disturbance than that through which the mystics pass. It is also, I think, fully explicable, whereas mystical experience cannot be explained.

Conversion usually takes place during that period of strain and stress known as adolescence. The growing boy or girl begins to realise life's perplexities, difficulties and dangers. The sense of internal conflict is often acute. Desire to act aright is at war with insurgent and perhaps hitherto unknown appetites and passions. A great sense of need arises which may last for long and produce acute dejection: in language which has unfortunately become somewhat old-fashioned, there is a profound conviction of sin from which no release seems possible. Suddenly all is changed. Help from on high has come. Discords are harmonised. The period of storm and stress ends. "God's in His heaven: all's right with the world." The prodigal son returns home and God in His fatherly love says: "This my son was dead and is alive again: was lost and is found".

Of course, conversion does not always occur during adolescence. Sometimes, as with St Paul, the spiritual crisis happens at a more mature stage of life. But it always ends a period of spiritual struggle and brings escape from some inward tension. With St Paul, for instance, there came release from a career of persecution which he instinctively (or, in other words, below the level of consciousness) felt to be wrong.

Conversion is unlike mystical experience in that it can be induced. Inge has coined the phrase that "religion is better caught than taught"; and, when the time is ripe for the crisis of conversion, emotion rather than teaching will effect the ardently sought release.

There is nothing holy or beautiful which cannot be defiled; and conversion can be degraded by unscrupulous 'revivalists' so that for them it is merely a method of making money. The novel entitled *Elmer Gantry* was written with the exaggeration born of desire to expose an evil; but I fear that in the religious life of America there does exist a misuse, such as its author describes, of emotion which ought to be held sacred.

§467. *The psychology of conversion.*

Most psychologists are agreed that in conversion there is suddenly brought into consciousness a process of synthesis for which preparation has been made in the 'unconscious mind'. Modern psychology is a subject, still in a state of ferment, in which extravagant theories are not seldom reared on an exiguous basis of fact. But one of its assured conclusions seems to be that logical processes can take place below the level of consciousness. Ideas buried in the unconscious mind can form the source of chains of sound reasoning of which we are unaware; and, in the end, the conclusions reached can by some uprush dominate the conscious mind. If the ideas are harmful, or false, lunacy may develop, as Hart* has shewn in a brilliant little volume. There are times, on the other hand, when such 'unconscious cerebration' will help the mathematician or man of science towards the discovery which he seeks. The fact that spiritual harmony is obtained by a similar process of 'unconscious thinking' offers an explanation of conversion. Through storm and stress harmony has been reached in the lower levels of the mind. And the influence of some person, who probably has passed through the same crisis but who in any case can by suggestion effect the desired release, leads to the flooding of full consciousness by light and peace.

Had such a tumultuous release never taken place it is possible that gradually a sense of inward unity would have filtered through to consciousness. With the placid 'once-born' type of William James' famous classification some such process probably occurs. Certainly in some religious communions the necessity of conversion seems to be replaced by the steady influence of 'church teaching' and sacramental worship.

§ 468. *The value of conversion.*

What is to be our attitude towards conversion? As William James says, to him who has had the experience it is a "real, definite and memorable event". I would add that it is profoundly healthy. Further, if it can be brought to pass through the influence of some earnest religious leader, it will enable him to give of the best within himself in the most helpful way possible.

The evangelical movement in England in the eighteenth century, that spiritual cleansing of the nation which we associate with Wesley (1703–1791) and Whitefield (1714–1770), worked almost entirely through conversion: and its deep and lasting influence testifies to the value of such spiritual experience. The great Wesley, it will be remembered, believed that he found himself and his mission in an hour of conversion on May 24, 1738.

* Bernard Hart, *The Psychology of Insanity.* Cambridge University Press, 3rd ed. 1916 and later.

Similarly, if we take the greatest religious movement in England during the last half-century, that of the Salvation Army, we find conversion in the forefront of its programme of the reclaiming of outcasts, the raising of the fallen. 'Blood and Fire'; no words could better typify Christian conversion. The burning sense of anguish, the ardent longing for release, the memory of the sacrifice of Christ, the blood outpoured for many to be the new wine of the Kingdom of God—all are joined in the crisis which 'saves sinners'.

Of late the evangelical churches in England—I cannot speak of Scotland—seem to have lost something of their enthusiasm for conversion. Unless they can recapture the spiritual power of which it is the essential outcome they will die. To the spiritual aesthete conversion may seem somewhat vulgar: any deep and strong emotion may offend those who prefer superficial amenities. But churches die of respectability just as they become a nuisance through superstition. Conversion takes a man so fully into the realities of the spiritual world that he ignores respectability and has no need of superstition. Thus conversion has been the mainspring of the free spiritual life of English evangelicalism.

§ 469. *Conversion and 'fundamentalism'.*

The reason why conversion is regarded with mistrust by many who ought to welcome its power is that at the present time it is temporarily associated with 'fundamentalism'. Such association, of course, is purely accidental and can have no permanence. Conversion is the sudden conviction that all man's powers and passions can be given to God's service: it is, to use somewhat ecclesiastical language, the consecration of personality. Such a psychological process has no inherent or natural connection with a belief that all the books of the Bible are so inspired that it is infallible. In fact, the process and the belief are singularly remote, the one from the other. But conversion has been misused by fundamentalist leaders, who have taken advantage of their ascendancy at the moment of crisis to instil belief in the verbal inspiration of the Scriptures. It has, therefore, somewhat 'lost caste' with educated people.

In addition it must be admitted that, in the reaction following the War, religion in all communions has become more 'institutionalised': the priest has displaced the prophet. Now, conversion is a disturbing factor to the priest and his ordered system. It tends to be explosive and may easily result not only in free criticism but also in new ventures in search of deeper spiritual reality. I highly esteem the Methodist Church and would say nothing which seemed to disparage it; but I sometimes wonder whether John Wesley would not to-day be an explosive force within it although it owes its very existence to his conversion.

All these considerations lead me to think that, in the religious revival which will assuredly, though perhaps tardily, follow the present unrest, conversion will become once again a great spiritual force. It will be associated, not with fundamentalism, but with a belief that the world described by science is the realm of God. The Bible will be, not a miracle of infallibility, but a storehouse of spiritual treasure. I fancy that the traditional creeds will lose the authority which some now claim for them. When men have inward certainty their faith does not need the buttress of a creed; and obvious disadvantages attach to creeds fashioned by men whose assumptions and modes of thought differed from our own.

§ 470. *Mystical experience.*

We have previously described what it seemed convenient to call normal religious experience, and we said that essentially it consists in the process whereby we grow to understand that goodness, beauty and truth express the nature of Ultimate Reality, and that through them some measure of communion is possible with the God Whose attributes they are.

We have now to consider mystical experience, the abnormal or super-normal religious experience which is so puzzling and yet so important in the history of religion. Essentially it consists of experience in which the subject believes that he has come into direct communication with Ultimate Reality. The veils, says the mystic, normally hide God. His presence is indirectly apprehended, His nature inferred by the activity of the mind. But there come states of the soul when the veils are removed and Supreme Reality is revealed to us. These states constitute mystical experience.

How far are they rightly to be given the supreme importance which mystics claim for them? Are they not rather pathological, psychological abnormalities which yield illusion? Before we attempt to answer such questions we may make certain relevant statements as to which there is general agreement. Mystical experience, as it is described by those to whom it comes, is fairly uniform in its essential characteristics. As we strip away interpretation which clings closely to most attempts to describe what is fundamental, there is revealed a state of consciousness which is independent of time, place, sex and creed. Indian, Mohammedan and Christian mystics of ancient, medieval and modern times, agree remarkably in their description of mystical experience and in the importance which they attach to it.

Unfortunately the highest form of the mystical state can only be described by negatives: a 'blank trance' which is infinitely precious and satisfying seems to be as adequate a description as we can frame.

Certain approximations to, or simulations of, the mystical state can be produced by drugs. Alcohol produces a sense of escape into a larger world, more sympathetic and more joyous than that in which the sober man finds himself. Nitrous oxide mocks us by pretending to give us an amazing insight into the truth of things: then full consciousness returns and we babble doggerel as we try to tell others of the profound depths that we have reached. Other drugs have like effects and I suppose that it will be generally agreed that all such are pathological. Yet there remains the possibility that the drugs actually open avenues of consciousness which are normally closed and that the harmful effects of most of them coexist to an uncertain extent with an enhancement of perception.

The practice of asceticism resembles the use of drugs in that by it mystical states can be induced. But, though hunger and sleeplessness seem to be able at times to produce the genuine thing, hallucinations and hysterical conflicts are so often also present as to make it clear that extravagant asceticism is no less dangerous than drugs.

We hardly need to say explicitly that by no means all religious people have mystical experience; but, *per contra*, some of those to whom such experience comes are only religious in the vague sense that they find through their religion fellowship with the unseen. Possibly the flashes of deep-seated satisfaction which come in response to prayer are analogous to the overpowering revelation of the mystical state. But, alike from the intuitive sense of the meaning and purposiveness of life that characterises quiet religious faith and from the inward unity attained in conversion, mystical exaltation can be separated by its non-intellectual content and its intensity.

We have said that mysticism is independent of creed. Such a result necessarily follows from the non-intellectual content of the highest forms of mystical experience. But the ecstatic sense of union with the Absolute leads naturally, as William James says, to a monistic and optimistic interpretation of the Universe. Medieval Christian mystics were often pantheistic in their outlook: and it is generally true that mysticism leads more readily to pantheistic optimism than to any other type of belief.

§ 471. *Illustrations of mystical experience.*

The pagan mysticism of classical antiquity at its best is to be seen in Plotinus (A.D. *ca.* 205–270). In a famous passage from the sixth book of his *Enneads* he describes the state of one who has a vision of God*:

> In this state the seer does not see or distinguish or imagine two things; he becomes another, he ceases to be himself or to belong to himself. He belongs to God and is one with Him, like two concentric circles; they are one when they coincide, and two only when they are separated. It is only in this sense that the Soul is other than God. Therefore this vision is hard to describe. For how can one describe, as other than oneself, that which, when one saw it, seemed to be one with oneself?
>
> This is no doubt why in the mysteries we are forbidden to reveal them to the uninitiated. That which is divine is ineffable, and cannot be shown to those who have not had the happiness to see it. Since in the vision there were not two things, but seer and seen were one, if a man could preserve the memory of what he was when he was mingled with the divine, he would have in himself an image of God. For he was then one with God, and retained no difference, either in relation to himself or to others. Nothing stirred within him, neither anger nor concupiscence nor even reason or spiritual perception or his own personality, if we may say so. Caught up in an ecstasy, tranquil and alone with God, he enjoyed an imperturbable calm; shut up in his proper essence he declined not to either side, he turned not even to himself; he was in a state of perfect stability; he had become stability itself.

Having thus explained, so far as is possible, the content of supreme mystical experience, Plotinus a little later endeavours also to describe its nature. He fails, of course, but his failure is illuminating:

> Perhaps we ought not to speak of *vision*; it is rather another mode of seeing, an ecstasy and simplification, an abandonment of oneself, a desire for immediate contact, a stability, a deep intention to unite oneself with what is to be seen in the sanctuary.

These passages filtered from Neo-platonism, through the writer called Dionysius the Areopagite†, to the Christian Middle Ages and have thus been influential in standardising a mystical type for Western Europe. Numerous other descriptions of the form and content of the mystical

---

* The translations are those of W. R. Inge, *The Philosophy of Plotinus.* 2 vols. Longmans, vol. II, 1918, pp. 140, 141.

† Thomas Whittaker (*The Neo-platonists.* Cambridge, 2nd ed. 1918, p. 187) accepts the generally held belief that this writer was a Christian platonist, trained in the Athenian School, who possibly had been a hearer of Proclus (A.D. 410–485).

state exist. I will not reproduce those to which access can readily be obtained in the standard textbooks on mysticism. It is, however, perhaps worth while to give the words in which Tennyson* revealed that to him there came 'frequently' an experience that was essentially of the mystical type:

I have never had any revelations through anaesthetics, but a kind of waking trance—this for lack of a better word—I have frequently had, quite up from boyhood, when I have been all alone. This has come upon me through repeating my own name to myself silently, till all at once, as it were out of the intensity of the consciousness of individuality, individuality itself seemed to dissolve and fade away into boundless being, and this not a confused state but the clearest, the surest of the surest, utterly beyond words—where death was an almost laughable impossibility—the loss of personality (if so it were) seeming no extinction, but the only true life. I am ashamed of my feeble description. Have I not said the state is utterly beyond words?

Professor Tyndall, in a letter, recalls Tennyson saying of this condition: "By God Almighty! there is no delusion in the matter! It is no nebulous ecstasy, but a state of transcendent wonder, associated with absolute clearness of mind".

My own experience, if I may be allowed to make a personal intrusion, has been similar. Four or five times in life, the first time when I was a boy some fourteen years old and the last time at the age of thirty-three, I have felt, enjoyed and wondered at a sudden exaltation which seemed to carry with it an understanding of the innermost nature of things. So vivid has been the experience that I could to-day go to the exact spot in the street of the Oxfordshire village where the flash of revelation first came. Always such experience has occurred in sunshine and out-of-doors, never in church. Always it has been unexpected. Always I have been alone. There has never been ill-health as an exciting cause. On the last occasion, which still remains vivid, I sat down in the early afternoon on a piece of bare turf in a fern-covered moor near the sea. I remember that I was going to bathe from a stretch of shingle to which the few people who stayed in the village seldom went. Suddenly the noise of the insects was hushed. Time seemed to stop. A sense of infinite power and peace came upon me. I can best liken the combination of timelessness with amazing fullness of existence to the feeling one gets in watching the rim of a great silent fly-wheel or the unmoving surface of a deep, strongly flowing river. Nothing happened: yet existence was completely full. All was clear. I was in a world where the confusion and waste and loss inseparable from time had vanished. At the heart

---

* Quoted by William James, *Varieties of Religious Experience.* Longmans, 1912, p. 384.

of the world there was power and peace and eternal life. How long this blank trance, so full and so empty, lasted I cannot say. Probably a very short time indeed. It passed, leaving me neither tired in body nor mentally irritable. The memory remains. And it is because an inexplicable quality of supreme significance attaches to it that it remains precious.

§ 472. *The 'dark night of the soul'.*

No account of mystical experience, however brief, can be satisfactory if it ignores the period of distress usually called the dark night of the soul. This period often, though by no means invariably*, precedes the supreme revelation and is commonly regarded as a necessary stage when mystical illumination is deliberately sought and artificial means, other than drugs, are used to produce it. Probably we ought to see, in the agonies of despair which some mystics describe, the course of a fierce struggle to overcome the sensuality and selfishness which shut out God.

No uncontaminated religious fervour, or true spiritual understanding, can be reached without some measure of renunciation and self-discipline. The paradoxes which express this truth are the most familiar in religious literature. We die to live and lose to find. "He that hateth his life in this world shall keep it unto life eternal." "If any man would be my disciple, let him deny himself and take up a cross and follow me." As Pratt†, in his psychological study of the religious consciousness, says truly: "Moral purity is the necessary condition of the mystic life. The soul that is filled with the love of sin will have no room for the love of God".

On such truths the practice of asceticism and all else that belongs to the purgative way have been based. But a study of what various mystics have done 'to subdue the flesh' is painful and not seldom disgusting. The source-books of the subject are full of exaggerations of renunciation which are horribly pathological. They are, as Pratt says, obviously associated with the dualistic view of human nature generally held when the tradition of catholic mysticism was formed: that soul and body are joined together temporarily in rather external fashion and that they carry on a constant warfare with each other. Such a belief naturally led to austerities which we now find shocking.

---

* For instance, W. R. Inge says that "there is not a trace in Plotinus of the 'dark night of the soul', the experience of dereliction". *Loc. cit.* vol. II, p. 150.

† J. B. Pratt, *The Religious Consciousness.* Macmillan, 1921, p. 375.

Our modern aim is so to strengthen and discipline the body as to fit it both for intellectual activity and also for spiritual understanding. A due amount of sleep, an adequate though moderate amount of simple food, some exercise in the fresh air and contact with unspoiled nature: by such means we seek to keep the body in health and the mind whole-some. Of course, if such constitute the background of man's physical life, spiritual restlessness and moral conflict need not, and probably will not, be absent from the life of his soul. But after inward struggle and victory we may expect that there will come spiritual understand-ing; and, if God so please, there may possibly follow the higher vision which the mystics prize.

We moderns who reject the old dualism of body and soul do not find it necessary to harm the one that the other may be stronger and more beautiful. We know that the phrase "the flesh lusteth against the spirit" is a metaphor: sin and saintliness alike arise in the mind, which together with the body forms that unit which we term man. Hence a tortured body is likely to produce a warped mind. Bodily health will, by the very nature of our being, minister to religious health; and health of body should be regarded as a pre-requisite alike for outstanding intellectual achievement and for exceptional religious perception*.

These conclusions will be challenged by those who take a perverted delight in the austerities which have preceded mystical states. Such will claim that horrible forms of asceticism were necessary to the ex-perience which followed them. I grant that it is possible to contend that, for instance, Henry Suso (1295–1366), the fourteenth-century German ascetic, would never have known the joy of the mystical trance but for the austerities which he practised. But against such con-tentions one quotation is sufficient. "In order not to be able to avoid the bites of the vermin (for he did not bathe during the twenty-two years) he put his hands in slings during the night." We say bluntly that, if God will not give the highest revelation of Himself save to those who use such methods, the world which He has made is not rational.

We grant that ill-health is at times associated with unexpectedly great achievement and that there is a consumptive mysticism of the cloister which may be compared to the consumptive genius of the Brontës or of Keats. But no one would pretend that literary excellence can only be produced by tuberculosis: and we can confidently assert

* Charles Darwin's genius triumphed over, though it may none the less have been impaired by, chronic ill-health.

that the highest mystical experience which can be safely accepted as a revelation of God will come to the man or woman who is wholesome and healthy in mind and body alike. Such a one, in trying to be loyal to the highest aspiration which God has planted within him, will not escape inward conflict. Quite possibly he will pass through a period of distress which without exaggeration may be described as the dark night of the soul. But he will be under no necessity to ill-treat his body. It will suffice that within his soul he should continue the mental and moral and spiritual struggle that has brought man from barbarism and is slowly fitting him for citizenship of the Kingdom of God.

§ 473. *The worth of mystical experience.*

What must be our verdict as to mystical experience? Is it, as the mystics claim, a state in which the soul reaches a stark simplicity which enables it directly to perceive the Spiritual Unity in which the world has its being? Those of us who believe that the religious valuation of life gives us knowledge of the mind and will of God will not dismiss as impossible the claims which mystics put forward. The intensity of conviction which results from mystical experience is in itself remarkable. The mystics are quite certain that God has revealed Himself. From many lands and from different ages they speak with an inward assurance which is most impressive. The world for them is not a chaos of loose ends, nor an arena of conflict between ultimate controlling powers hostile to each other. Beneath apparent confusion there is unity, rule by a single Spiritual Principle. And, moreover, waste and loss, evil and suffering, do not belong to the Real: "the heart of the Eternal is most wonderfully kind".

Yet all would wish that the mystics had more to tell us. They waver between pantheism and theism, often inclining to the former. And, after some states which closely simulate those of pure mysticism, the moral dangers of pantheism are not always avoided. A study of primitive religion shews conclusively that pseudo-religious exaltation and moral laxity can coexist: emotional satisfaction then leaves the moral law disregarded. Just as drugs seem to link mystical experience to physiological degeneracy, so apparently experience, which at the least resembles the mystical, can be associated with moral disorder. But on the other hand, as against such doubts, it may be urged that, in the world of our experience, gold is seldom found unmixed with base metal: we do not despise the gold because it must be, as it were, rescued from impurity.

For what it is worth I give my own opinion that in mystical experience there *is* a richer stronger intuition of the Divine than men normally possess. The mystic gets nearer to the inner nature of things; and, if he is really one of the pure in heart, he is blessed with a true vision of God. But others who have had no such exceptional vision granted to them may be not less worthy children of the Kingdom of God which they help to create. Moreover, I would strongly re-assert what has already been emphasised in § 448, that there is nothing rightly to be described as supernatural even in the most intense mystical experience. What is received, though it be exceptional, is natural; it is not different in kind from the understanding which suddenly unravels mental or moral perplexity. No one will say that John Wesley's religious experience lacked depth or strength: yet we have his affirmation: "I pretend to no extraordinary revelations or gifts of the Holy Ghost, none but what every Christian may receive, and ought to expect and pray for".

It is, however, unavoidable that science should be agnostic with regard to mysticism. Experiment is impossible, save with pathological mysticism induced by extravagant asceticism or drugs. With what we may call uncontaminated mysticism there is no possibility of creating a "uniform repetition of likenesses", to use Hort's phrase; and such uniformity is the basis of the synthetic knowledge which science exists to organise.

But we may not unfairly remark that science must be equally agnostic with regard to the source and nature of those uprushes of creative power from which come great art. What makes the great artist? Is his work a proof that he has been given some special intuition of God, Who is the source of all beauty? To these and other similar questions science can give no satisfying answer. But it is at all events certain that, just as the Philistine* has no reason to despise the artist's work, so the man of science may not term the mystic mad. There *are* diversities of gifts given to men: and reflection upon their source almost always leaves us puzzled.

§ 474. *Induced experience.*

Every student of electrodynamics knows that, if a variable electric current passes through a circuit, it will cause an induced current to

---

* We use the term 'Philistine' with the popular significance which it has obtained from the writings of Matthew Arnold. Modern research has established that the Philistines were more cultured than their Israelite enemies.

appear in an adjacent circuit. Religious experience and belief can be similarly induced, if a person susceptible to suggestion comes under the influence of one with religious enthusiasm and strongly held beliefs. The fact that religious experience of the more emotional type can be thus induced and used to produce dogmatic conviction is of great practical importance and deserves a brief examination. Just as conversion can at the appropriate time be, as it were, precipitated by the psychological process of suggestion, so normal religious experience can be induced alike by personal influence and by suitably chosen modes of worship.

The most simple examples of such induced religious experience result from ordinary teaching in sunday school or catechism class. The beliefs of the teacher, especially if they are emotional rather than intellectual convictions, are caught by the pupil. The pupil ought to be given a resolve that he will be loyal to the moral law and a certainty that through reason, beauty and goodness some measure of communion can be gained with God, the Source of that law. But, unhappily, it is quite possible that he will get, by a process best described as mental infection, a whole dogmatic system, accepted with emotional fervour but irrationally and merely because the teacher holds it.

The power of the teacher's 'suggestion' is enhanced if it be associated with an appropriate type of worship. Such worship, if shrewdly designed, will by creed-repetition or ritual, or in some other way, reenforce the fundamental suggestion and make the emotions and beliefs associated with it permanent fixtures in the mind.

Induced religious experience is, under normal circumstances, predominantly second-hand, the one in whom it appears being passive and contributing no more than a child who learns the multiplication table. Even so, religion thus received may be entirely valuable if, owing to the wisdom and integrity of the teacher, it is moral and spiritual. But induced religion is usually partly good and partly bad, a certain induced spiritual exaltation being allied to imperfect truth or defective morality. Such is typical of the nun, whose religion is normally of the non-critical induced type and who generally combines genuine devotion and self-denial with pettiness, obscurantism and intolerance.

Sometimes induced religion is almost wholly evil. We then witness, with the vanishing of the moral element, the implanting of a mixture of ferocity and religious fervour. Free religious experience among normal Western Europeans often leads to 'heresy'; but it would never have produced the cruelties of the Inquisition. These shew the devilish character which can be given to induced religion when regard for the safety of a Church replaces service to God.

§ 475. *The problem of public worship.*

The ordering of worship so that wholesome elements in religion may be duly emphasised is highly important. When the puritan wished to express the sternness of moral obligation he made his meeting-places gaunt and strong. On the other hand, the emotional aspects of religion are best sustained by worship in which sound and light and colour and even smell all play their part. Music, candles, coloured images, rich windows and incense are adjuncts of worship of very varied value. All are factors in the emotional appeal made by a 'catholic service'. Unfortunately, such a mode of worship is, in actual fact, rarely beautiful, for it is made to satisfy the facile emotion which is chilled by pure beauty though excited by tawdriness and sentiment.

During the present century many churches in England have lost much by cheapening their appeal. The reaction against the puritan ugliness of the Victorian era was wholesome. But catholic tawdriness is aesthetically degrading and morally relaxing. I believe that if we could associate Christian worship with a severe and satisfying beauty, ecclesiastical standards of truth and righteousness would improve. Bad taste, evasion and hypocrisy are natural allies; and the religion which they foster or capture is a danger to the community.

It is sometimes urged, in defence of cheapened worship, that higher and aesthetically richer forms make no appeal. Undoubtedly there is great need for such education of the average churchgoer that his, or her, soul may be attuned to the best. But churches exist for such a purpose; and they condemn themselves if they assert that their manifest duty is too difficult a form of service to God.

§ 476. *Sacraments.*

No consideration of worship, as it exists among us to foster religious experience, can ignore the use of sacraments. So often is their fundamental simplicity obscured that it is well to set out quite obvious illustrations of the use of symbols or signs to deepen religious understanding and to strengthen religious aspiration. Think, for example, of the Christian who wishes to encourage devotion to ideal aims and to teach the redemptive power of self-sacrifice. He naturally seeks to recall the life and death of Christ. The Cross thus becomes an effective symbol, an inspiration to much that is highest in the religious life of man.

When, in addition, it is desired to emphasise union between men who seek to further the aims and to follow the example of Christ, the repetition of His last meal with His followers becomes central in worship. Entrance into the society of those who seek in purity of heart to serve Christ is naturally symbolised by baptism, wherein the washing away of all that is unworthy is signified. The Cross is perhaps the simplest of Christian sacraments: for to the man, before whose mind it rises as a bulwark against moral cowardice and as an incentive to self-sacrifice, it is an outward and visible sign of an inward and spiritual grace.

A sacrament is, of course, a psychological process; and its value is largely, if not entirely, due to the power of suggestion. It is not a *mere* sign of some desire or a *mere* memorial of some event; but there is in it a measure of efficacy. It works: it makes the desire more effective: it causes the memorial to become an active influence. Much of the misunderstanding as to the nature of 'sacramental grace' would disappear if the false isolation of the two Christian 'sacraments of the Gospel' were brought to an end. There are many true parallels to these in the social life of man; and through Nature there can be gained satisfying revelations of God's power and care and of His expression of Himself through beauty. In fact, though 'the sacraments of the Gospel' be but two in number, the sacraments of human life are not seven but seventy times seven.

We cannot conclude even a brief discussion of sacramental worship without emphasising that induced sacramental experience, such that he who receives it fancies himself privileged to enter some supernatural realm, is dangerous. In the first place, the notion is not true. In all human experience the spiritual emerges from the natural; and, as was stated in § 448, there exists no realm of super-Nature which is peculiarly God's own as opposed to a realm of Nature where His control and presence are imperfect. In the second place, so to isolate sacramental experience as to make it virtually an exclusive channel of a particular type of Divine grace is to create in human thought yet another artificial opposition which has no existence in fact. Judged by the fruits of his religious life the Quaker experiences the presence and power of God in Christ as compellingly as the catholic. Yet for the most part his religious experience is to be classed as direct rather than induced: it is certainly not sacramental in the narrow catholic sense. We may add that the religious exaltation which comes from the pure beauty of

Nature—the wind across the uplands, sun in spring-time on rain-washed meadows—such religious experience is also direct and not induced; and though there is in it no primary moral appeal, yet it makes for pureness of living because the natural unity between beauty and goodness somehow expresses the fundamental value-structure of the Universe to which we belong.

§ 477. *The necessity for guided religious experience.*

The danger of all induced religion is that the induced experience may be emotionally satisfying but morally barren, and that the beliefs held as a result of what is essentially second-hand enthusiasm may have little or no truth in them. The operative principle in highly emotional types of induced religion is, as we have said, that process of suggestion which is a primitive human trait associated with the herd-instinct of gregarious animals; and, for this reason, primitive human fancies and superstitions are easily conveyed by it. Religious emotion, if it is not to be dangerous, must be severely disciplined by the reason and must also be permeated by a sense of obedience to the moral law. For this reason it should always be subject to the guidance, direct or indirect, of some great religious teacher.

Probably the finest religious experience possible to the average man is that which, on the one hand, is spontaneous and free but which also, on the other hand, finds itself strengthened and deepened by the guidance of Christ. Heart and head will then combine to discover in Christ's teaching an explanation of, or an incentive to, all that is deepest, strongest and finest in human religious feeling. Induction has done its work when it has given a man confidence in the free judgment by which he sees the greatness of Christ's revelation of the Divine. He can then, not uncritically but after reasoned argument, create from that revelation an active faith which will not easily degenerate.

The authority of a great religious teacher must always be freely and inwardly accepted: the external compulsion of custom or tradition is of little value. If an accepted religion be mainly based on custom or tradition it will rapidly decay under adverse circumstances. Whenever, as during a great war, the moral level of the community falls, low types of religious emotion spread rapidly by suggestion. And similarly when, owing to rapid changes in the culture of a people, an opportunity is given to intellectual anarchy, ancient types of religious credulity reappear under thin disguises. The people who succumb to these semi-barbarous manifestations of the religious instinct are sublimely unconscious of their fall. Examples come readily to the mind. When, after each calamity that overtook the nation, the prophets of Israel had to fight against the recrudescence of Canaanite cults, they were contending against people who were profoundly certain that they alone knew the true direction of religious progress. England to-day is filled with misguided men and women who similarly believe that in embracing some retrograde superstition they are ministering to a religious revival.

§ 478. *The revival of pagan sacramentalism.*

A singularly good example of the revival of superstition in a period of intellectual anarchy and religious decay is to be found, as we saw in § 440, in the recrudescence in England of beliefs connected with the Mass. The rejection of transubstantiation was a crucial factor in the struggle of the Reformation: and the rejection carried with it, as the literature of the time abundantly proves, repudiation of the idea that a Spiritual Presence was associated after consecration with the bread and wine of Holy Communion. During the present century this belief has revived in a most extraordinary fashion. Other doctrines and practices discarded at the Reformation have similarly re-established themselves. We have witnessed, in fact, in the Church of England within a quarter of a century the significant process of change which transformed the faith of St Paul into catholicism.

The statement that the catholicising of Christianity was the paganising of it is more true than most epigrams. To a certain extent St Paul facilitated the process. He was a Jew of the Dispersion, brought up in Tarsus on the southern coast of Asia Minor, in the centre of the region where, as we know from Plutarch, Mithraism was flourishing a century before the death of Christ. St Paul used with familiarity the language of the mysteries; and possibly, or even probably, ideas associated with these cults influenced his presentation of the Christian faith. But careful scholars, for the most part, find in the sacramental teaching of St Paul little more than a superficial resemblance to the mystery-religions. Now these faiths from the time of the Punic Wars to the eventual triumph of Christianity were active within the Roman world. Of their fundamental nature Cumont* says: "The purity and holiness imparted by the practice of sacred ceremonies were the indispensable condition for obtaining eternal life. The mysteries promised a blessed

---

* F. Cumont, *Oriental Religions in Roman Paganism.* English translation, Kegan Paul, 1911, p. 209.

immortality to their initiates: claimed to reveal to them infallible means of effecting their salvation".

Thus the mystery-religions worked by stimulating religious emotion; and the belief which the emotion affirmed and preserved was what we should now term magical or mechanical sacramentalism. Such sacramentalism associates itself naturally with conceptions like 'holy food' and derives strength from the notion that the Divine can be embodied in inanimate things.

It must be remembered that the mysteries were a sort of conglomerate of religious myths, cults and beliefs drawn for the most part from the older paganism of what we now call the Near East. In this conglomerate elements derived from Syrian sources were important: the Syrian type of paganism was so attractive that two Roman Emperors desired to give it official status.

Now, throughout Syria, as Biblical archaeologists have made clear, sacred stones or pillars were important features in primitive religion. For instance, among the Israelites, Beth-el, 'the House of God', owing to an association (whether of fact or story) with the stone of Jacob's dream, became under the monarchy the most popular sanctuary of the Northern Kingdom. Frazer* remarks that "even the prophet Hosea appears to have regarded a standing-stone or pillar as an indispensable adjunct of a holy place dedicated to the worship of Jehovah". In later times Hebrew religious leaders saw that such stones were a hindrance to religious progress: the 'high places' were destroyed: sacrificial worship was centred in Jerusalem and the synagogue replaced the local sanctuary. But the old regard for the sacred stone persisted through Syria. It exists to-day, for the Black Stone at Mecca has a central place in local Mohammedan devotion.

Moreover, as Frazer* says, "originally the deity seems to have been conceived as actually resident in the stones: it was his awful presence which conferred on them their sanctity". The belief lasted long: as Cumont says, "the power of this Semitic litholatry equalled its persistence". Well into the Christian era the rough stones called bethels were still regarded "as the residence of the god, or rather, as the matter in which the god was embodied†". In Greek they are called significantly λίθοι ἔμψυχοι‡. Modern catholicism seems far removed from

---

* Sir J. G. Frazer, *Folk-lore in the Old Testament*. Macmillan, vol. II, 1919, p. 59.

† Cumont, *op. cit.* p. 116.

‡ Cumont gives the references, *op. cit.* p. 244.

ancient bethel-cults; but we need only transfer the Divine indwelling from a stone to a piece of bread and we obtain the exact belief which transubstantiation tries to make plausible. Just as the stone or pillar was to an Israelite of the ninth century before Christ an indispensable adjunct of a holy place dedicated to Jehovah, so a piece of consecrated bread for the modern catholic makes especially holy a church dedicated to Christ.

To trace the extent to which catholicism resulted from the infiltration of ancient paganism into Christianity would be a lengthy and unprofitable task. It suffices to say that, during the decline of the human critical faculty which was so marked in classical civilisation after the beginning of the second century* of our era, Christianity was gradually assimilated to the mysteries. The catholicism which resulted was such that it and the opposed paganism "moved in the same intellectual and moral sphere,† and a man could actually pass from one to the other without shock or interruption. Sometimes when reading the long works of the last Latin writers...scholars could well ask whether their authors were pagan or Christian ".

The truth that catholicism arose from a transformation of primitive Christianity in the atmosphere of the pagan mysteries is often denied; but the known facts are decisive. It is to be regretted that detailed evidence is not as full as we could wish, inasmuch as documents describing the mystery-beliefs have largely perished. Their destruction was probably deliberate. Yet enough remains to shew that the beliefs of catholicism repudiated by a sound instinct at the Reformation were precisely those mystery-religion accretions which were alien from the moral and spiritual simplicity of Christ's teaching.

§ 479. *Religious degeneration.*

The influence within catholicism of ideas associated with the Mass, 'holy' water, the relics of saints, and so forth, shews the prodigious vitality of primitive religious beliefs. A new faith may appear to replace these lower beliefs by a purer form of religion: yet after a time they are

---

* The decline has been demonstrated in detail in the writings of Dr Charles Singer. See, for instance, his article on 'Ancient Medicine' in *Science and Civilisation*, edited by F. S. Marvin. Oxford University Press, 1923, especially pp. 70, 71.

† The interaction between the two forms of faith is well described by Samuel Dill, *Roman Society in the Last Century of the Western Empire*. Macmillan, 1898. "In truth, the line between Christian and pagan was long wavering and uncertain" (p. 11).

found growing within it. A reformation may seem to sweep them away: in due course at some period of moral and religious anarchy they return. Alike in Western Europe, in Persia, in India and in China we can see the same phenomenon.

The spiritual monism of the Vedanta, for instance, has been successfully invaded by popular Hinduism. Popular Buddhism in China is recognised as degenerate by all who have studied its origin. The researches of such a scholar as J. H. Moulton into the teaching of Zoroaster equally prove the decay of a fine form of faith under the pernicious influence of semi-barbarous practices and beliefs. He says* that Zoroastrianism, "as its founder left it, is absolutely monotheistic, free from any unworthy views of God, earnest and practical, and untainted by asceticism; and if in later times it fell below its founder's too lofty ideals, and became corrupted with ritualistic puerilities and a worship of saints and angels which seriously compromises monotheism, it may be doubted whether it goes beyond the corruptions of Christianity in many of the more superstitious corners of modern Europe".

Perhaps such phenomena ought not to surprise us. Man's thoughts and feelings change but slowly. Though he has probably been on the earth for well-nigh a million years it is only, as it were, yesterday that he began to cast off religious barbarism. All the great religions of mankind are due to leaders who emerged in the millennium which began in the seventh century before Christ. About the same time natural science emerged among the Ionian Greeks. Thus science and moralised religion are only some 2500 years old: we must expect that, for a long time to come, the advance in culture of which they are the expression will be insecure.

Accurate thought is fatiguing and moral enthusiasm is easily chilled by the pressure of circumstance. Religious prophets resemble leaders in scientific discovery in that they are alike rare. We need to look far ahead if we would reassure ourselves that, notwithstanding retrograde movements in human society, God is active among men, patiently leading them towards the ideal Kingdom of Christ's vision.

§ 480. *Religious ecstasy must be subject to morality and reason.*

Any study of religious experience will be gravely defective unless some attempt is made to assess the value of such experience as, when rationalised, leads to beliefs which are untrue. What are we to say of

* J. H. Moulton, *The Christian Religion in the Study and the Street.* Hodder and Stoughton, 1919, p. 180.

the worship of an Hindu idol? The idol is grotesque and the ceremonies of which it is the centre are, to our thinking, uncouth, noisy, absurd, barbaric. Yet some of the worshippers as they leave the idol's presence will shew in their faces a glow of religious exaltation: and an Hindu with a university training will gravely use the fact as a proof that the god has deigned to dwell within the image, and to give his grace to those who have approached him with faithfulness and joy.

Plainly, in such a phenomenon, the influence of heredity combines with traditional rites to preserve the psychological atmosphere in which erroneous notions thrive. We, with a different mental ancestry, would be merely repelled by such rites: we should find it impossible to persuade ourselves that the god was present within the, to us, repulsive figure. Yet the religious fervour of an Hindu under such circumstances is genuine: his belief is often invincible. The fervour may have no moral content, yet it is a sign of conviction of communion with the god. We may hesitate wholly to condemn it in itself, yet some of its manifestations will only too probably be deplorable. In fact, religious ecstasy is highly dangerous unless it is subject both to morality and reason.

We must even admit that, whenever Christian religious enthusiasm has flared high, antinomianism, a sort of impatient disregard for the moral law, has been in the background. There is something primitive in strong religious emotion and, unless disciplined by reason and morality, it evokes ugly, nasty concomitants of primitive religion. Science and puritanism resemble one another in that both are austere: the discipline of the mind in the one corresponds to the moral discipline of the other. The popular emotional types of religion need to be controlled by both science and puritanism if their ultimate outcome is not to be harmful.

§ 481. *Religious experience and dogmatic assertion.*

Such considerations will put us on our guard against the use of religious experience to establish dogma. Dogmas, of course, are merely assertions that certain propositions in the domain of religious thought are true. Each dogma which we are asked to accept must therefore be investigated by the dry light of reason. In the first place, there must be an examination of the facts of experience or experiment on which it rests. Then enquiry must be made into the legitimacy of the arguments by which the dogma is derived from the accepted facts. Finally, if after such critical investigation the dogma seems to merit acceptance, its congruity with our general view of the world must be considered.

As a rule the religious enthusiast passes directly from some striking experience to beliefs which the experience does not guarantee.

An illustration from current controversy will give point to these obvious generalities. I quote from a private letter written to convince me that Christ is 'really present' in the consecrated elements of the sacrament of Holy Communion. The writer, a churchworker and formerly a 'moderate' churchwoman, recalls how she went to stay at a convent and there, after a few days, was led to pray in a side-chapel where "the Blessed Sacrament was reserved".

Immediately I entered I was gripped by a sense of a Holy Presence, the Presence of God, so that I trembled as I knelt. Then I had to go lower on my knees. I could not help myself falling on my face. Then I was flooded with the love of God as well as awed by His nearness. I could not move for a long time. When at length I felt I must rise and leave the Chapel, I trembled so that I could scarcely walk. From that time my happiest hours of communion with our Lord were spent in that Presence. I approached It with fear and trembling each time.

She added, however, somewhat later in the same letter: "I cannot say that now I have such exceptional experience". None the less she urged that in every church the consecrated elements should be 're-served' so that such experience might be possible. Obviously, the experience does not prove the dogma of a 'Real Spiritual Presence' associated with, or inherent in, the consecrated bread and wine. Were we to allow our churchworker's argument we should equally have to allow the educated Hindu's 'proof' that his god is in the idol. In each case there was religious exaltation induced by environmental conditions. But the churchworker had an experience analogous to conversion while the religious exaltation of the Hindu results from normal worship and racial traditions learned in childhood. Of course, the crisis of the churchworker is easily explained as the result of suggestion operating in the lower unconscious levels of her mind. She had heard much argument as to the value of 'reservation'; and, unknown to herself, had in her unconscious mind accepted the doctrine of a spiritual presence connected with the consecrated elements. The sudden uprush of latent convictions had a memorable splendour; but significantly there was no repetition of the experience after the period of crisis had passed. The new belief with its emotional atmosphere was within a few days firmly established. The poor woman in whose mind it lodged proved herself ready to receive harmful suggestion, and in the end was overcome by a false dogma.

§ 482. *The duty of religious teachers.*

It is the duty of religious teachers to set religious experience so free from erroneous suggestion that from such experience goodness comes in natural alliance with truth. Moreover, religious teachers cannot preserve truth unless they assert the authority of reason in matters of faith. Hort said with great wisdom more than thirty years ago*: "There can be no surer sign of decrepitude and decay in faith than a prevalent nervousness about naming and commending reason, an unwillingness to allude to its existence except under wrappings of language which suggest that it is but a necessary evil". Hort also wrote of "our present cowardice", which he described as "of modern growth". Unfortunately, in the generation which has passed since his words were published, evasion and a nervous fear of reason among influential Christian leaders have allowed and even encouraged falsehood to flourish.

By all means let religious enthusiasm be stimulated. The man or woman to whom come moments of spiritual exaltation is to be envied. To be sure that one is enfolded by a Divine presence and power is to find a pearl of great price. But let it be remembered that spiritual exaltation which is built on falsehood is an evil thing. The great religious teacher is one in whom religious emotion is not only strong but also pure; and who, to preserve its purity, is quick to test by the dry light of reason the knowledge which such emotion seems to give him. When in such a one moral earnestness is joined to spiritual enthusiasm we ought to recognise a true prophet of God.

* F. J. A. Hort, *The Way, the Truth, the Life.* Macmillan, 1897, p. 176.

Lecture xx

IMMORTALITY

§ 483. *Soul and body.*

In approaching the subject of immortality we must first remind ourselves of what science has to say with regard to man. Does he consist of a living body animated by a soul? Can he legitimately for purposes of thought be separated into body, soul and spirit, to use language derived from the standard versions of the New Testament? The answer must be, as previous enquiry has shewn, that such divisions represent convenient ways of speaking: they must not be taken to indicate any possibility known to ourselves of actual severance. Man's body and his life cannot be separated: the two form the living organism. Similarly, his consciousness is not a separable element: it belongs to the organism. In the process of evolution increased complexity of function and structure in the organism has proceeded *pari passu* with the development of consciousness. The latter mysteriously accompanies the complex physiological and physical processes which are made possible by elaborate structural organisation.

We have in a previous discussion in Lecture XVII (§ 444) rejected the notion of psycho-physical parallelism and have contended that concurrent psychical and physical phenomena are two aspects of a single process of change. From this standpoint we must conclude that in so far as there is a duality of soul and body it is a duality in unity: we cannot rightly speak of an immaterial soul present in a material body. Thus what is usually called 'animism' must be rejected. We cannot, in fact, in the light of modern knowledge refuse to accept what Hort termed "an ultimate position, not proved, but likely to be true". This position Hort stated in the form*: "Man's whole mental and spiritual nature is conditioned by his physical nature and its pathological states, no mental or spiritual movement taking place without a concomitant physical movement".

Now, such conclusions are in conflict with what many would argue to be a very strong Christian tradition. In the Middle Ages death was supposed to occur when the soul left the body: and naïve medieval paintings portraying the soul's departure still survive in church frescoes and in picture galleries. In our hymns similar ideas linger:

* Hort, *loc. cit.* p. 188.

"On the resurrection morning soul and body meet again". We have had in the course of these lectures repeatedly to protest against the dualisms of popular thought: and among such dualisms that of soul and body must be abandoned whenever we desire to use strictly accurate language.

We thus acknowledge that science can rightly assert that man's mental powers and spiritual aspirations are intimately and, so far as our knowledge goes, indissolubly linked to his physical organisation. Damage to the mechanism of the brain or to some biochemical process of the body will often lead to mental and spiritual degeneracy. 'Sleepy sickness', for instance, is a disease caused apparently by a virus which sets up a destructive inflammation of certain portions of the brain and ganglia; its painful after-consequences of moral depravity are now generally recognised. Thus, as we have previously insisted, if mind and body are separable the body is primary: although a healthy mind undoubtedly has an influence tending to keep the body in health, lesions in the body are relatively more potent in harming the mind.

§ 484. *The resurrection of the body.*

It is interesting to recognise that ancient popular thought by a sound instinct emphasised the mind's need of its own body that it might function properly. Hence the life after death was conceived to be bound up with the resurrection of the body (or, more strictly, of the flesh). Modern chemistry has made everyone of any education familiar with the fact that the atoms of which the matter of our bodies consists are distributed by the decay which follows death and may afterwards enter into the bodies of other human beings. Thus 'a resurrection of the flesh', in which the old material was supposed to be gathered together once more, has become incredible.

The phrase 'resurrection of the body', which occurs in the usual translation of the Apostles' Creed, is therefore held to be a mere synonym for the survival of personality unless, by a species of interpretation which is absolutely groundless, it is taken to apply to the Resurrection of Christ. In such changes we have an illustration of the familiar fact that, when the intended meaning of some clause of a venerated document becomes impossible, the clause is not discarded. If it cannot be ignored, a new significance is attached to it. The document thus preserves that character of infallibility which is wrongly supposed to enhance its spiritual value.

§ 485. *Man's decisive separation from the lower animals.*

The descent of man from lower animals, which has not been in doubt since Darwin published his *Descent of Man* in the year 1871, has made it necessary for us to recognise that, alike in his psychological, physiological and physical organisation, man is akin to less highly organised mammals. The ground of his mental, and probably even of his spiritual, faculties can be discovered in such lower animals. But from this fact it is illegitimate to conclude that there is not a gap of great significance separating man from the anthropoids. Man has, and they have not, the power of creating abstract concepts. His self-consciousness is rational and ethical in ways to which they can offer no true parallel. Our power of recognising the existence in the Universe of Absolute Values to which we must be loyal has created in us what we call 'conscience'. The obligations of conscience derive their strength from our instinct that goodness and truth express the spiritual character of the Universe: in the language of Christian belief, in conscience we perceive God's laws. Hence arises the close association of conscience with the aspirations on which civilisation is based.

Now observation leads us to conclude that not even the highest of the anthropoids has any faculty of conscience resembling our own. Blind instincts, unrefined and undeveloped by reason, cannot be regarded as a true analogue. Little profit is gained by discussions as to whether in such a development as that which has led to man we observe a difference in kind or in degree. Inasmuch as the highest anthropoids have an extremely rudimentary faculty of speech, one might argue that therefore in language the difference between them and ourselves is merely a difference of degree. Yet from speech and from the associated development of writing such things as Gifford Lectures have resulted. No one will pretend that such lectures, good or bad, could be intelligible to our anthropoid cousins. In fact, the realm of intellectual abstractions, of spiritual aspiration and achievement, is man's realm. Into it none of the lower animals can enter. For this reason, as I hold, immortality in the form of eternal life can be predicated of man but not of the animals from which he has sprung.

§ 486. *The background of belief in immortality: pantheism and impersonal immortality.*

I personally am convinced that, in Rashdall's words*, "belief in God and belief in Immortality must in the long run stand or fall to-

* See 'The Resurrection and Immortality' in H. Rashdall, *Doctrine and Development*. Methuen, 1898, p. 183.

gether". Of course, if anything resembling a mechanical theory of the Universe is true, no argument for human immortality can exist. The blind forces which, on the assumptions of naturalism, have made man will at his death destroy him and all that is of value in him. Similarly, if pantheism be the true explanation of the riddle of the Universe, there is hardly likely to be a place in that Universe for the survival of human personality. For if God, the immanent ground of all that is, be the Reality that is differentiated into individuals existing in space-time, it would seem that human personality can be only a bundle of accidents: it will not be an end in itself but, in so far as the time-process is not illusory, a means to some end beyond itself. In no living organism, in fact, can there be more of permanent individuality than in the raindrop which falls once again into the sea.

As is well known, Hinduism in its standard theosophical books, *the Upanishads*, postulates that, immanent in the world which serves as its body, there is a supreme though impersonal soul termed Brahma. Furthermore, the soul of man is deemed to have an almost endless series of lives in which retribution is suffered for evil deeds done in previous phases of existence. The finite experience of the soul is thus, as C. F. Andrews says, "a curse, a chain, a fetter". In the end the individual soul can by purification and enlightenment find salvation by absorption into the soul of the world. Thus absorbed it remains in a state of *nirvana* or blessedness, unconscious but immortal: it has realised its own identity with the Supreme.

The doctrine of transmigration or re-incarnation appears to have arisen before the year 500 B.C. Its association with belief in *karma*, or retribution, grew up gradually as men felt the need of some explanation of undeserved suffering. Transmigration and retribution, thus welded together to overcome man's sense of the apparent injustice of the present scheme of things, have maintained a strangely persistent influence. During the ninth century of the Christian era the Vedanta philosophy was completed by Shankara when he added the doctrine of *maya*, or illusion. For Shankara illusion caused by ignorance gives rise to phenomena: and the impersonal Brahma permeating all things is the only Reality.

We may describe such a philosophy as a variant of spiritual or pantheistic monism. The defects in it are obvious. There is no evidence for the doctrine of re-incarnation; and that guilt should endure when memory is destroyed does not satisfy our Western European sense of justice. Furthermore, the place of individual consciousness in the system is manifestly unsatisfactory. In the end such consciousness is absorbed into the impersonal world-soul; yet we must allow that, inasmuch as it is personal, it is of a higher order of being than that within which it is finally merged. I therefore conclude that we must reject alike the re-incarnation and the unconscious immortality of Hindu thought. Such beliefs do not suffice to give a rational explanation of the riddle of human life.

§ 487. *Spinoza and immortality.*

The West has its theories of Divine Immanence. Such theories as have affiliations with the teaching of Spinoza (1632–1677) attract some men, who think thereby that they can make a bridge between religious feeling and the conclusions of science, and that they can also find an argument for human immortality. But the God of Spinoza has little likeness to the God of the Christian revelation; and any immortality which Spinozism allows to human individuals will assuredly not satisfy the Christian hope.

For Spinoza, God is the one Substance which underlies all that is. He is neither mind nor matter but He manifests Himself in both. Mind and matter are thus different attributes of Spinoza's God. For Spinoza, therefore, everything is Divine, whence we have the familiar description of Him as 'the God-intoxicated man'. Hence also he has been accused of denying altogether the reality of the world; and for this reason Hegel described him as acosmist in contrast to the term atheist which others felt to be appropriate. Inasmuch as matter is for us a mental construction, Spinoza has a valid argument for his assumption that one and the same substance underlies both matter and mind. But we cannot make any adequate conception of such substance: it is, in Rashdall's phrase, merely "an unknowable ground of phenomena".

Spinoza's God cannot be worshipped: the 'intellectual love' which the philosopher could offer would be rightly deemed by all theists to be a poor substitute for their own devotion. Spinoza avoided the ascription to his one Substance of personality. If God is perfect, it is not in a moral sense. He is not considered to have a will and does not therefore act towards an end. According to Spinoza final causes are human inventions.

Coherent with his general system is Spinoza's doctrine that at death personal distinctions between man and man vanish: imagination and memory expire with the body. In fact, nothing is eternal in its own right save God Himself. Though the essence of things is eternal, their existence is not.

It is not unfair to say that, when stripped of its theistic language, Spinoza's system is a variant of naturalism. As his phrase *Deus sive Natura* shews, he "identified the world and God as completely as he identified the properties of a triangle with the triangle itself*". The general argument against naturalism which we have previously advanced in Lecture XVII holds good, for those who accept it, against Spinoza's main conclusions. As a thinker his fame is secure: his remarkable insight constantly appears in his writings. Yet any man who is certain that no metaphysical system can be satisfactory in which human freedom is denied and the moral law deprived of primary significance will feel it impossible to accept Spinoza's position. To the philosopher freedom and contingency are alike illusions. He excludes choice from will and forbids us to pass moral judgments. We ought in his opinion neither to regret our so-called bad actions, nor to pride ourselves on those we judge to be good. In spite of his intellectual austerity Spinoza was willing that philosophy should make concessions to popular religious feeling which ought to be refused. "Faith does not demand that doctrines should be true so much as that they should be pious."

§ 488. *God as the Absolute.*

The nineteenth century saw the rise in Germany of a number of important philosophical systems. They had in common an idealist character: they rightly interpreted Nature in terms of mind. In all, moreover, God was regarded as (or replaced by) the Absolute, a supreme Unity reached largely by a process of abstraction conjoined with *à priori* speculation. The comprehensive systems associated with the names of Fichte (1762–1814), Hegel (1770–1831) and Schelling (1775–1854) do not admit of brief description; and between different Hegelian schools there were wide differences. But, speaking generally, we can say that the One of Absolutism is neither objective nor exclusively subjective. It must not even be conceived as a unity of subject and object, but it is rather an all-inclusive Self-consciousness that transcends both.

Philosophies of this kind fail to find room for such a notion of the finite self as will allow of its continued existence after death as a separate centre of consciousness within the Absolute. They offer instead, in the characteristic words of Bosanquet (1848–1923), "the eternal reality of the Absolute as that realisation of our self which we instinctively demand and desire". When God as the Absolute is all-inclusive, it is possible to think of Him as a Self-consciousness which is active in and

* James Ward, *The Realm of Ends.* Cambridge University Press, 1911, p. 234.

through finite selves. But it would then appear that such selves owe such differences from the Absolute as they exhibit to the fact that they are associated with finite physical bodies. When the bodies dissolve it would therefore seem inevitable that the paramount claims of the Absolute should lead to absorption. In fact, if the Absolute be all-inclusive it seems impossible that any finite self can be independently real: it will at most 'qualify' the Absolute as an adjective qualifies a noun.

§ 489. *The rejection of Absolutist theories.*

Against the view that God is an all-inclusive Absolute, which unfolds Itself in the world in the self-consciousness of humanity, strong arguments can be brought. In the first place, if God is so constituted, then every human being is a part of Him including, for example, Cesare Borgia and Rasputin. A conclusion so shocking to the moral sense carries its own condemnation. But, in the second place, an examination of the nature of human consciousness negatives the belief.

We may fairly contend that we cannot explain the higher by the lower. Hence, because we ourselves think, will and feel, God must be a conscious Being in whose consciousness at the very least there must be experiences analogous to thinking, willing and feeling. But it is surely impossible that such a Self can include a number of finite selves. For consider the nature of human individuality. Our thoughts, feelings and volitions are our own: every element of consciousness is unique. If some other individual thinks as I think, or feels as I feel, his thoughts and feelings are his own and not mine. When we say that another's feelings are the same as our own we are, of course, speaking of their content and not of the feelings themselves. Such content is an abstraction and only has real existence in the individual in whom the feelings are experiences. Any doubts which this statement may cause can be set at rest by reflection upon the difference between toothache in oneself and knowledge of exactly similar toothache in another. Thus, though God may know all that I think or feel, I cannot pretend that my thought or feeling is a part of God.

The conclusion follows that if, as we have seen reason to believe, God is at the very least a Self, my finite self cannot be a part of God. It is perhaps worth while to add that if we were to begin by defining God as the all-inclusive Absolute, all finite selves would be, in so far as they were allowed to be real, parts of God. But such a God could not be a Self: He would be an aggregate lacking unity such as exists in human personality and therefore a Being of a lower order than ourselves.

It is often held that mystical experience points to the possibility of a type of union with God in which the finite self is lost. From this fact it is argued that what differentiates the finite self from God is some mere appearance. As against such an argument we must set the fact that moral purity is necessary for an undimmed knowledge of God and that such purity cannot be gained without struggle. Such a struggle in itself is surely real or we as individuals have no real being in ourselves. The necessity for such struggle, moreover, negatives the notion that every finite consciousness is by its very nature a part of God. We can, however, rightly admit, as we said in §6, the much more limited contention that there is a certain community of nature between God and man.

§490. *The self as* Ego.

We have now set forth reasons which, as it seems to me, should lead us to reject the notion that God is an all-inclusive Absolute. Were such a true solution of the problem of 'the One and the many', we should be compelled to abandon belief in human immortality.

Let us now approach the fundamental problem in a different way. First we will consider the finite individual and then later, as an outcome of our enquiry, argue as to the persistence of human personality. There is much to be said for such a procedure, inasmuch as our primary conviction is that the soul or self exists as the subject of experience.

Now there are two ways of regarding the self. We may, on the one hand, think of it objectively, when it tends to become a synthesis of our thoughts and desires. Or, on the other hand, we may take the self as the *ego*, the active centre of all experience, correlating and fusing together all that is presented to it. An *ego* thus accepted, we may remark, is very different from the conception of the soul as a substratum giving support to psychical states. Such a substratum does not, in fact, correspond to anything in human personality which can be reached by critical analysis.

The self, as the *ego* given in immediate experience, is fundamental. Furthermore, the self as a concept differs from the *ego* in that it is, as James Ward says, an "objective construction". Whenever we reflect upon the *ego* we are likely to put in its place the conceptual self. Thus the *ego* is for thought elusive: reflection upon it may easily give rise to contradictions. Yet the *ego* remains the basis of all intellectual activity because we have a direct experience of it as the centre of all consciousness, the unifying factor in all psychical processes. Moreover, this *ego* is real, the most real thing we know. Of those who would deny its reality, we must ask whether none the less they think that its experience can be valid and why such a self is able to distinguish between appearance and reality. Enquiries of this character allow us to claim that the *ego* is real, whatever else can be rightly thus described.

But, granting the fact, is the *ego* immortal? That the psychical life of man is vastly important there is no doubt. But equally undoubted is it that, though the body can exist when the mind is a wreck, the mind often suffers when the functions of the body are impaired. Moreover, the mind cannot exist, or at any rate manifest its existence, when the type of coordination which we call life has ceased. There is then some reason—there are those who would deem it a conclusive reason—for the belief that the *ego* perishes with the death of the organism through or in which it acts.

Now it must be admitted that the *ego* comes into being with the birth and growth of the individual. Furthermore, there seems to be general agreement that no satisfactory metaphysical proof can be offered that any element in such a creature born in time is intrinsically immortal. If we could assume pre-existence we could advance strong arguments in favour of an intrinsic capacity for persistence on the part of the *ego*. But any theory of pre-existence must, as we have seen, be rejected as improbable: and, in any event, continued existence without memory would not be personal survival. In brief, the general conclusion of Christian philosophers seems to be that, without bringing in value-judgments and especially ethical considerations, it is impossible to give even a moderately satisfactory argument in favour of personal immortality. I personally hold that no belief in personal immortality can be argumentatively maintained save as a result of precisely those considerations which are necessary to establish ethical, or Christian, theism.

§ 491. *Christian theism and immortality.*

We recall that it was the existence of our value-judgments and, in particular, of the moral law which led us, in §§ 459–462, to the belief that the absolute values goodness, beauty and truth are attributes of God. We thus reached the conclusion that God is not merely the ground of all that is. Not merely is His will the cause of events; but His rule and guidance of the Universe are purposive and His purpose is good. God is thus revealed as the God of ethical theism.

Now our contention is, as we have previously stated it in Rashdall's words, that belief in such a God and belief in Immortality stand or fall together. The argument which supports this contention is, in essentials, simple. We are forced to assume that the Universe is rational. The assumption is largely confirmed by our experience and, unless it were true, the Universe would be unknowable. In that case God's works and ways would be unintelligible and experience would not lead to any understanding of Him. Now if, on the contrary, the character of the ordering of all that happens is for our thought rational, we are forced to conclude that God would not have allowed the majority of human beings to have lives, so wretched and incomplete as we observe them to be, were it not that earthly existence is but the first part, a mere beginning, of the complete life of the human spirit.

We may put the same consideration somewhat differently and say that, if Christian theism be true, we must create an understanding of man's place in the scheme of things which shall not be out of harmony with the nature of God as revealed by Christ. But such a harmony cannot exist unless this life is a probation or, more probably, an education for another which shall be both fuller and better. If the Universe be rational, man's potentialities must have opportunities of realisation; and on earth such opportunities do not come to the majority of men.

Think, for instance, of the eagerness for knowledge, the over-powering thirst, of the scholar or man of science: and contrast it with the meagre satisfaction that at most is possible even when circumstances are especially favourable. Even with Newton, as a famous saying attests, the feeling was strong that he was but a child on the seashore with the great ocean of truth lying all undiscovered beyond his sight. Is the artist ever satisfied with his attempt to create beauty? In the truism that art is long and life is short, the ceaseless desire for fuller opportunities has been crystallised. Similarly, when men search for holiness and religious understanding they never on earth reach their goal. Furthermore, when men reflect upon life's manifest unfairness and injustice and review the undeserved inequalities of fortune by which the good suffer and the wicked are made happy rather than unhappy, they cannot accept belief in God's just government of mankind, unless it be true that the grave is not the end of human existence.

In brief, our plea for personal survival can be set out as follows. We have been led by the processes of reason to postulate that the world is the realm of Creative Spirit, of Mind which is purposive. Argument from the existence of the Moral Law or, in other words, of man's feeling that he is compelled to believe that goodness is objectively valid—such argument leads us to the conclusion that the Creative Spirit, in and for Whom the Universe exists, is good. But our arguments must be pronounced unsatisfactory, and the conclusions derived from them must be rejected, unless personal immortality be a fact.

Thus the witness of the moral consciousness and a conviction that the Universe is rational are the bases of our belief that human personality survives bodily death. It is not that we greedily demand another life to make amends for what we have suffered here. Probably most religious men ask nothing for themselves: their attitude is rather "though He slay me, yet will I trust Him". Yet it is our profound conviction that, to use words suggested by Henry Sidgwick* (1838–1900), the good of the individual must be in some way identified with Universal Good. If no such identification is possible, the scheme of things, as we are compelled to regard it, is fundamentally irrational.

§ 492. *Immortality and the conservation of values.*

A somewhat different form of the foregoing argument for human immortality is sometimes put forward. Its basis is an axiom which the Danish religious philosopher H. Höffding has expressed in the form, "no value perishes out of world". For Höffding† (1843–1931) "faith in the conservation of value constitutes the essence of religion". Similarly, true religious experience is an understanding that there is union between value and reality. A fundamental misfit between the two is the assumption of a non-religious pessimism. God, in fact, is the source not only of reality but also of value: we may even say that reality apart from value is meaningless. With this line of thought goes a saying of Plotinus, quoted by Inge, "none of the things that really are can perish".

On the other hand, Höffding insists that "neither our concept of value nor our concept of reality is complete or can be completed". The former is empirical and the latter ideal. He further maintains that the confusion of particular definite values with eternal values is irreligious. He will not therefore allow that faith in the conservation of value necessarily leads to belief in personal immortality. "Of the relation of the individual to the great kingdom of values we can form no clear idea: hence we can assign no grounds either for affirmation or negation." Höffding, however, allows that the mere possibility of the conservation of value extending beyond the sphere of human life seems to assume

* Henry Sidgwick, *Methods of Ethics.* 3rd ed. Macmillan, 1884, p. 504.

† H. Höffding, *The Philosophy of Religion.* English translation. Macmillan, 1914, p. 130. The question of personal immortality is considered by Höffding in §§ 84, 85.

the continued existence of mental life; and such continuity *may* be effected by the conservation of individual psychical beings.

My own conclusions are more positive. Goodness, beauty and truth are attributes of God; and it seems to me that such values when once manifested are eternal and indestructible with Him. In so far as man's personality is permeated by these values, it also becomes eternal and indestructible. For, were it to perish, the values which it carries would perish also and Höffding's axiom would be contradicted. Moreover, such values are associated not with impersonal being but with finite personality; and, therefore, if they are to persist, the finite self must be immortal.

The conviction, that in all changes which take place in time values are conserved, results, of course, from our beliefs that the Universe is rational and its Ruler beneficent and wise. Such a Ruler would be untrue to His nature were He to create values, or allow His creatures to manifest them, and then allow them to perish. Such action would render His activity purposeless: God's Universe would, in fact, be meaningless.

§ 493. *Pantheism and theism.*

Our conclusions may now be expressed in antitheses which, perhaps somewhat too violently, separate the opposing religious positions open to thoughtful men at the present time.

When scientific knowledge and method are made the approach to religion, it is almost certain that some form of naturalism will at first be reached. As the inadequacies of naturalism become evident and it is seen that Nature must be interpreted in terms of mind or spirit there are, in the main, two alternatives between which a choice has to be made. They are pantheism and theism.

In pantheism God is immanent. He is sole and ultimate reality: all has come from Him: all returns to Him. Merely, moreover, by using a personal pronoun to describe Absolute Spirit we limit its all-inclusive character. God is impersonal. Though Spirit manifests self-consciousness in humanity and elsewhere, our labour and struggle, and the change and development through which we pass, are illusions. God is eternally the same: time is unreal: the end and the beginning are one.

In theism, on the other hand, God is primarily transcendent, the Creator of the World. Though active within the world, He is outside it. The finite spirits to whom He has given birth are not parts of Himself. They are His creatures but in some measure free. Moreover, their life

in time is not an illusion. Their struggles are real and of eternal significance. God is both the ground of their being and also the source of
the Good which they seek. As they conquer evil they find unity with
one another and with Him. The final harmony thus attained is life
eternal in the Kingdom of God.

I believe that the scientific approach to religion leads far more
naturally to theism than to pantheism. If the latter expresses the
ultimate character of the Universe, all the processes which science so
laboriously investigates are unreal. Terrestrial evolution itself, and
men as its products, are alike without ultimate significance. We may
think that new values arise, that epigenesis is actually taking place;
but we are mistaken. Obviously science cannot accept such conclusions without admitting that its realm is a land of vain shadows. But
equally, if any such philosophy is true, human life is without meaning:
it cannot be a realm of ends. Truth and falsehood, good and evil,
evolutionary progress and decay, matter nothing when the illusion
which we call time fades away.

Now science can only be valuable if it is actually a search for truth
in which the end can be attained. We need not go so far as to assert that
the labour and development, necessary to and characteristic of science,
are ultimate realities; but they are means whereby truth is reached and
man is brought nearer to God Who is the Source of Truth. Similarly,
both the struggle for goodness and suffering in the service of righteousness are not mere appearances in a world of illusions. They are means
whereby new values are created and old values are preserved. They add
to the richness of the kingdom of God, which shall come in its perfection
when—we know not how—time shall be no more.

For the pantheist temporal relations are illusory: science is the pursuit of shadows, and personal immortality is a hope or a desire based
upon misunderstanding. For the theist the existence in time of finite
spirits is no illusion: science, like suffering for goodness, brings man
nearer God; and personal immortality is in the end the life with God
which explains all that we are and would be. For the theist also the
evolutionary process described by science is evidence of purpose in the
Universe and thus ranks as one of the main grounds of his faith. It
describes the creative activity of God and hints at the nature of the
self-imposed limitations under which His purpose is being achieved.

Though theism is thus the almost inevitable conclusion to which
the man of science is led when he rejects naturalism, we must admit
that both abstract speculation and the religious instincts of the mass

of mankind tend towards a pantheistic explanation of the Universe. Vedantist Hinduism, Platonism, medieval mysticism, Spinozism and modern Absolutism can all be claimed for pantheism. Of the world-religions only Judaism, Christianity and Mohammedanism are staunch to the theistic position, and even their mystics are often tempted to change their allegiance. We must agree with the mystic that the Highest is eternally present to those who have eyes to see and ears to hear; and we need not and must not deny that the Supreme Goodness can always be found and enjoyed by those who can escape the snares and illusions of the sensuous world. But, on the one hand, we ourselves are not in essence divine; and, on the other hand, we are not accidents ever combining and dissolving in a realm of shadows. We are potentially immortal; and such glimpses of Supreme Reality as the mystics get are but a foretaste of the final joy for which free spirits were created.

Christian theism thus postulates an ultimate multiplicity of existence. It is therefore technically a form of pluralism which, because it asserts the independence of particular monads or elements in the world, is less intellectually satisfying than a monism in which all finite spirits are differentiations of a supreme unity.

We do not, however, in accepting Christian theism deny interconnection between God and finite spirits. The spirits themselves constitute in their freedom a plurality, not of individuals in isolation, but of individuals seeking unity. God, in creating them, has made them to be co-workers with Himself; and they satisfy His intention in so far as they do not misuse their freedom. He Himself is the ground of their unity. In fact, though in all experience we must begin with the many, for our knowledge is public knowledge obtained by comparing our own perceptions with those of other subjects of experience, yet we reach the One as we try to understand why the world is not a chaos.

Theism implies that, beyond the many subjects of experience, there is one transcendent Subject Who comprehends the whole. The active immanent presence of one Supreme Spirit Who knows all is an assurance that the interconnection of the many is itself a unity and thus offers such a solution as is possible of the problem of the unity and multiplicity of existence.

The great prophets of ethical religion have always felt bidden to urge their fellows to search for righteousness. Men of science seek truth. If the ideals which animate science and ethical religion be conjoined in an endeavour to understand the Universe, there naturally emerges ethical theism with its corollary of personal immortality. In fact, if we are agreed that goodness and truth alike belong to Ultimate Reality, the great Jewish prophets, not excluding the Greatest of them, were natural forerunners of modern men of science; and ethical theism is a faith harmonious with the aspirations of all.

§494. *Immortality and time.*

Belief in personal immortality is, we have seen, bound up with the acceptance of ethical theism. We reject pantheism primarily because its acceptance would imply that the struggle for goodness is illusory. We are therefore committed to the view that the time-process is for finite spirits of fundamental and enduring significance. Time is thus real: in fact, as Rashdall* has said, "you cannot believe in progress if you do not believe in real time". Christian theology regards God as actively concerned with the efforts of His creatures to attain righteousness. The belief is justified by the fact—again I quote Rashdall—that "the evils of an earlier stage in the time-process appear to be most rationally explained as a means to the good realised in the later". We must then assume that God and His creatures alike have, in James Ward's words, "a certain fundamental relation to the temporal process of the world's evolution". It is difficult to see how therefore God can be static, changeless and perfect. Doubtless absolute perfection and activity can be conjoined. But, on the Christian view, the temporal process leads to an enrichment of God's kingdom and therefore presumably to an enrichment of His own being.

We must not ignore the metaphysical contradictions to which belief in the reality of time thus leads. Absolutist philosophers and mystics alike have felt, and doubtless will continue to feel, their force. Hegel spoke of time as Chronos begetting and devouring his children. Inge† adopts the same attitude when he describes time as "always hurling its own products into nothingness". For him "the present is an unextended point, dividing an unreal past from an unreal future". In accepting such a position he is in the succession of a line of mystics going back to Plotinus: "to exist in time is to exist imperfectly". In §82 we referred to Descartes' opinion: "le temps présent ne dépend point de celui qui l'a immédiatement précédé: c'est pourquoi il n'est

---

* *Vide* 'The Idea of Progress' in H. Rashdall, *Ideas and Ideals*, edited by Major and Cross, Blackwell, 1928, pp. 78–93. Rashdall is explicitly criticising Inge's position.

† *Vide* 'Survival and Immortality' in W. R. Inge, *Outspoken Essays, First Series*. Longmans, 1919, p. 272.

pas besoin d'une moindre cause pour conserver une chose, que pour la produire la première fois*". For Kant†, space and time are real within experience: we may even describe them as constituents of the objects of our experience. But Kant regards them as ideal in relation to the realm (if any such realm exists) of 'things in themselves'.

I personally do not believe that, with our present knowledge, we can reach any satisfactory solution of the problem of the relation of God to time. In the physical discussions associated with relativity we were led to see how difficult is the apparently simple idea of simultaneity. The perplexing relation between past and future in Minkowski's world was indicated in § 100 by a striking quotation from Weyl. When to such perplexities as to the character of time is added the impossibility of our understanding God's transcendence of the finite, we may well admit that we are in a region where our mental powers fail to give us guidance.

Similarly, we can give no sufficient answer to enquiries as to whether the life after death is at first, or ultimately, a life in time. It is, by our argument, a life in which the values of earthly existence are preserved; and therefore, at any rate in its final stage of perfection when the purity of these values is unsullied, it will be life in full and perfect communion with God. This mode of being we call Eternal Life. Such a life is other than mere survival. Possibly its nature is indicated by Höffding's suggestion that eternity is that which expresses permanence of value during the alteration which takes place in time. The mystics get a foretaste of eternal life in those depths of religious experience which seem to be timeless. Possibly also, as Rashdall allows, the temporal aspect of the Universe is not the only aspect. Certainly it cannot be true to say *tout court* that God is in time: probably the notion that time is in Him expresses more nearly the truth about Him and His relation to the world.

Nevertheless, we must always return, as to solid rock, to the conviction that the world-process, as a process in time, is not meaningless. Man's spiritual struggles in time realise a good which otherwise would not exist. Values are in themselves supra-temporal abstractions; but when they are manifested in beings within time they are imperishable realities. Our life here is a pilgrimage and quite possibly after death will continue to be such. The pilgrimage is to the Eternal City; and,

---

* *Oeuvres de Descartes* (cited in § 82). T. I, p. 458 [Objections et Réponses, 1641].

† *Vide* Immanuel Kant's *Critique of Pure Reason*. Translated by F. Max Müller. Macmillan, 1907, Supplement XI, pp. 732–4.

when the City is reached, the time-process may, and probably will, be transcended. But, because of that process, the City will be alike richer and fuller. As time fades into eternity Reality may become static once again; but the values manifested and actually created in time will endure.

§ 495. *Personality and the psycho-physical organism.*

We may fairly say that, for those who accept ethical theism, the time-process is real or, at the very least, contributes to reality. They thus regard human personality at its highest as alike transformed by, and the seat of, the supreme values. These values are valid of reality; and personality, as manifested in the psycho-physical organism, through them becomes immortal. In other language, spiritual struggle makes human beings both worthy, and the recipients, of eternal life.

Yet, conclusive for us though such an argument may be, we must acknowledge that it is profoundly difficult to understand how personality can survive the dissolution of the organism. The organism is the product of heredity and environment, a unity of physical structure and physiological function and of consciousness correlated to both. Under the conditions of existence known to us, personality cannot be severed from the whole complex organism. Now we can, of course, give free rein to fancy and imagine that after bodily death the personality that has been created during life will receive an appropriate tabernacle: a man's life would thus, as it were, create a form appropriate to the next stage of the soul's development. Such a possibility is not an unworthy aid to imagination. We certainly seem forced to speculate that, after death, there must be continuity of experience, if personality is to be preserved. Moreover, having regard to the imperfections of human personality as we observe it, such continuity must apparently extend throughout a series of lives during which evil is overcome by goodness and falsehood by truth.

The biologist will demur to any such play of fancy and point out that continuity of personal life seems inseparable from continuity alike of organism and environment. But our belief in personal immortality is not the consequence of the knowledge given by natural science: it results from facts of the moral consciousness and from our belief in the rationality of the Universe.

We cannot expect science even to hint at the way in which personality shall exist in the life after death. We must be content to say with

Boutroux* that "it has not been proved, and it seems unprovable, that the actual body is the adequate cause and not a purely contingent condition, of our spiritual life". Even Bosanquet† admitted that "there may be future gradations of experience continuous with our finite selves". We postulate such gradations because future continuity with our present selves is a necessary truth if, as we have seen reason to believe, this Universe is ruled by a Creator Who is both wise and good. Such continuity will enable us to complete that pursuit of ideal aims which here is usually most incomplete. It will render possible such enrichment of personality by goodness, beauty and truth as will lead to the perfection which alone is fit for the Kingdom of God. That we cannot see how the process will be continued or the end achieved matters little, for is it not true that the process by which consciousness has come to be associated with the living organism remains a profound enigma?

CONCLUSION

§ 496. *The present and the immediate future of religious faith.*

Thus with a question-mark I come to the conclusion of these lectures. The journey has been long and at times fatiguing; but it has been the fault of the lecturer and not of his subject if the course has been dull. For, of all the surprises of this surprising world in which we find ourselves, none are so exciting, so stimulating and so significant as the discoveries which I have tried to set forth. It is probably true to say that in my own lifetime we have witnessed more rapid changes in fundamental beliefs and a greater enlargement of knowledge than in any equal period in the past. Inevitably the necessary readjustment of ideas has led temporarily to intellectual anarchy: and such disorder has intensified the revolt from Christian moral standards which had its origin in the agonies of the Great War.

Of the future it is rash to prophesy. Yet I cannot refrain from expressing my own conviction that both the moral and intellectual essentials of the Christian outlook will survive any temporary eclipse. The humane ideals which we rightly associate with Christ's teaching have lost none of their ascendancy over the minds of men: they are far

---

* E. Boutroux, *Science and Religion in Contemporary Philosophy.* English translation, Duckworth, 1909, p. 323. Boutroux is quoting William James.

† B. Bosanquet, *The Value and Destiny of the Individual.* Macmillan, 1913, p. 288.

more powerful now than when a united Church dominated Western Europe. Standards of international ethics have steadily risen of late years, in part owing to the influence of Christian ideals and in part owing to a recoil from the disastrous Machiavellianism which preceded the Great War. The social services of the principal European nations are now organised with a regard for those enduring illness, unemployment or old age, more generous than ever in the history of humanity. Christian sentiment has warmly supported such social reform and individuals actuated by Christian principles have been among its strongest advocates.

Again, the history of Great Britain shews that organised Christian communions during the nineteenth century had a steady concern with elementary and higher education. No one could say that such concern was wholly selfish or deny that the spread of education had led to a considerable refinement of conduct. Coarse vice has certainly diminished during recent generations.

It must, however, be admitted that attempts during the same period to add to the fullness of human life by developing the higher emotions associated with sex have been many, and that some of them have been dangerous. But the sex-legislation and sex-teaching of the Catholic Church were in the past at times deplorable: the Christian (though not, perhaps, the ecclesiastical) attitude towards sex to-day is probably more direct and wholesome, more like that of Christ, than at any previous period of Christian history. Christian influence may possibly fail in the immediate future to check sexual laxity; but its success will depend upon the extent to which Christian belief maintains itself.

Were the disintegration of religious certainty which has taken place during the last half-century to continue, so that scepticism became well-nigh universal, there would occur such a decline alike in sexual morality and in humane idealism as took place under similar circumstances in the first half of the eighteenth century. But the primary object of these lectures has been to shew that the new knowledge of our era should not lead to scepticism or to religious indifference. Belief in God as Christ revealed Him is in no way inconsistent with acceptance of the standpoint created by modern science.

§ 497. *The character of the lectures.*

Some may be disappointed at the limited character of the conclusion thus reached and may complain that I have made no attempt to uphold the distinctive dogmas of Christianity or to subject them to critical analysis. But, were I to have done so, I should have infringed the restrictions laid down by Lord Gifford when he founded these lectureships. He desired, in language which sounds to us quaint, that his lecturers should think upon "the true knowledge of God, that is of the Being, Nature and Attributes of the Infinite or the All, of the First and the Only Cause, that is, the One and Only Substance and Being, and the true and felt knowledge (not mere nominal knowledge) of the relations of man and of the universe to Him". His lecturers might be of any religion or way of thinking or of no religion; but he desired them to be reverent, "sincere lovers of and earnest inquirers after truth". They were to treat their subject as a strictly natural science, "without reference to or reliance upon any supposed special exceptional or so-called miraculous revelation". Such a restriction is, of course, decisive against any attempt to argue in favour of beliefs peculiar to Christianity. But I have sought to shew that ethical theism, which Judaism and Christianity alike derived from the ancient Hebrew prophets, is a form of belief no less reasonable now than in any past era.

§ 498. *The advance of knowledge.*

Will the advance of knowledge continue to be as rapid in the next century as in the last hundred years? My instinct is to return a negative answer to this question. We, who are heirs of the European Renaissance, have lately passed through a second revolution of outlook and now need a period of quiet assimilation and of general readjustment. Of late the pace of scientific discovery has been disquietingly fast. The intellectual gulf between the leaders of science and the educated citizen is dangerously wide. The present lectures, for instance, set forth only such new knowledge as ought (apart, of course, from the mathematical reasoning by which it is reached) to be familiar to, and a background for the belief of, a well-educated man: but it is not probable that the ideas here presented will be absorbed into the general consciousness of the community before several generations have passed. Of course, I am not blind to the possibility that we may need a period of quiet absorption and fail to get it. But, if one may judge by the past, periods of quiescence and rapid advance alternate.

Moreover, the needs of an epoch influence quite directly the mental activities of its leaders of thought. Thus I imagine that, as the pace of discovery slackens, the twentieth century will see the gradual creation, or consolidation, of a new scientific orthodoxy which will be used as a background to religious belief. The result in Great Britain will be a conflict concerning the reformulation of Christianity similar to that which was waged after the Renaissance. There will, as formerly, be a struggle between new knowledge and old sympathies, the recurring opposition of progress and reaction. The outcome of the struggle will be indecisive, for such warfare of the spirit never ends; but it will mark a stage in the advance of that slowly flowing tide of religious understanding which will, as we believe, in due time cover the earth.

§ 499. *Here and hereafter.*

I now end a piece of work which for more than six years has absorbed my vacations and occupied all my leisure hours. The task has been singularly enjoyable: in itself, and also because by its means I have escaped from the pettiness and insincerities of ecclesiastical disorder to learn of the men, now living, who are making discoveries as significant as any in human history. I have, in truth, been rarely fortunate in having had to try to understand the intellectual splendour of our own great era of scientific achievement. As I have followed the rapidly changing growth of knowledge I have felt that I too shared the excitement of research and the joy of discovery. Moreover, I too have realised how vast is our ignorance of the world in which we find ourselves and to which we belong. Can it be, I am compelled to ask, that with such a feeling of ignorance I shall pass to a realm where knowledge is not, because consciousness has ceased? Must we allow that the desire to understand God's works and ways, which is one of the strongest and purest of human passions, is a vain and hopeless by-product of man's search for material comfort. Do we but rise for a moment above the waters of unconsciousness and, after a brief glance around, sink again to eternal oblivion? If such is indeed our fate, then surely the mystery of human life is unfathomable: unreason must sit enthroned above meaningless change.

Now I, for one, cannot believe that within a few years my attempt to understand the Universe will have ceased. So, as I come to the end of these lectures, I turn to whatever awaits me with hope and courage. The world is full of surprises and perplexities: but it is not a chaos. There is order within it. Reason and beauty and much goodness have gone to its making. I am, like each of yourselves, one of its children. Our high thoughts and hopes and desires belong to the life of the Spirit manifested within it. Behind the world, controlling Nature, is the Creative Spirit to Whom we are somehow akin. That Spirit is not a cold foe working through blind and pitiless forces; but is the source of our aspirations, friendly to our search for knowledge, the kindly guardian of our destinies. Therefore I am certain that our search will not end with death: labour and struggle will not be in vain. At the last we shall know even as we are known.

Gibbon's reflections* when he finished his great history have often been quoted and naturally come into our thoughts as now we go our separate ways. "A sober melancholy was spread over my mind, by the idea that I had taken an everlasting leave of an old and agreeable companion, and that whatsoever might be the future date of my history, the life of the historian might be short and precarious." We, I feel, end any piece of work to which we put our hands with a confidence which Gibbon did not possess. To no companion of earth's short journey need we give an everlasting farewell. What we begin here we shall finish hereafter, if indeed it be worth the finishing. The fact that life is short and precarious matters little, inasmuch as those who have travelled with us here shall be our companions beyond the grave, if we and they alike seek the City of God.

* See, for instance, p. xxv of 'The Life and Writings of Edward Gibbon', prefixed to *The History of the Decline and Fall of the Roman Empire*. 8 vols. Cadell, 1838.

APPENDIX

Note to page 85.

The quantities u_{jk} are, by definition, covariant differentials of a function of position u. We wish to prove that, if $a = -K$ and b is a constant, the partial differential equations

$$u_{jk} = g_{jk}(au + b), \quad j, k = 1, 2, \ldots n, \qquad \ldots\ldots(1)$$

when the coefficients g_{jk} belong to the metric of a space of constant Riemannian curvature K, admit an integral which also satisfies the equation

$$au + b = \frac{u}{2}\left\{ -K + \frac{1}{u^2}\Sigma_l u^l u_l \right\}.$$

The proof depends on the theory of the solution of systems of total differential equations.

We may write the equation (1) in the form

$$\frac{\partial u_j}{\partial x_k} = \sum_{l=1}^{n} \{jk, l\} u_l + g_{jk}(au + b).$$

Suppose now that the quantities u_j, $j = 1, 2, \ldots n$, are not covariant derivatives of u, but that they are arbitrary functions save that they are given by the set of total differential equations

$$du_j = \sum_{k=1}^{n}\left[\sum_{l=1}^{n} \{jk, l\} u_l + g_{jk}(au + b) \right] dx_k, \quad j = 1, 2, \ldots n, \qquad \ldots\ldots(2)$$

where u is a given function of position.

Such a set of total differential equations is completely integrable if a set of n integral relations between the u's and the x's can be found, each of which involves an arbitrary constant.

The necessary and sufficient conditions that the set (2) should be of this character are that the equalities

$$\frac{\partial}{\partial x_i}\left[\sum_{l=1}^{n} \{jk, l\} u_l + g_{jk}(au + b) \right] = \frac{\partial}{\partial x_k}\left[\sum_{l=1}^{n} \{ji, l\} u_l + g_{ji}(au + b) \right] \qquad \ldots\ldots(3)$$

should be satisfied* for all values of i, j, k.

Now by the equations (2), we have

$$\frac{\partial u_l}{\partial x_i} = \Sigma_m \{li, m\} u_m + g_{li}(au + b). \qquad \ldots\ldots(4)$$

---

* See, for example, A. R. Forsyth, *Theory of Differential Equations*. Part I. Cambridge University Press, 1890, p. 51.

Using this result, the equality (3) may be written

$$\Sigma_l u_l \left[\frac{\partial}{\partial x_i} \{jk, l\} - \frac{\partial}{\partial x_k} \{ji, l\} \right] + \Sigma_{lm} [\{jk, l\}\{li, m\} - \{ji, l\}\{lk, m\}] u_m$$

$$+ (au + b) \left\{ \Sigma_l [\{jk, l\}g_{li} - \{ji, l\}g_{lk}] + \frac{\partial g_{jk}}{\partial x_i} - \frac{\partial g_{ji}}{\partial x_k} \right\}$$

$$+ a \left(g_{jk} \frac{\partial u}{\partial x_i} - g_{ji} \frac{\partial u}{\partial x_k} \right) = 0.$$

But

$$\Sigma_l [\{jk, l\}g_{li} - \{ji, l\}g_{lk}] = [jk, i] - [ji, k] = \frac{\partial g_{ji}}{\partial x_k} - \frac{\partial g_{jk}}{\partial x_i}.$$

Hence, if we recall the value of Riemann's symbol of the second kind given in § 63, the equality (3) may be written

$$\Sigma_l \{jl, ki\} u_l + a \left(g_{jk} \frac{\partial u}{\partial x_i} - g_{ji} \frac{\partial u}{\partial x_k} \right) = 0.$$

Now the functions g_{jk} belong to a space of constant Riemannian curvature K. Hence, by § 68, we have

$$(jh, ki) = K (g_{jk}g_{hi} - g_{ji}g_{hk}).$$

Multiply both sides of this result by g^{hl}, and sum for all values of h from 1 to n. We get

$$\{jl, ki\} = K (g_{jk}g_i^l - g_{ji}g_k^l).$$

Thus the necessary and sufficient conditions that the set of equations (2) may be completely integrable are that

$$g_{jk} \left(Ku_i + a \frac{\partial u}{\partial x_i} \right) = g_{ji} \left(Ku_k + a \frac{\partial u}{\partial x_k} \right),$$

for $j, i, k = 1, 2, \dots n$.

So far we have treated u as an arbitrary function of position. Suppose now that it is given in terms of $x_i, u_j, i, j = 1, 2, \dots n$, by the equation

$$au + b = \frac{u}{2} \left\{ -K + \frac{1}{u^2} \Sigma_{kl} g^{kl} u_k u_l \right\}, \qquad \dots\dots(5)$$

where a, b, K are all constants.

If we differentiate this equality with respect to x_m we get

$$\{u(2a + K) + b\} \frac{\partial u}{\partial x_m} = \Sigma_l u^l \frac{\partial u_l}{\partial x_m} + \tfrac{1}{2} \Sigma_{kl} u_k u_l \frac{\partial g^{kl}}{\partial x_m}.$$

Now we know that $\qquad \Sigma_\alpha g^{\alpha k} g_{\alpha\beta} = g_\beta^k.$

Hence $\qquad \Sigma_\alpha g_{\alpha\beta} \frac{\partial g^{\alpha k}}{\partial x_m} = - \Sigma_\alpha g^{\alpha k} \frac{\partial g_{\alpha\beta}}{\partial x_m}.$

Multiply both sides of this equality by $g^{\beta l}$ and sum for all values of β from 1 to n. We get

$$\frac{\partial g^{kl}}{\partial x_m} = -\Sigma_{\alpha\beta} g^{k\alpha} g^{l\beta} \frac{\partial g_{\alpha\beta}}{\partial x_m}.$$

Consider now the expression

$$\Sigma_{l\alpha} u^l \{lm, \alpha\} u_\alpha.$$

By the relation connecting Christoffel's functions of the first and second kinds it is equal to

$$\Sigma_{l\alpha\beta} u^l u_\alpha g^{\alpha\beta} [lm, \beta] = \tfrac{1}{2} \Sigma_{l\beta} u^l u^\beta \left\{ \frac{\partial g_{l\beta}}{\partial x_m} + \frac{\partial g_{m\beta}}{\partial x_l} - \frac{\partial g_{lm}}{\partial x_\beta} \right\} = \tfrac{1}{2} \Sigma_{l\beta} u^l u^\beta \frac{\partial g_{l\beta}}{\partial x_m}$$

$$= \tfrac{1}{2} \Sigma_{kl\alpha\beta} u_k u_l g^{k\alpha} g^{l\beta} \frac{\partial g_{\alpha\beta}}{\partial x_m} = -\tfrac{1}{2} \Sigma_{kl} u_k u_l \frac{\partial g^{kl}}{\partial x_m}.$$

We therefore have

$$\{u(2a + K) + b\} \frac{\partial u}{\partial x_m} = \Sigma_l u^l \left[\frac{\partial u_l}{\partial x_m} - \Sigma_\alpha u_\alpha \{lm, \alpha\} \right],$$

so that, by equation (4),

$$\{u(2a + K) + b\} \frac{\partial u}{\partial x_m} = \Sigma_l u^l g_{lm} (au + b).$$

This result can, of course, be written in the form

$$\{u(2a + K) + b\} \frac{\partial u}{\partial x_m} = (au + b) u_m. \qquad \ldots\ldots(6)$$

Hence the necessary and sufficient conditions that the set of equations (2) should be completely integrable are

$$\left\{ K + \frac{a(au + b)}{u(2a + K) + b} \right\} (g_{jk} u_i - g_{ji} u_k) = 0,$$

or

$$(a + K) \frac{u(a + K) + b}{u(2a + K) + b} (g_{jk} u_i - g_{ji} u_k) = 0.$$

All the conditions are therefore satisfied if $a = -K$.

Further, if $a = -K$, we shall have, by (6),

$$u_m = \partial u / \partial x_m, \quad m = 1, 2, \ldots n;$$

and thus the quantities u_m will be the partial differentials of u.

We see then that, if $a = -K$ and b is a constant, we can find a function of position u such that

$$u_{jk} = g_{jk} (au + b),$$

while, in addition,

$$au + b = \frac{u}{2} \left\{ -K + \frac{1}{u^2} \Sigma_l u_l u^l \right\}.$$

The proposition assumed in the text is therefore established.

INDEX

[The numbers refer to the pages.]

Abbot, C. G., 353
Aberdeen, 438
Absolute, God as the, 641
— motion, 134
— rotation, 100–1, 134–5
— (Kelvin) scale of temperature, 233–4
— simultaneity, 103, 134
— space, 99, 100
— temperature, 230, 234
— time, 101–2, 281
— values, 606–8
— zero, 229–30, 404
Absolute Differential Calculus, Levi-Civita, cited, 55
Absolutist theories rejected, 642–3
Absorption lines, 251–3
Acanthodrilidae, 431
Acceleration, 17
'Accidents', of matter, 570
Acheulean tools, 532, 534
Acosmist, 640
Acquired characters, inheritance of, *see* Lamarckism
Action, described, 266–7
— has no quality, 267
— is atomic, 266
— quantisation of, 264
— quantum of, 261
— unit of, 261, 584
Adams, W. S., 349
Adamson, R., 568
Addison, J., 559
Adiabatics, 235
Africa, primitive man and, 528–9, 534
Agar, W. E., 513
Age of the Earth, Holmes, cited, 423
Agnostic naturalism, 575–7
Alaska land-bridge, 431, 468, 526
Albinism, 485, 486, 518
Alcohol, and enlarged experience, 618
— and genetic change, 516, 517
Alexander, S., 590, 591
Algae, 425, 435
Algol, 362
Alkalis, the, 25
Allelomorphs, 483
Almagest, the, of Ptolemy, 311
α-rays, 211, 212, 225
Alpine race, 538
Amber, 193
America, in Tertiary times, 468
— North, development of the horse in, 431–2

America, North, origin of primates in, 526
— — religious life in, 614
— — telescopes in, 337
— South, flat-nosed monkeys of, 526
— — termites in, 453
— United States of, 459, 525–6
American Naturalist, cited, 498
Amino-acids, 415
Ammonia, 415
Amoeba, 412, 434
Amphibia, 426
— passage to reptile, 472
— sex-mechanism in, 447
— transition from fish to, 471
Amphioxus, 471
Analogue, Euclidean, of hyperbolic geometry, 39–44
Analysis, spectrum-, 221
Anatidae, 461
Andalusian poultry, 478, 514–15
Andrews, C. F., 639
Andrews, C. W., 526
Andromeda nebula, 370, 374, 377, 378, 379, 396, 397
Angiosperms, 440, 441, 442
Angle, in general manifold, 64
— measurement of, 58
— of parallelism, 35, 38, 39, 43, 44
Anglican clergymen, 459
Ångström unit, 259, 405
Angular diameter, apparent, of Betelgeux, 339
— momentum of earth, 331
Animals, first marine, 425
Animism, 9, 546, 636
Annales de la Société Scientifique de Bruxelles, cited, 381
Annihilation of matter, hypothesis of, 205, 307, 356, 404–6
Annual parallax, 339
Anselm, 594
Anthropoid apes, 429, 460
Anthropoids, man's kinship with the great, 459, 469, 473, 502, 525, 526–8
Anti-cathode, 263, 285
Antinomianism, Christian, 633
Ants, 452–4
Apes, anthropoid, 429, 460, 469, 473, 502, 526–8
Appendicitis, 465
Appendix to the lectures, 658–60
Aquinas, Thomas, 594, 595
Archaeozoic era, 423, 424

Archimedes, 311
Arcturus, 336
Argon, 274
Argument, cosmological, 595–6
— moral for theism, 596, 605–8
— ontological, 594–5
— teleological, 597–9
Aristarchus, 311
Aristotle, 15, 21, 311, 595
Arnold, M., 624
Arrangement and Creative Activity, 302
Arthropods, 469, 470–1
Asceticism and mysticism, 618
— horrible forms of, 622
Ascidians, 418, 463
Asexual spores, 443
Associated characters, defined, 477, 478
Aston, F. W., 26, 220, 356
Astronomical measures of distance, 339
Astronomy, Russell-Dugan-Stewart, cited, 335
Astronomy and Cosmogony, Jeans, cited, 364, 376, 397
Astrophysical Journal, cited, 341, 373, 379
Asymmetry in primitive organisms, 416
Atheism, 520
Atom, appearance of, 24
— Bohr's model, 217
— definition of, 21
— helium, 213
— hydrogen, 213
— size of, 24, 215, 216
— super-gigantic, of Lemaître, 408
— weight of hydrogen-, 24
Atom and the Bohr Theory of its Structure, Kramers and Holst, cited, 224
Atomic energy and frequency of radiation, 263–4
— nuclei, 215, 305
— number, 26, 213, 214, 215, 306
— number and characteristic X-rays, connection between, 287–8
— theory of Dalton, 21
— weight, 22, 24, 26, 213, 214
Atomic Structure and Spectral Lines, Sommerfeld, cited, 214, 287
Atoms, chemical combination of, 219
— of radio-active substances, 212, 305
Aurignacian art, 544
— cave-paintings, 536
— culture, 537
Australia, 428
Australian aborigines, 537, 538, 545, 611
— evolution, 539
Automata, conscious, 582
Averages, statistical, and free-will, 224–5
Avogadro's hypothesis, 22, 23

Axes of reference, 31
Azilian period, totemism in, 549
Azimuthal quantum-number, 272

Bacon, Roger, 13
Bacon, Roger, Essays on, cited, 13
Bacteria, 415, 435
Bacteriophage, 415
Baillie, Sir J. B., 609
Balmer, J. J., 222
Balmer-Ritz series, 223, 267–8, 270, 271
Barkla, C. G., 206, 285, 288
Barnacles, 448
Barnard, E. E., 326, 357
'Barred spirals', 375, 376, 396
Bateson, W., 445, 461, 479, 515
Baur, E., 493, 513
Bean, scarlet-runner, 513
Beauty, 606, 609
— in science, 599–600
Becquerel, H., 206, 207
Bees, 452–7
Beginning of things, speculation as to, 408
Behring Straits, 538
Beltrami, E., 84, 87
Bending of light rays, 174–6
Bentley, Richard, 177, 396
Bergson, H., 456
Berkeley, Bishop George, 135, 203, 556, 557, 558, 560, 562, 571, 572, 573, 574
Berkeley's Works, cited, 135, 558, 560
Berliner Berichte, cited, 190
Bernard, Claude, 434
Beryllium, 25, 215, 225
β-Lyrae, 362
β-rays, 20, 212, 405, 498
Betelgeux, 339, 354
Beth-el, 630
Bethune-Baker, J. F., Christian doctrine of Incarnation, 7
Beyond the Electron, Thomson, cited, 199
Bianchi's identities, 73, 83, 147
Bible, the, 1, 610, 616–17
Bidlake, J., 420
Billion, defined, 8
Binary stars, 354, 358–61, 362
— — origin of the wide, 363, 402
Binding forces in space, 52, 191
Biological evolution, duration of, 2
Birds, 447
— origin of, 427, 428, 472
— vestigial ovary of, 467
Black-body radiation, 249, 253, 261, 325
Black, Davidson, 531
'Blank trance', the, 618
Blastula, 463
'Bleeding', or haemophilia, 485, 489–90
Blending inheritance, 484, 509

Blink microscope, 357
Body and soul, 636–7
— resurrection of, 637
Bohr, Niels, 199, 213
— model of the atom, 214, 217–19, 222, 223, 250, 261, 271, 288, 575
— — — truth of, 575
— quantised orbits, 264
Bohr's correspondence principle, 284
— hydrogen spectrum, 267 et seq.
Bohr-Sommerfeld, 271, 273, 275
Bolometer, 255
Bolometric magnitude, 352
Boltwood, B., 423
Bolyai, W., 32, 35
Borgia, Cesare, 642
Born, M., 275, 278
Bosanquet, B., 641, 653
Botanical eras, the great, 438
Boule, Marcellin, 526, 527, 533, 545
'Boundary-stones', of the Universe, 344, 365
Boutroux, E., 598, 653
Bowen, I. S., 373
Boyle, R., 13, 15
Boyle's law, 23, 228
Brachyphalangy, 497
Bragg, Sir W. H., 205, 211, 303–4
Bragg, W. L., 303–4
Brahé, Tycho, 312, 313
Brahma, 639
Brain, man's, 473, 527, 543
— of Neanderthal man, 544
Breuil, H., 525, 534
Brontës, the, 622
Bronze, 541
Broom, R., 472, 503
Brose, H. L., 214, 287
Brünn, 475
Bruno, Giordano, 312, 323, 520
Buddhism, 632
Buffon, J. L., 504
Bulletin of the Astronomical Institutes of the Netherlands, cited, 379, 381
Bulletin of the John Rylands Library, Manchester, cited, 458
Burial, primitive, 534, 535, 544, 545
Burnham, S. W., 358
Bushmen, South African, 535–8, 545
Butterfly, cabbage-white, 511–12

Cabanis, P. J. G., 581
Cactuses, 502
Caird, Edward, 556
Calcium, 207
Calculus of tensors, 51, 68, 137
Cambrian era, 372, 411, 423, 424, 425, 435, 469

Camel family, 431, 432
Canaanite cults, 629
Canals on Mars, 326–7
Carbohydrates, 414
Carbon, 21, 207, 215, 301–3, 325, 414, 416, 417, 418
Carbon-dioxide, 16, 21, 325, 414
— mean-square velocity of, 322
Carboniferous era, 210, 423, 424, 426, 437, 438, 440, 472
Carnivora, 473
Carnot, S., 231
Carnot's cycle, 235
— efficiency function, 233
— principle, 232, 236, 253
— reversible engine, 231
Carp, Chinese, 516
Carslaw, H. S., 33
Cartesian dualism, 554, 590
Carthaginians, 545
Caspian Sea, 538
Castor, a multiple stellar system, 358
Catalysts, 415
Cathode-rays, 262, 263, 285
Catholic church, sex-legislation of, 654
— mysticism, dualism in, 621
— theology, 1, 519, 589
Catholicism, and paganism, 631
— source of, 629
Causality, notion of, 309
Causation, efficient, 567, 569, 585, 595
— — and mutations, 579
Cause, 567–9
— and effect, Mach's view of, 569
Causes, final, in Spinoza's thought, 640
Cave-paintings, Aurignacian, 536
Cell-division, 435, 445
Cell-fusion, 435, 445
Cells, reproductive, 444
Centaurus, super-system of galaxies in, 378
Centrifugal force, 134
Cephalopods, 418
Cepheid variables, 345, 362, 377
— — in globular clusters, 344
Chadwick, J., 225
Chamberlin, T. C., 318
Chancelade man, 535
Chapman, S., 351
Characteristic X-rays, 285
Characters, genetic, 446, 447, 478, 480
— mutant, 482
Charges and electrons, 195
Charles' law, 228, 229
Chellean eoliths, 540
— man, 430
— tools, 531–2, 534
Chemistry, organic, 414, 417

Cheshire cat, 20

China, 632

Chinese carp, 516

— discovery of magnetic needle, 193

Chlorine, 25, 219, 417

Chlorophyll, 414, 417, 435

Chordates, 470, 471

Chou Kou Tien, 531

Christ, Resurrection of, 637

Christ-Spirit, 522, 523, 524

Christian mystics, 618

— theism and immortality, 644–6

Christian Religion in the Study and the Street, Moulton, cited, 632

Christoffel, E. B., 51, 138

Christoffel, Riemann-, tensor, 66

Christoffel's symbol of the first kind, 55, 138

— — of the second kind, 62, 138

Chromatin, 417, 444

Chromosomes, 444 *et seq.*, 481, 482

— changes in the gross morphology of the, 483

Chrysanthemums, 450

Church of England, decay in, 573

Civilisation, classical, 631

— dawn of, 543

— Graeco-Roman, 448, 460

— Western, 460

Clausius, R. J. E., 236

Cleopatra, 451

Clifford, W. K., 51, 97, 159, 576

Clifford's speculations as to space, 203, 381–2

Climatic changes, 540

Clock-time, 28–9

— ideal, 29

Clouds of Magellan, 345, 379

Club-foot, 485, 487

Club-mosses, 426, 436

Clusters, globular, 343–4, 365

— moving, 364, 365, 368

— open, 343

Coblentz, W. W., thermocouple of, 352

Cockcroft, J. D., 226

Coefficients of potential, 137

Collected Essays, Huxley, cited, 556, 576

Collisions, superelastic and inelastic, 252

Colloidal carbon compounds, 415

— solutions, 413

Colour-blindness, 485, 489–91

Colour-index, 258

Coma-Virgo region, super-galaxy in, 379

Combs, in fowls, 478

Combustion, nature of, 16

Comet's mass, 317

— tail, 243–4

Common Sense of the Exact Sciences, Clifford, cited, 159, 381

Companion of Sirius, 348–9

Complex atoms and disintegration, 342

— chromosome changes, 483, 500

Composition of velocities, 122, 123

Compton effect, 252, 406

Concerning the Nature of Things, Bragg, cited, 205

Congruence, 36, 37

Conscience, 638

Conscious Purpose, 599

Consciousness, an epiphenomenon, 577, 582

— nitrogen and loss of, 581

— problem of, 310, 580–2

Conservation of energy, 4, 18, 154, 231

— of energy, in Einsteinian mechanics, 180–3

— of energy, in Lemaître's cosmos, 383

— of mass, 4, 16, 18, 20

— of momentum, 154, 181

Constant, Einstein's, 160–1, 169, 382

— of gravitation, 167, 169, 173, 315–16, 321, 399

— of hyperbolic space, 37

— Planck's, 200, 261 *et seq.*, 280

— Rydberg's, 222, 268

Contentio Veritatis, Rashdall in, cited, 564

Contingency, 589

Continuity, equation of, 150–1

— of space, 52

Continuous groups, 46, 47

Continuum, objective domain of perception, 554

— space-time, 114

Contraction, Fitzgerald-Lorentz, 108, 118

Contravariants, 58, 63, 69, 127

Conversion, 613–17

— and 'fundamentalism', 616, 617

— psychology of, 614, 615

— value of, 615, 616

Coordinates, 30, 31

— Gaussian, 53

— geodesic, 72, 73, 182

Copernican system of astronomy, 323

Copernicus, N., 312, 556, 567

Copper, 327, 418

—discovery of, 541

Cordaiteae, 502

Cordaites, 442

Correspondence principle, of Bohr, 284

Cosmic evolution, theories of, 407

— — time-scales of, 389

— process, man and the, 522

— rays, 201, 404–6, 408

— time, 394

Cosmological argument, 595–6
— term, defined, 186
Cosmology, Jewish, 1
Cosmos, alternative expansion hypothesis, 391
— and man, 395
— as home of intelligent beings, 403–4
— de Sitter's, 142, 166, 187–9, 380
— Einstein's, total mass of, 186
— — time-cylindrical, 184–6, 380, 387
— expansion of, 381 *et seq.* (*see* Lemaître's cosmos)
— final state of the, 404
— Newtonian-Euclidean, 184
— of expanding Euclidean type, 393–4
— probable origin of, 395–6
— probable size of, 389–90
— use of term, 184
Coster, D., 214
Coulomb's law, 194
Counter-reformation, 323
Covariant differentiation, 83, 143 *et seq.*
Covariants, 58, 63, 70
Cradle of humanity, 538–9
Creation, modern view of, 2
— traditional view of, 1
— vestigial organs and, 465
Creative activity, 191, 419
— — arrangement and, 302
— Mind, 599
— Power, intervention of, 240
— power of genius, 624
— Spirit, 656
— — world as realm of, 645
Creed, the Apostles', 637
Creeds, 617
Cretaceous era, 424, 427, 428, 440, 441, 442, 453
Cretan culture, 541
Critical Philosophy of Immanuel Kant, Caird, cited, 556
Critique of Pure Reason, Kant, cited, 572, 651
Cro-Magnons, 535
Crookes, Sir W., 206
Crookes' tube, 202, 206, 207 220
Cross, F. L., 650
Cross, the, as a sacrament, 626
'Crossing-over', 480–1
Crustaceans, 425–6
Crystal spheres, planets in, 311
Crystals, 300
— measurements of, and by, X-rays, 303–4
Culture, Aurignacian, 537
— Cretan, 541
— Neolithic, 537
— Palaeolithic, 535, 537

Cumont, F., 629, 630
Curvature, Gaussian, 33, 56, 76–8
— Riemannian, 57, 162–4, 166
Curve, limiting, 36, 38
— of error, 506
Cycad-like forms, 426
Cycads, 438–9
Cynodonts, 427
Cytology, 444 *et seq.*, 481
Cytoplasm, 443, 444

Dalton, J., 228
Dalton's atomic theory, 21
Darien, 179
Darwin, Charles, 420, 421, 459, 461, 462, 468, 484, 506, 507, 509, 513, 528, 529, 597, 598, 622, 638
— — achievement of, 504–5
Darwin, C. G., 199, 274
Darwin, Erasmus, 504
Darwin, Sir Francis, 509, 598
Darwin, Sir George H., 333, 334
Das Relativitätsprinzip, Lorentz, Einstein and Minkowski, cited, 98
Davisson, C. J., 198
Dawson, C., 530
Dead, Neanderthal, burial of the, 534, 544
— Reindeer age burial, 535, 545
Deaf-mutism, 518
de Broglie, L., 199, 275, 278, 281
Decimal system, Carboniferous origin of, 472
Decline and Fall of the Roman Empire, Gibbon, cited, 657
Degeneration, of elephants, 468
— of quantum orbits, 271
— religious, 631–2
Deinotherium, 534
Deism, 597, 599
Deity, *nisus* towards, 591
De Magnete, Gilbert, cited, 193
Dementia praecox, 496
Democritus, 21, 559
Density, 'proper', 158
— — and invariant-mass density, 125
— tensor-, defined, 181
de Quatrefages, A., 535
De Revolutionibus Orbium Coelestium, Copernicus, cited, 567
Descartes, R., 98, 556, 594, 650
Descent of Man, Darwin, cited, 528, 638
de Sitter, W., 104, 379, 380, 381, 388, 390, 393, 394
de Sitter's cosmos, 142, 166, 187–9, 380
Determinism, 224
— and uncertainty-relations, 309–10
— mechanistic, 408, 577–80
Deus sive Natura, of Spinoza, 641

*Development of English Theology in the
    Nineteenth Century*, Storr, cited, 420
Development of Modern Philosophy, Adam-
    son, cited, 568
Devonian era, 423, 424, 426, 429, 435,
    438, 470, 471, 474
de Vries, H., 475, 506
Diameter of Betelgeux, apparent angular,
    339
Diamond, 301–2, 303
Diatomic molecules, 23
Dicotyledons, 441
'Dictionary' method of proof, of Poin-
    caré, 39, 42
Dictionary of National Biography, cited,
    420
Die Naturwissenschaften, cited, 114
Differential calculus, invention by New-
    ton, 313
— galactic rotation, 341, 366–8
Differentiation, covariant, 83, 143 *et seq.*
Difflugia corona, 460
Diffraction, 201, 275, 284, 291–9
— centres, 297
— grating, 198, 278, 337
— of electrons, 198–9
'Diffraction disc', 337
Digits, in primitive vertebrates, 472
Dill, Sir Samuel, 631
Dinosaurs, 427
Dionysius the Areopagite, 619
Diploid, 445, 451–2, 454, 501
Dipnoi, 425
Dirac, P. A. M., 275, 278
Direction, integral change of, 77
— of evolutionary change, 455, 467, 518
Discovery, cited, 423
Disorder, ecclesiastical, 656
— of energy, 238
Dispersive character of a medium, de-
    fined, 276
Divergence, 142–7
— of energy- and world-tensors, 160
— of stress-tensor, 150, 154
Divine intervention, need of, 408–10
Doctrine and Development, Rashdall,
    cited, 638
Dogma and religious experience, 633
Domain of Natural Science, Hobson,
    cited, 573, 579
Dominant characters defined, 476–8
— mutations, frequency of, 486
Doppler effect in Lemaître cosmos,
    387–9
Doppler's principle, 177, 185, 189, 244–6,
    336, 337, 357, 379, 380
Dordogne region, 535
Drinkwater, H., 488

Drosophila melanogaster, 450, 460, 480,
    483, 485, 486, 489, 499, 500, 515, 518
Drugs and mystical state, 618, 623
Dryopithecus, 527
Dubois, E., 469, 530
du Bois-Reymond, E., 578
Duck-billed platypus, 460
Dugan, R. S., 335
Dürken, B., 452, 461, 511–12
Düsseldorf, 533
Dwarf stars, 346–7
'Dwarfs, white', 347, 348–9, 370
— — and Einstein effect, 176, 349
Dwarf-stuff, Russell's, 371
Dynamical equations, Minkowski's world,
    128–32

Ear-muscles, vestigial, 465–6
Earth, age of, 209–10, 355, 413, 423
— first appearance of life, 411
— future of the, 371
— in ancient speculation, 311
— 'in the beginning', 413–14
— shape, size, density, mass, 314
Earth, The, Jeffreys, cited, 331, 423, 540
Earth-moon system, origin of, 319–20
— — the end of, 334–5
— — the future of, 334
— — the past of, 333
Earth's atmosphere, 323
— initial gases, 414, 417
— position in galactic universe, 368
— strata, ages of, 421–3
Earthworms, 431
Echinoderms, 425, 470–1
Eclipse, total of 1919, 176
Eclipsing binary stars, 354, 362
Ecstasy, religious, 632–3
Eddington, Sir A. S., 107, 113, 116, 134,
    177, 243, 254, 308, 346, 347, 381, 384
Effective temperature of a star, 248, 352
Efficiency function, 233
— of a heat engine, defined, 231
— of a reversible engine, 234
Ego, the, 643
Egypt, 541
— Neolithic, 549
Einstein, A., 2, 16, 19, 20–1, 90, 98, 114,
    160, 179, 201, 281, 313, 381, 393, 560,
    580, 588
— and absolute rotation, 135
— and gravitational force, 136
— and photo-electric effect, 262
— effect and density of white dwarfs,
    348–9
— principle of inertia of energy, 20–1
— quantum conditions, 265–6
— world-tensor, 139–42

Einsteinian dynamics, problem of two bodies in, 169
Einstein's cosmos, instability of, 384
— — size of, 389–90
— deduction of Lorentz transformation, 110–11
— equations for the orbit of a planet, 172–3
— formula for negative absorption, 208
— general principle of relativity formulated, 137
— gravitational equations, 160, 161, 166, 172–7, 382, 392
— law of gravitation, 178
— special principle of relativity formulated, 107
— (time-cylindrical) cosmos, 142, 184–6, 380, 384, 387
— — — total mass of, 186
— unified system of field-equations, 190
Einstein's Unified Field Equations, Levi-Civita, cited, 190
Electric current, field of, 200
Electrical Age, 541
— theory of matter, Lecture vii
Electricity, ancient knowledge of, 193
— and matter, 193 *et seq.*
Electro-magnetic field, 20, 189, 195, 200
— nature of light, 240
— theory of light, 201, 240–1
Electron, 20, 26, 195, 223–4, 305, 307–8
— destruction of, 206
— inertia of, 202
— nature of, 197–200
— size of, 215–16
— 'spinning', 273–4
Electrons, creation of, 205
— forces between, 197
— substance in protons and, 572
Electrostatic field, 195
— unit, 194
Element, spectra of an, 221
Elements, fundamental, of organic chemistry, 414
— of matter, 15, 21, 25, 213–15, 306
— periodic system of the, 273–5
— radioactive, 207–9, 225
— the different groups of, 218
Elements of Non-Euclidean Geometry, Carslaw, cited, 33
Elements, The, Euclid, cited, 34, 46
Elephant, 429, 525, 539
Elephants, degeneration of, 468
Ellipse, 321, 359
Elliptic geometry, 44–5, 95
— orbits, of hydrogen atom, 269–70
— — quantum conditions for, 264–5
Elmer Gantry, reference to, 614

Embryo of mammals and man, 463–5
Embryology and evolution, 462–5
Emergence, in evolution, 417
— of man, 527–9
— purposiveness in, 592–3
Empty space-time, curvature of, 161–6
— — gravitational equations of, 161
Enchiridion Metaphysicum, More, cited, 100
Encounters, stellar, 399–402
Encyklopädie der Mathematischen Wissenschaften, cited, 80
Endocrine glands, 493, 496
Energy, conservation of, 4, 18, 154, 180–3, 572
— kinetic, 18
— nature of, 17
— of matter, 204–5, 307
— of primitive organisms, source of, 416
— of solar radiation, 353–6
— of solar radiation, source of, 355–6
— potential, 182
— quality and quantity of, 231
Energy-density of equilibrium radiation, 247, 253, 254
— relation to pressure, 247
Energy-tensor, 154–6
— for a perfect fluid, 156
Engram, 509
Enneads, of Plotinus, cited, 619
Enquiry Concerning Human Understanding, Hume, cited, 567
'Entail of sin', 458
Entelechy, 561
Entropy, 236–8, 266, 580
— and direction of time, 238
— and end of Universe, 239–40, 409
Environment and evolutionary change, 467, 514
Enzymes, 415
Eocene era, 424, 429, 431, 453, 466, 473, 526
Eötvös, R., 136
Eozoic era, 424
Epicurus, 559
Epicycles, theory of, 311
Epigenesis, 648
Equation of continuity, 150–1
Equations, fundamental, of general relativity, 161
Equatorial horizontal parallax, 315
— quantum-number, 272
Equilibrium radiation, 247–9, 253
— stable thermal, 237
— theory of the tides, 328–9
Equipartition of energy, 261, 364
Era, the present scientific, 656
Eratosthenes, 311

Escape, velocity of, 321–2
Eskimos, 535, 545
Essay Concerning Human Understanding, Locke, cited, 570
Eternal Life, 648, 651
Ether, sub-, 277
— the, 100, 202–4, 241, 295, 308
Ethical monotheism, 5, 551, 599–608, 644, 649, 655
Ethical values, 473, 600–8
Ethics, international, 654
Euclid, 29, 30, 32, 34, 35, 44, 46, 48
Euphorbias, 502
Eurypterids, 426, 470–1
Events, or point-instants, 98
Evidences of Christianity, Paley, cited, 597
Evil, problem of, 3, 6, 435, 521
Evolution and geographical distribution of animals, 467–9
— and religious prejudice, 459
— duration of, 2
— in Australia, 539
— main arguments for, 462–9
— missing links in, 469–70
— of animals, 459–75
— of intelligent beings, 402–4
— of modern man from ape-like stock, 469, 525–30
— plant-, 434–43
— radical process of, 598
— raw material of, 515–18
— terrestrial and human sight, 259
— the machinery of, Lecture xv
Evolution, Kerr, cited, 432, 505
Evolution of Man, Elliot Smith, cited, 530, 533
Evolutionary change and environment, 467
— process, future of, 502
Exaltation, pseudo-religious, 623
Exclusion principle, Pauli, 274–5
Existence and value, 601
Expanding cosmos (Lemaître's), 381 et seq.
— — alternative hypothesis, 393
— gas, work done by, 230
Expansion of solids, liquids, and gases, 227
Experience and space-time continuum, 561
— the basis of geometry, 560, 574
— collective, 555–6
— individual, 554
— mystical, 617–24
— mystical, illustrations of, 619–21
— religious, see Lecture xix
Experimental science, validity of, 583

Exposition du système du monde, Laplace, cited, 318
Extinct Plants and Problems of Evolution, Scott, cited, 435
Extrapolation, 340, 406–8
Eye, defects in human, 485, 487, 490, 597
Eye-colour in man, 477, 478
'Eyeless', in drosophila, 515

Faber, G. S., 420
Fabre, J. H., 454
Factorial inheritance, 478
Faith, decay in, 635
— rational and irrational, 9–10
Fall, Adam's, 1, 2
Fall, pre-mundane, 521
Faraday, M., 54, 161, 189, 195, 541
Fayum in Egypt, 526
Fechner's law, 255–6
Feeble-minded, Royal Commission on, Report, cited, 494
Feeble-mindedness, Goddard, cited, 493
Feeble-mindedness, 491–5, 518
— and genius, 492
Ferns, 426, 437, 439
Fichte, J. T., 641
Field-equations, Maxwell's, 189
Filter-passing viruses, 415
'Fine structure' of hydrogen lines, 223
Finzi's formula, 84
Fire, primitive use of, 531, 534, 544, 546
Fischer, E., 493
Fisher, R. A., 481, 484, 505, 507, 508, 518
Fishes, 425–6
— teleostean, sex-mechanism in, 447
Fitness of the Environment, Henderson, cited, 418
Fitzgerald, E., quotation from, 524
Fitzgerald, G. F., 110
Fitzgerald-Lorentz contraction, 108, 118–19
Fizeau, H. L., 123, 244
Flesh and spirit, 622
Flint, H. T., 199
Flood, the, 370, 462
Fluctuations, 506, 512–14, 516
Fluorescence, 252
Fluorine, 226
Folk-lore in the Old Testament, Frazer, cited, 630
'Forbidden lines', 373
Force, defined, 17
— Mach's view of, 568
Form, according to Kant, 191
Forsyth, A. R., 658
Fossil Men, Boule, cited, 526, 527, 533, 545

Fotheringham, J. K., 331
Foucault's pendulum, 101
Foundling Hospital, 179
'Four-acceleration' vector, 128
'Four-velocity' vector, 127, 128
Fourier, J. B. J., 277
Fourth Gospel, 523
France, changes of climate in, 540
Fraunhofer's lines, 251–3
Frazer, Sir J. G., 548, 630
Freedom, human, 565, 582–5
Free-will, 2–3
— in inanimate nature, 224–5
Frequency, of radiation, defined, 241
Fresnel, A. J., 201, 290, 291
Friedman, A., 142, 186, 381, 392
Frog, parthenogenesis of, 452
Fundamental equations, of general relativity, 161
— identities, of general relativity, 147–8
'Fundamentalism', 616–17
Fungi, 435

Galactic nebulae, 372–3
— plane, 340
— — sun's position in, 341, 368
— universe, 336–74, 403
— — age of (according to Jeans), 356, 363–4, 407
— — centre of, 366, 403
— — life in, 401–2
— — period of the rotation of the, 368
— — shape and size of, 340–1
— — unity of, 341–2
Galaxies, super-, systems of, 378–9
Galilean mesh-system, 136–7
— space-time, 139
Galileo, 14, 15, 336, 357
— persecution of, 312
Gametes, 443
γ-rays, 200, 201, 212, 309, 405, 498
Ganoids, 426, 471, 474
Gas, mean free path in a, 23
— work done by expanding, 230
Gaseous spectra, 373
Gases, expansion of, 227
— initial, of earth, 413–14, 417
— kinetic theory of, 22–4, 229
— pressure of, 23, 228
Gaskell, W. H., 470
Gastrula, 463
Gates, R. Ruggles, 486, 489, 490, 492
Gaunilo, 594
Gauss, 51, 52, 560
— intrinsic geometry of a surface, 52–3
Gaussian coordinates, 53, 181
— curvature, 33, 56, 76–8
Gay-Lussac, J. L., 228

Geikie, James, 429
Gene, reality of, 575
— the, 444, 445, 516
Gene-losses and evolution, 515
General Catalogue of Double Stars, Burnham, cited, 358
General principle of relativity, 137
— relativity, Lecture vi
Genes, heterozygous, 482
— homozygous, 482
— linear order of, 481
Genetic change and alcohol, 516, 517
Genetic variation, see Lecture xv
— — and predestination, 523–4
Genetical Theory of Natural Selection, Fisher, cited, 481, 484, 507, 518
Genius and feeble-mindedness, 492
Geodesic coordinates, 72–3, 182
Geodesics, 30, 33, 55
— are autoparallel curves, 59
— in the Lemaître cosmos, 384–5
Geodesic surface, defined, 56, 79
Geographical distribution of animals and evolution, 467–9
— isolation and new varieties, 468
Geological formations, main, 423 et seq.
— record, 420–33
— — and evolution, 462
Geology and the origin of life, 411
Geometry, elliptic, 44–5, 95
— experience as basis of, 560, 574
— Lobatchewskyan or hyperbolic, 32, 33, 34–44, 91–4
— object of, 10
— Riemannian or spherical, 32, 33, 36, 44–6, 91, 94–7
— self-consistency of hyperbolic, 39–40
Gerlach, W., 274
Germer, L. H., 198
Germ-plasm, changes in the, 483
Gesammelte Mathematische Werke, Riemann, cited, 51
Giant and dwarf stars, 346–7
Giant-stuff, 371
Gibbon, E., 657
Gifford lectures, 577, 638
Gifford, Lord, 655
Gilbert, William, 193
Gill-slits, in vertebrate embryo, 464
Glacial epochs, 426, 429, 438, 442, 534, 540
Globular clusters, 343–4, 365
Glucose, formation of, 414
God and creative activity, 420, 502, 520–2, 592
— — man, 7
— — nature, 5, 13, 179, 191, 306
— — personality, 518

God, as source of absolute values, 605, 608
— attributes of, 606
— belief in, Lecture xviii
— existence of, 593–4
— faith in, 599–600
— in Spinoza's thought, 640
— sternness of, 523
— transcendence of, 519–20
God the Invisible King, Wells, cited, 522
Goddard, H. H., 493
Goethe, J. W. von, 515
Gold, early extraction of, 541
Goldschmidt, R., 452
Good, the Absolute, idea of, 604
'Good-seeing' and 'bad-seeing', 326
Gorilla and man compared, 473, 525
Graeco-Roman, or classical, civilisation, 448, 460, 631
Graphite, 301–2
Grasses, evolution of modern, 473
Grating, crossed, 297
— diffraction, 198, 278, 292–9, 337
— reflection, 296
— transmission, 292
Gravitation, and warping of space-time, 177
— law of, a disguised identity, 178
— Newton's law of, 5, 177, 313
Gravitational equations, Einstein's, 160–1, 166–76
— tensor, Einstein's, 147–8
Gravity and inertia, 18–19
Gray, T., quotation from, 369
Great Ice Age, Geikie, cited, 429
Great Nebulae, *see* Nebulae, Great
Greece, golden age of, 15
Greeks, the Ionian, 311, 632
'Greenhouse effect', 317, 325
Greenland, 540
Greensand, the Lower, 441
Grimaldi cave, 535
— negroids, 535, 536
Groups, continuous, 46–7
— sub-groups of rotation, 47–8
Group-velocity, 275–8
Gryphaeae, 502
Gulick, J. T., 468
Gymnosperms, 439

Haeckel, E., 463
Haematite, or red ochre, 535
Haemoglobin, 418
Haemophilia, 485, 489–90
Hafnium, 215
Hairlessness, in rabbits, 497
Haldane, J. B. S., 507
Haldane, J. S., 561, 562, 563, 591, 592, 598
Halley, E., 330, 336

Hamilton, Sir W. R., 265
Hamilton's principle of Least Action, 265–6
Hanson, F. B., 499
Haploid, 445, 449, 451–2, 454, 456, 458, 501
Harris, J. Rendel, 458
Hart, Bernard, 615
Heat, 16, 227
— a form of motion, 159
— and Light, Lecture viii
— mechanical equivalent of, 18
Hebrews and use of iron, 541
Hegel, G. W. F., 640, 641, 650
Heidelberg man, 532
Heisenberg, W., 278
— uncertainty-relations, 3, 199, 279–81, 282, 283, 309, 580, 584
Helen of Troy, 451
Heliocentric theory, 312
Helium, 25, 197, 213, 217
— formation of, 405
— mean-square velocity of, 322
Helium-nucleus, 211
Helmholtz, H. von, 51, 238, 597
Henderson, L. J., 418
Henze, F. W. M., 418
Herbaceous plants, 442
Herbart, J. F., 567
Herbivorous mammals, 473–4
Herd-instinct, 473–4
Heredity and religion, 633
— laws of, 475 *et seq.*
Heredity in Man, Gates, cited, 486, 489, 490, 492
Herglotz, G., 162
Hermaphrodite, 448, 501
Herschel, Sir William, 358
Hertz, H. R., 240
Hertzsprung, E., 346–7, 349
Heterozygous, 446, 482
Hevesy, G. von, 214
Heys, F., 499
Hilbert's axiom, 34–5, 92
Himalayas, 526
Hindu religion, 633, 634
Hinduism, 632, 639, 649
Hipparchus, 311
Histoire de l'Astronomie ancienne, Tannery, cited, 323
Hobson, E. W., 573, 579, 583
Höffding, H., 646, 647, 651
Hoffmann, G., 404
Holmes, A., 355, 423, 471
Holmgren, 454
Holst, H., 224
Holstein-Friesian cattle, genetic defects in, 497

Holy Communion, 573, 627, 629, 634
Homaloidal, 80, 97, 381
Homogeneous space, defined, 47
Homoplasy, 502
Homo sapiens, 469, 533, 534–8, 545
— — antiquity of, 536
Homozygous, 446, 482
— factor, lethal, 497
Hopwood, A. T., 502
Horace, quoted, 89
Hormic process, 508
Horograph, 77
Horse, evolution of, 431–2
— lethal factor in, 497
— vestigial toe of, 466
Hort, F. J. A., 527, 624, 635, 636
Housman, A. E., quoted, 521
How to draw a straight line, Kempe, cited, 30
Hubble, E., 370, 372, 374, 375, 378, 379, 390
Huggins, Sir W., 342
Hull, G. F., 243
Human Heredity, Baur—Fischer—Lenz, cited, 493, 513
Human evolution, Wallace's theory of, 542
— intelligence, evolution of, 542
Human sight, and its limitations, 259–60
Humanity, cradle of, 538–9
Humboldt, F. H. A. von, 184
Hume, D., 410, 557, 558, 559, 567, 571
Hume, Huxley, cited, 581
Huntington's chorea, 496
Huxley, Julian, 498
Huxley, T. H., 427, 462, 522, 556, 576, 581
Huyghens' principle, 291, 292
Hyacinths, 449
Hybrids, 450, 460–1, 476 *et seq.*
Hydrocarbons, 414
Hydrogen, 207, 414, 417, 418
— atom, 213, 217, 273–4
— — and Bohr orbits, 283
— — diameter of, 216, 269
— — elliptic orbits in, 269–70
— mean-square velocity of, 322
— nucleus, *see* Proton
— spectrum, 222–3, 267 *et seq.*
— two forms of, 274
Hyperbolic geometry, Lecture iii, 91–4
— space, constant of, 37
Hypothyroidism, 494

Iberians, 537
Idealism, 9, 562
Ideas and Ideals, Rashdall, cited, 650
Identities, fundamental, of general relativity, 147–8

Immortality, 571, Lecture xx
— and ethical theism, 644
— and time, 650–2
— and value, 646–7
Impulse radiation, 285
Inanimate nature, free-will in, 224
Inbreeding, 498
Incarnation, Christian doctrine of, 7
Independent assortment, law of, 478–80
Indeterminacy, principle of, 279
Index of refraction, 241
India, 610, 632
— Southern, religion in, 551
Indian mystics, 618
Indicator-diagram, 235
Individuality and value, 601
Induced experience, 624–5
Inertia and gravity, 18, 19
— Galilean law of, 14–15
— of electron, 202
— of energy, Einstein's principle, 20–1, 133
— of light, 204
Inertial mass, 19
— — equality with gravitational mass, 135–6
Infallibility, Biblical, 616
Inge, W. R., 5, 522, 563, 593, 607, 621, 646, 650
Inheritable qualities, 505
Inheritance, by blending, 484
— laws of, 475 *et seq.*
— of acquired characters, *see* Lamarckism
— particulate or factorial, 478, 484
Innate concept of the understanding, Kant's, 569
Inquisition, the, 625
Insanity, 491–2, 495–6
Insects, earliest flying, 426
— parthenogenesis in, 451
— sex-mechanism in, 447
Instinct and intelligence, 456
Instinct and the Unconscious, Rivers, cited, 496
Intellect, synthetic activity of the, 556–7
Intensity of radiation, defined, 243
Interference bands, 339
— of light, 201, 275, 290–1
Interferometer, 337–9
Internal Constitution of the Stars, Eddington, cited, 254
Interpolation, 406
Interpretation of the Atom, Soddy, cited, 207, 208, 212, 216
Inter-sexes, 448–9, 450
Interstellar space and cosmic rays, 404
Intersubjective intercourse, 562
Intrinsic geometry of a surface, 52–3

Introduction to Wave Mechanics, de Broglie, cited, 199, 278
Invariable sequence, 2–3, 12, 309, 519, 568–9, 579
Invariant, covariant derivatives of, 143
Invariant mass, 125, 130, 382
Invertebrates, 469–70
Iodine, 417
Ionian Greeks, 632
Ionised atoms, 197, 273
Ions, 196, 220
Iron, 418, 541
— Age, 541
Island universes, 378
Isobars, 220, 307
Isolated particle, gravitational field of, 170
Isothermals, 235, 236
Isotopes, 26, 215, 218, 219–20, 307
Isotropic radiation, defined, 246
— — pressure of, 159, 247
Isotropic space, defined, 47
Israel, 629

Jacobian ellipsoids, 376
James, William, 551, 553, 566, 576, 581, 593, 595, 610, 612, 615, 618, 620
Japanese horses, genetic defect in, 497
Java, 529
Java ape-man, 530
— — date of, 541
Jeans, Sir J. H., 133, 318, 322, 356, 363, 364, 365, 375, 376, 393, 396, 397, 399, 401, 402, 403, 407
Jeffreys, H., 318, 320, 331, 333, 334, 423, 471, 540
Jehovah, 630–1
Jennings, H. S., 460, 513
Jesus Christ, 457–8, 523, 524, 613
Jesus Human and Divine, Rashdall, cited, 7
Jewish cosmology, 1, 2
Johannsen, W., 512, 513
Joule, J. P., 18, 23, 159, 230, 231
Judaism, 649
Judgments, ethical, 603–4
— qualitative, 600
Jupiter, 314, 317, 319, 368
— discovery of moons of, 312
Jurassic rocks, 424, 427, 428

Kabyles of Algeria, 535
Kammerer, P., 511
Kant, I., 190, 191, 318, 395, 558, 559, 560, 561, 563, 568, 569, 570, 572, 573, 574, 588, 593, 594, 651
— paradox of, 556
Kapteyn, J. C., 351, 365, 366

Karma, 639
Keats, J., 622
— quoted, 179
Kelvin, Lord, 230, 238, 239, 568
Kelvin's scale of temperature, 233, 234
Kempe, Sir A. B., 30
Kepler, J., 270, 312, 313, 332
Kepler's laws, 313
Kerr, J. Graham, 432–3, 505
Kidneys, in lower vertebrates and man, 464
Kidston, R., 440
Kirchhoff, G. R., 251, 574
Kirchhoff's law, 250–1
Kiwi, vestigial wings of, 466
Knowledge, advance of, 655
— public, 555–6
Kohlschütter, A., 349
Kolhörster, W., 404
Kowalewsky, A., 463
Kramers, H. A., 224
Krüger 60, 354

Lagrange, J. L., 265
Lamarck, Chevalier de, 505, 508
Lamarckism, 508, 510–12, 514–16
Laplace, P. S., 318, 395, 407, 409, 578, 579, 580, 583, 584
Lattice, 297
— constants, 303
— space-, 298–9
Laue, M. von, 303
Lavoisier, A. L., 16
Law of gravitation, 5, 177, 178, 313
— of inertia, Galileo, 14–15
— of kinetics, 126
Laws of motion, Newton, 14, 17, 125, 150, 266
— of Nature, 3, 12, 519, 568, 603
— reversible in time, 238, 580
— statistical, 580
Lebedew, P., 243
Lectures, the, purpose of, 5
— range of, 13
Lectures and Essays, Clifford, cited, 97
Leibniz, G. W., 224, 560, 566, 567, 570
Lemaître, G., 142, 186, 407–8, 409
Lemaître's cosmos, 381 *et seq.*
— — conservation of energy in, 383–4
— — Doppler effect in, 387–9
— — expansion of, 386–7, 407
— — geodesics in, 384–5
— — mass of, 390
— — perplexities of, 392–3
— — pressure, density and mass, 385–7
— — radius of, 390
— — rate of expansion of, 388

Lemaître's cosmos, time-scales of, 388–9, 393, 395, 402
Lemuroids, 526
Lemurs, 525, 526
Length, 'proper', defined, 108
Lenz, F., 493
Lessons on Phenomena common to Animals and Vegetables, Bernard, cited, 434
Lethal factors, sex-linked, 447
— mutations, 490, 497–8, 517
Levi-Civita, T., 51, 55, 138, 190
Lias, 527
Lie, Sophus, 47
Life, adaptability of, 327
Life elsewhere in the cosmos, 403–4
— elsewhere in the galactic universe, 401–2, 520
— eternal, 651
— nature of, 419
— origin of, 411–20
— origin of, and geology, 411–12
— the first, 416
Life and Letters of Charles Darwin, Darwin, cited, 598
Light, 240 *et seq.*, 308–9
— diffraction of, 201, 275, 284, 291–9
— inertia of, 204
— interference of, 201, 275, 290–1
— polarisation of, 242
— speed of, 102
— ultra-violet, 201, 263
— visible, wave-lengths of, 201
Light-quanta, or photons, 201, 276, 279
Light-rays and human sight, 8, 255–60
Light-year, defined, 339
Likenesses, uniform repetitions of, 586, 624
Lilliput, 300, 305
Limiting curve, defined, 36
Lindblad, B., 366
Lindemann, F. A., 200, 282, 283, 284, 287, 310
Line, Euclid's definition of a straight, 30
— straight, in non-Euclidean space, 33
Line-element in hyperbolic geometry, 38, 89
— in Riemann's generalised space, 53–4
— in space of constant curvature, 83 *et seq.*
— in spherical space, 89
Linear order of genes, 481
— oscillator, 264
Lines, absorption, 251–3
— Euclid's definition of parallel, 34
— green 'nebulium', 373
— hydrogen, 271–2
— — in Sirius, 342
— iron and calcium, in sun, 342

Lines, spectral, 288–9
Lingula, 527
Linkage-groups, 444, 479–80, 481–2
Linnaeus, C., 462, 525
Liquids, expansion of, 227
Lithium, 215
— bombardment of, 226, 307
Litholatry, Semitic, 630
Liverworts, 436
Lobatchewsky, N. J., 32, 34, 35, 48, 560
— hyperbolic geometry of, 32–44, 89, 91, 92–3
Lobatchewskyan space, volume of, 93–4
Locke, John, 570
Lockyer, Sir N., 342
Lorentz, H. A., 98, 110, 137
Lorentz transformation-equations, 109–12, 115, 116, 122, 246
Lotze, H., 567
Lowell, P., 317
Lucas, H. M., 15
Lucretius, 559
Luke, Gospel of St, 457
Lunar theory, 330
Lung-fishes, 425
Lungs, in viper, 467
Lycopods, 436
Lyell, Sir C., 420, 462, 504

Mach, Ernst, 24, 101, 568, 569, 571, 574
Mach's view of absolute rotation, 101, 135
Maclaurin's spheroids, 376
— theorem, use of, 73
Maeterlinck, M., 454
Magdalenian art, 544
— culture, 430
Magellanic clouds, 345, 379
Magic, and religion, 547
— nature of, 546–7
— non-religious, 548
Magical sacramentalism, 630
Magnesium, in chlorophyll, 417
Magnetic field, due to moving charge, 195
— needle, 193
Magnetism, ancient knowledge of, 193
Magnetism and Electricity, Maxwell, cited, 193
Magnitude, absolute, defined, 257
— measures of visual, 256–7
Main sequence, the, 346
Major, H. D. A., 650
Malay Archipelago, 525
Mammalian development, uniqueness of, 539
Mammals, 441
— age of, 424, 428 *et seq.*
— herbivorous, 473–4
— placental, defined, 429

Mammals, sex-mechanism in, 447
— the first, 438
— transition from reptiles to, 427, 472
Mammoth, the, 430, 535, 544
Man, a product of evolutionary change, 504
— and the cosmic process, 522
— and the cosmos, 395
— antiquity of, 539–41
— development of brain, 527, 543
— difference from lower animals, 638
— vestigial organs in, 465–6
Man's emergence, 527–9
— — place and time of, 528–9
— end, 432–3
— kinship with the great anthropoids, 473
— origin and past, Lecture xvi
— place among the primates, 525
Mariotte, E., 228
Mark, Gospel of St, 458
Marmoutier, 594
Marriage of feeble-minded, 495
Mars, 314, 324
— markings on, 326–7
— possible life on, 326
Marsupials, 428, 429, 539
Marvin, F. S., 631
Mass, and energy, 131–3
— and weight, 18–19
— conservation of, 4, 16, 18, 20
— equality of inertial and gravitational, 135–6
— gravitational, 19
Mass, the Roman, 629
Mass, inertial, 19
— invariant, 125, 130
— physical, 125, 130
— varying measure of, 132, 196, 202
Mass-luminosity law, 361–2, 371
Mass-spectrograph of Aston, 220
Material world, mind and the, 310
Materialism, 310, 553, 576
Mathematical Papers, Clifford, cited, 51, 160, 203
Mathematical Theory of Relativity, Eddington, cited, 113
Mathematics, need of, 13
Matter, see Lecture ii
— and mind, dualism of, 563
— annihilation of, 205, 307, 356, 404–6
— 'conservation' of, 16
— energy of, 20, 132–3, 204–5
— in ancient speculation, 15
— nature of, 564
Matthew, Gospel of St, 457
Mauer, 532
— jaw, 533

Maupertuis, P. L. M. de, 264
Maxwell, J. Clerk, 26, 189, 193, 195, 201, 228, 237, 239, 240, 241, 243, 364, 566
Maya, 639
Mean free path in a gas, defined, 23
Mean-square velocity, of a gas, 322
Measurement, our modes of, 179–80
Measures of matter and momentum, 178
Mecca, Black Stone at, 630
Mechanical equivalent of heat, 18
Mechanics and geometry, connection between, 159–60
Mechanistic determinism, 577–80
Mediterranean race, 537
Mediums, spiritualistic, 587
Melotte, P., 351
Mendel, Gregor, and the significance of his work, 475
Mendeléev's Periodic Table, 25, 26, 214, 218, 289
Mendelism, 475–503
Mendel's first law, 477–8
— fundamental experiment, 475–6
— law of independent assortment, 478–80
— laws, departures from, 478, 486–8
— — Morgan's restatement of, 480–2
Mental defectives, 491–5
— — and marriage, 494
— mutations in humanity, 491–6
Mentone, 535
Merck's rhinoceros, 430
Mercury, motion of perihelion of, 173–4, 314
Mesh-system, Galilean, 136
Mesozoic era, 423, 424, 426, 427, 428, 438, 439, 453, 474
Metal Age, the, 537, 541
Metaphysics, necessity of, 552–3
Metastable states of an atom, 373
Metazoa, 443, 444
Meteoric hypothesis, 412
Methodist Church, 617
Methods of Ethics, Sidgwick, cited, 646
Metric, 155, 160
— Schwarzschild's, 171, 174, 176–7
Miastor, 451
Michelson, A. A., interferometer of, 337
Michelson-Morley experiment, 98, 104–5, 107, 203
Michelson's experiment as to tides, 329
Micro-organisms, 415–16, 432
Microphthalmia, 487
Microscope and light, 279–80, 305
Microscopic and macroscopic equations, 125–6
Milky Way, 340, 343, 344, 350–1, 370, 372, 377, 403, 405

Milky Way, pole of, 351
Miller, N., 488
Millikan, R. A., 202, 404, 405, 500
Milne, E. A., 370, 394
Mind and matter, 310, 580–2, 640
— dualism of matter and, 563
— emergence of, 419
— human and Divine, 179–80, 306
— synthetic activity of the, 574
— the unconscious, 615
— versus material protection, 474
Minkowski, H., 98, 116, 394
Minkowski's world, 116, 117, 266, 561, 651
— — dynamical equations in, 128–32
— — 'four-acceleration' vector in, 127
— — 'four-velocity' vector in, 127
— — order of events in, 119–21
— — proper-time in, 127
Miocene era, 424, 429, 430, 453, 466, 526, 529
Miracle, 592
'Missing links', 469–70, 528
Mithraism, 629
Mneme, The, Semon, cited, 509
Mnemic theory, 509
Models, mechanical, 193, 568
Modernists, 457
Mohammedan mystics, 618
Mohammedanism, 630, 649
Mohr, O. L., 497
Moir, J. Reid, 531
Molecule, defined, 22
Molecules, and ascent to life, 415–16
— and temperature, 282
— Maxwell on, 26–7
— types of, 23
Moments, or covariants, defined, 58
Momentum, conservation of, 154, 181
— our measures of, 178
Momentum-density, 152
Monadology of Leibniz, 566
Monads, 3, 591
— Universe of, 224, 566
Monatomic gases, 25
— molecules, 23
'Mongolian' idiots, 494
Monism, 588, 639, 649
Monkeys, 526
— loss of teeth in, 526
Monochromatic radiation, 242, 263, 405
— waves, 277
Monocotyledons, 442, 502
Monoecious, 448, 501
Monotheism, ethical, 5, 551, 599–608, 644, 649, 655
Monotremes, 428, 429
Montana, 424

Month, sidereal, 330, 332
Monthly Notices of the Roya Astronomical Society, cited, 320, 331, 381
Moon, has no atmosphere, 320, 323
— mass and density of, 319
— motion of, effect of tidal friction, 331–3
— origin of the, 319–20
— origin of the, resonance theory of, 320
— visual magnitude of full, 257
Moons of planets, 314
— of planets, retrograde motion of, 314
Moral argument, the, 605–6
— consciousness, rise of, 473, 601–3
— principles, objective validity of, 603
Moral Values and the Idea of God, Sorley, cited, 600, 607
More, Henry, 100, 559
Morgan, C. Lloyd, 508, 590
Morgan, T. H., 448, 450, 451, 460, 480, 489, 514, 515
Moseley, H. G. J., 26, 214, 215, 288
Moses, 550
Mosses, 436
Moths, 447
Motion, absolute, 134
— Newton's laws of, 14, 17, 125, 150
Moulton, F. R., 318
Moulton, J. H., 632
Mount Wilson, 100-inch reflector of, 349, 352, 372, 374, 378, 407
Moustierian culture, 430, 534
— flints, 533
Moving clusters, 364
Müller, F. Max, 572, 651
Müller, George, 612
Muller, H. J., 498, 499
Multiple stellar systems, 358
Mutant characters, 482–3
Mutation, process of, 447
Mutational change, direction of, 455, 467, 518
Mutation-rates, 508, 517
Mutations, 3, 482 et seq., 506, 514, 516, 517
— and efficient causation, 579
— and short-wave radiation, 498–500
— dominant, 482, 486
— in humanity, 485 et seq.
— in humanity, mental, 491–6
— in humanity, persistence of, 488–9
— lack of ethical quality in, 3, 520
— lethal, 490, 497–8, 517
— recessive, 482
— reversal of, 498
Mutually orthogonal axes, in n dimensions, 162
Myers, F. W. H., 611
Mystery-religions, 629–31

Mystical experience, 617–24
— — illustrations of, 619–21
— — personal, 620–1
— — worth of, 623–4
— state and drugs, 618, 623
— — highest form of, 618
— states, normal and super-normal, 610
Mysticism and pantheism, 623, 649
— and science, 624
— catholic, dualism in, 621
— consumptive, 622
— naturalness of, 589
Mystics, Indian, Mohammedan and Christian, 618

Napoleon, 583
Nares, E., 420
Natural and spiritual, 590
— and supernatural, dualism of, 519, 588–90, 592
— selection, 468, 505, 506–8
Naturalism, agnostic, 5, 575–7
Naturalism and Agnosticism, Ward, cited, 576, 577
Nature and moral law, 605
— anthropomorphic interpretation of, 567
— efficient causation in, 585
— laws of, 3, 12, 568, 603
— rational principle of, 596
— resourcefulness of, 451, 477, 503
Neanderthal man, 430, 532–4, 536, 544
Nebulae, extra-galactic, *see* Nebulae, Great
— galactic, 372–3
— Great (or extra-galactic), 374–98
— — distances of the, 377–8
— — enigma of arms of, 397
— — number of, 374
— — shapes of the, 375–6
— — sizes of the, 378–9
— — spectra of the, 376–7
— — velocities of recession of the, 379–81, 387–8
— observing of the, 372
— planetary, 370, 374
'Nebulium' lines, 373, 405
Negroids, Grimaldi, 535, 536
Neolithic burials, 538
— culture, 537
— Egypt, totemism in, 549
— man, 430
Neon, 25, 218, 274
Neo-Platonism, 619
Neo-Platonists, The, Whittaker, cited, 619
Neptune, 314, 317
Neutrons, 226

New Conceptions of Matter, Darwin, cited, 199, 274
New Testament narratives, 457
New Theory of Vision, Berkeley, cited, 573
Newton, Sir I., 14, 17, 35, 155, 173, 336, 543, 557, 559, 560, 561, 580, 583, 645
— Arian beliefs of, 557
— *Four Letters of Bentley*, cited, 177, 396
Newton's belief in absolute space, 100
— dynamical equations of motion, 150–4
— law of gravitation, 5, 177, 178, 312
— laws of motion, 14, 17, 125, 150, 266
— picture of cosmic evolution, 395–6
— view of absolute rotation, 101
Newtonian constant of gravitation, 167, 169, 173, 315–16, 321, 399
Newtonian-Euclidean cosmos, 184, 392
New Zealand, 466
Nicholas of Cusa, 324
Nichols, E. F., 243
Nictitating membrane, 465
Nirvana, 639
Nisus towards deity, 591
Niton, 25, 208, 218
Nitrogen, 207, 414, 417
— and loss of consciousness, 581
— mean-square velocity of, 322
Nitrous oxide, 618
Noble, H. R., 203
'Noble' elements, 218
Nordics, 537
Nova Aquilae, 369
Novae, in spiral nebulae, 377
— or temporary stars, 368–70
Nuclei, problems of atomic, 225
Nucleus, atomic, 194, 215, 307
— hydrogen-, or proton, 197, 213, 216
— of a reproductive cell, 444–5
Numerical tests and heredity laws, 475
Nun, religion of the, 625

Object, conceptual, 556
— defined, 554
Objective validity in ethics, 602
Objects, *extra nos* and *praeter nos*, 563
Obscuring regions, of cosmos, 350
Ocean, age of earth's, 423
Ochre, red, or haematite, 545
Oeuvres de Descartes, cited, 98, 651
Oeuvres mathématiques de Riemann, cited, 51
Old Testament, 311
Oligocene era, 424, 429, 453, 466, 473, 526
Oliver, C. P., 499
Omar Khayyam, 524
On the Immortality of the Soul, Hume, cited, 571

On the Limits of Natural Knowledge, du Bois-Reymond, cited, 578
On the Nature of Things, Lucretius, cited, 559
'Once-born', the, 615
Ontogeny, 463
Ontological argument, 594–5
Oort, J. H., 341, 366, 367, 368, 390
Ophiuchus, 366
Optical pairs of stars, 358
Opticks, Newton, cited, 558
Orbits, quantised, 265 *et seq.*
Ordovician rocks, 424, 425
Organism, psycho-physical, 652
Organisms and self-protection, 474
— constitution of, 504
— primitive, 416–17
Oriental Religions in Roman Paganism, Cumont, cited, 629, 630
Origin of Species, Darwin, cited, 420, 459, 461, 505, 597, 598
Origin of the Human Skeleton, Broom, cited, 472
Origin of the Vertebrates, Gaskell, cited, 470
Orthodoxy, a new scientific, 655
Oscillator, linear, 264
Osmium, 348
Osthoff, H., 493
Ostracoderms, 470, 471
Outspoken Essays, Inge, cited, 5, 522, 563, 593, 650
Ovaries, in birds, 467
Ovum, 443, 444, 445, 447
Oxygen, 207, 325, 327, 414, 416, 417, 418
— mean-square velocity of, 322
Oxyhaemoglobin, 418

Paedogenesis, 451
Palaeolithic culture, 535, 537, 547
— era, 537–8, 541
Palaeozoic era, 423, 424, 425, 426, 469
Paley, William, 597
Panama, Isthmus of, 468, 526
Pantheism, 520, 599
— and mysticism, 623
— and theism, 647–50
Parallax, annual, 339, 340, 343
— equatorial horizontal, 315
— measurements, 314
Parallaxes, spectroscopic, 349
Parallel displacement, infinitesimal, 59–66
— — — along a geodesic, 60
— — — in *n*-dimensional manifolds, 64
— — — of a versor, 61
— — — of tangential vectors, 62–3
— — — round an infinitesimal parallelogram, 64–6

Parallel lines, defined, 34
Parallelism, angle of, 35, 38, 39, 43, 44
— psycho-physical, 580–2, 636
— — error in, 582
— with respect to a surface, 59
Paramecium, 513
Parameters, or contravariants, 58
Parsec, 257
— defined, 340
Parthenogenesis, 445, 451, 454, 477
— artificial, 452
Particle, isolated, gravitational field of, 170
Particulate inheritance, 478, 484
Patagonians, 538
Patterson, J. T., 499
Paul, St, 590, 610, 629
— — conversion of, 614
Pauli, W., 80
Pauli's exclusion principle, 218, 274, 275
Pearson, Karl, 159, 381, 491, 574
Peas, Mendel's experiments with edible, 475 *et seq.*
Pekár, D., 136
Pekin man, 531–2, 544
Pendulum, 29
— Foucault's, 101
Percy pedigree, 488
Pérès' formula, 71, 75, 76, 79, 81
Perihelion of Mercury, motion of, 173–4, 314
Periodic Table of Mendeléev, 25, 26, 214, 218, 289
Permian era, 424, 426, 427, 472, 473
Perseus, moving cluster in, 364
Persia, 632
Personality and the psycho-physical organism, 652–3
— dissociation of, 587
Phallic worship, 546
Phase of light wave, defined, 291
Phase-velocity, 276
'Philistine', 624
Philistines and Cretan culture, 541
Philosophical Essay on Probabilities, Laplace, cited, 578
Philosophy, Indian, time in, 98
— the Newtonian, 557–9
Philosophy of Plotinus, Inge, cited, 619, 621
Philosophy of Religion, Höffding, cited, 646
Phlogiston, 16, 227
Phosphorus, in protoplasm, 417
Photo-electric effect, 262–3, 275
Photon, 201, 276, 279
Phyla, 463, 469
Phylogeny, 463

Physical and the psychical, 310
Physical mass, 125, 130
Physical Significance of the Quantum Theory, Lindemann, cited, 200, 282
Physics as the science of mutual relations, 308
Pilgrim, G. E., 526, 527
Piltdown remains, 530–1
Pistil, 461, 501
Pithecanthropus erectus, 469, 530
Placenta, 429, 463
Placental mammals, 371, 429, 511
Planck, M., 261
Planck's law, 254–5, 405
— constant, 200, 261 *et seq.*, 280 *et seq.*
— — and mental processes, 310, 584
Plane transmission grating, theory of, 295–7
— waves, direct passage through a slit, 293–5
Planes of reference, defined, 31
Planetary nebulae, 370, 374
— perturbations, of the moon, 330
— systems, formation of, 318, 398–401
— — number of, 401–2
— — number of, in spiral nebulae, 403
Planets, atmospheres on, 322–3
— existence of life on, 324 *et seq.*
— moons of, 314
— moons of, retrograde motion of, 314
Plants and animals, similarity of, 434
— evolution of, 434–43
— flowering, 429
— herbaceous, 442
— marine, 425, 439
— monoecious, 448
— the most primitive, 435
Plaskett, J. S., 366
Plaskett's star, 361, 362
Plato, 9, 504
Platonism, 100, 649
Platonist, Cambridge, 559
Platypus, 460
Playfair's axiom, 32
Pleistocene era, 424, 429, 430, 431, 432, 442, 528, 530, 532, 534
Pliocene era, 424, 429, 442, 530
— — man's probable appearance in, 529
Plotinus, 619, 621, 646, 650
Pluralism, 649
Plutarch, 629
Pluto, 314
Pluto's orbit, period, mass, diameter, 317
Poincaré, H., 12, 17, 39, 49, 96, 97, 224, 281, 307
Point-instants, 30, 98
Polar quantum-number, 272
Polarisation, of light, 242

Pollen, 461, 501
Polyploids, defined, 449
Polyploidy, and sex, 450
Popular Scientific Lectures, Mach, cited, 568, 569, 571
Potassium, 25–6, 218
— faintly radio-active, 214
— in protoplasm, 500
Potential, coefficients of, 137
— energy, 182
Pratt, J. B., 611, 621
Prayer, 611–13
— answers to, 612
— petitionary, 613
Pre-Cambrian rocks, age of, 210
Predestination, 496, 523
Pre-existence, 644
Pre-history, human, 2
Pressure at the centre of the sun, 316
— in a fluid, 158–9
— of gases, 227
— of isotropic radiation, 247
— of solar radiation, 243
Pressure-shift, defined, 244
Primary qualities, 570
Primates, 429, 474, 525–7
— development of the, 526–7
— the earliest, 525–6
Primitive religion, 545–51, 609–10
Primrose, mutually infertile varieties, 461
Principia, Newton, cited, 100, 101, 312, 558, 578
Principle, Carnot's, 232, 233, 234
— Huyghens', 291, 292
Principles of Geology, Lyell, cited, 420
Principles of Human Knowledge, Berkeley, cited, 558
Principles of Psychology, James, cited, 566, 576, 581
Pringle-Pattison, A. S., 606
Proceedings of the National Academy of Sciences, cited, 393
Procrustes, bed of, 562
Proper motion, stellar, defined, 357
'Proper' density, 125, 158, 266, 382
— length, 108
— mass or invariant mass, 125, 130, 382
— time, 113, 127, 267
— volume, 124–5, 267
Protactinium, 207
Protagoras, 573
Proteins, 415, 417
Prothallus, 436, 437, 501
Proton, 197, 306–8
— size of, 215–16
Protons and electrons, substance in, 572
Protoplasm, 417, 434, 500
Protozoa, 443

Proxima Centauri, distance from the sun, 336
— — parallax of, 343
Pseudo-energy-tensor, 182–3
Pseudo-sphere, 93
'Psychic unity', 502
Psychology of Insanity, Hart, cited, 615
Psycho-physical organism, the, 652
— parallelism, 580–2, 636
— — error in, 582
Pteridosperms, 437, 439
Pterodactyls, 427
Ptolemaic system of astronomy, 311, 337
Ptolemy, 311, 336
Public worship, 626
Punic Wars, 629
Punnett, R. C., 479
Puppis, V., 354, 362
Pure strains and hybrids, 475–6, 477, 480
Purgative way, 621
Puritanism and science, 633
Purity of the gametes, law of, 480
Purkinje effect, 257–8
Pyrheliometer, 353
Pythagoras' theorem, 32, 54
Pythagorean doctrine, 311
Python, vestigial legs of, 466

Quaker, the, 627
Qualities, primary and secondary, 570
Quality, 601
Quantisation of action, 264
Quantised elliptic orbits, 265
— orbits, 264
Quantum conditions, Einstein, 265, 266
— — general, 264, 265
— law, Einstein, 201, 262–3
— — Planck, 261–2
— numbers, 265
— — azimuthal and radial, 272
— of action, 261
— of light, 201, 276, 279
— theory and Röntgen rays, Lecture ix
— — present state of, 281–4
Queensland, 536

Racial mean, 505
Radial quantum-number, 272
Radiation, absorption of, 252
— and human sight, 258–60
— black-body, 249, 253, 261, 325
— described, 200, 241
— equilibrium-, 159, 247–9, 253–4
— from planets, 250
— from sun and stars, 249
— intensity of, 242–3
— isotropic, 23, 246
— — pressure of, 247

Radiation, monochromatic, 242, 263, 405
— pressure of, 243
— 'proper' mass of, 159
— short-wave, and mutations, 498–500, 517
— stellar, 351–3
— — source of, 205, 355–6
— various forms of, 201
— within a star, 250, 251
Radiator, perfect, defined, 248
Radio-active atoms and determinism, 224, 305
— decomposition, 208–9, 211–12, 219
Radioactivity, 207–8
Radium, 207, 208, 275
Radius of spherical curvature, defined, 164
Radon, 208, 218
Rankine, W. J. M., 238
Rashdall, Hastings, 7, 564, 605–6, 638, 640, 644, 650, 651
Rasmuson, 364
Rasputin, 642
Rationality of the Universe, 645, 652
Rayleigh, Lord, 261, 275
Rays, 'cosmic', 201, 404–6, 408
'Real Spiritual Presence', 573, 634
Realism, defined, 563
— moderate, 6, 563–5
— naïve, 553, 563
— physical, 553–4
Reality, scene of, Weyl, 122, 651
Realm of Ends, Ward, cited, 565, 566, 641
Recessive characters, defined, 476
Reck, H., 534
Red ochre, or haematite, 545
Reflections on the Motive Power of Heat, Carnot, cited, 231
Reformation, the, 629, 631
Refraction, index of, 241
Reincarnation, 639
Reindeer Age, 535–6
— — burials, 535, 545
— — civilisation, 544–5
Reiter, H., 493
Relativity, Einstein, cited, 107
Relativity, general principle of, 137
— general theory of, Lecture vi
— general theory of, as applied to density of white dwarfs, 348–9
— restricted principle of, 107
— special theory of, 10, Lecture v
Religion, primitive, 545–51, 609–10
— — and totemism, 549
— — characteristics of, 545
— — development of, 550–1
— — in relation to magic, 547

Religious consciousness, psychology of, 10, Lecture xix
— credulity, reappearance of, 628
— degeneration, 573, 631–2
— ecstasy, 632–3
— experience and dogmatic assertion, 633
— experience and suggestion, 625
— — induction of, 624–5
— — necessity for guided, 628
— faith, future of, 653–4
— prejudice and evolution, 459
— teachers, authority of, 628
— — duty of, 635
Religious Consciousness, Pratt, cited, 611, 621
Renaissance, the, 656
Report of the Mental Deficiency Committee, cited, 494
Reproductive cells, 444
Reptiles, 426
— age of, 424
— mammal-like, 427
— transition from amphibians, 472
Reptilian birds, 427
'Reservation', 634
Resonance, 252
— theory of moon's origin, 320
Resurrection of the body, 637
Reversal of mutations, 498
Reversible engine, Carnot's, 231–3
Rhinoceros, Etruscan, 429, 532
— Merck's, 430
— woolly, 430
Rhodesia, 541
Rhyniaceae, 438
Rhynie chert-bed, 438
Ricci, G., 51, 138
Ricci's lemma, 144
Riemann, Bernhard, 30, 32, 51, 90, 159, 560
Riemann-Christoffel tensor, 66–8, 138–9
Riemann, general theory of space, 51–97
— surface, 265
Riemannian curvature, 57, 162–4, 166
— or spherical, geometry, 32, 33, 36, 44–6, 48, 91
— space, volume of spherical or, 94–5
— — properties of, 96
Riemann's symbol of the first kind, 57, 66, 139
— — of the second kind, 66, 139
Rigid body, displacements of, 41, 46–9
Rings, of Saturn, 335
Ritz, W., 222
Rivers, W. H. R., 495, 496
Rocks, measurement of age of, 422
— oldest known igneous, 423

Roman church and date of creation, 420
— — and Galileo, 312
— — and Giordano Bruno, 323
— — and transubstantiation, 573
— — opposition to evolution, 459
Roman Society in the Last Century of the Western Empire, Dill, cited, 631
Romanes Lecture, Huxley's, 522
Römer, O., 102
Römerian time, 152
Röntgen's X-rays, *see* X-rays, 206, 284 *et seq.*
Roses, cultivated, origin of, 450
Rotation, absolute, 100, 101, 134
— cause of nebular, 397
— sub-groups of, 47–8
Rotifer, 451–2
Rowland, H. A., 293
Rowland grating, 303
Rupp, E., 198
Russell, Bertrand, Earl, 210, 225
Russell, H. N., 335, 371
Russell-Hertzsprung diagram, 346–7, 349
Rutherford, Lord, 25, 211, 267
Rydberg's constant, 222, 268
R.Z. Lyrae, 357

Sabatier, A., 611
Saccheri's quadrilateral, 35–6
Sacrament, synonym for consecrated elements, 634
Sacramental theory, dualism in, 627
Sacramentalism, magical, 630
— pagan, 629
Sacraments, 626–8
— and suggestion, 627
— number of, 627
Sagittarius, 341, 344, 366, 377
Saints, relics of, 631
Salvation Army, 616
Sandwich Islands, snails in, 468
Sanger, C. P., 15
Saturn, 314, 319, 335
Scalar product, defined, 64
Scattering points, 297
Scepticism of Hume, 559
Schelling, F. W. J., 641
Schiaparelli, G. V., 326
Schlosser, M., 526
Scholasticism, medieval, 458
Schouten, J. A., 75
Schrödinger, E., 199, 275, 278, 281
Schur, F., theorem of, 82–3
Schwarzschild, K., 171, 174, 176–7, 243
Science and Civilisation, Singer in, cited, 631
Science and moralised religion, antiquity of, 632

Science and puritanism, 633
— limitations of, 10
— nature of the progress of, 4
Science and Religion in Contemporary Philosophy, Boutroux, cited, 598, 653
Science et l'Hypothèse, Poincaré, cited, 12, 96, 224, 281
Sciences and Philosophy, Haldane, cited, 561, 591
Scorpio, 366
Scorpio-Centaurus group of clusters, 364
Scorpions, 425
Scott, D. H., 435, 441
Scott, Sir Walter, quoted, 28
Séances, 587
Seares, F. H., 341, 344, 351, 364, 366
Secondary qualities, 570
Secular acceleration, sidereal, 331
— perturbations, 330
Seed-ferns, 437
Seeds, 437
Seeliger, H. von, 184
Selective mating, 495
Semitic litholatry, 630
Semon, R. W., 509
Sensorium, 558, 559
Sequence, invariable, 2–3, 12, 309, 568–9, 579
Series, K-, L- and M-, of spectral lines, 288–9
Serpent, as totem, 550
Seward, A. C., 439
Sex, 443–58
— basal facts, 443
— secondary differences of, 443–4
Sex-chromosomes, 444, 446 *et seq.*
Sexes in humanity, roughly equal in numbers, 447
Sex-linked characters, 447, 448, 478, 480
— defects, 487, 489–91
— lethal factors, 447
Sex-mechanism, an alternative, 447–8
— in animals and plants, 501–2
Sexual cycle, 501
— fusion, 445
Seymouria, 472
Shankara, 639
Shapley, H., 344, 345, 365, 366, 374, 378
Shark, 464, 473
'Shell-shock', 495
Short-fingeredness, 497
Sickness, 'sleepy', 637
Sidereal month, 330, 332
— secular acceleration, 331
Sidgwick, H., 646
Siegbahn, M., 288
Silurian era, 424, 425, 426, 435, 470, 471

Similar figures, in different geometries, 90, 91
Simocephalus, 513
Simon, L., 509
Simultaneity, 103, 134
Singer, C., 631
Sirius, 336, 348–9
— companion of, 177, 348–9
— spectral lines and temperature, 342
Sivalik Hills, 526–7
Sivapithecus, 527
Skin-colour inheritance, 485
'Sleepy sickness', 637
Slime-moulds, 434
Slipher, V. M., 379
Smith, G. Elliot, 502, 530, 531, 533, 538
Snails, 468
Social problem group, the, 495
Soddy, F., 207, 208, 212, 216
Solar apex, defined, 357
— constant, 353
— radiation, energy of, 353–6
— system, 310–35
— — ancient observations of, 311, 330
— — existence of life on planets of, 324–7, 403
— — Laplace's theory of origin of, 318
— — members of, 314
— — modern theory of origin of, 318–19, 398–401, 407
— tides, 334–5
Solid Geometry, Frost, cited, 77
Solids, expansion of, 227
Solipsism, 555
Sommerfeld, A., 214, 217, 223, 261, 270, 271, 287
Sommerfeld-Bohr, 271, 273, 275
Sommerfeld-Wilson quantum conditions, 265–6
Sorley, W. R., 600, 607
Soul and body, 636–7
— as substratum, 643
— dark night of the, 621–3
Sound-waves and light-waves, compared, 295
Space, absolute, 99, 100
— and time, concepts of, 281–4
— binding forces in, 52
— Clifford's speculations, 203–4
— continuity of, 52
— dispersive character of, 276
— 'elliptic', 45, 95
— finite, 49–50, 96, 183
— flat, 80–1
— given in experience, 560, 573–4
— homogeneous, isotropic and unbounded, 47

Space, intuitions of, 28–9
— measurements in, 28–9
— numerical representation of three-dimensional, 31
— Riemannian, properties of, 96
— separation from time, 30
— volume of Lobatchewskyan, 93, 94
— volume of Riemannian, 94, 95
Space-lattice, diffraction by, 298–9
Space-time, Lecture v
— continuum, interval in the, 114–19
— gravitation and warping of, 177
— Weyl's picture, 122
Space, Time, and Deity, Alexander, cited, 590
Space, Time and Gravitation, Eddington, cited, 107, 116, 134, 177
Space—Time—Matter, Weyl, cited, 54, 89, 122
Space—Time—Motion, Vasilief, cited, 15
Special theory of relativity, Lecture v
— — of relativity, dynamical equations in, 128–32
— — of relativity, fundamental result of, 105–7
— — of relativity, time-measurements in, 112–14
Species, destruction of, 431–2
— nature of, 460–2
— special creation of, 542
Spectator, The, cited, 559
Spectra, gaseous, 373
— stellar, 341–2
Spectral type of a star, 342
Spectrograph, mass-, 220
Spectroscope, 221, 242, 244–5, 337
Spectroscopic and visual binaries, contrast between, 362–3
— binaries, 354, 358, 359
— — masses of, 360–1
— — number of, 359
— — origin of, 363
— — periods and eccentricities of, 363
— parallaxes, 349–50
— work, pioneers in, 342
Spectrum of an element, 221
— of hydrogen, 222–3, 267 *et seq.*
— X-ray, origin of, 286
Spectrum-analysis, 221
Spectrum-shift, 176
Speech, human, development of, 543
— in lower animals, 543
Spencer, H., 507, 576
Spermatozoon, 443, 444, 445, 447
Spherical curvature, defined, 164
— or Riemannian, geometry, 32, 33, 36, 44–6, 91, 94–7

Spherical, space, Einstein tensor for, 141
'Spinning' electron, 200, 273–4
Spinoza, B., 565, 566, 588, 640
— concept of God, 640
Spinozism, 649
Spin-quantum, 274
Spiral nebulae, 375–6, 396–7. *See also* Great nebulae *and* Extra-galactic nebulae
— — as island universes, 378
— — enigma of arms of, 397–8
— — novae in, 377
— — number of planetary systems in, 403
'Spirals, barred', 375, 376, 396
Spirit and flesh, 622
Spiritual activity and understanding, 310
Spiritualism, 587
Spontaneous generation, 412–13
Spores, asexual, 443
— described, 437, 501
Sporophyte, 501
'Sports', 505, 516
Stahl, G. E., 16
Stamen, 461, 501
'Standard candles', cepheids as, 345
Star-cloud, local, 340, 398
— — diameter and velocity of, 341
Star-density, local, 343, 399, 401
'Star-streaming', 365, 368
— vertex of, 368
Stark effect, 272
Stars, ages of, 363
— diameters of, 339, 353
— distances of the, 343
— distribution of, 350–1
— frequency of encounters between, 398–401
— future of the, 371
— giant and dwarf, 346–7
— in ancient speculation, 336
— motions of, 357–8
— origin of, 396–7
— parallaxes of, 340, 343
— radial velocities of, 357
— radiation emitted by, 354–5
— spectra of the, 341
— tangential velocities of, 357
— total number of, 350–1
Statuettes, upper Palaeolithic, 544
Stefan's constant, 254, 352
— law, 253–4, 325
Stellar encounters, frequency of, 398–401
— evolution, 347
— radiation, 351–2
— spectra, 341–2
— velocities in space, 357
Stern, O., 274

Stewart, Balfour, 239, 249
Stewart, J. Q., 335
Stoic creed, cycles in, 239
Storr, V. F., 420
Straight line, length of, in Riemannian geometry, 45
— — the, 30, 33
Strata of the earth, ages of, 421–3
Stress-tensor, defined, 148, 154
— for perfect fluid, 156
Strömberg, G., 367, 379
'Sub-ether', 277
Sub-groups, 47, 48
Subject of experience, defined, 554
Subject-object relation, 554
Substance, 191, 553–4, 570–3
Substantial, 307
Sugar, 415
— solutions, polarisation by, 416
Suggestion and religious experience, 625
— in sacraments, 627
Sulphur in protein, 417
Sun, absolute magnitude of, 345
— future of, 371
— mean distance, from the earth, 314–15
— pressure at centre of the, 316
— visual magnitude of, 257
Sun's atmosphere, 323
— mass and mean density, 316
— mean parallax and diameter, 315
— motion, 336
— position in galactic plane, 341
— radiant energy, 353–6
— — — source of, 355–6
— temperature, 342, 354
Super-galaxies, 378–9
Supernatural dualism, 519, 588–90, 592
Super-sexes, 449–51
Superstition, a nuisance, 616
— opportunity of, 11
Surface, geodesic, defined, 56, 79
Survival of the fittest, defined, 507
Suso, H., 622
Symphalangism, 488
Syria, religion in, 630
System of Animate Nature, Thomson, cited, 456
Systems, physico-chemical, heat in, 237, 239

Tail, the, in man, 464–5, 466
Tait, P. G., 239
Talbot pedigree, 488
Talgai skull, 536
Tanganyika, 534
Tannery, P., 323
Tarsier, 525
Tarsus, 629

Taurus cluster, 364
Taylor's theorem, used, 37
Teeth, in monkeys, apes and men, 460, 525, 526
Teleological argument, 597–9
Telepathic perception, 587
Telescope, 336, 340
Temperature, 227–8
— effective, of a star, 248, 352
— Kelvin scale of, 233–4
Tennyson, Lord, mystical experience of, 620
— — quoted, 28
Tensor, covariant derivatives of, 144
— divergence of, 145
— Einstein's world-, 139
— energy-stress-, defined, 154–6
— notion of a, 69
— Riemann-Christoffel, 66–8, 138, 139
— symmetrical, defined, 145
— transformation-equations of a, 68–9
Tensor-density, defined, 181
Tensor-equation, significance of, 70
Tensors, calculus of, 51, 68, 137
— world-, 73
Termites, 453–4
— productivity of queen, 454
Terrestrial evolution, human sight and, 259
Tertiary era, 423, 424, 428, 441, 442
— — geography of, 430
Tetraploid, defined, 449
Texas, 472
Theism and pantheism, 647–50
Theology, basis of, 5
Theory of Differential Equations, Part i, Forsyth, cited, 658
Theory of Good and Evil, Rashdall, cited, 605–6
Theory of Heat, Maxwell, cited, 27, 228, 239
Theory of the Gene, Morgan, cited, 448, 451, 480, 514
Thermal equilibrium, stable, 237
Thermocouple, 352
Thermodynamical equilibrium, 249
Thermodynamics, 230, 237
— first law of, 231
— second law of, 206, 231, 233, 237, 239, 392, 409, 580, 595
— reversal of second law, 239
Thermometer, air, 229–30, 234
Theromorphs, 426, 473
'Things in themselves', 563, 577, 586, 589, 651
Thomson, G. P., 198, 277
Thomson, Sir J. A., 452, 456, 461
Thomson, Sir J. J., 25, 193, 195, 199

Thorium, 405
Thorium, disintegration of, 207–8
Thyroid, 493
Tibet, 532, 538
Tidal friction, 327, 329–35, 363, 540
— — and moon's motion, 331–3
Tides, 327 et seq.
— cause of, 328
— equilibrium theory of, 328–9
— Michelson's experiment, 329
Tides, The, Darwin, cited, 333
Tiger, the sabre-toothed, 430
Time, absolute, 101, 102, 281
— 'before' and 'after', 120–1
— creation in, 392
— direction of and entropy, 238
— given in experience, 560
— intuitions of, 28
— measurements of, 28–9
— reality of, 392, 409, 648, 650
— separation from space, 30
Time-relations, within consciousness, 561
Time-scales of cosmic evolution, 388–9,
    393, 395, 402, 407
Tornier, 516
Torsion balance, 136
Totemism, 549–50
Tractrix, 93
Transcendental knowledge, defined, 190
Transformation-equation of a tensor,
    68–9
Transmigration, 639
Transmission grating, described, 292
Transubstantiation, 570, 573, 629
Treatise on Natural Philosophy, Thomson
    and Tait, cited, 77
Tree-shrews, 525
Triassic era, 424, 427, 439
Trilobites, 411, 425, 426, 469
Triploid, defined, 449
— form of drosophila, 450
Trouton, F. T., 203
Truth, 604, 606, 609
Two bodies, problem of, 169
Tycho's star, 368
Tylor, Sir E. B., 546
Tyndall, J., 620

Ultimate Reality, 617
Uncertainty-relations, and determinism,
    309, 584
— of Heisenberg, 3, 199, 279–81, 282,
    283, 580
'Unconscious cerebration', 615
'Uniformitarian' geological theory, 462
Uniformity of nature, and origin of life, 412
Unit, astronomical, defined, 315, 317
— of action, defined, 261

Unit-cell, of a crystal, 300
Universe, a finite, 49–50
— earth's place in the, 2
— end of, and entropy, 239
— of monads, 224
— rationality of the, 645, 652
— size of, 390
— time-process in, 238
— unity of, 518
Unseen Universe, Tait and Stewart, cited,
    239
Upanishads, the, 639
Uranium atom, average life of, 210
— atomic number of, 215, 219
— disintegration of, 207–8, 355
— puzzle of, 210–11
Uranium-lead ratio, 209, 422
Uranus, 314
Urea, synthesis of, 413
Ursa Major, 364
Ussher, Archbishop James, 420

Validity, objective, defined, 602, 603
Value, 601
— and reality, 646
Value and Destiny of the Individual,
    Bosanquet, cited, 653
Values, absolute, 606–8
— — and objective reality, 607
— conservation of, 646
Vanadium, 327, 418
van Rhijn, P. J., 351
Variations, genetic, 505–6, 518–19
— — and predestination, 523–4
— — origin of, 508–9
Varieties of Religious Experience, James,
    cited, 593, 612, 620
Vasilief, A. C., 15
Vector, covariant components of, 143
— divergence of, 144
Vedanta, 632, 639
Vedantist Hinduism, 649
Velocities, composition of, 122–3
— of recession of great nebulae, 382 et
    seq., 394
— of recession of great nebulae, de
    Sitter's formula, 380, 388
— stellar, in space, 357
Velocity of escape, theory of, 321–2
Venus, 314, 368
— atmosphere of, 324–5
— life on, 324–6
— surface-temperature of, 325
Vertebrates, embryology of the, 463–4
— origin of the, 470–1
Vestigial organs, 460, 465–7
Vibrations, atomic, 176
Viper, lungs in, 467

Virgin Birth, the, 457–8
— births, 451
Visual and spectroscopic binaries, contrast between, 362–3
— binaries, 354, 358–9
— — discovery of, 358
— — eccentricities of, 363
— — masses of, 360
— — origin of, 363
— — periods of revolution of, 359
'Vital force', 561
Vogt, Karl, 581
Void, the, 559
Volition, loophole for, 584
Volume and 'proper' volume, 124
V Puppis, 354, 362

Walcott, C. D., 424
Wallace, A. R., 542
Wallis, J., 90
Walton, E. T. S., 226
War, the Great, 653
Ward, James, 224, 554, 564, 565, 566, 576, 577, 589, 603, 641, 643, 650
Warping, of space-time, 177, 191
Wasps, 452–3
Water, 'holy', 631
Water-vapour, 325, 327, 414
— mean-square velocity of, 322
Wave mechanics, 275 et seq.
— theory, of light and other radiation, 201, 240 et seq.
Wave-aspect of radiation, a makeshift, 283
Wave-front, 292
Wave-length, of radiation, 240
Wave-packet, 278
Waves, plane, and lattices, 295–9
— — direct passage through a slit, 293–5
Way, purgative, 621
Way of Modernism, Bethune-Baker, cited, 7
Way, the Truth, the Life, Hort, cited, 527, 635, 636
Weber, 255
Wegener, A., 426, 540
Weismann, A., 509, 510
Wells, H. G., 522
Wesley, John, 615, 617
— — and religious experience, 624

Weyl, Hermann, 54, 89, 122, 651
Whale, vestigial organs of the, 466
'White dwarfs', 347, 348–9, 370
White forelock, inheritance of, 488
'White-eye', in drosophila, 489
Whitefield, G., 615
Whitney, D. D., 451
Whittaker, T., 619
Wien, W., law of, 254, 255, 261
Wilson, C. T. R., 212
Wilson, Mount, 100-inch reflector of, 349, 352, 372, 374, 378, 407
Wilson-Sommerfeld quantum conditions, 265–6
Winge, O., 478
Wireless waves, 8, 201
Wöhler, F., 413
Wolf-Rayet spectrum, 369
Woodward, Sir A. S., 455, 530
World-formula of Laplace, 578, 580
World-tensor, Einstein's, 139
World-tensors, defined, 73
Worms, 425, 431
Worship, catholic, 626
— public, and beauty, 626
Wriedt, C., 497
Wundt, W., 611

X-chromosome, defined, 446
X-ray crystal analysis, 304–6
— spectra, 207, 219, 286, 290
X-rays, 200–1, 206, 284
— and genetic changes, 498–500
— characteristic, origin of, 286
— discovery of, 206
— impulse and characteristic, 285
— photography by, 207
— wave-lengths of, 201, 285

Y-chromosome, defined, 446
Yamane, J., 497
Young, Thomas, 290

Zeeman effect, 272
Zeitschrift für Physik, cited, 381
Zero, absolute, of temperature, 229–30, 283
Zirconium, 214
Zoroaster, 632
Zwicky, F., 380, 407

CAMBRIDGE: PRINTED BY

W. LEWIS, M.A.

AT THE UNIVERSITY PRESS